Introduction to the Theory of Statistics

McGRAW-HILL SERIES IN PROBABILITY AND STATISTICS

David Blackwell and Herbert Solomon, *Consulting Editors*

Bharucha-Reid Elements of the Theory of Markov Processes and Their Applications

Graybill Introduction to Linear Statistical Models, Volume I

Mood and Graybill Introduction to the Theory of Statistics

Wadsworth and Bryan Introduction to Probability and Random Variables

Weiss Statistical Decision Theory

Wolf Elements of Probability and Statistics

Introduction to the Theory of Statistics

Alexander M. Mood

Vice President, C-E-I-R, Inc.
Beverly Hills, California

Franklin A. Graybill

Director, Statistical Laboratory
Colorado State University
Fort Collins, Colorado

SECOND EDITION

McGRAW-HILL BOOK COMPANY, INC.

New York, San Francisco, Toronto, London

Introduction to the Theory of Statistics

 Library of Congress Catalog Card Number 62-18858

II

42861

To Harriet A.M.M.

and Danny and Kathy F.A.G.

Preface to the First Edition

This book developed from a set of notes which I prepared in 1945. At that time there was no modern text available specifically designed for beginning students of mathematical statistics. Since then the situation has been relieved considerably, and had I known in advance what books were in the making it is likely that I should not have embarked on this volume. However, it seemed sufficiently different from other presentations to give prospective teachers and students a useful alternative choice.

The aforementioned notes were used as text material for three years at Iowa State College in a course offered to senior and first-year graduate students. The only prerequisite for the course was one year of calculus, and this requirement indicates the level of the book. (The calculus class at Iowa State met four hours per week and included good coverage of Taylor series, partial differentiation, and multiple integration.) No previous knowledge of statistics is assumed.

This is a statistics book, not a mathematics book, as any mathematician will readily see. Little mathematical rigor is to be found in the derivations simply because it would be boring and largely a waste of time at this level. Of course rigorous thinking is quite essential to good statistics, and I have been at some pains to make a show of rigor and to instill an appreciation for rigor by pointing out various pitfalls of loose arguments.

While this text is primarily concerned with the theory of statistics, full cognizance has been taken of those students who fear that a moment may be wasted in mathematical frivolity. All new subjects are supplied with a little scenery from practical affairs, and, more important, a serious effort has been made in the problems to illustrate the variety of ways in which the theory may be applied.

The problems are an essential part of the book. They range from simple numerical examples to theorems needed in subsequent chapters. They include important subjects which could easily take precedence over material in the text; the relegation of subjects to problems was based rather on the feasibility of such a procedure than on the priority of the subject. For example, the matter of correlation is dealt with almost entirely in the problems. It seemed to me inefficient to cover multivariate situations twice in detail, i.e., with the regression model and with the correlation model. The emphasis in the text proper is on the more general regression model.

The author of a textbook is indebted to practically everyone who has touched the field, and I here bow to all statisticians. However, in giving credit to contributors one must draw the line somewhere, and I have simplified matters by drawing it very high; only the most eminent contributors are mentioned in the book.

My greatest personal debt is to S. S. Wilks, who kindled my interest in statistics and who was my mentor throughout my term of graduate study. Any merits which this book may have must be charged largely to his careful lectures and understanding direction of my studies.

My colleagues at Iowa State College have all contributed much to my understanding and general view of statistics. I am particularly aware of large debts to G. W. Brown, W. G. Cochran, and G. W. Snedecor. Among the many students who thoroughly revised the original notes by their excellent comments and suggestions I must mention H. D. Block, who gave the final manuscript a very careful and competent review. Margaret Kirwin and Ruth Burns accurately translated my scrawl into beautiful typescript. Bernice Brown and Miss Burns carefully proofread the entire set of galleys.

I am indebted to Catherine Thompson and Maxine Merrington, and to E. S. Pearson, editor of *Biometrika,* for permission to include Tables III and V, which are abridged versions of tables published in *Biometrika.* I am also indebted to Professors R. A. Fisher and Frank Yates, and to Messrs. Oliver and Boyd, Ltd., Edinburgh, for permission to reprint Table IV from their book "Statistical Tables for Use in Biological, Agricultural and Medical Research."

In the final chapter are some distribution-free tests which were developed jointly by G. W. Brown and myself at Iowa State College on a project sponsored by the Office of Naval Research. Professor Brown has very generously and graciously permitted me to include this material which should have first appeared in print under his name as well as mine. The tests referred to are presented in Sections 5, 6, 7, 8, and 9 of Chapter 16.

Alexander M. Mood

Preface to the Second Edition

Since the first edition of this book was published in 1950 many new statistical techniques have been made available and many techniques that were only in the domain of the mathematical statistician are now useful and demanded by the applied statistician. To include some of this material we have had to eliminate other material, else the book would have come to resemble a compendium. The general approach of presenting the theory with some connection to practical problems apparently contributed significantly to the success of the first edition and we have tried to maintain that feature in the present edition.

No previous course in statistics is required in order to study this book. The mathematical preparation required is the conventional first-year calculus course. Some familiarity with the arithmetic of matrices is desirable but not essential, since a discussion of the needed operations is provided in Chapter 9. Some of the sections which require matrix algebra are starred and may be omitted without interrupting the continuity of the book.

The authors owe a very large debt to Professor Herman Chernoff, who spent much time with large portions of the manuscript making extensive improvements, even to the point of rewriting several sections.

We also give grateful acknowledgment to Dr. David Weeks, who read the entire manuscript; to Terrence Connell, William Owen, and Scott Urquhart, who helped with the galleys; and to Dr. James Pachares, Dr. Leon Harter, and the Trustees of *Biometrika* for their kind permission to use their material in Tables VI, VII, and VIII.

Alexander M. Mood
Franklin A. Graybill

Contents

1

Introduction

1.1 Statistics

In order to place this book in its proper perspective, it is necessary to consider first what statistics is. The lay conception of statistics ordinarily includes the collection of large masses of data and the presentation of such data in tables or charts; it may also include the calculation of totals, averages, percentages, and the like. In any case, these more or less routine operations are a part, but only an incidental part, of statistics. Statistics is also concerned with the design of experiments, the design of sample surveys, data reduction and data processing, and many other things.

We shall describe statistics as the technology of the scientific method. Statistics provides tools for making decisions when conditions of uncertainty prevail. These tools may be of quite general application and useful in any field of science—physical, biological, social, etc. They are applicable not only to the scientific world but to the business world and the world of everyday affairs as well. On the other hand, certain tools may be particularly designed for special fields of research.

Statistics can be divided into two broad classifications: (1) descriptive statistics, which is concerned with summarizing data and describing these data, and (2) inferential statistics, which is concerned with the process of using data to make decisions about the more general case of which these data are a part. The process of making decisions about general situations on the basis of incomplete information that is contained in sample data is hazardous and cannot be done with certainty; probability is a measure of this uncertainty. There are two types of uncertainty with which we must contend: (1) uncertainty due to randomness and (2) uncertainty due to our ignorance of the true state of the system. We shall illustrate with an example.

A seed company, company A, grows a certain kind of flowers, harvests the seeds, and packages them in packets of 25 seeds each. A retail store purchases some of the packets and guarantees to its customers that at least 22 of the 25 seeds in each packet will grow or else it will give them another packet free of charge. The retailer has two types of uncertainty with which he must contend: (1) He is not sure what proportion p_A of the packages that the seed company has for sale will be acceptable (has at least 22 seeds that will grow) and (2) since the seed company has on the order of one million packages of the seed for sale and the retailer will buy only about 200 packages, he has another uncertainty facing him; namely, even if he knows that p_A proportion of the one million packages is acceptable, how can he be "sure" or "reasonably sure" that the p_A proportion of the 200 packages that *he buys* will be acceptable? Even if p_A is .99, i.e., if 990,000 of the one million packages that the seed company has for sale are acceptable, the retailer's 200 packages could be "accidentally" selected from the 10,000 unacceptable ones and he would lose money.

The first type of uncertainty, that of not knowing p_A, the proportion of acceptable packages that the seed company produced, is uncertainty due to one's ignorance of the state of the system (sometimes called the true state of nature). The second type of uncertainty is due to what is often referred to as "randomness."

The retailer can improve his position by experimentation (ask the company to run a germination test) by which he can make a "decision" as to what he believes the state of nature is (what p_A is). Even then he will never be able to determine p_A exactly and with certainty. If he knows what loss he will incur if he determines the proportion of acceptable packages to be p'_A when it really is p_A, then he will want to experiment and make decisions in such a manner as to minimize his loss in some fashion.

To make matters more complicated, another seed company (company B) now sells the same kind of flower seeds at the same price per package, so that the retailer must decide from which company he will buy. If p_A is greater than p_B, he will purchase from company A; otherwise he will buy his seeds from company B.

The retailer may conduct an experiment (ask each company to conduct germination tests) and take one of two actions: (a_1) buy from company A; or (a_2) buy from company B, depending on the outcome of the experiment and upon his evaluation of the loss that he might sustain if he makes a wrong decision.

The designing of the experiment, determining the number and kind of observations to make, and determining how to use the results to make "good" decisions are statistical problems.

Another division of the field of statistics worth brief consideration is that between the theory and the methodology.

The theory of statistics is a branch of applied mathematics. It has its roots in an area of pure mathematics known as the theory of probability, and, in fact, the complete structure of statistical theory in a broad sense may be thought of as including the theory of probability. It also includes other things not part of the formal theory of probability: theoretical consequences of the principle of randomization, various principles of estimation, and principles of testing hypotheses and, in general, a principle of decision making. These principles may be regarded as axioms which augment the axioms of probability theory.

The statistician is, of course, engaged in producing tools for research workers. Faced with a particular experimental problem, he constructs a mathematical model to fit the experimental situation as best he can, analyzes the model by mathematical methods, and finally devises procedures for dealing with the problem. He is guided in this work by the principles of the theory of statistics.

The statistician is also engaged in developing and extending the theory of statistics. There are many quite important problems of experimental design and statistical inference which remain untouched because the theory of statistics is not yet powerful enough to deal with them. The broad advance in the application of statistical methods during the past three decades was made possible by far-reaching developments in the theory which immediately preceded it.

It may be interesting to remark here on the origins of the theory of statistics. Certain areas of biological experimentation reached a point at which what are now called statistical methods were imperative if further progress was to be made. The essentials of statistical theory were then evolved by the biologists themselves. This parallels the natural history of almost any branch of abstract knowledge, but it is nevertheless curious in the case of statistics. For the theory of statistics appears to be a very natural development of the theory of probability, which is several hundred years old; somehow it was almost completely overlooked by workers in that field. Incidentally, the situation which created statistical theory still obtains; there are many areas of scientific experimentation ready and waiting for statistical methods which do not yet exist.

In contradistinction to the theory of statistics is the practice of statistics. There is a great body of tools and techniques for research workers which expands appreciably with the passing of each year. Until recent years the statistician was not much concerned with these tools, being content to pass them on to those who wished to use them. But as scientific research progresses, experiments become more complex and the statistical tools become correspondingly complex and specialized. In some areas the time has come when it is impossible for the research worker to become familiar with all the tools that might be useful to him. Furthermore, as tools become more specialized, they become less flexible: To fit a particular experiment, the tool often has to be modified, and this requires knowledge of statistical theory.

The use of statistical tools is not merely a matter of picking out the wrench that fits the bolt; it is more a matter of selecting the correct one of several wrenches which appear to fit the bolt about equally well but none of which fit it exactly. It is a long step from an algebraic formula to, for example, a nutrition experiment on hogs. There is nothing magic about the formula; it is merely a tool and, moreover, a tool derived from some mathematical model which may not represent the actual situation with great precision. In using the tool, one must make a whole series of judgments relative to the nature and magnitude of the various errors engendered by the discrepancies between the model and the actual experiment. These judgments cannot well be made by either the statistician or the experimenter, for they depend on both the nature of statistical theory and the nature of the experimental material.

To meet this development, the applied statistician has come on the scene. He is to be found in various industrial and academic research centers, and his function is, of course, to collaborate with the research workers in their experimentation and investigation. He must be completely familiar with both the theory and methodology of statistics, even though his work is concerned not with the field of statistics at all but with the field of application. We merely wish to observe here that applied statistics has developed to the point where it may be regarded as a field of interest in itself.

1.2 The Scope of This Book

This book is concerned with the theory rather than the applications of statistics. In the course of the development, many tools will be derived and discussed; a secondary purpose of the book is to make clear the conditions under which certain of the important statistical tools may be employed. But our primary purpose is the exposition of statistical theory.

The book is introductory in that no knowledge of statistics by the reader is presumed. And it is elementary in that no knowledge of mathematics beyond elementary calculus is presumed. However, some familiarity with the arithmetic of matrices is desirable but not essential. This restriction of the mathematical level is necessarily costly. We shall have to omit entirely many interesting but more technical developments of the theory; the generality of theorems will be reduced; it will be necessary to make statements without proof from time to time; mathematical rigor will be sacrificed at many points; and cumbersome arguments will sometimes have to be used when very simple arguments at a higher mathematical level exist. All these sacrifices, however, will inhibit our presentation rather less than one might suppose. The essential aspects of the theory are entirely comprehensible without higher mathematics.

Since statistical theory is founded on probability theory, we shall begin the study with a consideration of probability concepts and the development of certain probability theorems which will be required. Next we shall consider mathematical models which have been found by experience to approximate many common experimental situations. It will then be possible to study mathematically the problems of statistical inference and of the design and analysis of experiments and investigations.

1.3 Reference System

The chapters are divided into numbered sections; the numbering begins anew in each chapter. Theorems, definitions, examples, etc., are also numbered by chapter. Thus Sec. 5.3 refers to Sec. 3 of Chap. 5, Theorem 5.1 refers to Theorem 1 of Chap. 5, etc.

The equations are numbered anew in each section, and equation numbers are always enclosed in parentheses. Merely the equation number is given when referring to an equation in the same section; otherwise chapter and section numbers are prefixed. Thus equation (6) refers to the sixth equation of the same section, and equation (9.1.12) refers to the twelfth equation of the first section of the ninth chapter.

Numbers in brackets refer to the numbered references in the Bibliography at the end of each chapter.

1.4 Bibliography

1. Arrow, Kenneth J.: "Alternative approaches to the theory of choice in risk-taking situations," *Econometrica,* Vol. 19(1951), pp. 404–437.
2. Churchman, C. West.: "Theory of Experimental Inference," The Macmillan Company, New York, 1948.
3. Fisher, R. A.: "Statistical Methods and Scientific Inference," Hafner Publishing Company, New York, 1956.
4. Good, I. J.: "Probability and the Weighing of Evidence," Charles Griffin & Co., Ltd., London, and Hafner Publishing Company, New York, 1950.
5. Jeffreys, Harold: "Scientific Inference," Cambridge University Press, London, 1957.
6. Kolmogoroff, A. N.: "Foundations of the Theory of Probability," Chelsea Publishing Company, New York, 1950.
7. Lindley, D. V.: "Statistical inference," *Journal of the Royal Statistical Society,* Series B, Vol. 15(1953), pp. 30–76.
8. Neyman, Jerzy: "Outline of a theory of statistical estimation based on the classical theory of probability," *Philosophical Transactions of the Royal Society of London,* Series A, Vol. 236(1937), pp. 333–380.
9. Savage, Leonard J.: "The Foundations of Statistics," John Wiley & Sons, Inc., New York, 1954.

2

Probability

2.1 Introduction

One of the fundamental tools of statistics is probability, which had its beginnings with games of chance in the seventeenth century.

Games of chance, as the name implies, include such actions as spinning a roulette wheel, throwing dice, tossing a coin, drawing a card, etc., in which the outcome of a trial is uncertain. However, it is recognized that, even though the outcome of any particular trial may be uncertain, there is a *predictable* long-term outcome. It is known, for example, that in many throws of an ideal (balanced, symmetrical) coin about one-half of the trials will result in heads. It is this long-term predictable regularity that enables gaming houses to engage in the business.

A similar type of uncertainty and long-term regularity often occurs in experimental science. For example, in the science of genetics it is uncertain whether an offspring will be male or female, but in the long run it is known approximately what per cent of offspring will be male and what per cent will be female. A life insurance company cannot predict which persons in the United States will die at age 50, but it can predict quite satisfactorily *how many* people in the United States will die at that age.

First we shall discuss the classical or a priori theory of probability, then we shall discuss the frequency theory, and finally we shall develop the axiomatic approach; this is the order of the historical development of the theory.

2.2 Classical or A Priori Probability

As we stated in the previous section, the theory of probability in its early stages was closely associated with games of chance. This association prompted the classical definition. For example, suppose that we want the probability of the event that an ideal coin will turn up heads. We argue in this manner: Since there are only two ways that the coin can fall, heads or tails, and since the coin is well balanced, one would expect it to fall heads and tails with about equal frequency; hence, in the long run one would expect it to fall heads about one-half of the time, and so the probability of the event of a head will be given the value $\frac{1}{2}$.

This kind of reasoning prompted the following classical definition of probability:

Definition 2.1. *Classical Definition of Probability. If an event can occur in n mutually exclusive and equally likely ways and if n_A of these outcomes have an attribute A, then the probability of A is the fraction n_A/n.* We shall apply this definition to a few examples in order to illustrate its meaning.

If an ordinary die (one of a pair of dice) is tossed, there are six possible outcomes: Any one of the six numbered faces may turn up. These six outcomes are *mutually exclusive* since two or more faces cannot turn up simultaneously. And, if the die is fair, or true, the six outcomes are *equally likely;* i.e., it is expected that each face will appear with about equal frequency in the long run. Now suppose that we want the probability that the result of a toss be an even number. Three of the six possible outcomes have this attribute. The probability that an even number will appear when a die is tossed is therefore $3/6$ or $1/2$. Similarly, the probability that a five will appear when a die is tossed is $1/6$. The probability that the result of a toss will be greater than two is $2/3$.

To consider another example, suppose that a card is drawn at random from an ordinary deck of playing cards. The probability of drawing a spade is readily seen to be $13/52$, or $1/4$. The probability of drawing a number between 5 and 10, inclusive, is $24/52$, or $6/13$.

The application of the definition is straightforward enough in these simple cases, but it is not always so obvious. Careful attention must be paid to the qualifications "mutually exclusive" and "equally likely." Suppose that one wished to compute the probability of getting two heads if a coin were tossed twice. He might reason that there are three possible outcomes for the two tosses: two heads, two tails, or one head and one tail. One of these three outcomes has the desired attribute, i.e., two heads; therefore the probability is $1/3$. This reasoning is faulty because the three given outcomes are not equally likely. The third outcome, one head and one tail, can occur in two ways since the head may appear on the first toss and the tail on the second, or the head may appear on the second toss and the tail on the first. Thus there are four equally likely outcomes: HH, HT, TH, TT. The first of these has the desired attribute while the others do not. The correct probability is therefore $1/4$. The result would be the same if two ideal coins were tossed simultaneously.

Again, suppose that one wished to compute the probability that a card drawn from an ordinary well-shuffled deck will be an ace or a spade. In enumerating the favorable outcomes, he might count 4 aces and 13 spades and reason that there are 17 outcomes with the desired attribute. This is clearly incorrect because these 17 outcomes are not mutually exclusive, since the ace of spades is both an ace and a spade.

We note that, by the classical definition, probability is always a number between 0 and 1 inclusive. The ratio n_A/n must be a proper fraction since the total number of possible outcomes cannot be smaller than the number of outcomes with a specified attribute. If an event is certain to happen, its probability is 1; if it is certain not to happen, its probability is 0. Thus, the probability of obtaining an eight in tossing a die is 0. The probability that the outcome of tossing a die will be less than 10 is 1.

The probabilities determined by the classical definition are called a priori probabilities. When one states that the probability of obtaining a head in tossing a coin is $\frac{1}{2}$, he has arrived at this result purely by deductive reasoning. The result does not require that any coin be tossed or even be at hand. We say that, if the coin is true, the probability of a head is $\frac{1}{2}$, but this is little more than saying the same thing in two different ways. Nothing is said about how one can determine whether or not a particular coin is true.

The fact that we shall deal with ideal objects in developing a theory of probability will not trouble us, because that is a common requirement of mathematical systems. Geometry, for example, deals with conceptually perfect circles, lines with zero width, and so forth, but it is a useful branch of knowledge which can be applied to diverse practical problems.

There are some rather troublesome defects in the classical, or a priori, approach. It is obvious, for example, that the definition of probability must be modified somehow when the total number of possible outcomes is infinite. One might seek, for example, the probability that a positive integer drawn at random be even. The intuitive answer to this question is $\frac{1}{2}$. If one were pressed to justify this result on the basis of the definition, he might reason as follows: Suppose that we limit ourselves to the first 20 integers; 10 of these are even so that the ratio of favorable events to the total number is $\frac{10}{20}$, or $\frac{1}{2}$. Again, if the first 200 integers are considered, 100 of these are even, and the ratio is also $\frac{1}{2}$. In general, the first $2N$ integers contain N even integers; if we form the ratio $N/2N$ and let N become infinite so as to encompass the whole set of positive integers, the ratio remains $\frac{1}{2}$.

The above argument is plausible and the answer is plausible, but it is no simple matter to make the argument stand up. It depends, for example, on the natural ordering of the positive integers, and a different ordering could produce a different result. Thus, one could just as well order the integers in this way: 1, 3, 2; 5, 7, 4; 9, 11, 6; $\cdots$, taking the first pair of odd integers, then the first even integer; the second pair of odd integers, then the second even integer; and so forth. With this ordering, one could argue that the probability of drawing an even integer is $\frac{1}{3}$. The integers can also be ordered so that the ratio will oscillate and never approach any definite value as N increases.

There is another difficulty with the classical approach to the theory of probability which is deeper even than that arising in the case of an infinite number of outcomes. Suppose that we have a coin known to be biased in favor of heads (it is loaded so that a head is more likely to appear than a tail). The two possible outcomes of tossing the coin are not equally likely. What is the probability of a head? The classical definition leaves us completely helpless here.

Still another difficulty with the classical approach is encountered when we try to answer questions such as the following: What is the probability that a child born in Chicago will be a boy? or What is the probability that a male will die before age 50? or What is the probability that a cookie bought at a certain bakery will have less than three peanuts in it? or What is the probability that a light bulb will burn less than 100 hours? All these are legitimate questions which we want to bring into the realm of probability theory. However, questions of "symmetry," "equally likely," etc., cannot be answered as they could be in games of chance. Thus we shall have to alter or extend our definition to bring problems similar to the above into the framework of the theory. This more widely applicable probability is called a posteriori probability or frequency probability and will be discussed in the next section.

2.3 A Posteriori or Frequency Probability

A coin which seemed to be well balanced and symmetrical was tossed 100 times and the outcomes recorded in Table 2.1. The important thing to notice is how the relative frequency of heads tends to become quite stable and close to $\frac{1}{2}$. This is not unexpected, since the coin was symmetrical and it was anticipated that, in the long run, heads would occur about the same number of times as tails. For another example, a single die was thrown 300 times and the outcomes recorded in Table 2.2. Notice how close the relative frequency of a face with a one showing is to $\frac{1}{6}$; similarly for a two, three, four, five, and six. These results are not unexpected since the die which was used was quite symmetrical and balanced; it was expected that each face would occur with about equal frequency in the long run. This suggests that we might be willing to use this relative frequency in Table 2.1 as an approximation for the probability that the particular coin used will come up heads, or we might be willing to use the relative frequencies in Table 2.2 as approximations for the probabilities that various numbers on this die will appear.

In fact, it seems reasonable to assume for the coin experiment that there exists a number, label it p, which is the probability of a head. Now if the coin appears well balanced, symmetrical, and true, we might use Definition 2.1 and state that p is approximately equal to $\frac{1}{2}$. It is only an approximation to set p equal to $\frac{1}{2}$ since for this particular coin we cannot be certain that the two cases, heads and tails, are exactly equally likely. But by examining the balance and symmetry of the coin it may seem quite reasonable to assume that they are. Alternatively, the coin could be tossed a large number of times, the results recorded as in Table 2.1, and the relative frequency of a head used as an approximation for p. In the experiment with a die, the probability p_2 of a two showing could be approximated by using Definition 2.1 or by using the relative frequency in Table 2.2. The important thing is that we postulate that there is a

TABLE 2.1. RESULTS OF TOSSING A COIN 100 TIMES

Outcome	Frequency	Observed relative frequency	Long-run expected relative frequency of a balanced coin
H	56	.56	.50
T	44	.44	.50
Total	100	1.00	1.00

TABLE 2.2. RESULTS OF TOSSING A DIE 300 TIMES

Outcome	Frequency	Relative frequency	Long-run expected relative frequency of a balanced die
1	51	.170	.1667
2	54	.180	.1667
3	48	.160	.1667
4	51	.170	.1667
5	49	.163	.1667
6	47	.157	.1667
Total	300	1.000	1.0000

number p which is defined as the probability of a head with the coin, or a number p_2 which is the probability of a two showing in the throw of the die. Whether we use Definition 2.1 or the relative frequency for the probability p seems unimportant in the examples cited.

Suppose, as described above, that the coin is unbalanced so that we are quite certain from an examination that the two cases, heads and tails, are *not* equally likely to happen. In these cases a number p can still be postulated as the probability that a head shows, but the classical definition will not help us to find the value of p. We must use the frequency approach.

In many scientific investigations, observations are taken which have an element of uncertainty or unpredictability in them. As a very simple example, suppose that we want to predict whether the next baby born in a certain locality will be a male or a female. This is individually an uncertain event, but the results of groups of births can be dealt with satisfactorily. We find that a certain long-run regularity exists which is similar to the long-run regularity of the frequency ratio of a head when a coin is thrown. If, for example, we find upon examination of records that about 51 per cent of the births are male, it might be reasonable to postulate that the probability of a male birth in this locality is equal to a number p and take .51 as its approximation. This method of definition is sometimes referred to as statistical probability.

To make this idea more concrete, we shall assume that a series of observations (or experiments) can be made under quite uniform conditions. That is, an observation of an event is taken, then the event is repeated under similar conditions and another observation taken; this is repeated many times, and while the conditions are similar each time, there is an uncontrollable variation which is "haphazard" or "random" so that the observations are individually unpredictable. In many of these cases the observations fall into certain classes wherein the relative frequencies are quite stable. This suggests that we postulate a number p, called the probability of the event, and approximate p by the relative frequency with which the repeated observations satisfy the event. For instance, suppose that the experiment consists of sampling the population of a large city to see how many voters favor a certain proposal. The outcomes are "favor" or "do not favor," and each voter's response is unpredictable, but it is reasonable to postulate a number p as the probability that a given response will be "favor." The relative frequency of "favor" responses can be used as an approximate value for p.

As another example, suppose that the experiment or observation consists of sampling transistors from a large collection of transistors. We shall postulate that the probability of a given transistor being defective is p. We can approximate p by selecting several transistors at "random" from the collection and computing the relative frequency of the number defective.

The important thing is that we can *conceive* of a series of observations or experiments under rather uniform conditions. Then a number p can be postulated as the probability of the event A happening, and p can be approximated by the relative frequency of the event A in a series of experiments.

2.4 Probability Models

One of the aims of science is to predict and describe events in the world in which we live. One way in which this is done is to construct mathematical models which adequately describe the real world. For example, the equation $s = \frac{1}{2}gt^2$ expresses a certain relationship between the symbols s, g, and t. To use the equation $s = \frac{1}{2}gt^2$ in a real-world experience to predict s, the distance a body falls, as a function of the time t, the gravitational constant g must be known. The latter is a physical constant which must be measured by experimentation if the equation $s = \frac{1}{2}gt^2$ is to be useful. The reason for mentioning this equation is that we do a similar thing in probability theory; we construct a probability model which can be used to describe events in the real world. For example, it might be desirable to find an equation which could be used to predict the sex of each birth in a certain locality. The equation would be very complex, and none has been found. However, a probability model can be constructed which, while not very helpful in dealing with an individual event, is quite useful in dealing with groups of events. Therefore, we can postulate a number p which represents the probability that a birth will be a male. From this fundamental probability we can answer questions such as What is the probability that in ten births at least three will be males? or What is the probability that there will be three consecutive male births in the next five? To answer questions such as these and many other similar ones, we shall develop an idealized probability model.

We shall consider a theory of probability for only those situations which can be described by the outcomes of conceptual experiments. That is, we shall consider only those events which can conceivably be repeated under generally similar conditions. Thus male births, coin tossing, the number of automobiles, etc., are permissible, but questions such as What is the probability that my wife loves me? or What is the probability that World War II would not have happened?, etc., are not included.

We also require that every possible outcome of an experiment can be enumerated. For example, in the coin-tossing experiment there are two possible outcomes: heads and tails. We shall associate probabilities only with these outcomes. We add, however, that even if a certain outcome is impossible it can be included (its probability is 0). The main thing to remember is that every outcome which *can occur* must be included.

Each conceivable outcome of a conceptual experiment that can be repeated under similar conditions will be called a sample point, and the totality of conceivable outcomes (or sample points) will be called the sample space.

Before proceeding with the development of the theory, we shall give some examples.

Example 2.1. If a random experiment consists of throwing a coin two times, there are four conceivable outcomes: (H, H), (H, T), (T, H), (T, T). Thus there are four sample points which make up the sample space.

Example 2.2. If a random experiment consists of observing the sex of births in a certain population, there are two conceivable outcomes, male and female; hence, there are two sample points in the sample space.

Example 2.3. Suppose that a sample of 50 seeds is selected from a bag of seeds to see how many will germinate. The random experiment consists of drawing 50 seeds from the bag. The conceivable outcomes are the number of the 50 which germinate. There could be 0, 1, 2, · · · , or 50 that germinate, so that there are 51 sample points which make up the sample space.

Example 2.4. Suppose that 500 people are selected at random in a large city to see how many use a certain brand of milk. The conceivable number of the 500 people who use the brand of milk is 0, 1, 2, · · · , 500. Each of these 501 numbers is a sample point in the sample space.

Example 2.5. Suppose that a random experiment consists of asking television viewers in a certain city if they regularly watch three specified programs. There are eight conceivable outcomes: (YYY), (YYN), (YNY), (NYY), (YNN), (NYN), (NNY), (NNN), where (YNY) means "yes" to program one, "no" to program two, "yes" to program three, etc. The sample space consists of eight points.

Example 2.6. The sample space in the above examples consists of a finite number of points. We shall now give an example of a sample space that consists of an infinite number of points. Suppose that it is desired to determine the number of tosses of a coin that must be made until the first head appears. It can appear on the 1st, 2d, · · · , nth · · · toss. Actually the sample space will consist of a countable infinity of points (the same number of points as there are positive integers).

Example 2.7. In this example the sample space will contain as many points (called a continuum of points) as there are real positive numbers. Let the random experiment be selecting a random sample of one sixth-grade student in a certain city and recording his weight. The outcome can be any positive number. We may argue that no student could weigh less than one pound or more than 2000 pounds. This is true, but it does not matter if impossible outcomes are included so long as every conceivable outcome is enumerated. Therefore, this sample space can consist of all positive numbers.

2.5 Point Sets

We shall define certain operations on the set of points which make up the sample space and which are necessary for further development of the theory. A set of points, sometimes called simply a set, is an aggregate of elements having certain specified properties. A set could be the set of the first 10 integers or a collection of automobiles or of any other objects. *If s is a point or an element belonging to the set S, we shall write* $s \in S$.

Definition 2.2. *Two sets* S_1 *and* S_2 *are said to be equal if every element or point of* S_1 *is also a point of* S_2 *and every point of* S_2 *is also a point of* S_1, *that is, if* S_1 *and* S_2 *both contain exactly the same points. This will be indicated by writing* $S_1 = S_2$.

Definition 2.3. *If every element (or point) of a set* S_1 *is also an element of S, then* S_1 *will be called a subset of S, and we shall write this* $S_1 \subset S$.

Example 2.8. Let the set S be the integers x such that $x = 1, 2, 3, 4, 5, 6, 7$. This will be written $S = \{x: x = 1, 2, 3, 4, 5, 6, 7\}$. Let $S_1 = \{y: y = 1, 2, 3\}$. Then S_1 is a subset of S. If $S_2 = \{z: z = 1, 3, 5, 7\}$, then S_2 is not a subset of S_1, but S_2 is a subset of S.

Definition 2.4. *In each discussion there will be a universal set, the sample space S, such that all other sets in the discussion are subsets of S.*

Sometimes the sample space may not be explicitly indicated but will generally be clear from the context of the discussion.

Definition 2.5. *The complement of a set* S_1 *with respect to the sample space S will be the set of points that are in S but not in* S_1. *This will be indicated by* $S - S_1$ *or sometimes by* $\bar{S}_1$.

In Example 2.8 the set $\bar{S}_1$ is given by $\bar{S}_1 = \{x: x = 4, 5, 6, 7\}$, and $\bar{S}_2 = \{z: z = 2, 4, 6\}$.

Definition 2.6. *If a set* S_1 *contains no points, it will be called the null set, which will be indicated by* $\emptyset$.

We shall adopt the convention that the null set is a subset of every set and that every set is a subset of itself.

After the outcomes of a random experiment are enumerated and a sample space S defined, we shall want to discuss certain subsets of the sample space. For instance, in Example 2.3, we may want to ask the question, What is the probability that more than 30 seeds germinate? We are asking a question about a subset of S; the subset contains the elements $31, 32, \cdots, 50$. In our terminology, we shall say, What is the probability of the event A happening, where A is the subset $31, 32, \cdots, 50$? We can conceive of wanting answers to questions about many different kinds of events. This leads us to the following definition:

Definition 2.7. *An event A in the sample space S is defined to be a subset A of points in S, and when we say "The probability that event A occurs (happens)" we shall mean the probability that any point of A occurs.*

For example, in the above, when we ask the question, What is the probability that more than 30 seeds germinate?, we are, in essence, asking what the probability is that any point in the event A occurs, where $A = \{x: x = 31, 32, \cdots, 50\}$; if any point in A "occurs," we say that the event A (more than 30 seeds germinate) occurs.

Actually, if the sample space contains a continuum of points, as in

Example 2.7 above, we shall not define *every* subset to be an event but only *measurable* subsets. This term (measurable) is taken from advanced mathematics, and the reader need not be concerned about it in this book since every subset which we shall consider will be measurable and hence will be called an event.

In Example 2.7 we may want to ask the question, What is the probability that the student will weigh between 150 and 170 pounds? In our terminology we would ask, What is the probability of the event A, where $A = \{x: 150 < x < 170\}$?

Relative to a sample space S, suppose that S_1 and S_2 are two events, i.e., two subsets of S. Then two other events can be defined: (1) the set of points which are in both S_1 and S_2 and (2) the set of points which are in S_1 or in S_2 or in both S_1 and S_2. These are given in the next two definitions.

Definition 2.8. *Let S_1 and S_2 be any two events in the sample space S; then the event which consists of all points that are in S_1 or S_2 or both is called the union of S_1 and S_2 and written as $S_1 \cup S_2$.*

Example 2.9. Consider Example 2.5. Let S_1 be the event defined by the condition that "yes" is the answer for program number one; that is, S_1 contains the four points (YYY), (YYN), (YNY), (YNN). Let S_2 be the event defined by the condition that "no" is the answer for program number three; that is, S_2 contains the four points (YYN), (YNN), (NYN), (NNN). Then the set $S_1 \cup S_2$ contains the six points (YYY), (YYN), (YNY), (YNN), (NYN), (NNN).

Definition 2.9. *Let S_1 and S_2 be any two events in the sample space S; then the event which consists of all the points that are in both S_1 and S_2 is called the intersection of S_1 and S_2 and is written $S_1 \cap S_2$, or sometimes written S_1S_2.*

Example 2.10. If S_1 and S_2 are as defined in Example 2.9, the event $S_1 \cap S_2$ consists of the two points (YYN), (YNN).

From the definitions above the results below follow: S is the sample space; S_1 and S_2 are events in S.

1. $\bar{S} = \emptyset$.
2. If S_1 and S_2 have no common points (mutually exclusive sets), then $S_1 \cap S_2 = \emptyset$.
3. $S_1 \cap S = S_1$.
4. $S_1 \cup S = S$.
5. $S \cap \bar{S}_1 = S - S_1 = \bar{S}_1$.
6. $S_1 \cup S_1 = S_1$.
7. $S_1 \cap S_1 = S_1$.

Many other relationships between events can be shown to hold but these will be sufficient for our immediate purpose.

We shall classify the sample space into two types, *discrete* and *con-*

tinuous. This is for the purpose of aiding in explanations in further development of the theory. Actually, with tools of higher mathematics which are beyond the scope of this book, both of these types can be treated in one unifying theory.

Definition 2.10. *A sample space S is called discrete if it contains either (1) a finite number of points or (2) an infinite number of points (countable infinity) which can be put into a one-to-one correspondence with the positive integers.*

In Examples 2.1 to 2.5, the sample space contains a finite number of points and so it is discrete. In Example 2.6 there are an infinite number of points but they can be arranged in a sequence (a one-to-one correspondence with the positive integers), and so this sample space is also discrete. However, the sample space in Example 2.7 was taken to be all real numbers x, where $x > 0$, and these numbers cannot be put into a one-to-one correspondence with the positive integers. Thus, there are some sample spaces which are not discrete but contain what is called a continuum of points.

Definition 2.11. *A sample space S is called a continuous sample space if it contains a continuum of points.*

We shall conclude this section with some more examples, and then we shall give an axiomatic development of probability.

Example 2.11. Consider a random experiment of observing the length of life of electron tubes. The outcome can be any positive number, and so the sample space is continuous.

Example 2.12. Consider a random experiment which consists of selecting three persons at random from the employees of a certain company and recording the annual income of each person. The sample space consists of the triplets (x_1, x_2, x_3), where x_1, x_2, x_3 are the respective incomes of the three persons and each can assume any value greater than 0. Let the event A be defined by the condition that the total annual income of all three persons who are sampled exceeds \$15,000. This can be written as

$$A = \{(x_1, x_2, x_3): x_1 > 0, x_2 > 0, x_3 > 0; x_1 + x_2 + x_3 > \$15{,}000\}$$

Example 2.13. A random experiment consists of throwing two dice and observing the numbers that they show. The sample space consists of 36 points which are (1, 1), (1, 2), · · · , (6, 6), where the ordered pair of numbers represents the outcome of the first and second die, respectively. Let the event A be defined by the condition that the sum of the two faces that shows is equal to seven. The event A consists of six points which are (1, 6), (2, 5), (3, 4), (4, 3), (5, 2), (6, 1).

Example 2.14. In an agricultural experiment, the yield of five varieties of wheat is examined. The five varieties are all grown under rather uniform conditions. The outcome is a collection of five numbers (y_1, y_2, y_3, y_4, y_5), where y_i represents the yield of the ith variety, in bushels per acre. The sample space is continuous, since each y_i can conceivably be any real number greater than or equal to 0. In this example let the event A be defined by the conditions that y_2, y_3, y_4, y_5 are each 10 or more bushels per acre larger than y_1, the standard variety.

In our notation we write

$$A = \{(y_1, y_2, y_3, y_4, y_5): y_j \geq y_1 + 10; j = 2, 3, 4, 5; 0 \leq y_1\}$$

2.6 The Axiomatic Development of Probability

In the previous sections we have given the ideas of classical and frequency probabilities which can help us to answer important problems in experimental science. To aid in the solution of these problems, we shall develop a mathematical theory of probability and then show how this idealized model can be used in real-world problems.

First we shall state the axioms which will be used to develop the theory.

Let S be a sample space, and let A be any event in S; that is, A is any subset of S. Then P will be called a *probability function* on the sample space S if the following three axioms are satisfied.

Axiom 1. *$P(A)$ is a real number such that $P(A) \geq 0$ for every event A in S.*

Axiom 2. $P(S) = 1$.

Axiom 3. *If $S_1, S_2, \cdots$ is a sequence of mutually exclusive events in S, that is, if $S_i \cap S_j = \emptyset$ for $i \neq j = 1, 2, \cdots$, then*

$$P(S_1 \cup S_2 \cup \cdots) = P(S_1) + P(S_2) + \cdots$$

These axioms, which will be used to develop an idealized model, are motivated by the classical and frequency definitions of probability. Now we shall prove some theorems which are direct results of the axioms.

Theorem 2.1. *Let S be a sample space, and let P be a probability function on S; then the probability that the event A does not happen is $1 - P(A)$. This is written in point-set notation as $P(\bar{A}) = 1 - P(A)$.*

Proof. From Definition 2.6, $A \cap \bar{A} = \emptyset$; also $A \cup \bar{A} = S$, and so, by Axiom 2, we get $1 = P(S) = P(A \cup \bar{A})$. By Axiom 3, we have $1 = P(S) = P(A \cup \bar{A}) = P(A) + P(\bar{A})$, and the proof is complete.

Theorem 2.2. *Let S be a sample space with probability function P; then $0 \leq P(A) \leq 1$ for any event A in S.*

Proof. By Axiom 1, $P(A) \geq 0$, and so we need only show that $P(A) \leq 1$. From Theorem 2.1, $P(A) + P(\bar{A}) = 1$ but $P(\bar{A}) \geq 0$, by Axiom 1, and so $P(A) = 1 - P(\bar{A}) \leq 1$.

Theorem 2.3. *Let S be a sample space with a probability function P. If S_0 is the null set, then $P(S_0) = 0$.*

Proof. From the results in Sec. 2.5, we have $\bar{S} = S_0 = \emptyset$. From Axiom 3, we get $P(S \cup \bar{S}) = P(S) + P(\bar{S}) = P(S) + P(S_0)$. But $S \cup \bar{S} = S$ and $P(S) = 1$, and so $P(S_0) = 0$.

If these axioms and the resulting theorems are to aid us in developing a useful model, we must have a rule or function which will enable us to compute the probability for *every* event A (subset) of the sample space S. In the next few sections we shall explain how to construct such a function. We shall do this for three different sample spaces: (1) a discrete sample space with a finite number of points, where each point has the same probability; (2) a general discrete sample space, which will be discussed in Chap. 3; (3) a continuous sample space, which will be discussed in Chap. 4.

2.7 Discrete Sample Space with a Finite Number of Points

In certain kinds of problems, in which games of chance are notable examples, the sample space contains a finite number of points n, say, and the probability attached to each point is $1/n$.

In other words, in certain problems there are a finite number of arrangements (n), and it is often realistic to assume that the probability of each arrangement is $1/n$. The classical definition is generally sufficient for these problems, and combinatorial methods can be used for enumeration. We shall show how this special sample space (finite number of points with equal probability for each point) fits into the general theory, and then we shall demonstrate various methods which can be used to solve these problems.

Definition 2.12. *Let $s_1, s_2, \cdots, s_n$ be the n sample points in a discrete sample space S; the function P is called an equally likely probability function if it satisfies the following conditions:*

(*a*) $P(s_1) = P(s_2) = \cdots = P(s_n) = 1/n$.

(*b*) *Let A be an event which contains any n_A of the sample points s_i; then* $P(A) = n_A/n$.

Condition (*a*) states that each of the n points is equally likely and hence has probability $1/n$. Condition (*b*) states that the probability of an event which contains n_A of the n sample points is n_A/n. It is readily checked that this function satisfies Axioms 1, 2, and 3 and hence is a probability function. The equally likely probability function is exactly the same as that in Definition 2.1.

Example 2.15. Suppose that a random experiment consists of tossing a symmetrical balanced coin two times. The sample space S (outcomes) consists of four points (H, H) $= s_1$; (H, T) $= s_2$; (T, H) $= s_3$; (T, T) $= s_4$, where (H, T) means a head appeared on the first toss and a tail on the second toss, etc. It seems quite reasonable to attach the probability ¼ to each sample point. Suppose that A is the event "The first toss results in a head." Then $A = s_1 \cup s_2$. This event (subset) contains two points, and so $P(A) = 2/4 = 1/2$. Let the event B be the condition that at least one head appears; then $B = s_1 \cup s_2 \cup s_3$. B contains three points, and so $P(B) = 3/4$. Next suppose that we desire the probability that B does not occur, that is, $P(\bar{B})$. By Definition 2.5, $s_4 = \bar{B}$, and by Theorem 2.1, $1 - P(B) = P(\bar{B}) = P(s_4) = 1/4$, and so $P(\bar{B}) = 1/4$.

2.8 Permutations and Combinations

To compute the probability of an event A in a situation where Definition 2.1 or its equivalent Definition 2.12 applies (we shall assume that these definitions apply in Secs. 2.8 to 2.13) we need to evaluate the total number of equally likely, mutually exclusive arrangements n and the number n_A with attribute A. This sort of enumeration can often be facilitated by certain combinatorial formulas which will be developed now. They are based on the following two basic principles:

(*a*) *If an event A can occur in a total of m ways and if a different event B can occur in n ways, then the event A or B can occur in m + n ways provided that A and B cannot occur simultaneously.*

(*b*) *If an event A can occur in a total of m ways and if a different event B can occur in n ways, then the event A and B can occur in mn ways.*

These two ideas may be illustrated by letting A correspond to the drawing of a spade from a deck of cards and B correspond to the drawing of a heart. Each of these events can be done in 13 ways. The number of ways in which a heart or a spade can be drawn is obviously

$$13 + 13 = 26$$

To illustrate the second principle, suppose that two cards are drawn from the deck in such a way that one is a spade and the other is a heart. There are $13 \times 13 = 169$ ways of doing this, since with the ace of spades we may put any one of the 13 hearts, or with the king of spades we may put any one of the 13 hearts, and so on for all 13 of the spades.

The two principles may clearly be generalized to take account of more than two events. Thus, if three mutually exclusive events A, B, and C can occur in m, n, and p ways, respectively, the event A or B or C can occur in $m + n + p$ ways, and the event A and B and C can occur in mnp ways.

We shall now use the second of these principles to enumerate the number of arrangements of a set of objects. Let us consider the number of arrangements of the letters a, b, c. We can pick any one of the three to place in the first position; either of the remaining two may be put in the second position, and the third position must be filled by the unused letter. The filling of the first position is an event which can occur in three ways; the filling of the second position is an event which can occur in two ways; and the third event can occur in one way. The three events can occur together in $3 \times 2 \times 1 = 6$ ways. The six arrangements, or *permutations*, as they are called, are

$$abc,\ acb,\ bac,\ bca,\ cab,\ cba$$

In this simple example the elaborate method of counting was hardly worth while because it is easy enough to write down all the six permutations. But if we had asked for the number of permutations of six letters, we should have had

$$6 \times 5 \times 4 \times 3 \times 2 \times 1 = 720$$

permutations to write down.

It is obvious now that, in general, the number of permutations of n different objects is

$$n(n-1)(n-2)(n-3) \cdots (2)(1)$$

This product of an integer by all the positive integers smaller than it is usually denoted more briefly by $n!$ (read n factorial). Thus $2! = 2$, $3! = 6$, $4! = 24$, $5! = 120$, etc. Since

$$(n-1)! = \frac{n!}{n}$$

it is common to define $0!$ as 1, so that the relation will be consistent when $n = 1$.

Let us now enumerate the number of permutations that may be made from n objects if only r of the objects are used in any given permutation. Reasoning as before, the first position may be filled in n ways, the second position may be filled in $n - 1$ ways, and so forth. When we come to the rth position, we shall have used $r - 1$ of the objects so that $n - (r - 1)$ will remain from which we can choose. The number of permutations of n objects taken r at a time is therefore $n(n-1)(n-2) \cdots (n-r+1)$. The symbol $P_{n,r}$ is used to denote this number.

$$P_{n,r} = n(n-1)(n-2) \cdots (n-r+1) = \frac{n!}{(n-r)!} \qquad (1)$$

Thus the number of permutations of the four letters a, b, c, d taken two at a time is $P_{4,2} = 4 \times 3 = 12$. On putting $r = n$ in equation (1), we get the result stated earlier: that the number of permutations of n objects taken n at a time is $n!$.

With the aid of equation (1) we can now solve the following problem: In how many different ways can r objects be selected from n objects? $P_{n,r}$ counts all the possible selections as well as all the arrangements of each selection or *combination*. Two combinations are different if they are not made up of the same set of objects. Thus *abc* and *abd* are different three-letter combinations, while *abc* and *bac* are different permutations of the same combination. Let the symbol $\binom{n}{r}$ denote the number of different combinations. Then it is clear that $P_{n,r}$ equals $\binom{n}{r}$ times $r!$, since each combination of r objects has $r!$ arrangements. Therefore

$$\binom{n}{r} = \frac{P_{n,r}}{r!} = \frac{n(n-1)(n-2)\cdots(n-r+1)}{r!} = \frac{n!}{r!(n-r)!} \tag{2}$$

Another common symbol for this number is $C_{n,r}$, but we shall not use it in this text. The number of combinations of five objects taken three at a time is

$$\binom{5}{3} = \frac{5 \times 4 \times 3}{3!} = \frac{60}{6} = 10$$

The number $\binom{n}{r}$ may be given a different interpretation. It is the number of ways in which n objects may be divided into two groups, one group containing r objects, and the other group containing the other $n - r$ objects. Now suppose that we wish to divide n objects into three groups containing n_1, n_2, n_3 objects, respectively, with

$$n_1 + n_2 + n_3 = n$$

We shall first divide them into two groups containing n_1 and $n_2 + n_3$ objects. This may be done in $\binom{n}{n_1}$ ways. Then we may divide the second group into two groups containing n_2 and n_3 objects. This may be done in $\binom{n_2+n_3}{n_2}$ ways. If the second principle of enumeration is used, the total number of ways of doing the two divisions together is

$$\binom{n}{n_1}\binom{n_2+n_3}{n_2} = \frac{n!}{n_1!(n_2+n_3)!}\,\frac{(n_2+n_3)!}{n_2!n_3!} = \frac{n!}{n_1!n_2!n_3!}$$

This type of argument may be carried further to find the number of ways of dividing n objects into k groups containing $n_1, n_2, \cdots, n_k$ objects with $n_1 + n_2 + \cdots + n_k = n$. This number is readily found to be

$$\frac{n!}{n_1!n_2!\cdots n_k!} \tag{3}$$

Thus the number of ways of dividing four objects into three groups containing one, one, and two objects is

$$\frac{4!}{1!1!2!} = 12$$

The expression (3) also has a second interpretation. It is the number of different permutations of n objects when n_1 of the objects are alike and of one kind, n_2 are alike and of a second kind, and so forth. Referring to the numerical example above, there are 12 permutations of the letters a, b, c, c. In order to see that expression (3) gives the correct number, consider n different objects (for example, the letters $a, b, c, \cdots, p$) arranged in a definite order. Consider a division of this set of objects into k groups, the first group containing n_1 objects, the second n_2, and so forth. Now, in the original arrangement of objects, replace all the objects selected for the first group by 1's, all those selected for the second group by 2's, and so forth. The result will be a permutation of n_1 1's, n_2 2's, $\cdots, n_k$ k's. A little reflection will convince one that every division of the letters into the k groups corresponds to a different permutation of the integers and that this is the total set of permutations, because if there were another, there would be another division of the letters into k groups.

We have derived three formulas in this section, not only because they are useful but because their derivation serves to illustrate the application of the two principles of enumeration given at the beginning of the section. It is the methods that are important. The formulas will aid in solving many problems, but they are useless in many others, and one must then fall back on the elementary principles.

Example 2.16. If two cards are drawn from an ordinary deck, what is the probability that one will be a spade and the other a heart?

Since nothing is said about the order in which the spade and the heart should occur, this is a problem in combinations. To compute the probability, we must find the total number of possible outcomes, n, of two-card draws. This n is the number of points in the sample space S, and $1/n$ is the probability attached to each point. Then we must find the number of these points n_A that have the specified attribute. The total number of two-card combinations that can be made up from 52 cards is $\binom{52}{2} = 1326 = n$. We have seen before that there are $13 \times 13 = 169 = n_A$ different combinations with the required attribute. Therefore,

$$P(A) = \frac{n_A}{n} = 169/1326 = 13/102$$

This problem could also be solved by regarding the different two-card permutations as the set of possible outcomes. The denominator of the ratio would then be $P_{52,2} = 2652$. To get the numerator, we consider that each of the 169 two-card combinations has two permutations and get $2 \times 169 = 338$ as the number of permutations with the required attribute. Or we may start at the beginning as follows: The number of permutations in which the spade occurs first and the heart second is $13 \times 13 = 169$, by principle (*b*). The number with the heart first and the spade second is the same. Either of these sets of permutations satisfies the specification. By principle (*a*), the required number is $169 + 169 = 338$. Again we find the probability to be $^{13}\!/_{102}$.

Example 2.17. What is the probability that, of four cards drawn from an ordinary deck, at least three will be spades?

Here again we are interested in combinations. The total number of possible four-card combinations is $\binom{52}{4} = 270{,}725$. Thus the sample space S consists of $270{,}725 = n$ points, and the probability attached to each point is $1/n = 1/270{,}725$. To get the numerator n_A we consider the following: The specification, at least three spades, means either three or four. The number of four-card hands containing exactly three spades is $\binom{13}{3} 39 = 11{,}154$; the first factor is the number of three-card combinations of three spades, and the second is the number of ways in which a card may be selected from the other three suits; the product is taken in accordance with principle (*b*). The number of hands with all cards spades is $\binom{13}{4} = 715$. By principle (*a*), the number of hands with the required attribute is $11{,}154 + 715 = 11{,}869 = n_A$. The required probability is $P(A) = n_A/n = 11{,}869/270{,}725$.

One might attempt to find the numerator by the following method: The number of three-card combinations of spades is $\binom{13}{3} = 286$. The fourth card may be either a spade or not a spade, and after three spades have been selected, the fourth card may be selected from the whole set of 49 remaining cards. Thus the required number of hands is $49 \times 286 = 14{,}014$. This argument is faulty because the hands with four spades have been counted more than once. A specific three-card combination of spades is AKQ, and when the jack of spades is drawn from the remaining 49 cards, we have the combination AKQJ. But we also count this combination when the AQJ is considered and the king is drawn from the remaining 49 cards. It is now clear that the hands with four spades have been counted four times in the above figure. We can obtain the correct result by subtracting from it three times the number of hands with four spades. The result is

$$14{,}014 - 3\binom{13}{4} = 11{,}869$$

as before.

Example 2.18. Seven balls are tossed into four numbered boxes so that each ball falls in a box and is equally likely to fall in any of the boxes. What is the probability that the first box will contain exactly two balls?

Since the first ball may fall in any one of four ways, the second may fall in any one of four ways, and so forth, the total number of possible outcomes is, by principle (*b*), 4^7. To enumerate the number of outcomes with the desired attribute, let us first divide the seven balls into two groups, one containing two and the other five balls. This may be done in $\binom{7}{2}$ ways. Now the group of two will be put into the first box and the other five distributed among the other three boxes. This may be done, by the same reasoning as above, in 3^5 ways. The number of favorable outcomes is therefore $\binom{7}{2}3^5$, and the desired probability is

$$P(A) = \frac{n_A}{n} = \frac{\binom{7}{2}3^5}{4^7} = \frac{7 \times 3^6}{4^7} \cong .3115$$

(The symbol $\cong$ is used to denote approximate equality.)

2.9 Stirling's Formula

In finding numerical values of probabilities, one is often confronted with the evaluation of long factorial expressions which are troublesome to compute by direct multiplication. If an adding machine is available, and there are not a great number of factors in the expression, it is often convenient to use logarithms. However, when the factors become numerous, this method also becomes tedious, and much labor may be saved by using Stirling's formula, which gives an approximate value of $n!$. It is

$$n! \cong \sqrt{2\pi}e^{-n}n^{n+\frac{1}{2}} \tag{1}$$

where e is the Napierian base, 2.71828 · · · . A much more accurate approximation may be obtained by replacing the factor e^{-n} by $e^{-[n-(1/12n)]}$, but this refinement is rarely used. To indicate the accuracy of the formula, we may compute 10!, which is actually 3,628,800. Formula (1) using five-place logarithms gives

$$10! \cong 3{,}599{,}000$$

The more refined formula gives

$$10! \cong 3{,}629{,}000$$

The error in (1) for $n = 10$ is a little less than 1 per cent, and the percentage error decreases as n increases.

2.10 Sum and Product Notations

A sum of terms such as $n_3 + n_4 + n_5 + n_6 + n_7$ is often designated by the symbol $\sum_{i=3}^{7} n_i$. The Σ is the capital Greek letter sigma, and in this connection it is often called the *summation sign*. The letter i is called the *summation index*. The term following the Σ is called the *summand*. The $i = 3$ below Σ indicates that the first term of the sum is obtained by putting $i = 3$ in the summand. The 7 above the Σ indicates that the final term of the sum is obtained by putting $i = 7$ in the summand. The other terms of the sum are obtained by giving i the integral values between the limits 3 and 7. Thus

$$\sum_{j=2}^{5} (-1)^{j-2} j x^{2j} = 2x^4 - 3x^6 + 4x^8 - 5x^{10}$$

An analogous notation for a product is obtained by substituting the capital Greek letter Π for Σ. In this case the terms resulting from substituting the integers for the index are multiplied instead of added. Thus

$$\prod_{a=1}^{5} \left[c + (-1)^a \frac{a}{b} \right] = \left(c - \frac{1}{b}\right)\left(c + \frac{2}{b}\right)\left(c - \frac{3}{b}\right)\left(c + \frac{4}{b}\right)\left(c - \frac{5}{b}\right)$$

Using this notation, expression (2.8.3) derived previously may be written $n! \Big/ \prod_{i=1}^{k} n_i!$.

2.11 The Binomial and Multinomial Theorems

The expansion of the binomial expression $(x + y)^n$ is given in elementary algebra, and a proof of the correctness of the expansion is ordinarily by induction. We shall here expand the binomial by a simple combinatorial method which readily generalizes to the multinomial case. If we write the binomial in the form $(x + y)(x + y)(x + y) \cdots (x + y)$, which has n factors, the problem of finding the coefficient of one of the terms, say $x^{n-a}y^a$, reduces to the problem of finding the number of ways of dividing the n factors into two groups. The first term of the expansion is x^n, which is obtained by selecting the x from each of the factors. The next term is some coefficient times $x^{n-1}y$. This term arises by selecting the x from $n - 1$ of the factors and the y from the remaining one. The one from which y is taken may be chosen in any of n ways; hence the coefficient of $x^{n-1}y$ is n. In general, to get the coefficient of $x^{n-a}y^a$, we must count the number of ways of dividing the n factors into two groups so that one group contains a factors and the other $n - a$ factors; y is selected from each factor of the first group and x from each factor of the second group. The number of ways of dividing the n factors into two such groups is $\binom{n}{a}$, which is the desired coefficient. The binomial expansion is therefore

$$(x + y)^n = x^n + nx^{n-1}y + \binom{n}{2}x^{n-2}y^2 + \cdots + y^n$$

$$= \sum_{i=0}^{n} \binom{n}{i} x^{n-i}y^i \tag{1}$$

The multinomial theorem follows directly. If the expression

$$(x_1 + x_2 + \cdots + x_k)^n$$

is multiplied out, one will obtain terms of the form

$$Cx_1^{n_1}x_2^{n_2} \cdots x_k^{n_k}$$

where C is some coefficient and the exponents satisfy the relation

$$\sum_{i=1}^{k} n_i = n$$

We wish to determine C. Terms of the given form arise when x_1 is selected from n_1 of the n factors, x_2 is selected from n_2 of the remaining factors, and so forth. The number of ways of getting such a term is equal to the number of ways of dividing the n factors into k groups containing $n_1, n_2, \cdots, n_k$ factors. This is expression (2.8.3). Thus the general term of the multinomial expansion is

$$\frac{n!}{n_1!n_2! \cdots n_k!} x_1^{n_1}x_2^{n_2} \cdots x_k^{n_k} \qquad \text{or} \qquad n! \prod_{i=1}^{k} \frac{x_i^{n_i}}{n_i!}$$

and we may write

$$(x_1 + x_2 + \cdots + x_k)^n = \sum_{n_1, n_2, \cdots, n_k} n! \prod_{i=1}^{k} \frac{x_i^{n_i}}{n_i!} \tag{2}$$

We have indicated only that the summation is over the indices n_1, n_2,

$\cdots, n_k$. The range of each index is 0 to n, but they cannot all be summed independently over that range because we must have $\sum_{i=1}^{k} n_i = n$. The summation is over all sets of values of $n_1, n_2, \cdots, n_k$ such that their sum is n and such that each n_i is an integer in the range 0 to n inclusive. The sum is very troublesome to write down when n is large. We shall illustrate for a simple case.

$$(x_1 + x_2 + x_3)^4 = \sum_{n_1,n_2,n_3} \frac{4!}{n_1!n_2!n_3!} x_1^{n_1}x_2^{n_2}x_3^{n_3}$$

The sets of values of (n_1, n_2, n_3) which satisfy $n_1 + n_2 + n_3 = 4$ are (4, 0, 0), (3, 1, 0), (3, 0, 1), (2, 2, 0), (2, 1, 1), (2, 0, 2), (1, 3, 0), (1, 2, 1), (1, 1, 2), (1, 0, 3), (0, 4, 0), (0, 3, 1), (0, 2, 2), (0, 1, 3), (0, 0, 4). The sum therefore has 15 terms, the first few of which are

$$\begin{aligned}(x_1 + x_2 + x_3)^4 &= \frac{4!}{4!} x_1^4 + \frac{4!}{3!} x_1^3x_2 + \frac{4!}{3!} x_1^3x_3 + \frac{4!}{2!2!} x_1^2x_2^2 + \cdots + \frac{4!}{4!} x_3^4 \\ &= x_1^4 + 4x_1^3x_2 + 4x_1^3x_3 + 6x_1^2x_2^2 + \cdots + x_3^4\end{aligned}$$

A set of numbers such as (3, 1, 0) is called a three-part *partition* of four. (2, 6) is a two-part partition of eight. The 15 triplets of numbers listed above form the complete set of *ordered three-part partitions* of four. The partitions are called *ordered* because the same combination of three parts in a different order is counted as a different partition. If it is not specified that the partitions be ordered, the unordered ones are assumed; thus, the three-part partitions of four are simply (4, 0, 0), (3, 1, 0), (2, 2, 0), (2, 1, 1). In terms of the idea of partitions, the multinomial sum (2) may be described briefly as follows: The sum is taken over all ordered k-part partitions of n, the parts being $(n_1, n_2, \cdots, n_k)$.

2.12 Combinatorial Generating Functions

The enumeration of possible outcomes and of outcomes with a certain attribute can become quite complex. In fact, it is easy to state problems in which the enumeration is practically impossible. One of the most powerful devices for solving enumeration problems involves the use of what are called *generating functions*. The subject of combinatorial generating functions is a field of mathematics in itself, and we shall consider only a few simple cases here. We wish merely to indicate the nature of this method of analysis.

Let us consider the last illustration given in Example 2.18 where seven balls were tossed into four boxes, and consider

$$(x_1 + x_2 + x_3 + x_4)^7$$

The coefficient of a term such as $x_1^2x_2^4x_3$ in the expansion of this multinomial is given by formula (2.8.3) as $7!/2!4!1!0!$, which is just the number of ways of dividing seven objects into four groups so that the first contains two objects, the second four, and so forth. Thus any term in the multinomial expansion gives a description of a possible outcome; a factor such as x_i^5 means five balls have fallen in the ith box, and the numerical coefficient of the term gives the number of ways in which that outcome can occur. If the x's are now all replaced by 1's, the terms become simply $7!\Big/\prod_{i=1}^{4} n_i!$, and to get the whole set of possible outcomes, we need to sum this expression over all sets of the n_i whose sum is 7. This sum by the multinomial theorem is just

$$(1 + 1 + 1 + 1)^7 = 4^7$$

If we want the probability that the first box contains two balls, we shall sum $7\ /\Pi n_i!$ over all sets of n_i which have $n_1 = 2$. Let us rewrite the term as

$$\frac{7!}{2!5!}\,\frac{5!}{n_2!n_3!n_4!}$$

and now we wish to sum this over all sets so that $n_2 + n_3 + n_4 = 5$. If we multiply $5!/n_2!n_3!n_4!$ by $1^{n_2}1^{n_3}1^{n_4}$, we have the general term of $(1 + 1 + 1)^5$; hence the desired sum is $7!/2!5!$ times 3^5.

The polynomial $(x_1 + x_2 + x_3 + x_4)^7$ is a simple type of generating function; it is an algebraic expression which is given an interpretation in terms of the physical problem at hand. It may be used to answer any of the questions that may be asked about the physical problem to which it is related. Thus, if the number of ways in which the first two boxes can each contain at least two balls is required, we would add the coefficients of all terms in the generating function which have x_1 and x_2 with powers greater than or equal to 2.

Now let us consider another problem. An urn contains five black and four white balls. The balls are all drawn one by one from the urn, and the first three drawn are placed in a black box while the last six are placed in a white box. What is the probability that the number of black balls in the black box plus the number of white balls in the white box is equal to five?

We may solve this problem by considering the balls of each color to be numbered. The total number of ways of dividing the nine objects into two groups, the first containing three and the second six, is $\binom{9}{3}$. To get five balls to match the color of the box containing them, we must clearly have two black balls in the black box and three white ones in the white box. The black box may be filled $\binom{5}{2}\binom{4}{1}$ ways since there are $\binom{5}{2}$ ways of picking two black ones from the five black ones to be among the first three drawn and $\binom{4}{1}$ ways of choosing one white ball to be among the first three drawn. The probability is $\binom{5}{2}\binom{4}{1}\bigg/\binom{9}{3}$.

The following generating function may be related to this problem:

$$(x_1t + x_2)^5(x_1 + x_2t)^4$$

Here x_1 corresponds to the black box and x_2 to the white one. The first factor corresponds to the five black balls, and the second to the four white balls. We shall consider the coefficient of the term involving $x_1^3x_2^6$. It will be a polynomial in t, and if t were put equal to 1, the polynomial would have the value $\binom{9}{3}$, since then we should have the coefficient of $x_1^3x_2^6$ in $(x_1 + x_2)^9$. The coefficient of t^r in the polynomial is the number of ways in which r balls can fall in boxes of the same color as the balls. In forming a term in $x_1^3x_2^6$, we may choose certain of the x_1's from the factor $(x_1t + x_2)^5$ and the remainder from the other factor. Those chosen from the first factor represent black balls, and those chosen from the second represent white balls. Thus, when a black ball is associated with the black box, we get a factor t, and when a white ball is associated with the white box, we also get a factor t. The power of t then gives the total number of times a ball is associated with a box of its color. On expanding the generating function, one would find the coefficient of $x_1^3x_2^6t^5$ to be $\binom{5}{2}\binom{4}{1}$ as before.

The generating function is of no value for this simple problem, but it becomes useful if more than two colors are considered. Thus suppose that an urn contained n_1 balls of a given color, n_2 of a second color, and n_3 of a third color; and suppose that m_1 are drawn and placed in a box of the first color, m_2 are then drawn and placed in a box of the second color, and the remaining balls, say m_3 of them, are placed in a box of the third color. Let n be the total number of balls; then

$$n = n_1 + n_2 + n_3 = m_1 + m_2 + m_3$$

The coefficient of $x_1^{m_1}x_2^{m_2}x_3^{m_3}t^r$ in

$$(x_1t + x_2 + x_3)^{n_1}(x_1 + x_2t + x_3)^{n_2}(x_1 + x_2 + x_3t)^{n_3}$$

gives the number of ways in which r balls match the color of the box containing them. The coefficient is difficult to calculate in this case, but to find it is a straightforward procedure, while to find it without the generating function is considerably more troublesome.

We shall consider one other kind of generating function. If five dice are tossed, what is the probability that the sum of the spots will be 15?

Since the first die may fall in six ways, the second may fall in six ways, and so forth, the total number of possible outcomes is 6^5. Now we need the number of these outcomes that have a sum equal to 15. In the case of two dice, it is easy to write down all possible combinations which give a specified sum. Thus to obtain a sum of five, the two dice may fall (1, 4), (2, 3), (3, 2), (4, 1). These are the ordered two-part partitions of five when zero is excluded as a part. In our problem we must enumerate all the ordered five-part partitions of 15 which have all parts between one and six inclusive.

In problems involving partitions of numbers, there is a generating function which will usually materially simplify the enumeration. For the particular problem of counting the ways of getting 15 with five dice, let us consider the polynomial

$$(x + x^2 + x^3 + x^4 + x^5 + x^6)^5 \tag{1}$$

It is a polynomial in x in which the term of lowest degree is x^5 and the term of highest degree is x^{30}. Let us suppose that it is written as the product of five factors instead of as a fifth power. The first factor will be associated with the first die, the second factor with the second die, and so on. In the expansion of the quantity there will be a number of terms x^{15}; one, for example, will arise when x is selected from each of the first three factors and x^6 is selected from the remaining two factors. This situation corresponds to the appearance of a one on the first three dice, and a six on the other two. It is readily seen that there is a one-to-one correspondence between the ways in which x^{15} can arise in the expansion and the ways in which the five dice can total 15. Hence our required number is the coefficient of x^{15} in the expansion of the polynomial. This coefficient may be found most easily by use of the following identity:

$$\frac{1 - x^n}{1 - x} = 1 + x + x^2 + \cdots + x^{n-1} \tag{2}$$

which may be verified by multiplying both sides by $1 - x$. Using this identity, the generating function may be put in the form

$$\frac{x^5(1 - x^6)^5}{(1 - x)^5}$$

We may omit the factor x^5 and find the coefficient of x^{10} in what remains.

Now we need another identity:

$$\frac{1}{(1-x)^n} = 1 + \binom{n}{1}x + \binom{n+1}{2}x^2 + \binom{n+2}{3}x^3 + \cdots \qquad |x| < 1$$

$$= \sum_{i=0}^{\infty} \binom{n+i-1}{i} x^i \tag{3}$$

which reduces our problem to that of finding the coefficient of x^{10} in

$$(1 - x^6)^5 \sum_{i=0}^{\infty} \binom{4+i}{i} x^i$$

If the first factor is expanded, all but the first two terms have x to a higher power than 10 and may be neglected. And now the problem becomes that of finding the coefficient of x^{10} in

$$(1 - 5x^6) \sum_{i=0}^{\infty} \binom{4+i}{i} x^i$$

which has two terms in x^{10}: one when the 1 is multiplied by the term given by $i = 10$ in the sum, and the other when the $-5x^6$ is multiplied by the term given by $i = 4$ in the sum. The coefficient is therefore $\binom{14}{10} - 5\binom{8}{4}$, and the probability that we set out to find is

$$\frac{\binom{14}{10} - 5\binom{8}{4}}{6^5} = \frac{651}{7776} \cong .0837$$

These examples will serve to indicate the kind of attack that may be made on enumeration problems by means of generating functions. The method is powerful, but we cannot develop it here. We merely wish to point out the existence of the method.

2.13 Marginal Probability

Suppose in this section that the sample space S which consists of n points with probability $1/n$ is partitioned into r mutually exclusive (disjoint) subsets $A_1, A_2, \cdots, A_r$. Let $B_1, B_2, \cdots, B_s$ be another partition of S into s mutually exclusive (disjoint) subsets. The n points in S may then be classified in a two-way table, as in Table 2.3. Here we have indicated that n_{11} of the n outcomes have both the attribute A_1 and the attribute B_1; n_{12} have both the attribute A_1 and the attribute B_2; and in general n_{ij} of the outcomes have the attributes A_i and B_j.

The sum of all n_{ij} is n. As an example, we may consider the drawing of a card from an ordinary deck of playing cards. The 52 outcomes may be classified according to suit (say A_1, A_2, A_3, A_4) or according to denomination (say $B_1, B_2, \cdots, B_{13}$). In this example every n_{ij} is 1.

TABLE 2.3

	B_1	B_2	$\cdots$	B_s
A_1	n_{11}	n_{12}	$\cdots$	n_{1s}
A_2	n_{21}	n_{22}	$\cdots$	n_{2s}
$\vdots$	$\vdots$	$\vdots$		$\vdots$
A_r	n_{r1}	n_{r2}		n_{rs}

The probability of the event A_1 and B_3, for example, will sometimes be denoted by $P(A_1, B_3)$ instead of $P(A_1 \cap B_3)$, and the value of this probability is obviously n_{13}/n. In general,

$$P(A_i, B_j) = \frac{n_{ij}}{n}$$

We may be interested in only one of the criteria of classification, say A, and indifferent to the B classification. In this case B is omitted from the symbol, and the probability of A_2, say, is written $P(A_2)$, and

$$\begin{aligned} P(A_2) &= \frac{n_{21} + n_{22} + n_{23} + \cdots + n_{2s}}{n} \\ &= \sum_{j=1}^{s} \frac{n_{2j}}{n} \end{aligned}$$

This is called a *marginal probability*, and the term marginal is used whenever one or more criteria of classification are ignored. It is clear that

$$P(A_i) = \sum_{j=1}^{s} \frac{n_{ij}}{n}$$

or

$$P(A_i) = \sum_{j=1}^{s} P(A_i, B_j) \tag{1}$$

since $n_{ij}/n = P(A_i, B_j)$. Also the marginal probability of B_j is

$$P(B_j) = \sum_{i=1}^{r} P(A_i, B_j) \tag{2}$$

In point-set terminology, we have partitioned the sample space S into rs disjoint subsets where the general subset is denoted by $A_i \cap B_j$. Now,

$$A_i = (A_i \cap B_1) \cup (A_i \cap B_2) \cup (A_i \cap B_3) \cup \cdots \cup (A_i \cap B_s)$$

But since $(A_i \cap B_j) \cap (A_i \cap B_{j'}) = \emptyset$ when $j \neq j'$, we can use Axiom 3 and obtain

$$P(A_i) = P(A_i \cap B_1) + P(A_i \cap B_2) + \cdots + P(A_i \cap B_s)$$

or, in the simpler notation,

$$P(A_i) = \sum_{j=1}^{s} P(A_i, B_j) = \sum_{j=1}^{s} \frac{n_{ij}}{n}$$

In the card example, the probability that a card is an ace is the sum of the probabilities that it is the ace of spades, the ace of hearts, the ace of diamonds, and the ace of clubs.

In a more general situation, suppose that there are three criteria of classification, A, B, and C. Let n_{ijk} of the n possible outcomes have the specification A_i, B_j, C_k, and let the C classification be $C_1, C_2, \cdots, C_t$, with the A and B classes the same as before. The complete classification would be a three-way table consisting of t layers of two-way tables, each layer corresponding to a C_k. The marginal probability of, say, A_i and C_k is

$$P(A_i, C_k) = \sum_{j=1}^{s} P(A_i, B_j, C_k) \tag{3}$$

and the marginal probability of C_k is

$$P(C_k) = \sum_{i=1}^{r} \sum_{j=1}^{s} P(A_i, B_j, C_k) \tag{4}$$

$$= \sum_{i=1}^{r} P(A_i, C_k) \tag{5}$$

$$= \sum_{j=1}^{s} P(B_j, C_k) \tag{6}$$

The extension of these ideas to more than three criteria of classification is apparent.

2.14 Conditional Probability

Returning to the two-way classification in Table 2.3, suppose that the outcome of a random experiment is examined for one attribute but not for the other. We wish to find the probability that the other attribute has a specified value. The event, for example, may be B_3. What is the probability that it is also A_2? The total number of outcomes for A, given that B_3 has occurred, is $\sum_{i=1}^{r} n_{i3}$, and the number of favorable outcomes for A_2 is n_{23}. Thus the probability of A_2, given that B_3 has occurred, is $n_{23} \Big/ \sum_{i=1}^{r} n_{i3}$. This is called a *conditional probability* and is denoted by the symbol $P(A_2|B_3)$. In general (assume the denominators are not zero),

$$P(A_i|B_j) = \frac{n_{ij}}{\sum_{i=1}^{r} n_{ij}}$$

$$P(B_j|A_i) = \frac{n_{ij}}{\sum_{j=1}^{s} n_{ij}}$$

On dividing both the numerator and denominator of the fraction on the right by n, we have

$$P(A_i|B_j) = \frac{P(A_i, B_j)}{P(B_j)} \tag{1}$$

$$P(B_j|A_i) = \frac{P(A_i, B_j)}{P(A_i)} \tag{2}$$

or in another form

$$P(A_i,B_j) = P(A_i|B_j)P(B_j) \tag{3}$$

$$= P(B_j|A_i)P(A_i) \tag{4}$$

The last equation may be stated: The probability that an outcome will have the attribute A_i and B_j is equal to the marginal probability of A_i multiplied by the conditional probability of B_j, given that A_i has occurred.

The idea of conditional probability has a straightforward extension to situations involving more than two criteria of classification. In the case of three criteria, for example, it may be shown directly that

$$P(A_i, B_j|C_k) = \frac{P(A_i, B_j, C_k)}{P(C_k)} \tag{5}$$

$$P(A_i|B_j, C_k) = \frac{P(A_i, B_j, C_k)}{P(B_j, C_k)} \tag{6}$$

and also that

$$P(A_i\ B_j, C_k) = P(A_i, B_j|C_k)P(C_k) \tag{7}$$

$$= P(A_i|B_j, C_k)P(B_j, C_k) \tag{8}$$

$$= P(A_i|B_j, C_k)P(B_j|C_k)P(C_k) \tag{9}$$

Other similar relations could be obtained by permuting the letters A, B, C. Thus

$$P(B_j|A_i, C_k) = \frac{P(A_i, B_j, C_k)}{P(A_i, C_k)} \tag{10}$$

and

$$P(A_i, B_j, C_k) = P(B_j|A_i, C_k)P(A_i|C_k)P(C_k) \tag{11}$$

or

$$P(A_i, B_j, C_k) = P(B_j|A_i, C_k)P(C_k|A_i)P(A_i) \tag{12}$$

We shall not take the space to write out all such possible relations, but the student would do well to do so. These relations are fundamental in the theory of statistics and must be well understood. The above conditional probabilities are not defined if the denominator is 0. This is also true in what follows.

In describing conditional probability we have used a rather special sample space, one with a finite number of points, n, each with probability $1/n$. However, the idea is quite general and can be defined for discrete and continuous sample spaces as follows:

Definition 2.13. *Let A and B be two events in a sample space S such that $P(B) > 0$. The conditional probability of the event A, given that event B has happened, which is written $P(A|B)$, is*

$$P(A|B) = \frac{P(A, B)}{P(B)}$$

Example 2.19. An urn contains six red and four black balls. Two balls are drawn without replacement. What is the probability that the second ball is red if it is known that the first is red? Let us use the formula in Definition 2.13. Let B be the event that the first ball is red and A the event that the second ball is red. Thus $P(A, B)$ is the probability that both the first and the second ball are red. There are $\binom{10}{2}$ ways of drawing two balls from the urn, and so the sample space contains $\binom{10}{2}$ points each with probability $1\Big/\binom{10}{2}$. The number of ways of getting two red balls is $\binom{6}{2}$, and so $P(A, B) = \binom{6}{2}\Big/\binom{10}{2} = \frac{1}{3}$. Now $P(B)$ is the probability that the first ball drawn is red. This is clearly $\frac{6}{10}$. Thus $P(A|B) = \frac{1}{3}\Big/\frac{6}{10} = \frac{5}{9}$. This can, of course, be computed directly since, if the first ball is red, this leaves five red and four black balls in the urn, and so $P(A|B) = \frac{5}{9}$.

2.15 Two Basic Laws of Probability

If A and B are two mutually exclusive subsets (which means $A \cap B = \emptyset$, or, in other words, A and B cannot happen simultaneously), then Axiom 3 states that $P(A \cup B) = P(A) + P(B)$, or, in more suggestive notation, $P(A \text{ or } B) = P(A) + P(B)$. For any events A and B, mutually exclusive or not, we can obtain a similar formula.

Theorem 2.4. *Let S be a sample space with probability function P. If A and B are any two events in S, then*

$$P(A \cup B) = P(A) + P(B) - P(A, B)$$

or, in words, the probability that event A or event B or both occur is equal to the probability that event A occurs plus the probability that event B occurs minus the probability that events A and B both occur.

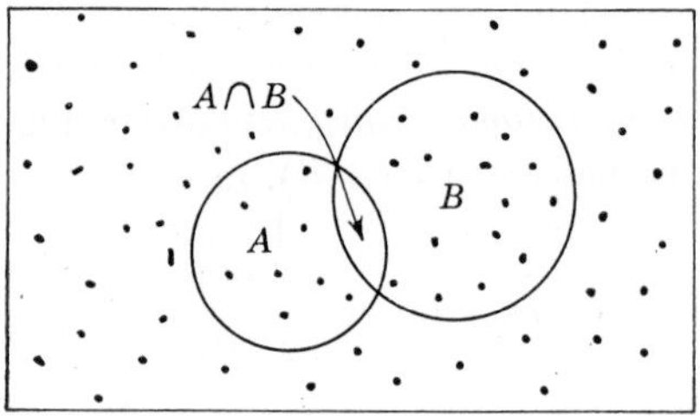

FIG. 2.1

Proof. From point-set algebra we get $A \cup B = A \cup (\bar{A} \cap B)$ (see Fig. 2.1). But A and $\bar{A} \cap B$ are disjoint, and so we apply Axiom 3 and get $P(A \cup B) = P[A \cup (\bar{A} \cap B)] = P(A) + P(\bar{A} \cap B)$. Now $B = (A \cap B) \cup (\bar{A} \cap B)$, and the two sets $(A \cap B)$ and $(\bar{A} \cap B)$ are disjoint. Applying Axiom 3 again gives

$$P(B) = P[(A \cap B) \cup (\bar{A} \cap B)] = P(A \cap B) + P(\bar{A} \cap B)$$

or $P(\bar{A} \cap B) = P(B) - P(A \cap B)$. Substituting $P(\bar{A} \cap B)$ into the equation above gives $P(A \cup B) = P(A) + P(B) - P(A \cap B)$, which completes the proof.

To demonstrate the theorem in a finite sample space S, where each point has probability $1/n$, let us refer to Table 2.3 and compute $P(A_1 \cup B_2)$. Now the probability that the events A_1 or B_2 occur is calculated by adding all n_{ij} in the first row and second column and dividing by n.

Thus

$$
\begin{aligned}
P(A_1 \text{ or } B_2) &= \frac{\sum_{j=1}^{s} n_{1j} + \sum_{i=2}^{r} n_{i2}}{n} \\
&= \frac{\sum_{j=1}^{s} n_{1j} + \sum_{i=1}^{r} n_{i2} - n_{12}}{n} \\
&= P(A_1) + P(B_2) - P(A_1, B_2)
\end{aligned}
$$

The situation is also illustrated in Fig. 2.1, where the sample space is represented by points in a plane and the two events A and B by circles. The event $A \cap B$ is the lenticular region common to both circles, and in adding the points in both circles these points are counted twice and must therefore be subtracted once.

We may generalize this law to account for more than two subsets; thus

$$
\begin{aligned}
P(A \text{ or } B \text{ or } C) = P(A) + P(B) + P(C) - P(A, B) \\
- P(A, C) - P(B, C) + P(A, B, C)
\end{aligned}
$$

as is easily verified by drawing a figure similar to Fig. 2.1 in which three circles intersect so as to have a region common to all three. The general law for h events, which may be proved by induction, is

$$
\begin{aligned}
P(A_1 \text{ or } A_2 \cdots \text{ or } A_h) = \sum_{i=1}^{h} P(A_i) - \sum_{\substack{ij \\ i<j}} P(A_i, A_j) \\
+ \sum_{\substack{i,j,k \\ i<j<k}} P(A_i, A_j, A_k) - \cdots \pm P(A_1, A_2, \cdots, A_h)
\end{aligned}
$$

where the second sum is over all combinations of the numbers $1, 2, \cdots, h$ taken two at a time, the third is over all combinations of the numbers taken three at a time, and so forth. If all the events are mutually exclusive, then all the probabilities in the sums beyond the first sum are 0.

We have essentially derived the multiplicative law of probabilities in defining conditional probability in Definition 2.13. In words, it states: *The probability of the events A and B is equal to the conditional probability of B, given A times the marginal probability of A.* In symbols,

$$
\begin{aligned}
P(A, B) &= P(A)P(B|A) \qquad (1) \\
&= P(B)P(A|B) \qquad (2)
\end{aligned}
$$

To demonstrate for a finite sample space where each point has probability $1/n$, let us refer to Fig. 2.1. Let n be the number of points in Fig.

2.1; let m_1 be the number of points in A (including those common to B), m_2 be the number in B, and m_3 be the number common to A and B. Then (assume $m_1 > 0$, $m_2 > 0$)

$$P(A, B) = \frac{m_3}{n}$$

$$P(A) = \frac{m_1}{n}$$

$$P(B) = \frac{m_2}{n}$$

$$P(A|B) = \frac{m_3}{m_2}$$

$$P(B|A) = \frac{m_3}{m_1}$$

whence (1) and (2) follow directly.

In general, we may show by induction that

$$P(A_1, A_2, \cdots, A_h) = P(A_1)P(A_2|A_1)P(A_3|A_1, A_2)P(A_4|A_1, A_2, A_3) \cdots P(A_h|A_1, A_2, \cdots, A_{h-1}) \quad (3)$$

and there are $h!$ such relations, which may be obtained by permuting the letters on the right-hand side.

2.16 Compound Events

The multiplicative law of probabilities is particularly useful in simplifying the computation of probabilities for compound events. A compound event is one that consists of two or more single events, as when a die is tossed twice or three cards are drawn one at a time from a deck. The following simple example will illustrate the method:

Two balls are drawn, one at a time, from an urn containing two black, three white, and four red balls. What is the probability that the first is red and the second is white? (The first is not replaced before the second is drawn.)

The outcomes of this compound event may be classified according to two criteria: the color of the first ball and the color of the second ball. We may therefore construct a table like Table 2.3. The A classification corresponds to the color of the first ball, and we shall let A_1, A_2, A_3 correspond to the colors black, white, and red, respectively. Similarly the classes B_1, B_2, B_3 will correspond to the same colors for the second ball. The total number of points in the sample space is $n = 9 \times 8 = 72$. It is not $\binom{9}{2} = 36$, because we are considering permutations, not combinations; i.e., we are not asking that one ball be red and one white; we require that the colors appear in a specific order. The complete table of outcomes is

	B_1	B_2	B_3
A_1	2	6	8
A_2	6	6	12
A_3	8	12	12

and the probability asked for in the problem is

$$P(A_3, B_2) = 12/72 = 1/6$$

By using the multiplicative law of probabilities, we need only consider the two separate events one at a time. Here we must use the law in the form

$$P(A_3, B_2) = P(A_3)P(B_2|A_3)$$

Now $P(A_3)$ is simply the probability of drawing a red ball in a single draw, which is $4/9$, and $P(B_2|A_3)$ is the probability of drawing a white one, given that a red one has already been drawn, which is $3/8$. The product of these two numbers gives the required probability

$$P(A_3, B_2) = 4/9 \times 3/8 = 1/6$$

The validity of the above technique is not obvious. It is not immediately evident that the marginal probability $P(A_3)$ can be computed by completely disregarding the second event, nor that the conditional probability corresponds to the simple physical event described above.

For a compound event consisting of two single events we need only consider a 2×2 table. Let A_1 correspond to a success on the first event and A_2 correspond to a failure, and let m_1 be the number of ways in which the first event can succeed, and m_2 be the number of ways in which it can fail. Let B_1 and B_2 be similarly defined for the second event. Let m_{11} and m_{12} be the numbers of ways in which the second event can succeed or fail if the first succeeds, and let m_{21} and m_{22} be the number of ways in which the second can succeed or fail if the first event fails. The 2×2 table is

	B_1	B_2
A_1	m_1m_{11}	m_1m_{12}
A_2	m_2m_{21}	m_2m_{22}

The total number of possible outcomes is

$$n = m_1 m_{11} + m_1 m_{12} + m_2 m_{21} + m_2 m_{22}$$

The required probability is

$$P(A_1, B_1) = \frac{m_1 m_{11}}{n} \tag{1}$$

The marginal probability $P(A_1)$ is

$$\frac{m_1 m_{11}}{n} + \frac{m_1 m_{12}}{n} = \frac{m_1(m_{11} + m_{12})}{m_1(m_{11} + m_{12}) + m_2(m_{21} + m_{22})} \tag{2}$$

Now the probability of a success on the first event without regard to the second is simply $m_1/(m_1 + m_2)$, which is not equal to the above expression unless

$$m_{11} + m_{12} = m_{21} + m_{22}$$

i.e., unless the total number of outcomes for the second event is the same, regardless of whether or not the first event is a success. The conditional probability is $m_{11}/(m_{11} + m_{12})$ and gives the probability of a success for the second event under the assumption that the first was a success.

We might be inclined to conclude that the conditional-probability approach is correct only if the number of outcomes for the second event is independent of the outcome of the first event. Precisely the opposite is true. The correct probability is

$$P(A_1, B_1) = \frac{m_1}{m_1 + m_2} \frac{m_{11}}{m_{11} + m_{12}} \tag{3}$$

and not the value $m_1 m_{11}/n$ given in equation (1).

The value computed by the conditional approach is always correct, while that computed by enumeration of outcomes is correct only if the number of outcomes for the second event is independent of the outcome of the first event.

A simple example will clarify the situation. Suppose that a coin is tossed, and if a head appears, a black ball is placed in an urn, while if a tail appears, a black ball and a white ball are placed in the urn. Then a ball is drawn from the urn. If a head is tossed, the ball will necessarily be black. Using H, T, B, W to represent heads, tails, black, and white, the three possible outcomes of this sequence are HB, TB, TW. These three outcomes are clearly not equally likely. If the experiment were repeated a number of times, we should expect the outcome HB to occur twice as often as either of the other two. $P(\text{HB}) = \frac{1}{2}$, not $\frac{1}{3}$.

In general, the possible outcomes of a compound event are not equally likely if the number of outcomes of the second event depends on the outcome of the first. However, if the definition can be applied to the constituent events separately, then it is possible to compute the probability of the compound event by using the method of conditional probabilities. Unfortunately, it is not possible to give a formal proof of these statements. We must simply rely on our intuition or, rather, on the import of whatever experimental evidence we may possess. Such evidence may be obtained, for example, by performing the above-described experiment a number of times.

Example 2.20. To illustrate further the method of conditional probabilities, let us compute the probability that, of five cards drawn from an ordinary deck, exactly two will be aces.

We shall suppose that the deck consists of four A's, representing aces, and 48 N's, representing not aces. To use conditional probabilities, we must assume that the five cards are drawn one at a time, and we must assume a particular order such as A, A, N, N, N. We shall use equation (2.15.3) with $h = 5$.

$$P(A, A, N, N, N) = P(A)P(A|A)P(N|A, A)P(N|A, A, N)P(N|A, A, N, N)$$

Now $P(A) = 4/52$; with one ace removed from the deck, $P(A|A) = 3/51$; with two aces removed from the deck, $P(N|A, A) = 48/50$. Proceeding thus,

$$P(A, A, N, N, N) = 4/52 \times 3/51 \times 48/50 \times 47/49 \times 46/48$$

This is the probability for the given order, but the problem did not specify any order, and so we must consider all possible orders. There are $5!/(2!3!) = 10$ permutations of two A's and three N's, and so we have 10 probabilities to evaluate, and the required probability, by the additive law, is the sum of these 10 probabilities. It is soon apparent, however, that all the probabilities are equal. Thus, for example,

$$P(N, A, N, N, A) = 48/52 \times 4/51 \times 47/50 \times 46/49 \times 3/48$$

which is the same as the above number except that the numerators are permuted. Clearly this will be the case for all permutations. Hence the required probability is

$$10P(A, A, N, N, N) = \frac{10 \times 4 \times 3 \times 47 \times 46}{52 \times 51 \times 50 \times 49} = .0399$$

Example 2.21. Six cards are drawn from an ordinary deck, with replacement. What is the probability that each of the four suits will be represented at least once among the six cards?

We shall solve the problem by finding first the probability that all the suits do not appear. Let A symbolize the appearance of all the suits and B symbolize the nonappearance of at least one of the suits; then $B = \bar{A}$.

Since either A or B is certain to happen,

$$P(A \text{ or } B) = 1$$

and since A and B are mutually exclusive,

$$P(A \text{ or } B) = P(A) + P(B) = 1$$

and

$$P(A) = 1 - P(B)$$

Thus, if we can find $P(B)$, $P(A)$ can be determined at once.

To get $P(B)$, let us classify the possible outcomes favorable to B into four sets: B_1 is the set of all outcomes in which spades are absent; B_2 is the set for which hearts are absent; B_3, diamonds absent; B_4, clubs absent. These sets are overlapping; an outcome which consists of only spades and hearts falls in B_3 and in B_4. Clearly

$$P(B) = P(B_1 \text{ or } B_2 \text{ or } B_3 \text{ or } B_4)$$

and

$$P(B) = \Sigma P(B_i) - \Sigma P(B_i, B_j) + \Sigma P(B_i, B_j, B_k) - P(B_1, B_2, B_3, B_4)$$

in which the sums are taken over all combinations of the subscripts. The probability $P(B_1)$ that a spade will not appear in the six draws is $(3/4)^6$, and the value is the same for all B_i; hence

$$\Sigma P(B_i) = 4(3/4)^6$$

The probability $P(B_1, B_2)$ that neither spades nor hearts will appear in the six draws is $(1/2)^6$ and is the same for all six pairs of the four suits taken two at a time; hence

$$\Sigma P(B_i, B_j) = 6(1/2)^6$$

Similarly

$$\Sigma P(B_i, B_j, B_k) = 4(1/4)^6$$

and

$$P(B_1, B_2, B_3, B_4) = 0$$

since the simultaneous nonappearance of every suit is impossible. The required probability is, therefore,

$$\begin{aligned} P(A) &= 1 - 4(3/4)^6 + 6(1/2)^6 - 4(1/4)^6 \\ &\cong .381 \end{aligned}$$

A slight alteration of this example will illustrate another useful technique.

Example 2.22. Cards are drawn one at a time, with replacement, from an ordinary deck until all suits have appeared at least once. What is the probability that six draws will be required?

Referring to the preceding example, let P_n denote the probability that all suits will be represented at least once if n cards are drawn. Clearly

$$P_n = 1 - 4(3/4)^n + 6(1/2)^n - 4(1/4)^n$$

Now suppose that we know the answer to the present problem for a general value of n. Let p_n denote this probability (that exactly n draws will be required to produce all the suits).

If n cards are drawn, the first appearance of each suit at least once may occur on the fourth draw, or the fifth, or the sixth, and so forth. Since these outcomes are mutually exclusive, we have

$$P_n = p_4 + p_5 + p_6 + \cdots + p_n$$

From this relation we conclude that

$$p_n = P_n - P_{n-1}$$

and in particular that

$$\begin{aligned} p_6 &= 1 - 4(3/4)^6 + 6(1/2)^6 - 4(1/4)^6 - [1 - 4(3/4)^5 + 6(1/2)^5 - 4(1/4)^5] \\ &= (3/4)^5 - 3(1/2)^5 + 3(1/4)^5 \\ &= .147 \end{aligned}$$

2.17 Independence

If $P(A|B)$ does not depend on the event B, we say that the two events A and B are independent. This is given in the following definition:

Definition 2.14. *Let A and B be two events in a sample space S. These events are said to be independent if any of the following is satisfied:*

$$\begin{aligned} &(a) \qquad P(A|B) = P(A) \\ &(b) \qquad P(B|A) = P(B) \qquad\qquad (1) \\ &(c) \qquad P(A, B) = P(A)P(B) \end{aligned}$$

For example, suppose that a die is thrown twice and that we want the probability that the results are to be a two and a three in that order,

$$P(2, 3) = P(2)P(3|2) = 1/6 \times 1/6 = P(2)P(3)$$

and so the two events are independent.

In Example 2.20 involving two aces in five cards, the five constituent events of the compound event will be independent if we require that each card drawn be replaced in the deck and the deck shuffled before the next card is drawn. The probability that the second card will be an ace is then $4/52$, instead of $3/51$. The probability that two aces will appear when five cards are drawn, with replacement, is

$$10(4/52)^2(48/52)^3 = .0465$$

2.18 Random Variables

In Examples 2.1, 2.2, and 2.5 the sample space is a set of arbitrary points, whereas in Examples 2.3, 2.4, 2.6, and 2.7, the sample space is a set of numbers. There is often an advantage in associating a set of real numbers with the outcome of a random experiment (with the sample space).

We can do this by defining a random variable.

Definition 2.15. *Let S be a sample space on which a probability function is defined. Let $\mathbf{x}$ be a real-valued function defined on S (the function $\mathbf{x}$ transforms points of S into points on the x axis). Then $\mathbf{x}$ is called a random variable (one-dimensional random variable).*

If s is a point in the sample space S and $\mathbf{x}$ is a random variable, then $\mathbf{x}(s)$ is the value of the random variable at s. For an illustration, consider Example 2.1, where the sample space consists of four points: $s_1 = $ (H, H); $s_2 = $ (H, T); $s_3 = $ (T, H); $s_4 = $ (T, T). Let $\mathbf{x}$ be a random variable which can assume the values x_1, x_2, x_3, x_4 defined by $x_i = $ number of heads in s_i. This can be represented by the following table:

Points in S	s_1	s_2	s_3	s_4
$\mathbf{x}(s)$	2	1	1	0

If we assume that S is a sample space on which an equally likely probability function is defined, we write

$$P(\mathbf{x} = 0) \text{ to mean } P[\{s: \mathbf{x}(s) = 0\}] = P(s_4) = \tfrac{1}{4}$$
$$P(\mathbf{x} = 1) \text{ to mean } P[\{s: \mathbf{x}(s) = 1\}] = P(s_2 \cup s_3) = \tfrac{1}{2}$$
$$P(\mathbf{x} = 2) \text{ to mean } P[\{s: \mathbf{x}(s) = 2\}] = P(s_1) = \tfrac{1}{4}$$

We shall not usually be concerned with the function $\mathbf{x}$ nor the sample space S but with the probability that the value of the random variable lies in a certain set A which we write as $P(\mathbf{x} \text{ in } A)$.

A density function of the random variable will be used to show how probabilities that the value of a random variable is in a certain set can be computed. This will be discussed in Chaps. 3 and 4. For the purposes of explanation in this book, random variables will be divided into two classes: (1) A random variable is called *discrete* if it assumes only a finite or a denumerable number of values (these are discussed in Chap. 3); (2) a random variable is called *continuous* if it assumes a continuum of values (these are discussed in Chap. 4).

Sometimes a one-dimensional random variable will not suit our purposes, and so we shall extend the definition.

Definition 2.16. *Let S be a sample space on which a probability distribution function is defined. Let* $\mathbf{x}$ *and* $\mathbf{y}$ *be two real-valued functions defined on S. Then the pair* $(\mathbf{x}, \mathbf{y})$ *is called a (two-dimensional) random variable, and the two random variables* $\mathbf{x}$ *and* $\mathbf{y}$ *are said to be jointly distributed. Thus a two-dimensional random variable transforms points of S into points in the xy plane.*

For any set A in the xy plane we shall be interested in $P[(\mathbf{x}, \mathbf{y})$ is in $A]$, which is to be taken to mean

$$P[\{s\colon (\mathbf{x}(s), \mathbf{y}(s)) \text{ is in } A\}]$$

A similar definition holds for the joint distribution of n random variables for any positive integer n. As with the one-dimensional random variable, we shall generally not be concerned with the sample space S nor the functions $\mathbf{x}$ and $\mathbf{y}$, but we shall define a density function which can be used to compute $P[(\mathbf{x}, \mathbf{y})$ is in $A]$. We shall state "$\mathbf{x}$ and $\mathbf{y}$ are jointly distributed random variables," and we shall sometimes use the words "random variable" and "the value of a random variable" interchangeably. For example when we say "a random variable $\mathbf{x}$ is equal to 1," or when we write $\mathbf{x} = 1$, etc., we shall mean "the value of a random variable $\mathbf{x}$ is equal to 1."

In Example 2.1, suppose that the function $\mathbf{x}$ is defined by

$\mathbf{x}$: number of heads in the first toss

Points in S	(H, H)	(H, T)	(T, H)	(T, T)
$\mathbf{x}(s)$	1	1	0	0

and let $\mathbf{y}$ be defined by

$\mathbf{y}$: number of heads in the second toss

Points in S	(H, H)	(H, T)	(T, H)	(T, T)
$\mathbf{y}(s)$	1	0	1	0

The two-dimensional random variable $(\mathbf{x}, \mathbf{y})$ is defined by

Points in S	(H, H)	(H, T)	(T, H)	(T, T)
Corresponding values of $(\mathbf{x}, \mathbf{y})$	(1, 1)	(1, 0)	(0, 1)	(0, 0)

We shall use boldface letters $\mathbf{U}$, $\mathbf{V}$, $\mathbf{W}$, $\mathbf{u}$, $\mathbf{v}$, $\mathbf{w}$, etc., or these letters with subscripts, to indicate random variables. We shall often use the word variate instead of random variable.

2.19 Problems

In this set of problems, when a probability is asked for, assume that all arrangements are equally likely. In each case define very carefully the sample space. In each problem where a probability is required, it is instructive to conceive of the random experiment and interpret the probability of the outcome as a frequency ratio. In a few of the problems an experiment can be performed and the computed probability compared with the observed frequency ratio.

1. Let A, B, C be events (subsets) in a sample space S defined by

$$\begin{aligned} S &= \{x: x = 1, 2, 3, 4, 5, 6, 7, 8, 9, 10\} \\ A &= \{x: x = 1, 3, 5, 7, 9\} \\ B &= \{x: x = 1, 2, 3, 4, 5, 6\} \\ C &= \{x: x = 5, 6, 7, 8, 9, 10\} \end{aligned}$$

Find the events:

(*a*) $A \cap (B \cap C)$ (*b*) $\overline{A \cup B}$ (*c*) $A \cup \bar{A}$

(*d*) $A \cup B \cup C$ (*e*) $\bar{C} \cap \bar{B}$ (*f*) $\bar{S}$

Using the definitions of A, B, C, and S, show that

(*g*) $A \cap (B \cup C) = (A \cap B) \cup (A \cap C)$ (*h*) $\overline{A \cup B} = \bar{A} \cap \bar{B}$

(*i*) $A \cup A = A$ (*j*) $A \cap A = A$

(*k*) $A \cup S = S$ (*l*) $A \cap \bar{A} = \emptyset$

(*m*) $\overline{A \cap B} = \bar{A} \cup \bar{B}$ (*n*) $A \cap (B \cap \bar{A}) = \emptyset$

2. Let A, B, C be events in a sample space S defined by

$$\begin{aligned} S &= \{x: 0 \le x \le 20\} \\ A &= \{x: 0 \le x \le 5\} \\ B &= \{x: 3 \le x \le 10\} \\ C &= \{x: 7 \le x \le 15\} \end{aligned}$$

Find the events:

(*a*) $A \cup B$; that is, either A occurs or B occurs or both A and B occur.

(*b*) $\bar{A}$; that is, A does not occur.

(*c*) $A \cap \bar{B}$; that is, A occurs and B does not occur.

(*d*) $A \cup (B \cap \bar{C})$; that is, A occurs or B occurs and C does not occur.

(*e*) $\overline{A \cup C}$; that is, neither A nor C occurs.

(*f*) $\bar{B}$; that is, B does not occur.

3. Let A, B be events in a sample space S defined by

$$\begin{aligned} S &= \{(x, y): x \ge 0, y \ge 0\} \\ A &= \{(x, y): x \ge 0, 0 \le y \le 5\} \\ B &= \{(x, y): x \ge 0, 5 \le y \le 10\} \end{aligned}$$

Find the events:

(a) $\bar{A}$ (b) $\bar{B}$ (c) $A \cap \bar{B}$
(d) $\overline{A \cap B}$ (e) $\bar{A} \cap \bar{B}$ (f) $\bar{A} \cap B$
(g) $A \cup \bar{B}$

4. Let A, B be events in a sample space S. Write out in words what each of the following means

(a) $\bar{A} \cup B$ (b) $\bar{A} \cup \bar{B}$ (c) $A \cap B$
(d) $\bar{A} \cap B$ (e) $\bar{A} \cap \bar{B}$ (f) $\bar{A} \cap A$

5. An urn contains 10 balls, 6 red and 4 green. Two balls are drawn at random, with replacement. Describe the sample space S and the probability function P. How many points does the sample space contain?

6. An urn contains four white balls and six black ones. What is the probability that one drawn at random will be white?

7. If two coins are tossed, what is the probability that a head and a tail will appear?

8. If a four-volume set of books is placed on a shelf in random order, what is the probability that they will be in the correct order?

9. What is the probability of obtaining three heads if three coins are tossed? What is the probability that at least two heads will appear? Toss three balanced coins 100 times and observe the frequency with which at least two heads appear.

10. An urn contains three white balls and two black ones. What is the probability that two balls drawn from the urn will both be black?

11. How many two-digit numbers can be formed with the integers 1, 2, 3, 4, 5, if duplication of the integers is not allowed? If duplication is allowed?

12. How many three-digit numbers can be formed from 0, 1, 2, 3, 4, if duplication is not allowed? How many of these are even?

13. In how many ways can a committee of three be chosen from nine men?

14. There are six roads from A to B and three roads from B to C. In how many ways can one go from A to C via B?

15. How many different sums of money can be formed with one each of the six kinds of coins minted by the United States Treasury?

16. In how many ways can six girls and four boys be divided into two groups of two boys and three girls each?

17. In a baseball league of eight teams, how many games will be necessary if each team is to play every other team twice at home?

18. How many football teams can be formed with 12 men who can play any line position and 10 men who can play any back position?

19. How many signals can a ship show with five different flags if there are five significant positions on the flagpole?

20. How many license plates can be made if they are to contain five symbols, the first two being letters and the last three integers?

21. How many diagonals are there in a twelve-sided polygon?

22. How many dominoes are there in a set from double 0 to double 12?

23. What is the probability of getting a seven with a pair of dice?

24. What is the probability that two cards drawn from an ordinary deck will be spades?

25. What is the probability that a five-card hand will contain exactly two aces? At least two aces?

26. What is the probability that a bridge hand will be a complete suit?

27. An urn contains five white, four red, and three black balls. Another contains five white, six red, and seven black balls. One ball is selected from each urn. What is the probability that they will be of the same color?

28. Show that $\binom{n}{r} = \binom{n}{n-r}$.

29. In how many ways can n different objects be divided into k groups containing $n_1, n_2, \cdots, n_k$ objects, if

$$n_1 + n_2 + \cdots + n_k = n - m \qquad \text{where } n > m$$

30. An urn contains m white and n black balls. k balls are drawn and laid aside, their color unnoticed. Then another ball is drawn. What is the probability that it is white?

31. Six dice are tossed. What is the probability that every possible number will appear?

32. Seven dice are tossed. What is the probability that every number appears?

33. What is the probability of getting a total of four points with three dice?

34. An urn contains 10 balls numbered from one to ten. Four balls are drawn, and suppose that x is the second smallest of the four numbers drawn. What is the probability that $x = 3$?

35. If n balls are tossed into k boxes so that each ball is equally likely to fall in any box, what is the probability that a specified box will contain m balls?

36. Show that $\sum_{i=1}^{n} CX_i = C \sum_{i=1}^{n} X_i$.

37. Show that $\prod_{i=1}^{n} CX_i^a = C^n \left(\prod_{i=1}^{n} X\right)^a$.

38. Show that $\left(\sum_{i=1}^{n} X_i\right)^2 = \sum_{i=1}^{n} \sum_{j=1}^{n} X_iX_j = \sum_{i=1}^{n} X_i^2 + \sum_{\substack{i=1 \\ i \neq j}}^{n} \sum_{j=1}^{n} X_iX_j$.

39. Show that $\prod_{i=1}^{2n+1} (x + n + 1 - i) = x \prod_{i=1}^{n} (x^2 - i^2)$.

40. Find the coefficient of x^6y^3 in the expansion of the binomial $(x^2 - ay)^5$.

41. Find the coefficient of $x^2y^2z^3$ in the expansion of the trinomial $(2x - y - z)^7$.

42. If six balls are tossed into three boxes so that each is equally likely to fall in any box, what is the probability that all boxes will be occupied?

43. The corners of a regular tetrahedron are numbered one, two, three, four. Five tetrahedra are tossed. What is the probability that the sum of the upturned corners will be 12?

44. The spades and hearts are removed from a deck of cards and placed face up in a row. The remaining cards are shuffled and dealt face up in a row beneath the row of spades and hearts. What is the probability that all the clubs will be beneath spades? What is the probability that, among the 26 pairs of cards, 16 pairs will consist of cards of the same color?

45. Six cards are drawn from an ordinary deck. What is the probability that there will be one pair (two aces, or two fives, for example) and four scattered cards? That there will be two pairs and two scattered cards?

46. The face cards are removed from an ordinary deck and the remainder divided into the four suits. A card is drawn at random from each suit. What is the probability that the total of the four numbers drawn is 20?

47. An urn contains three black balls, three white ones, and two red ones. Three balls are drawn and placed in a black box, then three more are drawn and placed in a white box, and the remaining two are put in a red box. What is the probability that all but two of the balls will fall in boxes corresponding to their colors?

48. An urn contains four white and five black balls; a second urn contains five white and four black ones. One ball is transferred from the first to the second urn; then a ball is drawn from the second urn. What is the probability that it is white?

49. In the above problem suppose that two balls, instead of one, are transferred from the first to the second urn. Find the probability that a ball then drawn from the second urn will be white.

50. If it is known that at least two heads appeared when five coins were tossed, what is the probability that the exact number of heads was three?

51. If a bridge player has seven spades, what is the probability that his partner has at least one spade? At least two spades?

52. If a bridge player and his partner have eight spades between them, what is the probability that the other five spades are split three and two in the opposing hands?

53. A bridge player and his partner hold all spades except K, 3, 2. What is the probability that they are split K and 3, 2 in the opposing hands? What is the probability that K or K, 2 or K, 3 or K, 3, 2 appears in a specified one of the two opposing hands?

54. A person repeatedly casts a pair of dice. He wins if he casts an eight before he casts a seven. What is his probability of winning? NOTE: $1 + x + x^2 + x^3 + \cdots = 1/(1 - x)$, if $|x| < 1$.

55. In a dice game a player casts a pair of dice twice. He wins if the two numbers thrown do not differ by more than two with the following exceptions: If he gets a three on the first throw, he must produce a four on the second throw; if he gets an eleven on the first throw, he must produce a ten on the second throw. What is his probability of winning?

56. The game of craps is played with two dice as follows: In a particular game one person throws the dice. He wins on the first throw if he gets 7 or 11 points; he loses on the first throw if he gets 2, 3, or 12 points. If he gets 4, 5, 6, 8, 9, or 10 points on the first throw, he continues to throw the dice repeatedly until he produces either a 7 or the number first thrown; in the latter case he wins, in the former he loses. What is his probability of winning?

57. In simple Mendelian inheritance, a physical characteristic of a plant or animal is determined by a single pair of genes. The color of peas is an example. Letting y and g represent yellow and green, peas will be green if the plant has the color-gene pair (g, g); they will be yellow if the color-gene pair is (y, y) or (y, g). In view of this last combination, yellow is said to be dominant to green. Progeny get one gene from each parent and are equally likely to get either gene from each parent's pair. If (y, y) peas are crossed with (g, g) peas, all the resulting peas will be (y, g) and yellow because of dominance. If (y, g) peas are crossed with (g, g) peas, the probability is .5 that the resulting peas will be yellow and is .5 that they will be green. In a large number of such crosses one would expect about half the resulting peas to be yellow, the remainder to be green. In crosses between (y, g) and (y, g) peas, what proportion would be expected to be yellow? What proportion of the yellow peas would be expected to be (y, y)?

58. Peas may be smooth or wrinkled, and this is a simple Mendelian character. Smooth is dominant to wrinkled so that (s, s) and (s, w) peas are smooth while (w, w) peas are wrinkled. If (y, g) (s, w) peas are crossed with (g, g) (w, w) peas, what are the possible outcomes and what are their associated probabilities? For the (y, g) (s, w) by (g, g) (s, w) cross? For the (y, g) (s, w) by (y, g) (s, w) cross?

59. Albinism in human beings is a simple Mendelian character. Let a and n represent albino and nonalbino; the latter is dominant, so that normal parents cannot have an albino child unless both are (n, a). Suppose that in a large population the proportion of n genes is p and the proportion of a genes is $q = 1 - p$, so that q^2 is the proportion of the individuals that are albinos. Assuming that albinism is not a factor in the selection of marriage partners or in the number of children of a particular marriage, what proportion of individuals of the next generation would be expected to be albinos? If albinos married only albinos and had as many children, on an average, as nonalbinos, what proportion of individuals in the next generation would be expected to be albinos?

60. It is known that an urn was filled by casting a die and putting in the urn white balls equal in number to that obtained on the throw of the die. Then black balls were added in a number determined by a second throw of the die. It is also known that the total number of balls in the urn is eight. What is the probability that the urn contains exactly five white balls?

61. Urn A contains two white and two black balls; urn B contains three white and two black balls. One ball is transferred from A to B; one ball is then drawn from B and turns out to be white. What is the probability that the transferred ball was white?

62. Each of six urns contains 12 black and white balls; one has eight white balls, two have six white balls, and three have four white balls. An urn is drawn at random, and three balls are drawn, without replacement, from that urn. Two of the three are white; the other is black. What is the probability that the urn drawn contained six white and six black balls?

63. Three newspapers, A, B, C, are published in a certain city. It is estimated from a survey that of the adult population:

20% read A
16% read B
14% read C
8% read both A and B
5% read both A and C
4% read both B and C
2% read all three

What percentage reads at least one of the papers? Of those that read at least one, what percentage reads both A and B?

64. Twelve dice are cast. What is the probability that each of the six faces will appear at least once?

65. A die is cast repeatedly until each of the six faces appears at least once. What is the probability that it must be cast exactly 10 times?

3

Discrete Random Variables

3.1 Introduction

In Chap. 2 we gave the axioms for a probability function and explained in detail how to construct it for a special sample space, one with a finite number of points each with the same probability. In this chapter we shall discuss a discrete random variable.

Definition 3.1. **x** *will be called a (one-dimensional) discrete random variable if it is a random variable that assumes only a finite or denumerable number of values on the x axis. Suppose that* **x** *assumes only the values* $x_1, x_2, \cdots, x_n, \cdots$ *and with probabilities* $f(x_1), f(x_2), \cdots, f(x_n), \cdots$ *and suppose that A is any subset of the points* $x_1, \cdots, x_n, \cdots$. *Then the probability of the event A (the probability that* **x** *is in A), written P(A), is defined as*

$$P(A) = \sum_A f(x)$$

where $\sum_A f(x)$ *means sum* $f(x)$ *over those values* x_i *that are in A.*

For example $P(\mathbf{x} = 2)$ will be taken to mean: the probability that the value of the random variable is equal to 2. $P(3 < \mathbf{x} < 5)$ will mean the probability that the value of the random variable is between 3 and 5, etc.

Of course, in any experimental situation, $f(x)$ is chosen to fit the particular problem at hand. We shall call $f(x)$ a *discrete density* or simply a *density*, and we shall sometimes say "**x** is distributed as $f(x)$," or "$f(x)$ is the distribution of **x**." Any function can be a discrete density if it satisfies

$$f(x_i) \geq 0 \qquad i = 1, 2, \cdots$$
$$\Sigma f(x_i) = 1$$

As an example, suppose that a random experiment consists of throwing four symmetrical coins and recording the number of heads. Let the outcome be the value of a random variable **x**; hence, **x** assumes values 0, 1, 2, 3, 4. To evaluate the density $f(x)$, the probability that x heads appear in four tosses, we note that the total number of ways that the four coins can fall is 2^4, since each coin can fall two ways. The number of ways in which x heads can occur is $\binom{4}{x}$; hence,

$$f(x) = \frac{\binom{4}{x}}{2^4} \qquad x = 0, 1, 2, 3, 4$$

Since

$$\sum_{x=0}^{4} f(x) = \frac{1}{2^4} \sum_{x=0}^{4} \binom{4}{x} = \frac{2^4}{2^4} = 1$$

and $f(x) \geq 0$ for $0 \leq x \leq 4$, $f(x)$ is a *discrete density*. We shall sometimes write $0 \leq x \leq 4$ for $x = 0, 1, 2, 3, 4$.

We may calculate $f(x)$ by giving **x** each of its possible values, and we may then plot the function as in Fig. 3.1, using vertical lines of length equal to $f(x)$ on some scale.

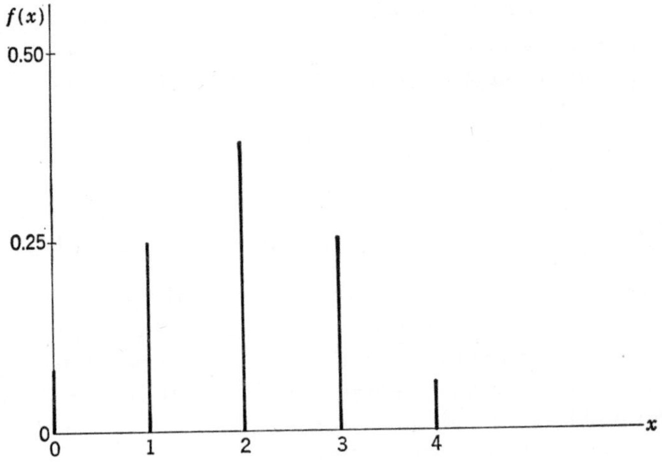

FIG. 3.1

It is useful to think of $f(x)$ as giving the relative frequency of occurrence of the separate values of **x**. Thus, suppose that the four coins were tossed a very large number of times. We should expect no heads to appear ($\mathbf{x} = 0$) in about one-sixteenth of the tosses; we should expect one head to appear ($\mathbf{x} = 1$) in about one-fourth of the tosses, and so forth. The graph of the density makes a number of things immediately evident: that the most likely number of heads is two, that one head can be expected to occur about four times as often as no heads, that three heads can be expected to occur about as often as one head, and so forth. The word "about" is used because of the fluctuations that accompany chance events. Thus, if a single coin is to be tossed 10 times, we expect five heads and five tails, on an average, but actually some other division of heads and tails is quite likely to occur in a given trial.

The results of an actual experiment in tossing four coins are given in the following table. Four coins were tossed 160 times and the number of heads counted on each toss.

RESULTS OF TOSSING FOUR COINS 160 TIMES

Number of heads	Actual relative frequency	Theoretical relative frequency
0	.038	.063
1	.256	.250
2	.350	.375
3	.281	.250
4	.075	.062

The agreement between actual and expected occurrences is none too good (it is to be remembered that the probability of a head may not have been exactly $\frac{1}{2}$ for each of the four coins actually used), but still the general character of the distribution of actual outcomes was fairly well indicated by the density $f(x)$.

If we know the density function of a random variable $\mathbf{x}$, we can supply the answer to any probability question pertaining to $\mathbf{x}$. Thus, referring again to our particular example, the probability of two heads is

$$P(\mathbf{x} = 2) = f(2) = \frac{\binom{4}{2}}{2^4} = \frac{3}{8}$$

The probability that the number of heads will be less than three is

$$P(\mathbf{x} < 3) = \sum_{x=0}^{2} f(x) = 11/16$$

The probability that the number of heads will be between one and three, inclusive, is

$$P(1 \leq \mathbf{x} \leq 3) = \sum_{x=1}^{3} f(x) = 7/8$$

Suppose that we wish to evaluate the conditional probability that the number of heads is less than three when it is known that the number of heads is less than four. Let A be the event that "less than three heads appear"; that is, $A = \{x : x = 0, 1, 2\}$. Let B be the event that "less than four heads appear"; that is, $B = \{x: x = 0, 1, 2, 3\}$. We want to evaluate $P(A|B)$. By the definition of conditional probability,

$$P(A|B) = \frac{P(A \cap B)}{P(B)}$$

Now $A \cap B = \{x: x = 0, 1, 2\}$, and so

$$P(A \cap B) = \sum_{x=0}^{2} f(x) = \frac{\sum_{x=0}^{2} \binom{4}{x}}{2^4} = \frac{11}{16}$$

Also

$$P(B) = \sum_{x=0}^{3} f(x) = \frac{\sum_{x=0}^{3} \binom{4}{x}}{2^4} = \frac{15}{16}$$

and so

$$P(A|B) = P(\mathbf{x} < 3 | \mathbf{x} < 4) = \frac{11/16}{15/16} = \frac{11}{15}$$

The relative-frequency interpretation is this: Suppose that four ideal coins are thrown a large number of times and the number of heads in each throw is recorded *only* in those cases in which less than four heads appear. The fraction of these cases (where less than four heads appear) in which less than three heads appear will be about $11/15$. It may be instructive for the reader actually to perform this experiment to check this result within sampling fluctuations.

3.2 Discrete Density Functions

The essential properties of discrete density functions have already been suggested in the preceding section, and we need only to describe them in somewhat more general language.

The set of possible outcomes of a chance event may be classified into a number of mutually exclusive classes according to some attribute. Associated with each class is a value of a *random variable*, or *variate*, $\mathbf{x}$. The density is a function which gives the probability that any specified value of $\mathbf{x}$ will occur.

The variate $\mathbf{x}$ may naturally describe the attribute, as was the case in the coin-tossing illustration, or it may be simply a code. Thus, in drawing balls from an urn, the classification may be according to color. We could define a random variable $\mathbf{x}$ by arbitrarily setting a correspondence between values of $\mathbf{x}$ and colors: $\mathbf{x} = 1$ corresponds to black; $\mathbf{x} = 2$ corresponds to red; and so forth. When a red ball is drawn, the variate has the value 2.

The density may be a mathematical formula, as was the case in the preceding section, or it may be a table. Thus, if an urn contains three black, two red, and five white balls, we may code the colors 1, 2, 3, respectively. We do not bother to construct a mathematical formula but describe the function by

x:	1	2	3
$f(x)$:	.3	.2	.5

The word *discrete* is used to distinguish the variate from *continuous* variates, which will be discussed in the next chapter.

Cumulative Distributions. It is quite often necessary to evaluate probabilities of the type $P(\mathbf{x} < 3)$, $P(1 \leq \mathbf{x} \leq 4)$, etc. In these cases and for other situations also, it is convenient to define a new function called the *cumulative distribution function.* For a discrete density $f(x_i)$, $i = 1, 2, \cdots$, the cumulative distribution $F(x)$ is defined by

$$F(x) = \Sigma f(x_i)$$

where the summation is over those values of i such that $x_i \leq x$. It is easily seen that $F(x) = P(\mathbf{x} \leq x)$ and that $P(a < \mathbf{x} \leq b) = F(b) - F(a)$. It can therefore be shown that for a discrete random variable it is possible to obtain the cumulative distribution from the density function and vice versa.

3.3 Multivariate Distributions

When the outcome of a chance event can be characterized in more than one way, the density is a function of more than one variable. Thus when a card is drawn from an ordinary deck, it may be characterized according to its suit and to its denomination. Let $\mathbf{x}$ be a random variable that can assume the values 1, 2, 3, 4 which correspond to the suits in some order (say spades, hearts, diamonds, clubs), and let $\mathbf{y}$ be a random variable that can assume the values $1, 2, \cdots, 13$ which correspond to the denominations ace, $2, \cdots, 10$, J, Q, K. Then $(\mathbf{x}, \mathbf{y})$ is a two-dimensional random variable. The probability of drawing a particular card will be denoted by $f(x, y)$, and if each card has equal probability of being drawn, clearly the density of $(\mathbf{x}, \mathbf{y})$ is

$$f(x, y) = \tfrac{1}{52} \qquad 1 \leq x \leq 4,\ 1 \leq y \leq 13 \tag{1}$$

This function may be plotted over a plane as in Fig. 3.2; the probabilities are represented by vertical lines at the points (x, y) in the horizontal plane where the probabilities are defined. In this case, the lines are of equal height.

To consider another example: Let four balls be drawn from an urn containing five black, six white, and seven red balls. Let $\mathbf{x}$ be the number of white balls drawn and $\mathbf{y}$ be the number of red balls drawn. The density of the two-dimensional random variable $(\mathbf{x}, \mathbf{y})$ is

$$f(x, y) = \frac{\binom{6}{x}\binom{7}{y}\binom{5}{4 - x - y}}{\binom{18}{4}} \qquad 0 \le x + y \le 4 \tag{2}$$

and its graph is shown in Fig. 3.3. In this example, we might consider defining a third random variable, $\mathbf{z}$, to be the number of black balls

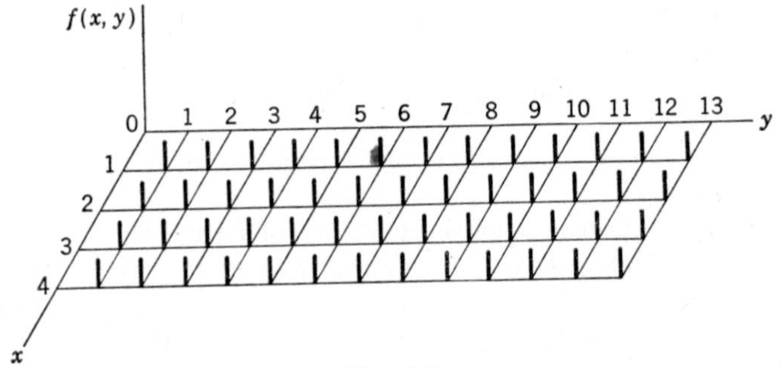

Fig. 3.2

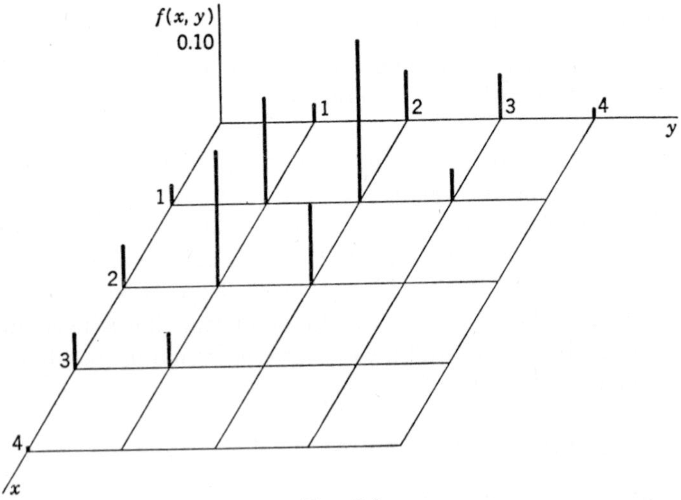

Fig. 3.3

drawn and obtain a trivariate distribution. But $\mathbf{z}$ is exactly determined by $\mathbf{x}$ and $\mathbf{y}$ since $\mathbf{z} = 4 - \mathbf{x} - \mathbf{y}$. No new information can be obtained by adding $\mathbf{z}$ to the set of random variables characterizing the outcomes, and, in fact, if **z** were included, the set of probabilities represented by $f(x, y, z)$ would be exactly the same set that we have already obtained using **x** and **y**.

A simpler example of functional dependence is that of tossing a coin, say four times. Let **x** be the number of heads and **y** be the number of tails. Since **x** + **y** must be equal to 4, the variables are functionally dependent; knowing one, the other is exactly determined. The density is

$$f(x, y) = \binom{4}{x}\left(\frac{1}{2}\right)^x\left(\frac{1}{2}\right)^y \qquad x + y = 4;\ x, y = 0, 1, 2, 3, 4$$

and its graph is given in Fig. 3.4. It gives us no more information than

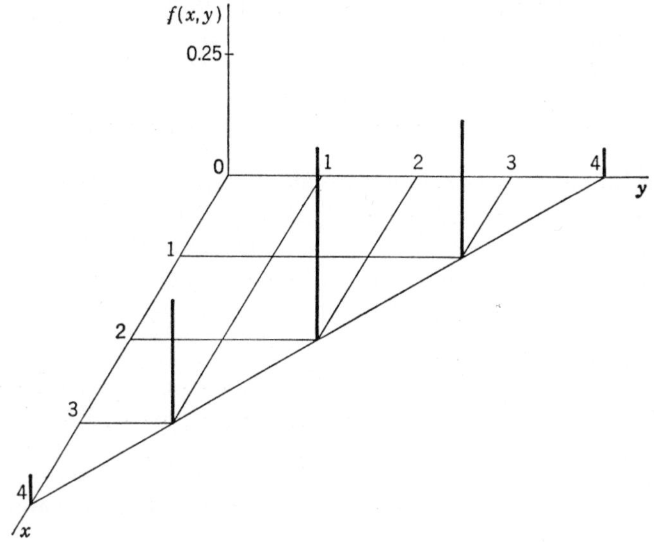

FIG. 3.4

the function used as an example in Sec. 3.1; the set of probabilities is exactly the same as before.

We have used the terms dependent and independent in two entirely different connections. In Chap. 2 we defined two events to be independent if the conditional probability of one, given the other, was equal to the marginal probability of the first. We shall in the future refer to this kind of independence as *independence in the probability sense.* Returning to the urn example: **x** and **y** are *functionally independent* (since **y** is not uniquely determined when **x** is known), but they are *dependent in the probability sense* (as we shall see).

In general the k-dimensional random variable $(\mathbf{x}_1, \mathbf{x}_2, \cdots, \mathbf{x}_k)$ is a k-dimensional discrete random variable if it can assume values only at a finite or denumerable number of points $(x_1, x_2, \cdots, x_k)$ in k-dimensional real space. Let $f(x_1, x_2, \cdots, x_k)$ be the probability that the value of the random variable is $(x_1, x_2, \cdots, x_k)$, that is $P(\mathbf{x}_1 = x_1, \mathbf{x}_2 = x_2, \cdots, \mathbf{x}_k = x_k) = f(x_1, x_2, \cdots, x_k)$, for every value that the random variable can assume. $f(x_1, x_2, \cdots, x_k)$ is called the (joint) density of the k-dimensional random variable. Let A be any subset of the set of values that the random variable can assume; then

$$P[(\mathbf{x}_1, \mathbf{x}_2, \cdots, \mathbf{x}_k) \text{ is in } A] = \sum_A f(x_1, x_2, \cdots, x_k)$$

where $\sum_A f(x_1, x_2, \cdots, x_k)$ means: sum the density over those points in A. Let $\mathbf{x}_{i_1}, \mathbf{x}_{i_2}, \cdots, \mathbf{x}_{i_t}$ be any subset of the discrete random variables $\mathbf{x}_1, \mathbf{x}_2, \cdots, \mathbf{x}_k$. The marginal density of the t-dimensional random variable $(\mathbf{x}_{i_1}, \mathbf{x}_{i_2}, \cdots, \mathbf{x}_{i_t})$ is

$$f_{i_1, i_2, \cdots, i_t}(x_{i_1}, x_{i_2}, \cdots, x_{i_t}) = \Sigma f(x_1, x_2, \cdots, x_k)$$

where the summation is for all variables except $x_{i_1}, x_{i_2}, \cdots, x_{i_t}$. Let $\mathbf{x}_{i_1}, \mathbf{x}_{i_2}, \cdots, \mathbf{x}_{i_t}$ and $\mathbf{x}_{j_1}, \mathbf{x}_{j_2}, \cdots, \mathbf{x}_{j_s}$ be two disjoint subsets of the discrete random variables $\mathbf{x}_1, \mathbf{x}_2, \cdots, \mathbf{x}_k$. The conditional density of the t-dimensional random variable $(\mathbf{x}_{i_1}, \mathbf{x}_{i_2}, \cdots, \mathbf{x}_{i_t})$ given the value $(x_{j_1}, x_{j_2}, \cdots, x_{j_s})$ of $(\mathbf{x}_{j_1}, \mathbf{x}_{j_2}, \cdots, \mathbf{x}_{j_s})$ is

$$g(x_{i_1}, x_{i_2}, \cdots, x_{i_t} | x_{j_1}, \cdots, x_{j_s}) = \frac{f_{i_1, i_2, \cdots, i_t, j_1, j_2, \cdots, j_s}(x_{i_1}, x_{i_2}, \cdots, x_{i_t}, x_{j_1}, x_{j_2}, \cdots, x_{j_s})}{f_{j_1, j_2, \cdots, j_s}(x_{j_1}, x_{j_2}, \cdots, x_{j_s})}$$

for all values of the x's for which the denominator is not zero. The discrete random variables $\mathbf{x}_1, \mathbf{x}_2, \cdots, \mathbf{x}_k$ are (mutually) independent if and only if

$$f(x_1, x_2, \cdots, x_k) = f_1(x_1) f_2(x_2) \cdots f_k(x_k)$$

for all values $(x_1, x_2, \cdots, x_k)$ for which the random variable $(\mathbf{x}_1, \mathbf{x}_2, \cdots, \mathbf{x}_k)$ is defined.

In the urn example, the marginal density of $\mathbf{x}$ is

$$f_1(x) = \sum_{y=0}^{4-x} f(x, y) = \frac{\binom{6}{x}\binom{12}{4-x}}{\binom{18}{4}} \qquad 0 \le x \le 4 \tag{3}$$

The sum may be performed by means of an algebraic identity, but here it is simpler to consider the problem anew as one involving 6 white balls and 12 that are not white. Similarly the marginal density of **y** is

$$f_2(y) = \sum_{x=0}^{4-y} f(x, y) = \frac{\binom{7}{y}\binom{11}{4-y}}{\binom{18}{4}} \qquad 0 \le y \le 4 \tag{4}$$

This density is plotted in Fig. 3.5. The height of the line at $y = 0$, which represents $f_2(0)$, is equal to the sum of the lengths of the vertical lines along the x axis in Fig. 3.3; $f_2(1)$ is the sum of the lengths of the vertical lines along the line $y = 1$ in Fig. 3.3, and so forth.

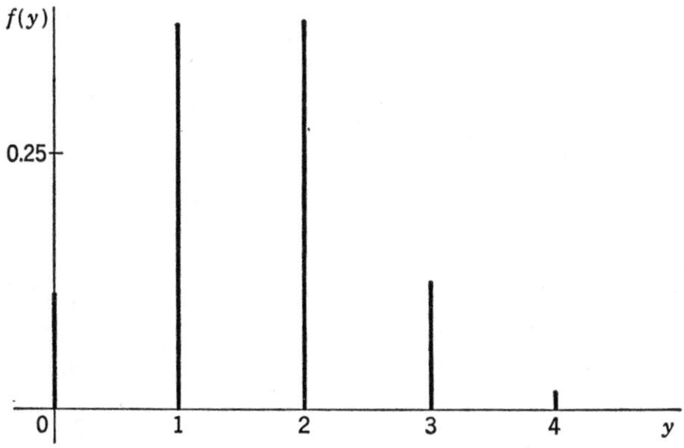

FIG. 3.5

The conditional density of **x**, given **y**, in the above urn problem is

$$g(x|y) = \frac{f(x, y)}{f_2(y)} = \frac{\binom{6}{x}\binom{5}{4-x-y}}{\binom{11}{4-y}} \qquad \begin{array}{l} 0 \le x \le 4 - y \\ y = 0, 1, 2, 3, 4 \end{array}$$

Similarly

$$h(y|x) = \frac{\binom{7}{y}\binom{5}{4-x-y}}{\binom{12}{4-x}} \qquad \begin{array}{l} 0 \le y \le 4 - x \\ x = 0, 1, 2, 3, 4 \end{array}$$

If **x** were given some specific value, say **x** = 1, we could plot the density $h(y|1)$ by giving y its successive values: 0, 1, 2, 3. The vertical lines would have the same relative heights as those along the line $x = 1$ in Fig. 3.3; their lengths would be increased by the factor $1/f_1(x)$ evaluated for $x = 1$ so that the sum of their lengths would be 1. We observe that

$h(y|x)$ is not equal to the marginal distribution of $\mathbf{y}$, so that $\mathbf{y}$ and $\mathbf{x}$ are not independent in the probability sense. Of course, the fact that the formula $h(y|x)$ involves x is sufficient evidence that the two variates are dependent in the probability sense. If, however, we had an example in which $h(y|x)$ did not involve x, it would still be possible for the two variates to be dependent because the limits of $\mathbf{y}$ might depend on $\mathbf{x}$. If both $h(y|x)$ and the limits of $\mathbf{y}$ do not involve $\mathbf{x}$, then the two variates will obviously be independent in the probability sense.

As an example of a distribution involving several variates, suppose that 12 cards are drawn without replacement from an ordinary deck, and let $\mathbf{x}_1$ be the number of aces, $\mathbf{x}_2$ be the number of deuces, $\mathbf{x}_3$ be the number of treys, and $\mathbf{x}_4$ be the number of fours. The density of these variates is given by a function of four variates and is, in fact,

$$f(x_1, x_2, x_3, x_4) = \frac{\binom{4}{x_1}\binom{4}{x_2}\binom{4}{x_3}\binom{4}{x_4}\binom{36}{12 - x_1 - x_2 - x_3 - x_4}}{\binom{52}{12}}$$

where the limits of each are $0 \le x_i \le 4$, subject to the restriction that $\Sigma x_i \le 12$. There are a large number of marginal and conditional distributions associated with this distribution; a few examples are

$$f_{23}(x_2, x_3) = \frac{\binom{4}{x_2}\binom{4}{x_3}\binom{44}{12 - x_2 - x_3}}{\binom{52}{12}} \qquad 0 \le x_i \le 4$$

$$f_4(x_4) = \frac{\binom{4}{x_4}\binom{48}{12 - x_4}}{\binom{52}{12}} \qquad 0 \le x_4 \le 4$$

$$g(x_2, x_4|x_1, x_3) = \frac{\binom{4}{x_2}\binom{4}{x_4}\binom{36}{12 - x_1 - x_2 - x_3 - x_4}}{\binom{44}{12 - x_1 - x_3}} \qquad \begin{array}{l} 0 \le x_i \le 4 \\ x_2 + x_4 \le 12 - x_1 - x_3 \end{array}$$

the first two being marginal distributions and the third a conditional distribution. The distribution $f(x_1, x_2, x_3, x_4)$ itself may in this case be regarded as a marginal distribution of some more detailed distribution, for example, the six-variate distribution of $\mathbf{x}_1, \mathbf{x}_2, \mathbf{x}_3, \mathbf{x}_4, \mathbf{x}_5, \mathbf{x}_6$, where $\mathbf{x}_5$ and $\mathbf{x}_6$ are the numbers of fives and sixes that appear among the 12 cards drawn.

We cannot plot the four-variate distribution; in fact, we have used all three dimensions of conceptual space in plotting bivariate distributions. This could have been avoided by using a different device; we might have used dots of different sizes rather than vertical lines and thus pictured the bivariate distributions in two dimensions. This method would not have given as clear a representation of the relative magnitude of the probabilities. Using the dots, we could get a pictorial representation of a

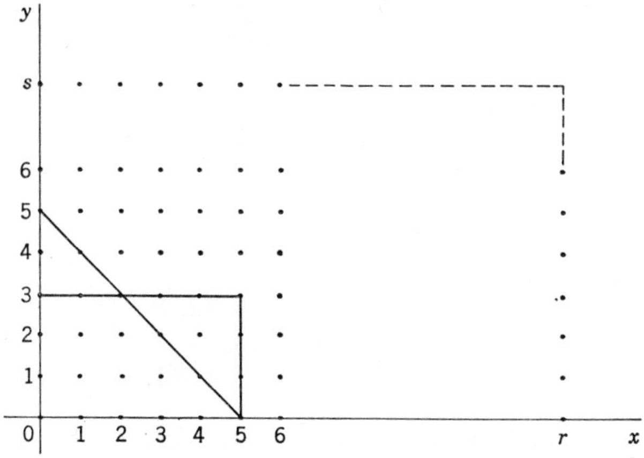

FIG. 3.6

trivariate distribution, but for more than three variates no simple graphical representation is possible.

The probability of any event is obtained by summing the density over all points in the region defined by the event. Suppose that a bivariate density $f(x, y)$ is defined for $x = 0, 1, 2, \cdots, r$ and $y = 0, 1, 2, \cdots, s$. The probability that $\mathbf{x} \leq 5$ and $\mathbf{y} \leq 3$ is obtained by summing $f(x, y)$ over the region defined by the inequalities (the rectangle in Fig. 3.6).

$$P(\mathbf{x} \leq 5, \mathbf{y} \leq 3) = \sum_{x=0}^{5} \sum_{y=0}^{3} f(x, y)$$

The probability that the sum of $\mathbf{x}$ and $\mathbf{y}$ is less than 5 is equal to the sum of $f(x, y)$ over all points below the line $x + y = 5$.

$$\begin{aligned} P(\mathbf{x} + \mathbf{y} < 5) &= f(0, 0) + f(1, 0) + f(2, 0) + f(3, 0) + f(4, 0) \\ &\quad + f(0, 1) + f(1, 1) + f(2, 1) + f(3, 1) \\ &\quad + f(0, 2) + f(1, 2) + f(2, 2) \\ &\quad + f(0, 3) + f(1, 3) \\ &\quad + f(0, 4) \\ &= \sum_{x=0}^{4} \sum_{y=0}^{4-x} f(x, y) = \sum_{y=0}^{4} \sum_{x=0}^{4-y} f(x, y) \end{aligned}$$

Some other examples are

$$P(\mathbf{x} + \mathbf{y} = 5) = \sum_{x=0}^{5} f(x, 5 - x)$$

$$P(\mathbf{x} \leq 2|\mathbf{y} = 3) = \sum_{x=0}^{2} g(x|3)$$

$$= \frac{\sum_{x=0}^{2} f(x, 3)}{\sum_{x=0}^{r} f(x, 3)}$$

$$P(\mathbf{x} \leq 2|\mathbf{y} > 3) = \frac{\sum_{x=0}^{2} \sum_{y=4}^{s} f(x, y)}{\sum_{x=0}^{r} \sum_{y=4}^{s} f(x, y)}$$

$$P(\mathbf{x} + \mathbf{y} = 2|\mathbf{x}^2 + \mathbf{y}^2 \leq 5)$$

$$= \frac{f(0, 2) + f(1, 1) + f(2, 0)}{f(0, 0) + f(0, 1) + f(0, 2) + f(1, 0) + f(1, 1) + f(1, 2) + f(2, 0) + f(2, 1)}$$

For three variables, the regions may be troublesome to visualize, and for more than three variables, we must rely on the analytical description of the region to determine the required sums. Some relatively easy examples are

$$P(\mathbf{x} \leq 3, \mathbf{y} \leq 4, 2 \leq \mathbf{z} \leq 6) = \sum_{x=0}^{3} \sum_{y=0}^{4} \sum_{z=2}^{6} f(x, y, z)$$

$$P(\mathbf{x} + \mathbf{y} = 4|\mathbf{z} = 2) = \sum_{x=0}^{4} f(x, 4 - x|2)$$

$$P(\mathbf{x} + \mathbf{y} + \mathbf{z} \leq 6) = \sum_{x=0}^{6} \sum_{y=0}^{6-x} \sum_{z=0}^{6-x-y} f(x, y, z)$$

$$P(\mathbf{x} + \mathbf{y} + \mathbf{z} = 6) = \sum_{x=0}^{6} \sum_{y=0}^{6-x} f(x, y, 6 - x - y)$$

3.4 The Binomial Distribution

The binomial distribution is one of the most frequently used discrete distributions in applications of the theory of statistics. It is the distribution associated with repeated trials of an experiment. Suppose that we denote by p the probability of a particular event. The event may be the occurrence of a head when a balanced coin is tossed, in which case $p = \frac{1}{2}$; it may be the occurrence of a seven when two symmetrical dice are cast, in which case $p = \frac{1}{6}$; it may be the occurrence of at least two aces when five cards are drawn at random from an ordinary deck, in which case

$$p = \frac{\binom{4}{2}\binom{48}{3} + \binom{4}{3}\binom{48}{2} + \binom{4}{4}\binom{48}{1}}{\binom{52}{5}}$$

Or, more generally, p may represent the probability of occurrence of some actual event to which no numerical a priori probability can be assigned.

Whatever the event, if the probability of its occurrence is p, the probability of its nonoccurrence is $1 - p$, since an event must either occur or not occur in a given trial. It will be convenient to denote $1 - p$ by q, and in speaking of a given trial we shall say that the probability of a success (occurrence) is p and the probability of a failure (nonoccurrence) is q, where $p + q = 1$.

Definition 3.2. *The random variable* $\mathbf{x}$ *is said to be distributed as a point binomial if the density is given by*

$$f(x) = p^x q^{1-x} \qquad x = 0, 1; 0 \leq p \leq 1$$

The random variable $\mathbf{x}$ which assumes only the values 0 or 1 can be interpreted by the following: $f(1)$ means the probability of a success; $f(0)$ means the probability of a failure. Clearly, $f(0) = q = 1 - p; f(1) = p$.

For example, if two dice are tossed and the probability of a seven is taken to be $\frac{1}{6}$, then the density of $\mathbf{x}$, the number of sevens occurring in one toss, is

$$f(x) = (\tfrac{1}{6})^x (\tfrac{5}{6})^{1-x} \qquad x = 0, 1$$

The probability of a seven is $f(1) = \frac{1}{6}$; the probability of no seven is $f(0) = \frac{5}{6}$.

Another important distribution will be defined next.

Definition 3.3. *Let the random variable* $\mathbf{x}$ *have a density given by*

$$f(x) = \binom{n}{x} p^x q^{n-x} \qquad x = 0, 1, 2, \cdots, n$$

This is the binomial distribution.

To investigate how this distribution can arise, we proceed as follows: The outcome of the ith trial forms a one-dimensional random variable which we denote by $\mathbf{x}_i$, where $\mathbf{x}_i = 0$ if the ith trial resulted in a failure and $\mathbf{x}_i = 1$ if the ith trial resulted in a success. Let $f(x_1, x_2, \cdots, x_n)$ be the probability that the random variable $\mathbf{x}_i = x_i$, $i = 1, 2, \cdots, n$, where $x_i = 0$ or 1. Since the random variables $\mathbf{x}_i$ are independent, we use the definition of independence to obtain

$$f(x_1, \cdots, x_n) = f(x_1)f(x_2) \cdots f(x_n)$$

But by the assumption that each random variable is a point binomial we get

$$\begin{aligned} f(x_1, x_2, \cdots, x_n) &= f(x_1)f(x_2) \cdots f(x_n) \\ &= p^{x_1}q^{1-x_1}p^{x_2}q^{1-x_2} \cdots p^{x_n}q^{1-x_n} \\ &= p^{\Sigma x_i}q^{n-\Sigma x_i} \qquad x_i = 0, 1 \end{aligned}$$

For example, for the particular set 0 0 1 0 1 1 1 we would get

$$f(0, 0, 1, 0, 1, 1, 1) = q\,q\,p\,q\,p\,p\,p$$

In fact, for any arrangement for which there are k successes (1) and $n - k$ failures (0), the probability is $p^k q^{n-k}$ since $\Sigma x_i = k$ if there are k 1's and $n - k$ 0's. But the total number of ways of arranging k 1's and $n - k$ 0's is $\binom{n}{k}$, and so the probability of exactly k successes is

$$\binom{n}{k} p^k q^{n-k} \qquad k = 0, 1, 2, \cdots, n$$

In summary, we have the following:

1. If the probability that an event occurs is p and the probability that it does not occur is $q = 1 - p$, then the density of the random variable $\mathbf{x}$ (the number of occurrences) is

$$f(x) = p^x q^{1-x} \qquad x = 0, 1$$

This is the *point binomial distribution.*

2. In n trials, let the probability of an event occurring in each trial be equal to p, and let all trials be independent. The density of the random variable $\mathbf{x}$ (the number of occurrences in n trials) is

$$f(x) = \binom{n}{x} p^x q^{n-x} \qquad x = 0, 1, 2, \cdots, n$$

This is the *binomial distribution.*

The density contains two other variables p and n (q is determined by p) of a different character. Their variation is between different binomial distributions; for a specific binomial distribution, p and n must be given numerical values. Variables of this kind are called *parameters.* The function actually represents a *two-parameter family* of distributions, and a specific member of the family is given when p and n are given specific values. The parameter n is called a *discrete parameter,* since it can have only the values 1, 2, 3, $\cdots$; it would be meaningless to speak of, say, 2.53 trials. But p is a *continuous parameter,* since it can conceivably have any value between 0 and 1. Thus it is possible for p to be .5, say, in the case of a true coin, or possibly .5000037 in the case of a slightly biased coin. Any arbitrarily chosen number between 0 and 1 is an allowable value of p.

Two particular binomial distributions are plotted in Fig. 3.7. In Fig. 3.7*a*, $p = .4$ and $n = 4$; in Fig. 3.7*b*, $p = .8$ and $n = 3$. In general, the binomial density has a maximum value determined as follows: Let m be the integral part of the number $(n + 1)p$ and let e be the fractional part. Thus if $n = 7$ and $p = .3$, we have $m = 2$ and $e = .4$. The largest value of $f(x)$ occurs when x is put equal to m; m is called the

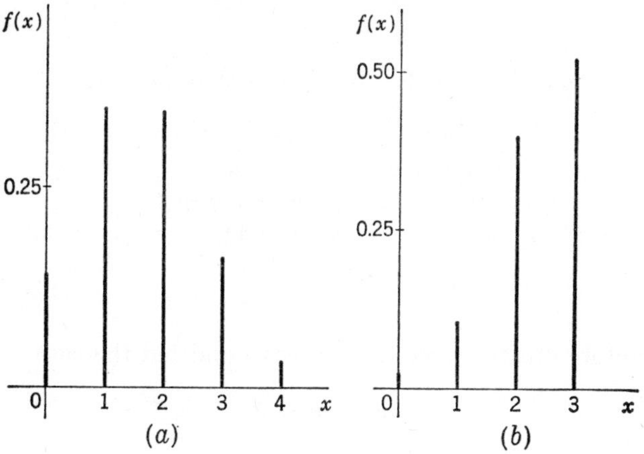

FIG. 3.7

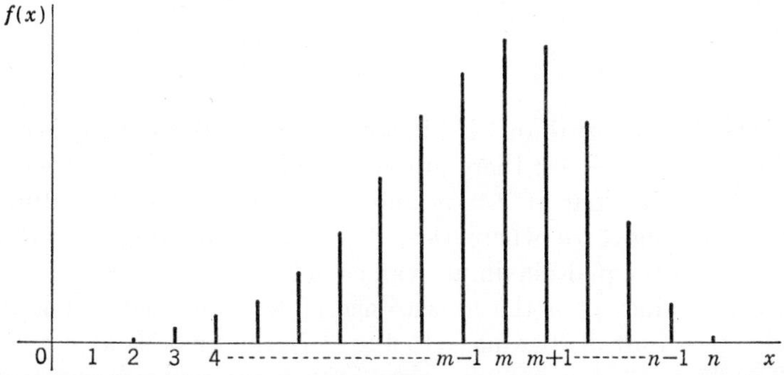

FIG. 3.8

modal value or simply the *mode* of x. To prove that this value of x maximizes $f(x)$, let us assume for the moment that e is not 0, and let us form the ratio $f(x + 1)/f(x)$. We wish to show that this ratio is less than 1 when x is greater than or equal to m, and greater than 1 when x is less than m. We are thinking of a situation such as that illustrated in Fig. 3.8. Now

$$\frac{f(x+1)}{f(x)} = \frac{p}{q}\,\frac{n-x}{x+1}$$

and if x is greater than or equal to m, then

$$\frac{p}{q}\frac{n-x}{x+1} \leq \frac{p}{q}\frac{n-m}{m+1}$$

On substituting $(n+1)p - e$ for m, the right-hand expression may be written

$$\frac{p}{q}\frac{n-m}{m+1} = \frac{(n+1) - [(1-e)/q]}{(n+1) + [(1-e)/p]}$$

which is certainly less than 1. If x is less than $m - 1$,

$$\begin{aligned}\frac{p}{q}\frac{n-x}{x+1} &> \frac{p}{q}\frac{n-(m-1)}{m}\\ &> \frac{p}{q}\frac{(n+1)q+e}{(n+1)p-e}\\ &> \frac{n+1+e/q}{n+1-e/p}\end{aligned}$$

and is therefore greater than 1. We have omitted the case

$$x = m - 1$$

Here

$$\begin{aligned}\frac{f(x+1)}{f(x)} &= \frac{p}{q}\frac{n-m+1}{m}\\ &= \frac{(n+1)+e/q}{(n+1)-e/p}\end{aligned}$$

which is again greater than 1 if e is not 0. If $e = 0$, the ratio is equal to 1, and $f(m) = f(m-1)$; there are two largest values of $f(x)$ which are equal and which occur at $x = m$ and at $x = m - 1$. This situation is illustrated in Fig. 3.7*a* where $(n+1)p = 2$ is an integer, so that $f(1)$ and $f(2)$ are two equal maximum values of $f(x)$.

For large values of n the appearance of the binomial distribution is generally like that of Fig. 3.8. In Fig. 3.7*b* the mode is at $x = n$ when $p = .8$ and $n = 3$, but as n increases, the mode moves away from the extreme right end of the range; thus, if $n = 100$, we have

$$101 \times .8 = 80.8$$

so that the mode is 80 and is well away from the extreme value of $x = 100$.

The computation of binomial probabilities becomes troublesome when n is large. Approximate methods can be developed for computing $\binom{n}{x} p^x q^{n-x}$, but we shall omit these because the computation of single terms is rarely required. In most applications, partial sums are needed.

Thus we may require the probability that $\mathbf{x}$ be greater than an integer a,

$$P(\mathbf{x} > a) = \sum_{x=a+1}^{n} f(x)$$

Methods of computing such sums will be given in Chaps. 7 and 11.

3.5 The Multinomial Distribution

The multinomial distribution is associated with repeated trials of an event which can have more than two outcomes. Thus the outcome of tossing a die may be any one of the six numbers 1, 2, $\cdot \cdot \cdot$, 6. If the event refers to the appearance of aces when, say, seven cards are drawn, there are five possible outcomes: 0, 1, 2, 3, or 4 aces.

In general, suppose that there are k possible outcomes of a chance event, and let the probabilities of these outcomes be denoted by p_1, p_2, $\cdot \cdot \cdot$, p_k. Obviously we must have

$$\sum_{i=1}^{k} p_i = 1 \tag{1}$$

just as $p + q = 1$ in the binomial case. Suppose that the event is repeated n times, and let $\mathbf{x}_1$ be the number of times the outcome associated with p_1 occurs, let $\mathbf{x}_2$ be the number of times the outcome associated with p_2 occurs, and so forth. The density for the random variables $\mathbf{x}_1$, $\mathbf{x}_2$, $\cdot \cdot \cdot$, $\mathbf{x}_{k-1}$ is

$$f(x_1, x_2, \cdot \cdot \cdot , x_{k-1}) = \frac{n!}{\prod_{i=1}^{k} x_i!} \prod_{i=1}^{k} p_i^{x_i} \qquad x_i = 0, 1, \cdot \cdot \cdot , n; \sum_{i=1}^{k} x_i = n \tag{2}$$

We have written the density as involving only $k - 1$ of the x_i's since only $k - 1$ of them are functionally independent; x_k is exactly determined by the relation $\sum_{1}^{k} x_i = n$ when the x_1, $\cdot \cdot \cdot$, x_{k-1} are specified. Thus this is a multivariate distribution involving $k - 1$ variates. The x_k on the right-hand side of (2) is to be interpreted as merely a symbol for the expression

$$n - x_1 - x_2 - \cdot \cdot \cdot - x_{k-1}$$

The expression (2) is a k-parameter family of distributions, the parameters being n, p_1, p_2, $\cdot \cdot \cdot$, p_{k-1}. The other variable p_k is, like q in the binomial distribution, exactly determined by

$$p_k = 1 - p_1 - p_2 - \cdot \cdot \cdot - p_{k-1}$$

A particular case of a multinomial distribution is obtained by putting, for example, $n = 3$, $k = 3$, $p_1 = .2$, $p_2 = .3$ to get

$$f(x_1, x_2) = \frac{3!}{x_1!x_2!(3 - x_1 - x_2)!} (.2)^{x_1}(.3)^{x_2}(.5)^{3-x_1-x_2}$$

This density is plotted in Fig. 3.9.

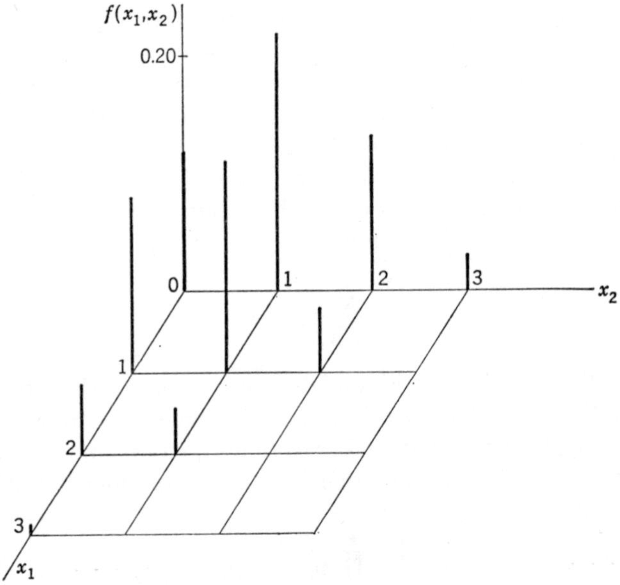

FIG. 3.9

3.6. The Poisson Distribution

The Poisson density is given in the following definition.

Definition 3.4. *The random variable* **x** *is distributed as a Poisson if the density is*

$$f(x) = \frac{e^{-m}m^x}{x!} \qquad x = 0, 1, 2, 3, \cdots \tag{1}$$

where m is any positive number.

Since the exponential e^m has the series expansion

$$e^m = 1 + m + \frac{m^2}{2!} + \cdots + \frac{m^x}{x!} + \cdots$$

it follows that

$$\sum_{x=0}^{\infty} f(x) = 1$$

The distribution has useful application in situations where a large number of objects are distributed over a large area. To consider a concrete example, suppose that a volume V of fluid contains a large number N of small organisms. It is assumed that the organisms have no social instincts and that they are as likely to appear in any part of the fluid as in any other part with the same volume. Now suppose that a drop of volume D is to be examined under a microscope, what is the probability that x organisms will be found in the drop? We assume that V is very much larger than D. Since the organisms are assumed to be distributed throughout the fluid with uniform probability, it follows that the probability that any given one of them may be found in D is D/V. And since they are assumed to have no social instincts, the occurrence of one in D has no effect on whether or not another occurs in D. The probability that x of them occur in D is therefore

$$\binom{N}{x}\left(\frac{D}{V}\right)^x\left(\frac{V-D}{V}\right)^{N-x} \tag{2}$$

We are also assuming here that the organisms are so small that the question of crowding may be neglected; all N of them would occupy no appreciable part of the volume D. The Poisson density is an approximation to the above expression, which is simply a binomial density in which $p = D/V$ is very small.

The Poisson distribution is obtained by letting V and N become infinite in such a way that the density of organisms $N/V = d$ remains constant. If we rewrite (2) in the form

$$\frac{N(N-1)(N-2)\cdots(N-x+1)}{x!N^x}\left(\frac{ND}{V}\right)^x\left(1-\frac{ND}{NV}\right)^{N-x}$$
$$= \frac{\left(1-\frac{1}{N}\right)\left(1-\frac{2}{N}\right)\cdots\left(1-\frac{x-1}{N}\right)(Dd)^x\left(1-\frac{Dd}{N}\right)^{N-x}}{x!}$$

the limit as N becomes infinite is readily seen to be

$$\frac{e^{-Dd}(Dd)^x}{x!}$$

which is the same form as (1) if we put $Dd = m$. This derivation shows that m is the average value of $\mathbf{x}$, since D, the volume of the portion examined, multiplied by the over-all density d gives the average number expected in the volume D.

We have gone into some detail in discussing this distribution because it is often erroneously applied to data which do not fulfill the assumptions required by the distribution. Thus it cannot be used, for example, in studying the distribution of insect larvae over some large crop area, because insects lay their eggs in clusters so that if one is found in a given small area, others are likely to be found there also.

The Poisson density is an approximation to the binomial density, $\binom{N}{x} p^x q^{N-x}$, when Np is large relative to p and N is large relative to Np. It is particularly useful when N is unknown.

3.7 Other Discrete Distributions

The *hypergeometric density* is

$$f(x) = \frac{\binom{m}{x}\binom{n}{r-x}}{\binom{m+n}{r}} \qquad x = 0, 1, \cdots, r \tag{1}$$

Equation (3.3.3) gives a special example. Equation (3.3.2) is an example of a bivariate hypergeometric distribution.

The *discrete uniform density* is

$$f(x) = \frac{1}{n} \qquad x = 1, 2, \cdots, n \tag{2}$$

The casting of a die provides an example.

The *negative binomial density* is

$$f(x) = p^r \binom{x+r-1}{r-1} q^x \qquad x = 0, 1, 2, \cdots; p + q = 1 \tag{3}$$

and $\Sigma f(x) = 1$ since

$$\sum_{x=0}^{\infty} \binom{x+r-1}{r-1} q^x = \frac{1}{(1-q)^r} = \frac{1}{p^r}$$

An example is provided by letting p be the probability of success and q be the probability of failure of a given event. Let $f(x)$ be the probability that exactly $x + r$ trials will be required to produce r successes. The last trial must be a success, and its probability is p. Among the other $x + r - 1$ trials there must be $r - 1$ successes, and the probability of this is

$$\binom{x+r-1}{r-1} p^{r-1} q^x$$

The product of these two probabilities gives the desired probability, $f(x)$, and is the same as (3).

3.8 Problems

Specify the values that the random variables can assume in every distribution. Do not obtain numerical answers which require lengthy computations.

1. Five cards are dealt from an ordinary deck. What is the density for the number of spades? What is the cumulative distribution?

2. Ten balls are tossed into four boxes so that each ball is equally likely to fall in any box. What is the density for the number of balls in the first box? What is the cumulative distribution?

3. A coin is tossed until a head appears. What is the density for the number of tosses?

4. What is the density for the number that appears when a die is cast? What is the cumulative distribution?

5. Two dice are cast. What is the density of the sum of the two numbers which appear?

6. Cards are drawn from an ordinary deck, without replacement, until a spade appears. What is the density for the number of draws?

7. Six dice are cast. What is the density of the number of ones and twos?

8. An urn contains m black and n white balls. k balls are drawn without replacement. What is the density of the number of white balls? Specify the range for the various relative sizes of m, n, and k.

9. Three coins are tossed n times. Find the joint density of $\mathbf{x}$, the number of times no heads appear; $\mathbf{y}$, the number of times one head appears; and $\mathbf{z}$, the number of times two heads appear.

10. A machine makes nails with an average of 1 per cent defective. What is the density of the number of defectives in a sample of 60 nails?

11. An urn contains 8 white and 12 black balls. Balls are drawn one by one, without replacement, until five white ones have appeared. Find the density of the total number drawn.

12. Six cards are drawn, without replacement, from an ordinary deck. Find the joint density of the number of aces and the number of kings.

13. Show that

$$\sum_{i=0}^{c} \binom{a}{i} \binom{b}{c-i} = \binom{a+b}{c}$$

by equating coefficients of x^c in

$$(1+x)^a(x+1)^b = (1+x)^{a+b}$$

Hence verify algebraically that the sum of the hypergeometric density is 1.

14. Use the result of Prob. 13 to find the marginal density of the number of aces from the result of Prob. 12.

15. In a town with 5000 adults, a sample of 100 are asked their opinion of a proposed municipal project; 60 are found to favor it and 40 to oppose it. If, in fact, the adults of the town were equally divided on the proposal, what would be the probability of obtaining a majority of 60 or more favoring it in a sample of 100?

16. A distributor of bean seeds determines from extensive tests that 5 per cent of a large batch of seeds will not germinate. He sells the seeds in packages of 200 and guarantees 90 per cent germination. What is the probability that a given package will violate the guarantee?

17. A manufacturing process is intended to produce electrical fuses with no more than 1 per cent defective. It is checked every hour by trying 10 fuses selected at random from the hour's production. If one or more of the 10 fail, the process is halted and carefully examined. If, in fact, its probability of producing a defective fuse is .01, what is the probability that the process will needlessly be examined in a given instance?

18. Referring to the above problem, how many fuses (instead of 10) should be tested if the manufacturer desires that the probability be about .95 that the process will be examined when it is producing 10 per cent defectives?

19. A has two pennies; B has one. They match pennies until one of them has all three. What is the density of the number of trials required to end the game?

20. Referring to the above problem, what is the density of the number of trials, given that A wins?

21. A die is cast 10 times. What is the probability that the number of ones and twos will not differ by more than two from its modal value?

22. A Poisson distribution has a double mode at $x = 1$ and $x = 2$; what is the probability that $\mathbf{x}$ will have one or the other of these two values?

23. Red-blood-cell deficiency may be determined by examining a specimen of the blood under a microscope. Suppose that a certain small fixed volume contains, on an average, 20 red cells for normal persons. What is the probability that a specimen from a normal person will contain less than 15 red cells?

24. An insurance company finds that .005 per cent of the population dies from a certain kind of accident each year. What is the probability that the company must pay off on more than 3 of 10,000 insured risks against such accidents in a given year?

25. A telephone switchboard handles 600 calls, on an average, during a rush hour. The board can make a maximum of 20 connections per minute. Use the Poisson distribution to evaluate the probability that the board will be overtaxed during any given minute.

26. A die is cast until a six appears. What is the probability that it must be cast more than five times?

27. Two dice are cast 10 times. Let $\mathbf{x}$ be the number of times no ones appear, and let $\mathbf{y}$ be the number of times two ones appear. What is the probability that $\mathbf{x}$ and $\mathbf{y}$ will each be less than 3?

28. In Prob. 27 what is the probability that $\mathbf{x} + \mathbf{y}$ will be 4? What is the probability that $\mathbf{x} + \mathbf{y}$ will be between 2 and 4 inclusive?

29. A die is cast 20 times. What is the probability that there will be at least twice as many ones and twos as there are threes?

30. Ten cards are drawn, without replacement, from an ordinary deck. What is the probability that the number of spades will exceed the number of clubs?

31. Suppose that a neutron passing through plutonium is equally likely to release one, two, or three other neutrons, and suppose that these second-generation neutrons are in turn each equally likely to release one, two, or three third-generation neutrons. What is the density of the number of third-generation neutrons?

32. Using the density of Prob. 12, find the conditional density of $\mathbf{x}$ (aces), given $\mathbf{y}$ (kings).

33. Using the density of Prob. 9, find the conditional density of $\mathbf{x}$ and $\mathbf{z}$, given $\mathbf{y}$.

Determine the sums required to compute the following probabilities, using density functions with as many variates as needed. Assume that all variates take the values $0, 1, 2, \cdots, m$.

34. $P(2\mathbf{x} + \mathbf{y} \leq 3)$

35. $P(\mathbf{x}^2 + \mathbf{y}^2 = 25)$

36. $P(\mathbf{x}^2 < 5 | 1 \leq \mathbf{y} \leq 6)$

37. $P(\mathbf{x} > 2\mathbf{y} - a), 0 < a < m$

38. $P(\mathbf{x} > \mathbf{y} > \mathbf{z})$

39. $P(\mathbf{x} + \mathbf{y} = 5 | \mathbf{y} = 3)$

40. $P(\mathbf{x} + \mathbf{y} = 5 | \mathbf{z} = 3)$

41. $P(\mathbf{x} \leq 3, \mathbf{y} \leq 4, \mathbf{z} \geq 5, \mathbf{w} \geq 6)$

42. $P(a \leq \mathbf{x} \leq b | \mathbf{y} = \mathbf{z}), 0 < a < b < m$

43. $P(\mathbf{x} > 2\mathbf{y} | \mathbf{x} > \mathbf{z})$

3.9 Bibliography

1. Clark, C.: "An Introduction to Statistics," John Wiley & Sons, Inc., New York, 1953.
2. Feller, W.: "An Introduction to Probability Theory and Its Applications," John Wiley & Sons, Inc., New York, 1950.
3. Fraser, D. A. S.: "Statistics—An Introduction," John Wiley & Sons, Inc., New York, 1958.
4. Fryer, H.: "Elements of Statistics," John Wiley & Sons, Inc., New York, 1954.
5. Hoel, P. G.: "Elementary Statistics," John Wiley & Sons, Inc., New York, 1960.
6. National Bureau of Standards: "Tables of the Binomial Probability Distribution," Applied Mathematics Series 6, 1950.
7. Rao, C. R.: "Advanced Statistical Methods in Biometric Research," John Wiley & Sons, Inc., New York, 1952.

4

Continuous Random Variables

4.1 Introduction

A continuous random variable can assume values that are not restricted to only isolated numbers but may have any value in a certain interval or collection of intervals on the x axis, the xy plane, etc.

To consider an example, suppose that a rifle is aimed at the center of a target and, after being clamped in that position, is fired several times. The bullets will not all strike the center, because minor variations in the weight of the bullets, in the shape of the bullets, in the effect of humidity and temperature on the powder, and other factors will cause variations in the trajectories of the bullets. After a few shots, the appearance of the target might be represented by Fig. 4.1. Let a random variable $\mathbf{x}$ have values that are horizontal deviations of the center of a hit from a vertical line through the center of the target. Clearly, $\mathbf{x}$ can assume a nondenumerable number of values.

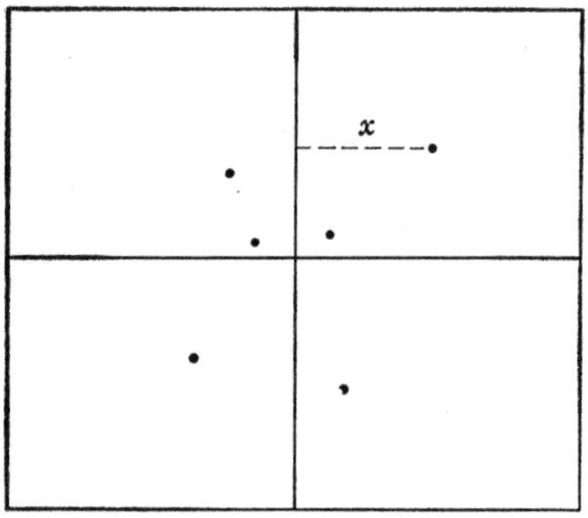

FIG. 4.1

This is a distinction between discrete and continuous random variables. A discrete random variable can take on a finite number of values or a denumerable infinity of values. A continuous random variable must take on a nondenumerable number of values.

4.2 Continuous Random Variables

In the case of discrete variates it is possible to have a nonzero probability associated with each admissible point, even when the number of points is infinite, and yet have the sum of the probabilities equal to 1. Thus if $\mathbf{x}$ is the number of tosses required to obtain a head with an ideal coin, we have seen that the density of $\mathbf{x}$ is

$$f(x) = (\tfrac{1}{2})^x \qquad x = 1, 2, 3, 4, \cdots$$

and

$$\sum_{x=1}^{\infty} f(x) = 1$$

In the case of a continuous variate this is not possible. The density will not sum to one unless practically all the points (all but a denumerable set) are given probability 0. Referring back to the horizontal deviations of rifle shots on a target, it is clear that all values of **x** within a small interval will be about equally likely, and it cannot reasonably be assumed that most of these points have probability 0 while some few others have nonzero probabilities.

We have encountered a difficulty which, it is to be pointed out, is purely logical. From a practical point of view the difficulty is obscured by the fact that we could not actually distinguish between a deviation of .5 inch and one of .500003 inch. We are limited by the accuracy of whatever measuring device we use, and a deviation can be identified only within a certain interval. Thus if we can measure only to within a hundredth of an inch, we might measure a deviation to be 4.26 inches. This would be interpreted to mean that the deviation lies somewhere in the interval 4.25 to 4.27 inches and might better be written $4.26 \pm .01$ to indicate this fact.

The logical problem is met by dealing with intervals rather than individual points. Let us first examine some empirical probabilities for intervals. Suppose that the rifle is fired 100 times at the target of Fig. 4.1, and suppose that the target area is divided into strips by drawing vertical lines on it 1 inch apart (see Fig. 4.2). Let the deviations x be negative to the left of the central line, and suppose that the vertical lines are drawn at $x = \pm 1, \pm 2, \pm 3$, and so on. Now for a given strip, say the one with $0 < x \leq 1$, the number of shots in that strip divided by 100 will be the relative frequency that a deviation will be between 0 and 1. We may tabulate a hypothetical distribution of shots and compute the empirical probabilities as in Table 4.1. The empirical distribution represented by this table could be plotted by using vertical lines, as was done with discrete distributions. However, we shall not plot a line at, say, the mid-point of each interval but shall prefer to use a rectangle with height equal to the relative frequency divided by the width of the

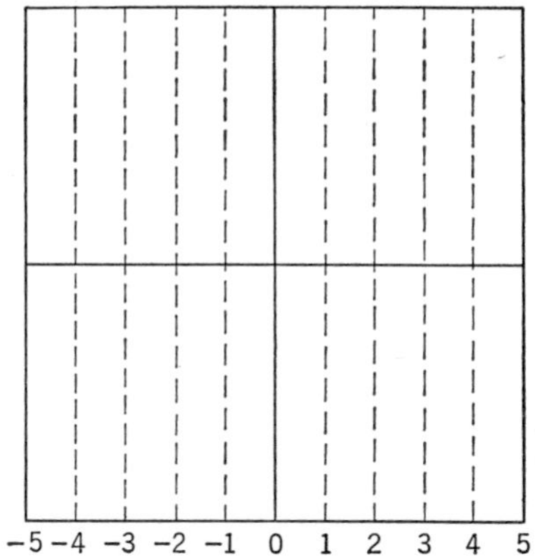

FIG. 4.2

TABLE 4.1

Strip	Number of shots	Relative frequency
$-5 < x \leq -4$	1	.01
$-4 < x \leq -3$	1	.01
$-3 < x \leq -2$	6	.06
$-2 < x \leq -1$	13	.13
$-1 < x \leq 0$	24	.24
$0 < x \leq 1$	27	.27
$1 < x \leq 2$	16	.16
$2 < x \leq 3$	7	.07
$3 < x \leq 4$	3	.03
$4 < x \leq 5$	2	.02

interval, and with a width equal to the width of the interval. This is done to indicate that the relative frequency refers to the whole interval rather than to any single point in the interval. The result is shown in Fig. 4.3.

Referring to Fig. 4.3, we note that the area of one of the rectangles is equal to the relative frequency for the interval corresponding to it, since the height of the rectangle is equal to the relative frequency and the base is 1. We shall focus attention on the areas rather than the heights.

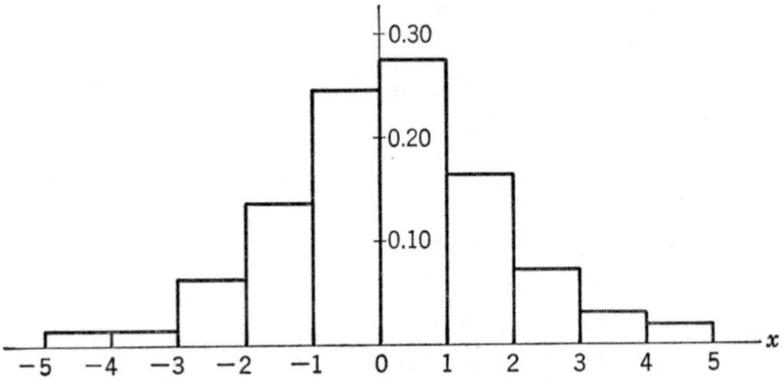

FIG. 4.3

The sum of the areas of all the rectangles is 1. It will be useful to let these relative frequencies be estimates of probability.

For intervals other than those chosen originally, we may also estimate probabilities. Thus we would estimate the probability that $0 < \mathbf{x} \leq 2$ by adding the areas of the two rectangles over that interval to get .43. To estimate the probability that, say, $-.25 < \mathbf{x} \leq 1.5$, we would compute the area over that interval to get

$$.06 + .27 + .08 = .41$$

If a second 100 shots were fired at the target, we could obtain another empirical distribution, which would in all likelihood be different from the first, although its general appearance might be similar. In constructing a theory of probability, we like to think of these observed relative frequencies as being estimates of some "true" probability. To this end we assume the existence of a function f such as that plotted in Fig. 4.4. We may not be able to specify the function, but we assume that there is some function which will give the correct probability for any *interval*. The probabilities are given by areas under the curve, not by values of the function. Thus

$$P(0 < \mathbf{x} \leq 1) = \int_0^1 f(x)\, dx$$

and this is the probability that is estimated by the area of the rectangle over the interval $0 < x \leq 1$ in Fig. 4.3. (Throughout this book all integrals will be Riemann integrals.)

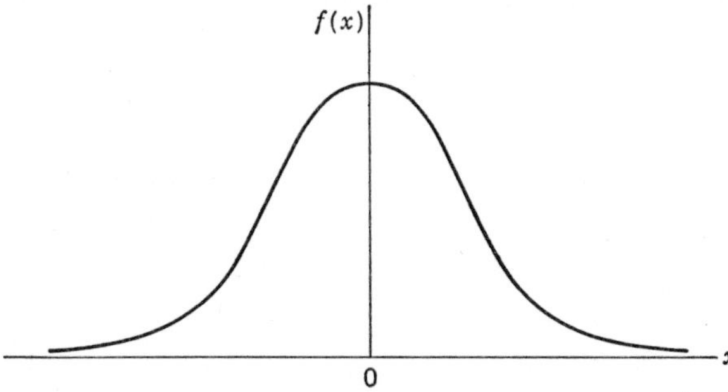

FIG. 4.4

The graph of the function f is thought of as a smooth curve rather than a step function for the following reasons: In the first place, it is recognized that the choice of intervals in any actual experiment is purely arbitrary. In the rifle experiment we could just as well have used intervals ½ inch long or intervals with end points at 1.2, 2.2, 3.2, for example, or we could have used intervals of different lengths: 0 to .5, .5 to 1.5, 1.5 to 3, for example. Thus the steps of the empirical distribution have no particular significance. In the second place, suppose that we consider two small intervals at a division point, say $1.9 < x \leq 2$ and $2 < x \leq 2.1$. Since the second interval is farther removed from the center than the first, we might expect its probability to be somewhat smaller, but it is not reasonable to suppose that a deviation is more than twice as likely to appear in the first interval, as is indicated in Fig. 4.3. The smooth curve gives a more reasonable relation between the two probabilities. In the third place, experiments with a large number of trials usually indicate that there are no abrupt changes in the curve. Thus if the rifle were fired, say, 1000 times, and if intervals $\frac{1}{10}$ inch wide were used, the steps would likely be much smaller than those of Fig. 4.3 and would approximate a smooth curve such as in Fig. 4.4 possibly.

In the foregoing discussion we have attempted to give an outline of how continuous random variables can arise and how relative frequency gives a notion of probability. Now we shall formulate this in a more concrete fashion.

Definition 4.1. *The random variable* $\mathbf{x}$ *will be called a (one-dimensional) continuous random variable if there exists a function f such that* $f(x) \geq 0$ *for all x in the interval* $-\infty < x < \infty$ *and such that for any event A*

$$P(A) = P(\mathbf{x} \text{ is in } A) = \int_A f(x)\,dx$$

$f(x)$ is called the density of $\mathbf{x}$, and we shall sometimes say "$\mathbf{x}$ is distributed as $f(x)$" or "$f(x)$ is the distribution of $\mathbf{x}$." The only event which

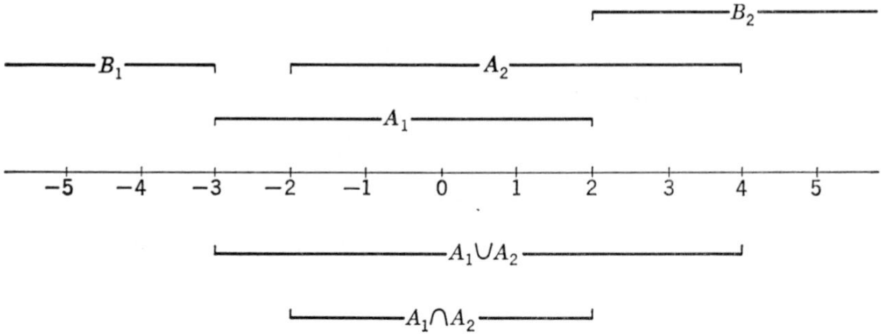

FIG. 4.5

we shall consider in this book for continuous random variables is an interval or a collection of a finite number of nonoverlapping intervals. For instance, in the example of the rifle target at the beginning of this chapter, let the two intervals A_1 and A_2 be defined by (see Fig. 4.5) $A_1 = \{x: -3 \leq x \leq 2\}$, $A_2 = \{x: -2 \leq x \leq 4\}$. The event "$A_1$ or A_2" is $A_1 \cup A_2 = \{x: -3 \leq x \leq 4\}$. The event "$A_1$ does not occur" is $\bar{A}_1 = B_1 \cup B_2$, where $B_1 = \{x: -\infty < x < -3\}$, $B_2 = \{x: 2 < x < \infty\}$. The event "$A_1$ and A_2" is $A_1 \cap A_2 = \{x: -2 \leq x \leq 2\}$. In this particular example the event (A_1 or A_2) is an interval, as is the event (A_1 and A_2); the event $\bar{A}_1$ is not an interval, but it is the union of two nonoverlapping intervals and hence is an event by our definition.

In this book we shall assume that continuous random variables have a density that is continuous except at most for a finite number of points.

Let A be defined by $A = \{x: a < x < b\}$. Then for a continuous random variable $\mathbf{x}$ with density $f(x)$,

$$P(a < \mathbf{x} < b) = P(A) = \int_A f(x)\,dx = \int_a^b f(x)\,dx$$

Since $\int_a^b f(x)\,dx$ is the same whether the interval is open, closed, open on the right or on the left, we have

$$P(a < \mathbf{x} < b) = P(a \leq \mathbf{x} < b) = P(a < \mathbf{x} \leq b) = P(a \leq \mathbf{x} \leq b)$$

Thus the integral at one point is 0; hence $P(\mathbf{x} = a) = 0$ for any number a. Now if A is not an interval but the union of a finite number of nonoverlapping intervals ($A = A_1 \cup A_2 \cup \cdots \cup A_k$, where $A_i \cap A_j = \emptyset$ for all $i \neq j$ and where $A_i = \{x: a_i < x < b_i\}$), then

$$\begin{aligned} P(A) = P(A_1 \cup A_2 \cup \cdots \cup A_k) &= \int_A f(x)\,dx \\ &= \int_{A_1} f(x)\,dx + \int_{A_2} f(x)\,dx + \cdots + \int_{A_k} f(x)\,dx \\ &= \int_{a_1}^{b_1} f(x)\,dx + \int_{a_2}^{b_2} f(x)\,dx + \cdots + \int_{a_k}^{b_k} f(x)\,dx \end{aligned}$$

equals the probability that the value of the random variable is between a_1 and b_1 or between a_2 and b_2 or $\cdots$ or between a_k and b_k. This essentially states that the probability of the value of a random variable occurring in a set A is the area between $f(x)$ and the x axis over that set. The density $f(x)$ may be a function which approximates a relative-frequency histogram as exemplified by Figs. 4.3 and 4.4, or $f(x)$ may be found from some fundamental theoretical reasoning. If the event A is the entire x axis, then $P(A)$ must be equal to 1, and we have

$$\int_{-\infty}^{\infty} f(x)\,dx = 1$$

Thus any function f can serve as a density of a continuous random variable $\mathbf{x}$ if it satisfies

$$\int_{-\infty}^{\infty} f(x)\,dx = 1$$
$$f(x) \geq 0 \qquad -\infty < x < \infty$$

Of course we want to choose f such that, for all a and b ($a < b$),

$$P(a < \mathbf{x} < b) = \int_a^b f(x)\,dx$$

in a particular applied problem has the meaning that it is the probability that the value of the random variable $\mathbf{x}$ is between a and b.

Any positive function over any arbitrarily chosen domain may be regarded as a density function for some random variable, provided that the function is multiplied by a constant which will make the integral of the function equal to 1. Thus the following function is a density function:

$$\begin{aligned} f(x) &= 0 & x &\leq 2 \\ &= \tfrac{1}{18}(3 + 2x) & 2 &< x < 4 \\ &= 0 & x &\geq 4 \end{aligned}$$

The value of the function is positive or zero, and

$$\begin{aligned} \int_{-\infty}^{\infty} f(x)\,dx &= \int_{-\infty}^{2} 0\,dx + \int_{2}^{4} \tfrac{1}{18}(3 + 2x)\,dx + \int_{4}^{\infty} 0\,dx \\ &= 0 + 1 + 0 \\ &= 1 \end{aligned}$$

The probability that a variate having this density will have a value in

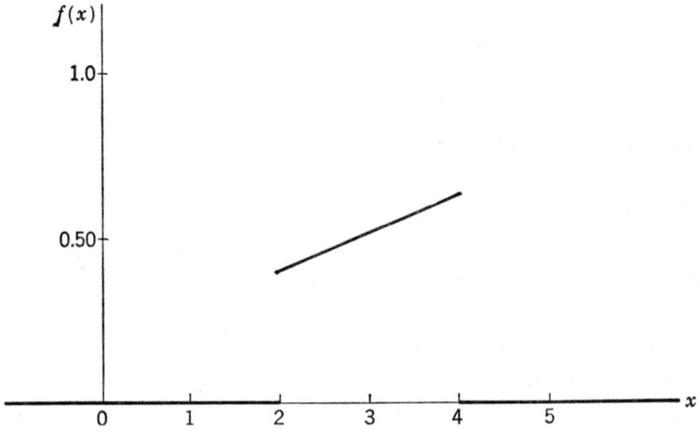

FIG. 4.6

the interval $2 < x < 3$, for example, is

$$\begin{aligned} P(2 < \mathbf{x} < 3) &= \int_{2}^{3} \tfrac{1}{18}(3 + 2x)\,dx \\ &= \tfrac{4}{9} \end{aligned}$$

The function is graphed in Fig. 4.6.

4.3 Multivariate Distributions

Going back to the rifle experiment, we may characterize each shot not only by its horizontal deviation x but by its vertical deviation y measured perpendicularly from a horizontal line through the center of the target. Suppose that a large number of shots are fired, and suppose that the target is divided into 1-inch squares by means of horizontal and vertical lines 1 inch apart. We could count the number of hits in each square and compute the relative frequency for each square. By plotting columns with heights equal to the relative frequency of each square, we might get a result such as that illustrated in Fig. 4.7. The volume of a column estimates the probability that a shot will fall in the square over which the column is constructed.

We shall idealize this situation by postulating the existence of a function f of x and y which would plot as a smooth surface over the xy plane.

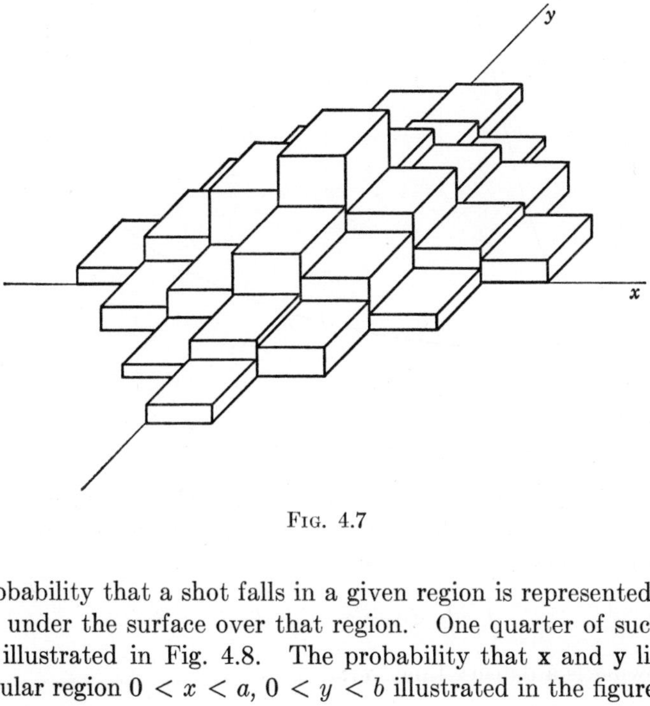

FIG. 4.7

The probability that a shot falls in a given region is represented by the volume under the surface over that region. One quarter of such a surface is illustrated in Fig. 4.8. The probability that **x** and **y** lie in the rectangular region $0 < x < a$, $0 < y < b$ illustrated in the figure is

$$P(0 < \mathbf{x} < a, 0 < \mathbf{y} < b) = \int_0^a \int_0^b f(x, y)\, dy\, dx \tag{1}$$

x and **y** are said to be jointly distributed continuous random variables if there exists a function f such that $f(x, y) \geq 0$ for all $-\infty < x < \infty$, $-\infty < y < \infty$ and such that for any event A

$$P(A) = P[(\mathbf{x}, \mathbf{y}) \text{ is in } A] = \int_A f(x, y)\, dy\, dx$$

We see that this requires

$$f(x, y) \geq 0 \qquad \text{for } -\infty < x < \infty,\ -\infty < y < \infty \tag{2}$$

$$\int_{-\infty}^{\infty} \int_{-\infty}^{\infty} f(x, y)\, dy\, dx = 1 \tag{3}$$

$f(x, y)$ is called the *joint density* of the random variables **x** and **y**.

A similar definition holds for the joint distribution of k continuous random variables.

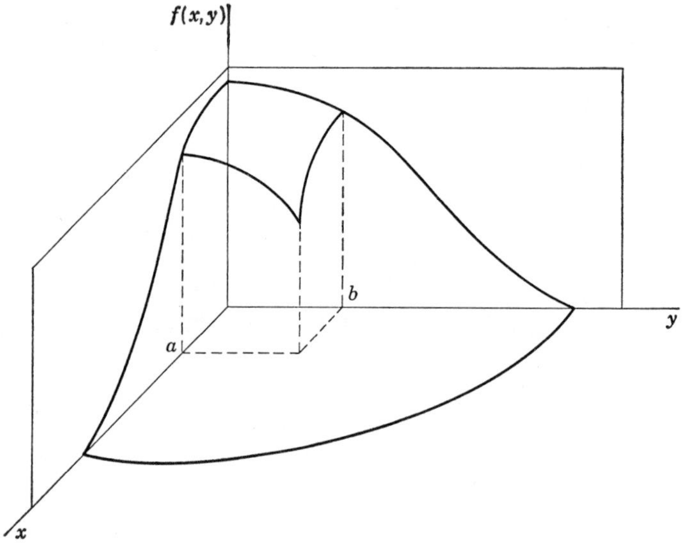

FIG. 4.8

As an illustration, $6 - x - y$ is positive over the rectangle $0 < x < 2$, $2 < y < 4$, for example; hence it may be used to define a joint density function over that region. Since

$$\int_0^2 \int_2^4 (6 - x - y)\, dy\, dx = 8$$

the following is a density function:

$$\begin{aligned} f(x, y) &= \tfrac{1}{8}(6 - x - y) \qquad && 0 < x < 2,\ 2 < y < 4 \\ &= 0 && \text{otherwise} \end{aligned} \tag{4}$$

If **x** and **y** are random variables having this density, the probability that they will fall (have a value) in the region $x < 1$, $y < 3$, for example, is

$$\begin{aligned} P(\mathbf{x} < 1, \mathbf{y} < 3) &= \int_{-\infty}^{1} \int_{-\infty}^{3} f(x, y)\, dy\, dx \\ &= \int_0^1 \int_2^3 \tfrac{1}{8}(6 - x - y)\, dy\, dx \\ &= \tfrac{3}{8} \end{aligned}$$

The probability that $\mathbf{x} + \mathbf{y}$ will be less than 3 is

$$P(\mathbf{x} + \mathbf{y} < 3) = \int_0^1 \int_2^{3-x} \tfrac{1}{8}(6 - x - y)\, dy\, dx$$
$$= \tfrac{5}{24}$$

The probability that $\mathbf{x} < 1$ when it is known that $\mathbf{y} < 3$ is

$$P(\mathbf{x} < 1 | \mathbf{y} < 3) = \frac{P(\mathbf{x} < 1, \mathbf{y} < 3)}{P(\mathbf{y} < 3)}$$

We have already computed the numerator of this expression, and the denominator is

$$P(\mathbf{y} < 3) = \int_0^2 \int_2^3 \tfrac{1}{8}(6 - x - y)\, dy\, dx$$
$$= \tfrac{5}{8}$$

Hence

$$P(\mathbf{x} < 1 | \mathbf{y} < 3) = \frac{\tfrac{3}{8}}{\tfrac{5}{8}} = \frac{3}{5}$$

The extension of these ideas to the case of more than two variates is apparent. In general, any function f may be regarded as a density function of k random variables, provided that

$$f(x_1, x_2, \cdots, x_k) \geq 0 \qquad -\infty < x_i < \infty \tag{5}$$
$$\int_{-\infty}^{\infty} \int_{-\infty}^{\infty} \cdots \int_{-\infty}^{\infty} f(x_1, x_2, \cdots, x_k)\, dx_1\, dx_2 \cdots dx_k = 1$$

The probability that the variate $(\mathbf{x}_1, \mathbf{x}_2, \cdots, \mathbf{x}_k)$ is in any given region of the k-dimensional space is obtained by integrating the density function over that region.

The function defined by

$$f(x_1, x_2, x_3, x_4) = 16x_1x_2x_3x_4 \qquad 0 < x_i < 1 \tag{6}$$
$$= 0 \qquad \text{otherwise}$$

is a density function since it satisfies the two requirements. The probability that the variate is in the region $x_1 < \tfrac{1}{2}$, $x_4 > \tfrac{1}{3}$ is

$$P(\mathbf{x}_1 < \tfrac{1}{2}, \mathbf{x}_4 > \tfrac{1}{3}) = \int_{\frac{1}{3}}^{\infty} \int_{-\infty}^{\infty} \int_{-\infty}^{\infty} \int_{-\infty}^{\frac{1}{2}} f(x_1, x_2, x_3, x_4)\, dx_1\, dx_2\, dx_3\, dx_4$$
$$= \int_{\frac{1}{3}}^{1} \int_0^1 \int_0^1 \int_0^{\frac{1}{2}} 16x_1x_2x_3x_4\, dx_1\, dx_2\, dx_3\, dx_4$$
$$= \tfrac{2}{9}$$

4.4 Cumulative Distributions

Since in the case of continuous variates the probabilities are given by integrals, it is often convenient to deal with the integrals of the densities rather than the densities themselves. Let $f(x)$ be a density for one variate (such as is plotted in Fig. 4.4, for example) and let

$$F(x) = \int_{-\infty}^{x} f(t)\,dt \tag{1}$$

$F(x)$ is the probability that the value of the random variable will be less than or equal to x. Thus

$$F(x) = P(\mathbf{x} \leq x) \qquad -\infty < x < \infty \tag{2}$$

F is called the *cumulative distribution function* of $\mathbf{x}$. The graph of a cumulative distribution function is illustrated in Fig. 4.9. If a function

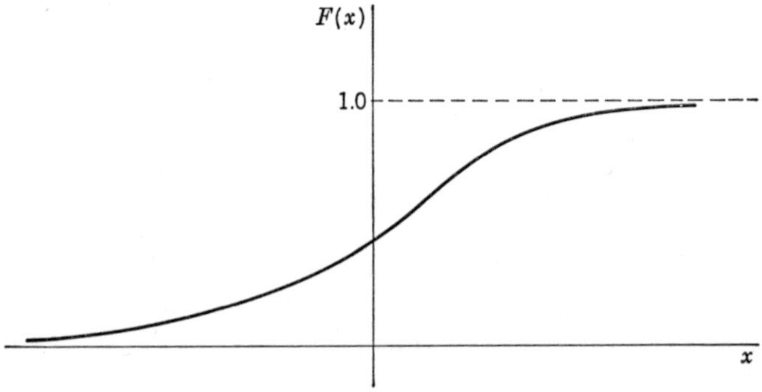

FIG. 4.9

F is the cumulative distribution of a continuous random variable, then

$$F \text{ is nondecreasing} \tag{3}$$
$$F(-\infty) = 0 \tag{4}$$
$$F(\infty) = 1 \tag{5}$$
$$F \text{ is continuous} \tag{6}$$

From the cumulative distribution, one can find the density, if it exists, by differentiating F at the points where F has a derivative; i.e.,

$$f(x) = \frac{dF(x)}{dx}$$

The probability that $\mathbf{x}$ falls in an interval $a < x \leq b$ is, in terms of the cumulative distribution,

$$\begin{aligned} P(a < \mathbf{x} \leq b) &= P(\mathbf{x} \leq b) - P(\mathbf{x} \leq a) \\ &= F(b) - F(a) \end{aligned} \tag{7}$$

Referring to the example at the end of Sec. 4.2, where

$$\begin{aligned} f(x) &= \tfrac{1}{18}(3 + 2x) \qquad && 2 < x < 4 \\ &= 0 && \text{otherwise} \end{aligned}$$

we find

$$\begin{aligned} F(x) &= 0 & x \le 2 \\ &= \int_2^x \tfrac{1}{18}(3 + 2t)\,dt = \tfrac{1}{18}(x^2 + 3x - 10) & 2 < x < 4 \\ &= 1 & x \ge 4 \end{aligned}$$

and

$$\begin{aligned} P(2 < \mathbf{x} < 3) &= F(3) - F(2) \\ &= \tfrac{1}{18}(9 + 9 - 10) - 0 \\ &= \tfrac{4}{9} \end{aligned}$$

The function is plotted in Fig. 4.10.

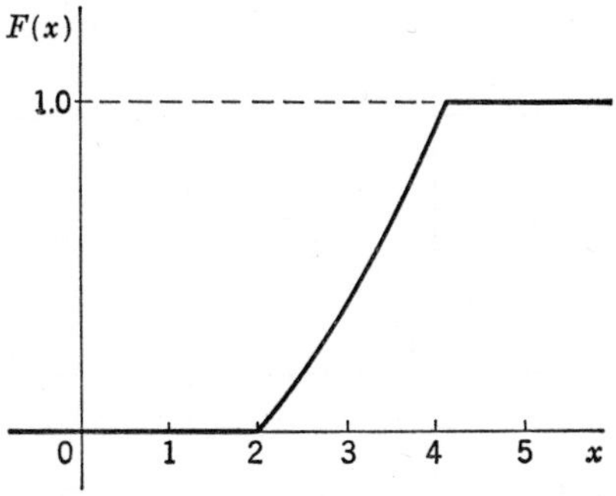

FIG. 4.10

For several variates the cumulative distribution is defined similarly:

$$F(x_1, x_2, \cdots, x_k) = \int_{-\infty}^{x_1} \int_{-\infty}^{x_2} \cdots \int_{-\infty}^{x_k} f(t_1, t_2, \cdots, t_k)\, dt_k\, dt_{k-1} \cdots dt_1 \tag{8}$$

where $f(x_1, x_2, \cdots, x_k)$ is the density. The value of the cumulative distribution at the point $(a_1, a_2, \cdots, a_k)$, for example, is the probability

$$\begin{aligned} P(\mathbf{x}_1 \le a_1, \mathbf{x}_2 \le a_2, \cdots, \mathbf{x}_k \le a_k) &= F(a_1, a_2, \cdots, a_k) \\ &= P(\mathbf{x}_1 < a_1, \mathbf{x}_2 < a_2, \cdots, \mathbf{x}_k < a_k) \end{aligned} \tag{9}$$

since for continuous random variables

$$F(x) = P(\mathbf{x} \le x) = P(\mathbf{x} < x)$$

Given the cumulative distribution F, the density may be found by differentiating F with respect to each of its variates when the derivatives exist:

$$f(x_1, x_2, \cdots, x_k) = \frac{\partial}{\partial x_1} \frac{\partial}{\partial x_2} \cdots \frac{\partial}{\partial x_k} F(x_1, x_2, \cdots, x_k) \tag{10}$$

To illustrate a cumulative distribution for two variates, we may use the density given in equation (4.3.4):

$$\begin{aligned} f(x, y) &= \tfrac{1}{8}(6 - x - y) \qquad 0 < x < 2, 2 < y < 4 \\ &= 0 \qquad \text{otherwise} \end{aligned} \tag{11}$$

There are nine regions in the xy plane to be taken account of in defining F; the nine regions are indicated in Fig. 4.11, in which the coordinates of the points of intersection of the lines are given. (The left vertical line coincides with the y axis.) This complication arises because of the

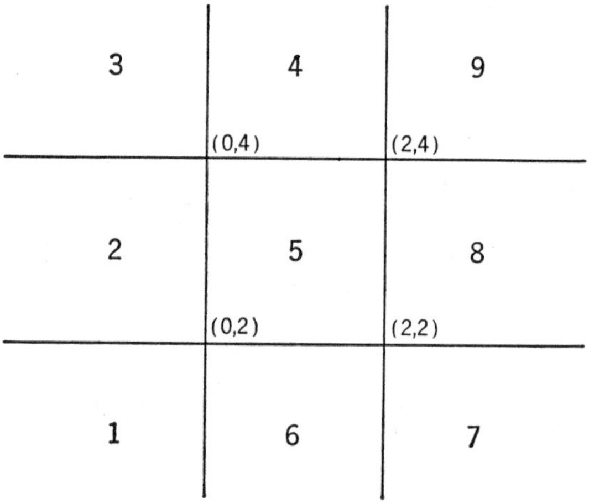

FIG. 4.11

piecewise definition of f. We could simply state that

$$F(x, y) = \int_{-\infty}^{x} \int_{-\infty}^{y} f(s, t)\, dt\, ds \tag{12}$$

but a more detailed characterization of the function will be required if it is to be useful. In region 1 of Fig. 4.11 $f(x, y)$ is 0; hence

$$F(x, y) = 0 \qquad x \le 0, y \le 2$$

In region 2, although y is greater than 2, we have $x \le 0$, so that (12) is still 0 since $f(s, t)$ never becomes positive over the range of integration. The same is true in regions 3, 6, 7. For x, y in region 5, the integrand is not 0 when $0 < s < x$, $2 < t < y$, and we have

$$\begin{aligned} F(x, y) &= \int_0^x \int_2^y \tfrac{1}{8}(6 - s - t)\, dt\, ds \\ &= \int_0^x \frac{1}{8}\left[(6 - s)(y - 2) - \frac{y^2}{2} + 2\right] ds \\ &= \tfrac{1}{16}x(y - 2)(10 - y - x) \qquad 0 < x < 2, 2 < y < 4 \end{aligned} \tag{13}$$

For any point in region 4, the integrand in (12) is positive when $0 < s < x$, $2 < t < 4$; hence

$$F(x, y) = \int_0^x \int_2^4 f(s, t)\, dt\, ds$$

and this integral may be computed by putting $y = 4$ in (13) to get

$$F(x, y) = \tfrac{1}{8}x(6 - x) \qquad 0 < x < 2,\ y \geq 4$$

Similarly, in region 8, $F(x, y) = F(2, y)$ when $x \geq 2$, so that

$$F(x, y) = \tfrac{1}{8}(y - 2)(8 - y) \qquad x \geq 2,\ 2 < y < 4$$

and in region 9, $F(x, y) = 1$. Combining these results,

$$\begin{aligned} F(x, y) &= 0 && x \leq 0 \text{ or } y \leq 2 \\ &= \tfrac{1}{16}x(y - 2)(10 - y - x) && 0 < x < 2,\ 2 < y < 4 \\ &= \tfrac{1}{8}x(6 - x) && 0 < x < 2,\ y \geq 4 \\ &= \tfrac{1}{8}(y - 2)(8 - y) && x \geq 2,\ 2 < y < 4 \\ &= 1 && x \geq 2,\ y \geq 4 \end{aligned} \qquad (14)$$

The function is plotted in Fig. 4.12.

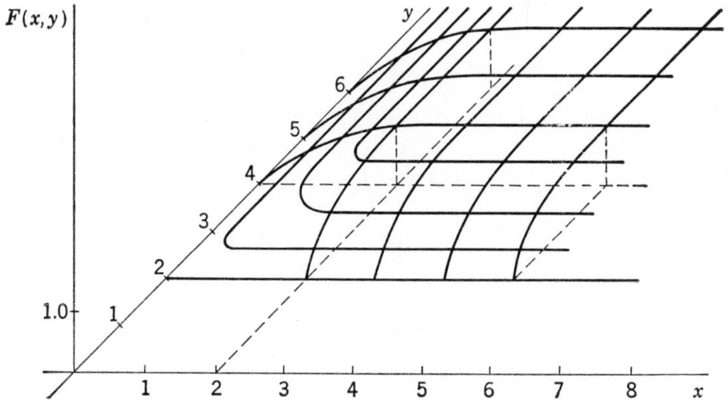

FIG. 4.12

The probability that $(\mathbf{x}, \mathbf{y})$ will fall in any rectangle, say $a_1 < x < b_1$, $a_2 < y < b_2$, may be written in terms of the cumulative distribution as follows:

$$\begin{aligned} P(a_1 < \mathbf{x} < b_1, a_2 < \mathbf{y} < b_2) &= P(\mathbf{x} < b_1, \mathbf{y} < b_2) - P(\mathbf{x} < a_1, \mathbf{y} < b_2) \\ &\quad - P(\mathbf{x} < b_1, \mathbf{y} < a_2) \\ &\qquad + P(\mathbf{x} < a_1, \mathbf{y} < a_2) \\ &= F(b_1, b_2) - F(a_1, b_2) - F(b_1, a_2) \\ &\quad + F(a_1, a_2) \end{aligned} \qquad (15)$$

Thus, in the above example,

$$\begin{aligned} P(0 < \mathbf{x} < 1, 3 < \mathbf{y} < 4) &= F(1,4) - F(0,4) - F(1,3) + F(0,3) \\ &= 5/8 - 0 - 3/8 + 0 \\ &= 1/4 \end{aligned}$$

These distributions can become quite complex for several variables, and in fact many important problems in applied statistics remain unsolved merely because the integrations required for their solution are too complex to perform.

In this book we shall ordinarily use small letters to denote probability density functions and the corresponding capital letters to represent their

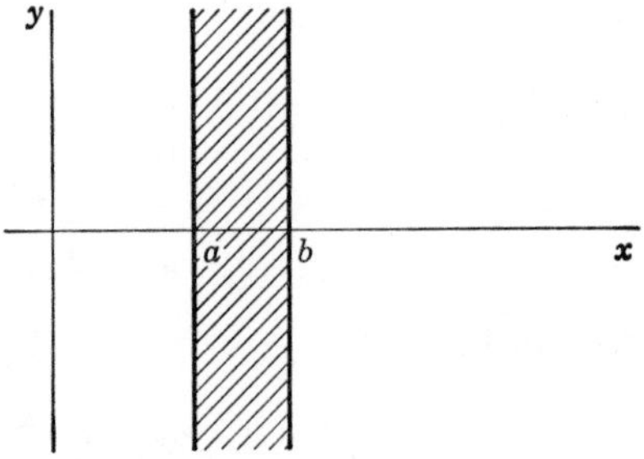

FIG. 4.13

cumulative forms. Thus, if **x** is continuous,

$$G(x) = \int_{-\infty}^{x} g(t)\, dt$$

or if the variate is discrete,

$$G(x) = \sum_{t \le x} g(t)$$

The word *density* will refer specifically to $g(x)$, while the phrase *cumulative distribution* will refer specifically to $G(x)$. The word *distribution* will be used as a more general term and may refer to either the density or its cumulative form.

4.5 Marginal Distributions

Associated with any distribution of more than one variable are several marginal distributions. Let $f(x, y)$ be a density for two continuous variates. We may be interested in only one of the variates, say **x**. We therefore seek a function of x which when integrated over an interval, say $a < x < b$, will give the probability that **x** will lie in that interval. In the xy plane such an interval corresponds to a strip, as illustrated in Fig. 4.13. The specification $a < x < b$ is satisfied by any point in the strip;

hence

$$P(a < \mathbf{x} < b) = \int_a^b \int_{-\infty}^{\infty} f(x, y)\, dy\, dx \tag{1}$$

Whatever the specification on $\mathbf{x}$, the limits of integration for y are $-\infty$ to $+\infty$, and so we may define a function, say

$$f_1(x) = \int_{-\infty}^{\infty} f(x, y)\, dy \tag{2}$$

and this function is the required marginal density, since

$$P(a < \mathbf{x} < b) = \int_a^b f_1(x)\, dx \tag{3}$$

for any pair of values a and b. Similarly the marginal density of $\mathbf{y}$ is

$$f_2(y) = \int_{-\infty}^{\infty} f(x, y)\, dx \tag{4}$$

In general, given any density $f(x_1, x_2, \cdots, x_k)$, one may find the marginal density of any subset of the variates by integrating the function with respect to all the other variates between the limits $-\infty$ and $+\infty$. Thus the marginal density of $\mathbf{x}_1$, $\mathbf{x}_2$, and $\mathbf{x}_4$, for example, is

$$f_{124}(x_1, x_2, x_4) = \int_{-\infty}^{\infty} \int_{-\infty}^{\infty} \cdots \int_{-\infty}^{\infty} f(x_1, x_2, \cdots, x_k)\, dx_3\, dx_5\, dx_6 \cdots dx_k \tag{5}$$

Referring to the distribution defined in equation (4.3.4), the marginal density of $\mathbf{x}$ is

$$\begin{aligned} f_1(x) &= \int_{-\infty}^{\infty} f(x, y)\, dy & -\infty < x < \infty \\ &= \int_2^4 \tfrac{1}{8}(6 - x - y)\, dy & 0 < x < 2 \\ &= \tfrac{1}{4}(3 - x) & 0 < x < 2 \\ &= 0 & x \leq 0 \text{ or } x \geq 2 \end{aligned} \tag{6}$$

The cumulative marginal distribution is easily found if the cumulative distribution is given. For two variables, the cumulative marginal distribution of $\mathbf{x}$ is

$$\begin{aligned} F_1(x) &= \int_{-\infty}^{x} \int_{-\infty}^{\infty} f(x, y)\, dy\, dx = \int_{-\infty}^{x} f_1(x)\, dx \\ &= F(x, \infty) \end{aligned} \tag{7}$$

Thus we need only let the variable in which we are not interested become infinite in the joint cumulative distribution. And in general, if $F(x_1, x_2, \cdots, x_k)$ is a k-variate cumulative distribution, the cumulative marginal distribution of $\mathbf{x}_1$, $\mathbf{x}_2$, $\mathbf{x}_4$, for example, is

$$F_{124}(x_1, x_2, x_4) = F(x_1, x_2, \infty, x_4, \infty, \cdots, \infty) \tag{8}$$

In our specific example we may find the cumulative marginal distribution of $\mathbf{x}$ by integrating $f_1(x)$; thus

$$\begin{aligned} F_1(x) &= \int_{-\infty}^{x} f_1(t)\, dt \\ &= 0 && x \leq 0 \\ &= \tfrac{1}{8}x(6 - x) && 0 < x < 2 \\ &= 1 && x \geq 2 \end{aligned} \tag{9}$$

The same result is obtained by letting y become infinite in $F(x, y)$ given by equations (4.4.14).

4.6 Conditional Distributions

We shall consider first a bivariate density, say $f(x, y)$, which might be represented by the surface of Fig. 4.8, for example. Suppose that a point $(\mathbf{x}, \mathbf{y})$ is drawn (a shot is fired at a target, for example), and suppose that the second variate $\mathbf{y}$ is observed but not the first. We seek a function, say $f(x|y)$, which will give the density of $\mathbf{x}$ when $\mathbf{y}$ is known, i.e., a function such that

$$P(a < \mathbf{x} < b|y) = \int_a^b f(x|y)\, dx \tag{1}$$

for any arbitrarily chosen a and b.

We define $f(x|y)$ only for values of y such that $f_2(y) > 0$. The definition is

$$f(x|y) = \frac{f(x, y)}{f_2(y)} \qquad \text{when } f_2(y) > 0 \tag{2}$$

By a similar definition, if $f_1(x)$ is the marginal density of $\mathbf{x}$, the conditional density of $\mathbf{y}$, given $\mathbf{x}$, is

$$f(y|x) = \frac{f(x, y)}{f_1(x)} \qquad \text{when } f_1(x) > 0 \tag{3}$$

The density $f(x|y)$ is a density of the variate $\mathbf{x}$; y is simply a parameter and will have some numerical value in any specific conditional density. Thus $f_2(c)$ is to be regarded as a constant. The joint density $f(x, y)$ plots as a surface over the xy plane. A plane perpendicular to the xy plane which intersects the xy plane on the line $y = c$ will intersect the surface in the curve $f(x, c)$. The area under this curve is

$$\int_{-\infty}^{\infty} f(x, c)\, dx = f_2(c)$$

Hence, if we divide $f(x, c)$ by $f_2(c)$, we obtain a density which is precisely $f(x|c)$.

For the particular density

$$f(x, y) = \tfrac{1}{8}(6 - x - y) \qquad 0 < x < 2,\ 2 < y < 4$$
$$= 0 \qquad \text{otherwise}$$

we have found in the preceding section that the marginal density of **x** is

$$f_1(x) = \tfrac{1}{4}(3 - x) \qquad 0 < x < 2$$
$$= 0 \qquad \text{otherwise}$$

In view of (3), the conditional density of **y** for fixed **x** is therefore

$$f(y|x) = \frac{6 - x - y}{2(3 - x)} \qquad 2 < y < 4,\ 0 < x < 2$$

Conditional distributions are defined analogously for multivariate distributions. Thus for five variates with a density $f(x_1, x_2, x_3, x_4, x_5)$, the conditional density of $\mathbf{x}_1$, $\mathbf{x}_2$, $\mathbf{x}_4$, given $\mathbf{x}_3$ and $\mathbf{x}_5$, is

$$f(x_1, x_2, x_4|x_3, x_5) = \frac{f(x_1, x_2, x_3, x_4, x_5)}{f_{35}(x_3, x_5)} \qquad \text{when } f_{35}(x_3, x_5) > 0$$

where $f_{35}(x_3, x_5)$ represents the marginal density of $\mathbf{x}_3$ and $\mathbf{x}_5$.

4.7 Independence

If the conditional density $f(x|y)$ does not involve y, then **x** is independent of **y** in the probability sense. Suppose that this is the case and that we represent $f(x|y)$ by $g(x)$. Since, from Sec. 4.6,

$$f(x|y) = g(x) = \frac{f(x, y)}{f_2(y)} \qquad \text{when } f_2(y) > 0 \tag{1}$$

it follows that

$$f(x, y) = g(x)f_2(y) \tag{2}$$

Hence the joint density of **x** and **y** is the product of two functions, one involving x only and the other involving y only. If we integrate (2) with respect to y, we find that $g(x)$ is simply the marginal density of **x**.

Definition 4.2. *The k variates $\mathbf{x}_1, \cdots, \mathbf{x}_k$ are independent in the probability sense if and only if their joint distribution is equal to the product of their marginal distributions.*

In general, if the conditional distribution of a subset of any set of variates is independent of the remaining fixed variables, then that subset is said to be independent of the remaining variables in the probability sense. The function defined in equation (4.3.6) provides an illustration:

$$f(x_1, x_2, x_3, x_4) = 16x_1x_2x_3x_4 \qquad 0 < x_i < 1 \text{ for all } i$$
$$= 0 \qquad \text{otherwise}$$

The marginal density of, say, $\mathbf{x}_2$ and $\mathbf{x}_4$ is

$$\begin{aligned} f_{24}(x_2, x_4) &= \int_{-\infty}^{\infty} \int_{-\infty}^{\infty} f(x_1, x_2, x_3, x_4)\, dx_1\, dx_3 \\ &= 4x_2x_4 \qquad 0 < x_2 < 1, 0 < x_4 < 1 \\ &= 0 \qquad \text{otherwise} \end{aligned}$$

Hence the conditional density of $\mathbf{x}_1$ and $\mathbf{x}_3$ is

$$\begin{aligned} f(x_1, x_3|x_2, x_4) &= 4x_1x_3 \qquad 0 < x_1 < 1, 0 < x_3 < 1 \\ &= 0 \qquad \text{otherwise} \end{aligned}$$

This function and its limits do not involve x_2 and x_4, so that the pair of random variables $(\mathbf{x}_1, \mathbf{x}_3)$ is independent of the pair $(\mathbf{x}_2, \mathbf{x}_4)$ in the probability sense. In fact, all four variates of this distribution are mutually independent, as may be deduced from the fact that the function may be factored into four functions each involving only one of the variates, and the limits are independent.

4.8 Random Sample

Consider the following experiment: A ball is drawn from an urn which contains six red and four black balls, and the color of the ball is noted. Let the outcome $\mathbf{x}_1$ be the number of red balls which are drawn; then the random variable $\mathbf{x}_1$ can assume only two values, 0 when no red ball is drawn (a black ball is drawn), and 1 when a red ball is drawn. Thus $\mathbf{x}_1$ is a random variable, and if the draw is such that each ball has the same chance of being selected the probability density is

$$f(x_1) = (6/10)^{x_1}(4/10)^{1-x_1} \qquad x_1 = 0, 1$$

Suppose that the ball which is drawn is replaced after its color is noted, and the experiment is repeated. Let the outcome of the second draw be denoted by $\mathbf{x}_2$; then the density of $\mathbf{x}_2$ is

$$f(x_2) = (6/10)^{x_2}(4/10)^{1-x_2} \qquad x_2 = 0, 1$$

Suppose further that, instead of looking at these two outcomes separately, we want the joint distribution of the two-dimensional random variable $(\mathbf{x}_1, \mathbf{x}_2)$. The physical experiment indicates that the joint density of the two-dimensional random variable could be written

$$\begin{aligned} g(x_1, x_2) = f(x_1)f(x_2) &= (6/10)^{x_1}(4/10)^{1-x_1}(6/10)^{x_2}(4/10)^{1-x_2} \\ &= (6/10)^{x_1+x_2}(4/10)^{2-(x_1+x_2)} \qquad x_1 = 0, 1 \\ & \qquad\qquad x_2 = 0, 1 \end{aligned}$$

When the joint density of a two-dimensional random variable is equal to the product of densities of each random variable and when the densities of each random variable are the same, we say that a random sample of size 2 is drawn from the density $f(x)$. These ideas can be extended to more than two random variables and also to continuous density functions. Thus we formulate the following definition:

Definition 4.3. *Let the n jointly independent random variables* $\mathbf{x}_1, \mathbf{x}_2, \cdots, \mathbf{x}_n$ *each have the same density* $f(x)$. *Then we say that* $\mathbf{x}_1, \mathbf{x}_2, \cdots, \mathbf{x}_n$ *is a random sample of size n from* $f(x)$. *The joint density of the n random variables* $\mathbf{x}_1, \mathbf{x}_2, \cdots, \mathbf{x}_n$ *is* $g(x_1, x_2, \cdots, x_n) = f(x_1)f(x_2) \cdots f(x_n)$.

For example, suppose that a random sample of size 3 is drawn from the density $f(x) = 1, 0 < x < 1$. What is the probability that the value of each random variable is between 0 and ½? We want

$$P(0 < \mathbf{x}_1 < \tfrac{1}{2}, 0 < \mathbf{x}_2 < \tfrac{1}{2}, 0 < \mathbf{x}_3 < \tfrac{1}{2}) = \int_0^{\frac{1}{2}} \int_0^{\frac{1}{2}} \int_0^{\frac{1}{2}} g(x_1, x_2, x_3)\, dx_1\, dx_2\, dx_3$$

but since the sample is random,

$$\begin{aligned} g(x_1, x_2, x_3) &= f(x_1)f(x_2)f(x_3) = 1 \cdot 1 \cdot 1 = 1 \qquad && 0 < x_i < 1 \\ &= 0 && \text{elsewhere} \end{aligned}$$

and so

$$P(0 < \mathbf{x}_1 < \tfrac{1}{2}, 0 < \mathbf{x}_2 < \tfrac{1}{2}, 0 < \mathbf{x}_3 < \tfrac{1}{2}) = \int_0^{\frac{1}{2}} \int_0^{\frac{1}{2}} \int_0^{\frac{1}{2}} 1 \cdot dx_1\, dx_2\, dx_3 = \tfrac{1}{8}$$

Suppose that we want to evaluate the probability that at least one of the random variables has a value that is between ½ and ¾. This can be evaluated by using the binomial distribution. We can think of the three random variables as three independent trials and the probability of a success on a single trial is p, where

$$\begin{aligned} p = P(\tfrac{1}{2} < \mathbf{x}_2 < \tfrac{3}{4}) &= P(\tfrac{1}{2} < \mathbf{x}_3 < \tfrac{3}{4}) = P(\tfrac{1}{2} < \mathbf{x}_1 < \tfrac{3}{4}) \\ &= \int_{\frac{1}{2}}^{\frac{3}{4}} 1 \cdot dx = \tfrac{1}{4} \end{aligned}$$

The probability of exactly k successes in three trials is given by the binomial distribution

$$P(k) = \binom{3}{k} p^k (1 - p)^{3-k} = \binom{3}{k} (\tfrac{1}{4})^k (\tfrac{3}{4})^{3-k} \qquad k = 0, 1, 2, 3$$

The probability of at least one success (at least one random variable has a value in the interval ½ to ¾) is

$$P(1) + P(2) + P(3) = \sum_{k=1}^{3} P(k) = 1 - P(0) = 1 - (\tfrac{3}{4})^3 = \tfrac{37}{64}$$

4.9 Derived Distributions

Sometimes it is important to be able to derive the density function of a random variable **y** from a knowledge of the density function of a random variable **x** when **y** is a function of **x**, say $\mathbf{y} = u(\mathbf{x})$. For example, suppose that the random variable **x** has density

$$\begin{aligned} f(x) &= 1 \qquad 0 < x < 1 \\ &= 0 \qquad \text{elsewhere} \end{aligned}$$

and suppose that we want to find the density of **y**, where $\mathbf{y} = 8\mathbf{x} - 2$. The distribution of **y** is called a derived distribution (derived from the distribution of **x**), and derived distributions play an extremely important role in statistics. There are many ways of obtaining the density functions of derived distributions, but we shall illustrate only one method here, the method of using the cumulative distribution. Other methods will be explained in detail in Chap. 10.

Let $g(y)$ be the density of **y**, and let $G(y)$ be the cumulative distribution of **y**. Now since $f(x) = 1$ for $0 < x < 1$ and 0 elsewhere, we have

$$\begin{aligned} F(x) &= P(\mathbf{x} \le x) = 0 && \text{for } x \le 0 \\ F(x) = P(\mathbf{x} \le x) &= \int_0^x f(t)\,dt = \int_0^x 1 \cdot dt = x && \text{for } 0 < x < 1 \\ F(x) &= P(\mathbf{x} \le x) = 1 && \text{for } x \ge 1 \end{aligned} \tag{1}$$

Now, by the definition of the cumulative distribution of **y**, we get

$$G(y) = P(\mathbf{y} \le y) \tag{2}$$

Substituting $\mathbf{y} = 8\mathbf{x} - 2$ into (2), we get

$$G(y) = P(8\mathbf{x} - 2 \le y) = P\left(\mathbf{x} \le \frac{y+2}{8}\right) \tag{3}$$

But, by (1), if we replace x with $\frac{y+2}{8}$, we get

$$G(y) = \begin{cases} P\left(\mathbf{x} \le \frac{y+2}{8}\right) = 0 & \text{if } \frac{y+2}{8} \le 0 \\ P\left(\mathbf{x} \le \frac{y+2}{8}\right) = \frac{y+2}{8} & \text{if } 0 < \frac{y+2}{8} < 1 \\ P\left(\mathbf{x} \le \frac{y+2}{8}\right) = 1 & \text{if } \frac{y+2}{8} \ge 1 \end{cases} \tag{4}$$

From (4),

$$\begin{aligned} G(y) &= 0 && \text{if } y \le -2 \\ &= \frac{y+2}{8} && \text{if } -2 < y < 6 \\ &= 1 && \text{if } 6 \le y \end{aligned}$$

To get the density, we differentiate $G(y)$ at points where the derivative exists, and we obtain

$$g(y) = \tfrac{1}{8} \qquad -2 < y < 6$$
$$= 0 \qquad \text{elsewhere}$$

This can be checked to be sure that it satisfies the conditions that qualify it for a density function.

For another example, let the random variable $\mathbf{x}$ have the density

$$f(x) = e^{-x} \qquad x > 0$$
$$= 0 \qquad \text{elsewhere}$$

Suppose that a random sample of size 2 denoted by $\mathbf{x}_1$, $\mathbf{x}_2$ is drawn from $f(x)$, and we want the density function of the random variable $\mathbf{y}$, where $\mathbf{y} = \mathbf{x}_1 + \mathbf{x}_2$. By the definition of a random sample, the joint density of

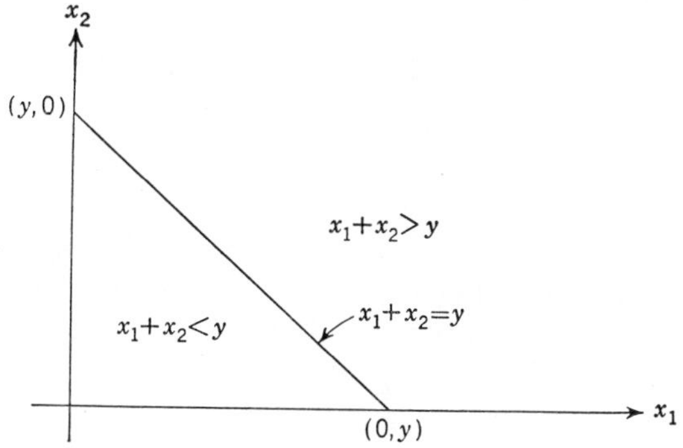

FIG. 4.14

the random variables $\mathbf{x}_1$ and $\mathbf{x}_2$ is

$$h(x_1, x_2) = e^{-x_1}e^{-x_2} \qquad x_1 > 0, x_2 > 0$$
$$= 0 \qquad \text{elsewhere}$$

To find the density of $\mathbf{y}$, call it $g(y)$, we shall first find the cumulative $G(y)$ and differentiate it. Now

$$G(y) = P(\mathbf{y} \le y) = P(\mathbf{x}_1 + \mathbf{x}_2 \le y)$$

But $P(\mathbf{x}_1 + \mathbf{x}_2 \le y)$ is the volume of $h(x_1, x_2)$ in the region $x_1 + x_2 \le y$. Since $h(x_1, x_2) = 0$ except when x_1 and x_2 are both positive, we need consider only the first quadrant in the x_1x_2 plane; see Fig. 4.14. The volume is

$$G(y) = P(\mathbf{y} \le y) = 0 \qquad \text{for } y \le 0$$

$$G(y) = P(\mathbf{y} \le y) = P(\mathbf{x}_1 + \mathbf{x}_2 \le y) = \int_0^y \int_0^{y-x_1} e^{-(x_1+x_2)}\, dx_2\, dx_1$$
$$= \int_0^y (e^{-x_1} - e^{-y})\, dx_1 = 1 - e^{-y} - ye^{-y} \qquad \text{for } y > 0$$

Thus we get

$$\begin{aligned} G(y) &= 0 && y \leq 0 \\ &= 1 - (1 + y)e^{-y} && y > 0 \end{aligned}$$

and

$$g(y) = \frac{dG(y)}{dy} = \begin{cases} 0 & y \leq 0 \\ ye^{-y} & y > 0 \end{cases}$$

or

$$\begin{aligned} g(y) &= ye^{-y} && y > 0 \\ &= 0 && \text{elsewhere} \end{aligned}$$

In defining a density we shall sometimes only specify it over the set where it is positive. For example, we shall sometimes write

$$\begin{aligned} f(x) &= 2x && 0 < x < 1 \\ &= 0 && \text{elsewhere} \end{aligned}$$

as

$$f(x) = 2x \qquad 0 < x < 1$$

4.10 Problems

In this set of problems $f(x)$ and $g(x)$ will represent density functions of the random variable $\mathbf{x}$; $f(x, y)$ will represent the joint density of the two random variables $\mathbf{x}$, $\mathbf{y}$; etc.

1. Let $\mathbf{x}$ be a random variable with density

$$\begin{aligned} f(x) &= \frac{1}{(x+1)^2} && x > 0 \\ &= 0 && \text{elsewhere} \end{aligned}$$

Let the events A_1, A_2, A_3 be defined by

$$\begin{aligned} A_1 &= \{x: -\infty < x < 0\} \\ A_2 &= \{x: 0 \leq x < \infty\} \\ A_3 &= \{x: 0 \leq x \leq 1\} \\ A_4 &= \{x: -6 \leq x \leq 0\} \end{aligned}$$

Find the probability of the following events:

(*a*) $\bar{A}_1$ (*b*) $\bar{A}_1 \cap A_2$
(*c*) $\bar{A}_1 \cup A_2$ (*d*) $\bar{A}_2 \cap A_1$
(*e*) $A_3 \cap A_2$ (*f*) $A_3 \cup A_2$
(*g*) $A_3 \cup A_1$ (*h*) $A_1 \cup A_4$
(*i*) $A_1 \cup A_2$ (*j*) $\bar{A}_3$
(*k*) $\bar{A}_4 \cap A_1$ (*l*) $A_3 \cap A_4$
(*m*) $(A_3 \cap A_4) \cap (A_1 \cup A_2)$ (*n*) $\bar{A}_2$
(*o*) $A_1 \cup A_3$ (*p*) $\overline{A_1 \cup A_3}$

2. Let the density of the random variable $\mathbf{x}$ be

$$f(x) = e^{-x} \qquad x > 0$$
$$= 0 \qquad x \leq 0$$

Find the probability of each event (*a*) through (*p*) in Prob. 1.

3. If the random variable $\mathbf{x}$ has the density $f(x) = 2x$ when $0 < x < 1$ and 0 elsewhere, find the probability that (*a*) $\mathbf{x} < \frac{1}{2}$, (*b*) $\frac{1}{4} < \mathbf{x} < \frac{1}{2}$, (*c*) $\mathbf{x} > \frac{3}{4}$, given that $\mathbf{x} > \frac{1}{2}$.

4. Define a density using $x(2 - x)$ over the set $0 < x < 2$. Find the probability that $a < \mathbf{x} < b$ if

(*a*) $0 < a < b < 2$ (*b*) $a < 0, 2 < b$

5. If $f(x) = 4x^3$ when $0 < x < 1$ and 0 otherwise, find the number a such that $\mathbf{x}$ is equally likely to be greater than or less than a. Find the number b such that the probability that $\mathbf{x}$ will exceed b is equal to .05.

6. A variate $\mathbf{x}$ has the density $f(x) = x/2$ when $0 < x < 2$ and 0 otherwise. If a random sample of size 2 is observed, what is the probability that both will be greater than 1? If three are observed, what is the probability that exactly 2 of them will be greater than 1?

7. A variate $\mathbf{x}$ has the density $f(x) = 1$ when $0 < x < 1$ and 0 otherwise. Determine the number a such that the probability will be .9 that at least one of four values of $\mathbf{x}$ drawn at random will exceed a.

8. Suppose that the life in hours of a certain kind of radio tube has the density $f(x) = 100/x^2$ when $x > 100$ and 0 when $x \leq 100$. What is the probability that none of three such tubes in a given radio set will have to be replaced during the first 150 hours of operation? What is the probability that all three of the original tubes will have been replaced during the first 150 hours?

9. A machine makes bolts with diameters distributed by the density $f(x) = K(x - .24)^2(x - .26)^2$ when $.24 < x < .26$ and 0 otherwise. K is the number which makes $\int_{-\infty}^{\infty} f(x)\,dx = 1$. Bolts must be scrapped if their diameters deviate from .25 by more than .008. What proportion of the bolts may be expected to be scrapped?

10. A bombing plane carrying three bombs flies directly above a railroad track. If a bomb falls within 40 feet of the track, the track will be sufficiently damaged to disrupt traffic. With a certain bombsight the density of points of impact of a bomb is

$$f(x) = \frac{100 + x}{10{,}000} \qquad -100 < x < 0$$
$$= \frac{100 - x}{10{,}000} \qquad 0 \leq x < 100$$
$$= 0 \qquad \text{elsewhere}$$

x represents the perpendicular deviation from the aiming point, which is the track in this case. If all three bombs are used, what is the probability that the track will be damaged?

11. Referring to the above problem, the plane can carry eight bombs of a smaller size, but one of these must hit within 15 feet of the track to damage it. Should the lighter or heavier bombs be used on this mission?

12. A country filling station is supplied with gasoline once a week. If its weekly volume of sales in thousands of gallons is distributed by $f(x) = 5(1 - x)^4$, $0 < x < 1$, what must be the capacity of its tank in order that the probability that its supply will be exhausted in a given week shall be .01?

13. A batch of small-caliber ammunition is accepted as satisfactory if none of a sample of five shots falls more than 2 feet from the center of a target at a given range. If $\mathbf{r}$, the distance from the target center of a given impact point, actually has the density

$$f(r) = \frac{2re^{-r^2}}{1 - e^{-9}}$$

$0 < r < 3$, for a given batch, what is the probability that the batch will be accepted?

14. If $f(x, y) = 1$, when $0 < x < 1$, $0 < y < 1$, and 0 otherwise, find the probability that (*a*) $\mathbf{x} < \frac{1}{2}$, $\mathbf{y} < \frac{1}{2}$; (*b*) $\mathbf{x} + \mathbf{y} < 1$; (*c*) $\mathbf{x} + \mathbf{y} > 1$; (*d*) $\mathbf{x} > 2\mathbf{y}$; (*e*) $\mathbf{x} > \frac{1}{3}$; (*f*) $\mathbf{x}^2 + \mathbf{y}^2 < \frac{1}{4}$; (*g*) $\mathbf{x} = \mathbf{y}$; (*h*) $\mathbf{x} > \frac{1}{2}$, given $\mathbf{y} < \frac{1}{2}$; (*i*) $\mathbf{x} > \mathbf{y}$, given $\mathbf{y} > \frac{1}{2}$.

15. If $f(x, y) = e^{-(x+y)}$ when $x > 0$, $y > 0$, and 0 otherwise, find $P(\mathbf{x} > 1)$; $P(a < \mathbf{x} + \mathbf{y} < b)$ if $0 < a < b$; $P(\mathbf{x} < \mathbf{y} | \mathbf{x} < 2\mathbf{y})$.

16. Using the distribution of Prob. 15, find the number a such that $P(\mathbf{x} + \mathbf{y} < a) = \frac{1}{2}$.

17. If three points are drawn at random from the density given in Prob. 15, what is the probability that at least one of them will fall in the square $0 < x < 1$, $0 < y < 1$?

18. A machine makes shafts with diameters $\mathbf{x}$, and a second machine makes bushings with inside diameters $\mathbf{y}$. Suppose that the density of $\mathbf{x}$ and $\mathbf{y}$ is $f(x, y) = 2500$, $.49 < x < .51$, $.51 < y < .53$, and 0 otherwise. A bushing fits a shaft satisfactorily if its diameter exceeds that of the shaft by at least .004 but not more than .036. What is the probability that a bushing and shaft chosen at random will fit?

19. Find and graph the cumulative distribution for the density given in Prob. 8. Use the cumulative distribution to find $P(150 < \mathbf{x} < 250)$.

20. Find and graph the cumulative distribution for the density given in Prob. 15, and use it to find $P(1 < \mathbf{x} < 2, 3 < \mathbf{y} < 4)$.

21. Find the marginal density of $\mathbf{x}$ for the distribution of Prob. 15.

(*a*) by integrating out y; (*b*) by using the result of Prob. 20 to get the cumulative marginal distribution, then differentiating the result.

22. Find the conditional density of $\mathbf{x}$, given $\mathbf{y}$, for the distribution of Prob. 15. What is the $P(0 < \mathbf{x} < 1|\mathbf{y} = 2)$?

23. If $f(x, y) = (n - 1)(n - 2)/(1 + x + y)^n$ when $x > 0$, $y > 0$, and 0 elsewhere, find $F(x, y)$, $f_1(x)$, $F_1(x)$, $f(y|x)$; assume $n > 2$.

24. If $f(x, y) = 24y(1 - x - y)$ over the triangle bounded by the axes and the line $x + y = 1$, and equals zero elsewhere, find $f(x|y)$.

25. If $f(x, y) = 3x$, $0 < y < x$, $0 < x < 1$, find the conditional density of $\mathbf{x}$, given $\mathbf{y}$.

26. If $f(x|y) = 3x^2/y^3$, $0 < x < y$, and $f_2(y) = 5y^4$, $0 < y < 1$, find $P(\mathbf{x} > \frac{1}{2})$.

27. If $f(x, y, z) = 8xyz$, $0 < x < 1$, $0 < y < 1$, $0 < z < 1$, find $P(\mathbf{x} < \mathbf{y} < \mathbf{z})$.

28. If $f(x) = 1/(1 + x)^2$, $x > 0$, find the density of $\mathbf{x}$, given that $\mathbf{x} > 1$.

29. If $f(x, y) = 1$, $0 < x < 1$, $0 < y < 1$, find the conditional density of $\mathbf{x}$ and $\mathbf{y}$, given that $\mathbf{y} < \mathbf{x}^n$, $n > 0$.

30. If $f(x) = 1$, $0 < x < 1$, find the density of $\mathbf{y} = 3\mathbf{x} + 1$. (Find first the cumulative distribution of $\mathbf{y}$ and then differentiate it.)

31. If $f(x) = 2xe^{-x^2}$, $x > 0$, find the density of $\mathbf{y} = \mathbf{x}^2$.

32. If $f(x, y) = 1$, $0 < x < 1$, $0 < y < 1$, find the density of $\mathbf{z} = \mathbf{x} + \mathbf{y}$.

33. If $f(x, y) = e^{-(x+y)}$, $x > 0$, $y > 0$, find the density of

$$\mathbf{z} = \frac{\mathbf{x} + \mathbf{y}}{2}$$

34. If $f(x, y) = 4xye^{-(x^2+y^2)}$, $x > 0$, $y > 0$, find the density of $\mathbf{z} = \sqrt{\mathbf{x}^2 + \mathbf{y}^2}$.

35. If $f(x, y) = 4xy$, $0 < x < 1$, $0 < y < 1$, find the joint density of $\mathbf{u} = \mathbf{x}^2$, $\mathbf{v} = \mathbf{y}^2$.

36. If $f(x, y) = 3x$, $0 < y < x$, $0 < x < 1$, find the density of $\mathbf{z} = \mathbf{x} - \mathbf{y}$.

37. If $f(x) = (1 + x)/2$, $-1 < x < 1$, find the density of $\mathbf{y} = \mathbf{x}^2$.

38. If $f(x, y) = 1$, $0 < x < 1$, $0 < y < 1$, find the density of $\mathbf{z}$ defined by $\mathbf{z} = \mathbf{x} + \mathbf{y}$ if $\mathbf{x} + \mathbf{y} < 1$, and $\mathbf{z} = \mathbf{x} + \mathbf{y} - 1$ if $\mathbf{x} + \mathbf{y} > 1$.

39. If $f(x, y) = e^{-(x+y)}$, $x > 0$, $y > 0$, find the joint density of $\mathbf{u} = \mathbf{x} + \mathbf{y}$ and $\mathbf{v} = \mathbf{x}$. What is the marginal density of $\mathbf{v}$?

40. If $f(x, y, z) = e^{-(x+y+z)}$, $x > 0$, $y > 0$, $z > 0$, find the density of their average $\mathbf{u} = (\mathbf{x} + \mathbf{y} + \mathbf{z})/3$.

41. If $f(x, y) = 4x(1 - y)$, $0 < x < 1$, $0 < y < 1$, find the density of $\mathbf{x}$, given that $\mathbf{y} < \frac{1}{2}$.

42. If $\mathbf{x}$ is distributed by $f(x)$, $x > 0$, find the density of $\mathbf{y} = a\mathbf{x}^2 + b$, $a > 0$.

43. If $\mathbf{x}$ is distributed by $f(x)$, $-\infty < x < \infty$, and if u is a function of

x defined by $y = u(x)$ such that the first derivative u' is positive and continuous for all x, find the density of $\mathbf{y}$ where $\mathbf{y} = u(\mathbf{x})$.

44. If $f(x, y) = g(x)g(y)$, $x > 0$, $y > 0$, find $P(\mathbf{x} > \mathbf{y})$.

45. If $f(x, y, z) = g(x)g(y)g(z)$, $x > 0$, $y > 0$, $z > 0$, what is the probability that the coordinates of a randomly drawn point $(\mathbf{x}, \mathbf{y}, \mathbf{z})$ will not satisfy either $\mathbf{x} > \mathbf{y} > \mathbf{z}$ or $\mathbf{x} < \mathbf{y} < \mathbf{z}$?

46. In which of the distributions defined in Probs. 23, 24, 32, 33, and 34 are the variates independent in the probability sense?

4.11 Bibliography

1. Brunk, H.: "An Introduction to Mathematical Statistics," Ginn & Company, Boston, 1960.
2. Clark, C.: "An Introduction to Statistics," John Wiley & Sons, Inc., New York, 1953.
3. Fraser, D. A. S.: "Statistics—An Introduction," John Wiley & Sons, Inc., New York, 1958.
4. Fryer, H.: "Elements of Statistics," John Wiley & Sons, Inc., New York, 1954.
5. Hoel, P. G.: "Elementary Statistics," John Wiley & Sons, Inc., New York, 1960.
6. Hogg, R., and A. Craig: "Introduction to Mathematical Statistics," The Macmillan Company, New York, 1959.
7. Rao, C. R.: "Advanced Statistical Methods in Biometric Research," John Wiley & Sons, Inc., New York, 1952.

5

Expected Values and Moments

5.1 Expected Values

The expected value of a random variable or any function of a random variable is obtained by finding the average value of the function over all possible values of the variable. To consider a specific example: If three ideal coins are tossed, the distribution of the number of heads that appear is the binomial

$$f(x) = \binom{3}{x}\left(\frac{1}{2}\right)^3 \qquad x = 0, 1, 2, 3 \tag{1}$$

For a specific value of $\mathbf{x}$, say $\mathbf{x} = 2$, we think of $f(2) = 3/8$ as the relative frequency with which two heads will appear in a large number of trials. Thus in 1000 trials we expect no heads to appear in about $1000 \times 1/8 = 125$ trials, one head to appear in $1000 \times 3/8 = 375$ trials, two heads in 375 trials, and three heads in 125 trials. Now let us find the average number of heads in the 1000 trials. The total number of heads is expected to be

$$125 \times 0 + 375 \times 1 + 375 \times 2 + 125 \times 3 = 1500$$

in the 1000 trials; thus the average is expected to be 1.5 heads per trial. This is the *expected value,* or *mean value,* of $\mathbf{x}$. It is clear that the same result would have been obtained had we merely multiplied all possible values of $\mathbf{x}$ by their probabilities and added the results; thus,

$$0 \times 1/8 + 1 \times 3/8 + 2 \times 3/8 + 3 \times 1/8 = 1.5$$

The expected value is a theoretical or ideal average. We do not actually expect $\mathbf{x}$ to take on its expected value in a given trial; in fact, that would be impossible in the present example. However, we might reasonably expect the average value of $\mathbf{x}$ in a great number of trials to be somewhere near the expected value of $\mathbf{x}$.

Definition 5.1. *Let* $\mathbf{x}$ *be a random variable with density* $f(x)$. *Then the expected value of* $\mathbf{x}$, $E(\mathbf{x})$, *is*

$$E(\mathbf{x}) = \sum_x xf(x)$$

if $\mathbf{x}$ *is discrete and*

$$E(\mathbf{x}) = \int_{-\infty}^{\infty} xf(x)\,dx$$

if $\mathbf{x}$ *is continuous.*

Actually these quantities are defined to be the expected value only if they are absolutely convergent. If they are not, we say that the expected value of $\mathbf{x}$ does not exist. Thus in the example above we have

$$E(\mathbf{x}) = \sum_{x=0}^{3} xf(x) = 1.5$$

Sometimes we are interested in the average or expected value of some function of a random variable $\mathbf{x}$ instead of $\mathbf{x}$ itself. For instance, we may be interested in the expected value of $2\mathbf{x}$ or $\mathbf{x}^2 + 1$, etc.

Theorem 5.1. *Let* $\mathbf{x}$ *be a random variable with density* $f(x)$. *The expected value of a function u of the random variable* $\mathbf{x}$ *is*

$$E[u(\mathbf{x})] = \sum_{x} u(x)f(x)$$

if $\mathbf{x}$ *is discrete and*

$$E[u(\mathbf{x})] = \int_{-\infty}^{\infty} u(x)f(x)\,dx$$

if $\mathbf{x}$ *is continuous.*

Again we remark that these quantities are defined to be the expected value only if they are absolutely convergent. The same holds for all expected values of random variables, and we shall not make this point again. The proof of Theorem 5.1 is beyond the scope of this book.

Example 5.1. Let $f(x)$ be given by (1), and if $u(\mathbf{x}) = \mathbf{x}^2 + 1$, then

$$E[u(\mathbf{x})] = E[\mathbf{x}^2 + 1] = \sum_{x=0}^{3} (x^2 + 1)f(x)$$
$$= 1 \times \tfrac{1}{8} + 2 \times \tfrac{3}{8} + 5 \times \tfrac{3}{8} + 10 \times \tfrac{1}{8} = 4$$

Next we shall define the expected value for multivariate random variables.

Definition 5.2. *Let* $(\mathbf{x}_1, \mathbf{x}_2, \cdots, \mathbf{x}_k)$ *be a k-dimensional random variable with density* $f(x_1, x_2, \cdots, x_k)$. *The expected value of* $\mathbf{x}_i$, *for any* $i = 1, 2, \cdots, k$, *is written* $E(\mathbf{x}_i)$ *and is defined by*

$$E(\mathbf{x}_i) = \sum_{x_1}\sum_{x_2} \cdots \sum_{x_k} x_i f(x_1, \cdots, x_k)$$

if the random variable is discrete and by

$$E(\mathbf{x}_i) = \int_{-\infty}^{\infty}\int_{-\infty}^{\infty} \cdots \int_{-\infty}^{\infty} x_i f(x_1, \cdots, x_k)\,dx_1\,dx_2 \cdots dx_k$$

if the random variable is continuous.

To find the expected value of a function of random variables, we can use the following theorem which will be given without proof.

Theorem 5.2. *Let* $(\mathbf{x}_1, \mathbf{x}_2, \cdots, \mathbf{x}_k)$ *be a k-dimensional random variable with density* $f(x_1, x_2, \cdots, x_k)$. *The expected value of a function u of the random variable is*

$$E[u(\mathbf{x}_1, \cdots, \mathbf{x}_k)] = \sum_{x_1}\sum_{x_2} \cdots \sum_{x_k} u(x_1, \cdots, x_k)f(x_1, \cdots, x_k)$$

if the random variable is discrete and

$$E[u(\mathbf{x}_1, \cdots, \mathbf{x}_k)] = \int_{-\infty}^{\infty}\int_{-\infty}^{\infty} \cdots \int_{-\infty}^{\infty} u(x_1, \cdots, x_k)f(x_1, \cdots, x_k)\, dx_1 \cdots dx_k$$

if the random variable is continuous.

Let us consider some examples.

Example 5.2. Let the two-dimensional random variable $(\mathbf{x}_1, \mathbf{x}_2)$ have the probability density

$$f(x_1, x_2) = p^{x_1+x_2}(1-p)^{2-(x_1+x_2)} \qquad x_1 = 0, 1;\ x_2 = 0, 1 \quad 0 < p < 1$$

Suppose that we want to evaluate the expected value of (*a*) $\mathbf{x}_1 + \mathbf{x}_2$; (*b*) $\mathbf{x}_1\mathbf{x}_2$; (*c*) $\mathbf{x}_1$. We get

$$(a)\ E(\mathbf{x}_1 + \mathbf{x}_2) = \sum_{x_1=0}^{1}\sum_{x_2=0}^{1} (x_1 + x_2)p^{x_1+x_2}(1-p)^{2-(x_1+x_2)} = 2p(1-p) + 2p^2 = 2p$$

$$(b)\ E(\mathbf{x}_1\mathbf{x}_2) = \sum_{x_1=0}^{1}\sum_{x_2=0}^{1} (x_1x_2)p^{x_1+x_2}(1-p)^{2-(x_1+x_2)} = p^2$$

$$(c)\ E(\mathbf{x}_1) = \sum_{x_1=0}^{1}\sum_{x_2=0}^{1} (x_1)p^{x_1+x_2}(1-p)^{2-(x_1+x_2)} = p(1-p) + p^2 = p$$

Example 5.3. Let $\mathbf{x}$ be a random variable with density

$$f(x) = 2x \quad 0 < x < 1$$
$$= 0 \quad \text{elsewhere}$$

Suppose that we want to find the expected value of $3\mathbf{x}^2 - 1$. Thus $u(\mathbf{x}) = 3\mathbf{x}^2 - 1$ and

$$E[u(\mathbf{x})] = E[3\mathbf{x}^2 - 1] = \int_0^1 (3x^2 - 1)2x\, dx = \tfrac{1}{2}$$

Example 5.4. Let the two-dimensional random variable $(\mathbf{x}_1, \mathbf{x}_2)$ have the density

$$\begin{aligned} f(x_1, x_2) &= 4x_1x_2 \qquad 0 < x_1 < 1, 0 < x_2 < 1 \\ &= 0 \qquad \text{elsewhere} \end{aligned}$$

Suppose that we want (*a*) $E(3\mathbf{x}_1 + 2\mathbf{x}_2)$; (*b*) $E(\mathbf{x}_1\mathbf{x}_2)$; (*c*) $E(\mathbf{x}_1)$. For (*a*) we obtain $u(\mathbf{x}_1, \mathbf{x}_2) = 3\mathbf{x}_1 + 2\mathbf{x}_2$ and

$$E[u(\mathbf{x}_1, \mathbf{x}_2)] = E(3\mathbf{x}_1 + 2\mathbf{x}_2) = \int_0^1 \int_0^1 (3x_1 + 2x_2)4x_1x_2 \, dx_1 \, dx_2 = 10/3$$

For (*b*) we get

$$E(\mathbf{x}_1\mathbf{x}_2) = \int_0^1 \int_0^1 (x_1x_2)(4x_1x_2) \, dx_1 \, dx_2 = 4/9$$

For (*c*) we get

$$E(\mathbf{x}_1) = \int_0^1 \int_0^1 x_1(4x_1x_2) \, dx_1 \, dx_2 = 2/3$$

We shall avoid confusing the expected-value notation with the functional notation by never using the letter E to represent a function. $E(\mathbf{g})$ will always represent the expected value of $\mathbf{g}$ and never the value of the function E at $\mathbf{g}$. In the remainder of this chapter we shall not distinguish between discrete and continuous density functions. Expected values will always be given in terms of integrals, but it is understood that the integrals are to be replaced by sums in specific problems which deal with discrete density functions.

Next we shall state some theorems on expected values.

Theorem 5.3. *Let* $\mathbf{x}$ *be a random variable with density* $f(x)$. *If* c *is a constant, then* $E(c) = c$.

Theorem 5.4. *Let* $\mathbf{x}$ *be a random variable with density* $f(x)$. *If* c *is a constant, then* $E[cu(\mathbf{x})] = cE[u(\mathbf{x})]$.

Theorem 5.5. *Let* $\mathbf{x}$ *be a random variable with density* $f(x)$. *Then the expected value of the sum of two functions of* $\mathbf{x}$ *is the sum of the expected values; that is,* $E[u(\mathbf{x}) + v(\mathbf{x})] = E[u(\mathbf{x})] + E[v(\mathbf{x})]$.

These results are special cases of the following more general theorem.

Theorem 5.6. *Let* $(\mathbf{x}_1, \mathbf{x}_2, \cdots, \mathbf{x}_k)$ *be a k-dimensional random variable with density* $f(x_1, x_2, \cdots, x_k)$, *and let* $c_1, c_2, \cdots, c_t$ *be t constants and* $u_1, u_2, \cdots, u_t$ *be t functions of the random variable. Then*

$$\begin{aligned} E[c_1u_1(\mathbf{x}_1, \mathbf{x}_2, \cdots, \mathbf{x}_k) + c_2u_2(\mathbf{x}_1, \mathbf{x}_2, \cdots, \mathbf{x}_k) + \cdots \\ + c_tu_t(\mathbf{x}_1, \mathbf{x}_2, \cdots, \mathbf{x}_k)] = c_1E[u_1(\mathbf{x}_1, \mathbf{x}_2, \cdots, \mathbf{x}_k)] \\ + c_2E[u_2(\mathbf{x}_1, \mathbf{x}_2, \cdots, \mathbf{x}_k)] + \cdots + c_tE[u_t(\mathbf{x}_1, \mathbf{x}_2, \cdots, \mathbf{x}_k)] \end{aligned}$$

The proof of these theorems will be left for the reader.

Example 5.5. Consider part (*a*) in Example 5.4. By Theorem 5.6 we get

$$E[3\mathbf{x}_1 + 2\mathbf{x}_2] = E[3\mathbf{x}_1] + E[2\mathbf{x}_2] = 3E(\mathbf{x}_1) + 2E(\mathbf{x}_2)$$
$$= 3 \cdot 2/3 + 2 \cdot 2/3 = 10/3$$

5.2 Moments

The moments of a distribution are the expected values of the powers of the random variable which has the given distribution. The rth moment of $\mathbf{x}$ is usually denoted by μ'_r and is defined as

$$\mu'_r = E(\mathbf{x}^r) = \int_{-\infty}^{\infty} x^r f(x)\,dx \tag{1}$$

The first moment μ'_1 is called the *mean* of $\mathbf{x}$. The moments about any arbitrary point a are defined as

$$E[(\mathbf{x} - a)^r] = \int_{-\infty}^{\infty} (x - a)^r f(x)\,dx \tag{2}$$

and when a is put equal to the mean, we have the moments about the mean, which are usually denoted by μ_r:

$$\mu_r = E[(\mathbf{x} - \mu'_1)^r] = \int_{-\infty}^{\infty} (x - \mu'_1)^r f(x)\,dx \tag{3}$$

We have

$$\begin{aligned} \mu_1 &= \int_{-\infty}^{\infty} xf(x)\,dx - \mu'_1 \int_{-\infty}^{\infty} f(x)\,dx \\ &= \mu'_1 - \mu'_1 = 0 \end{aligned} \tag{4}$$

and

$$\begin{aligned} \mu_2 &= \int_{-\infty}^{\infty} (x - \mu'_1)^2 f(x)\,dx \\ &= \int_{-\infty}^{\infty} [x^2 - 2x\mu'_1 + (\mu'_1)^2] f(x)\,dx \\ &= \mu'_2 - 2\mu'_1\mu'_1 + (\mu'_1)^2 \\ &= \mu'_2 - (\mu'_1)^2 \end{aligned} \tag{5}$$

This second moment about the mean is called the *variance* of $\mathbf{x}$.

The mean value of a variate locates the center of its distribution in the following sense: If the x axis is thought of as a bar with variable density, the density at any point being given by $f(x)$, then it is shown in elementary calculus that the value $x = \mu'_1$ is the center of gravity of the bar. Thus the mean may be thought of as a central value of the variate. For this reason it is often referred to as a location parameter —it tells one where the center of the distribution (in the center-of-gravity sense) lies on the x axis. Other central values are sometimes used to indicate the location of a distribution. One is the *median*, which is defined as the point at which a vertical line bisects the area under the curve $f(x)$. The median is therefore the point μ'', say, such that

$$\int_{-\infty}^{\mu''} f(x)\,dx = \tfrac{1}{2} = \int_{\mu''}^{\infty} f(x)\,dx \tag{6}$$

Another central value for densities with one maximum is the *mode*, which is the point, if it exists, at which f attains its maximum. One could easily devise other central values; these are the ones commonly used, and of the three the mean is by far the most useful. We shall often employ the symbol μ without the prime or subscript to denote the mean.

The variance μ_2 of a distribution is a measure of its spread, or dispersion. If most of the area under the curve lies near the mean, the variance will be small; while if the area is spread out over a considerable range, the variance will be large. Distributions with different variances

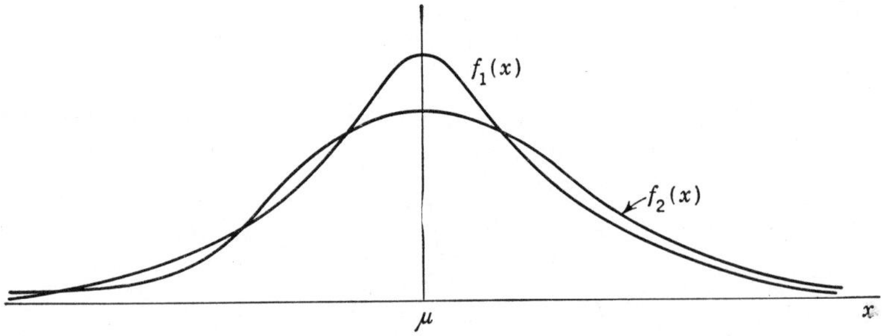

FIG. 5.1

are plotted in Fig. 6.3. The variance is necessarily positive or zero, since it is the integral or sum of nonnegative quantities. It will be zero only when the distribution is concentrated at one point, i.e., when the distribution is discrete and there is only one possible outcome. The symbol σ^2 is commonly used to denote the variance; the positive square root of the variance, σ, is called the *standard deviation.*

We shall look a little further into the manner in which the variance characterizes the distribution. Suppose that $f_1(x)$ and $f_2(x)$ are two densities with the same mean such that

$$\int_{\mu-a}^{\mu+a} [f_1(x) - f_2(x)]\,dx \geq 0 \tag{7}$$

for every value of a. Two such densities are illustrated in Fig. 5.1. It can be shown that in this case the variance σ_1^2 in the first density is smaller than the variance σ_2^2 in the second density. We shall not take the time to prove this in detail, but the argument is roughly this: Let

$$g(x) = f_1(x) - f_2(x)$$

where $f_1(x)$ and $f_2(x)$ satisfy (7). Since $\int_{-\infty}^{\infty} g(x)\,dx = 0$, the positive area between $g(x)$ and the x axis is equal to the negative area. Furthermore, in view of (7), every positive element of area $g(x')\,dx'$ may be balanced by a negative element $g(x'')\,dx''$ in such a way that x'' is farther from μ than x'. When these elements of area are multiplied by $(x - \mu)^2$, the negative elements will be multiplied by larger factors than their corresponding positive elements (see Fig. 5.2); hence

$$\int_{-\infty}^{\infty} (x - \mu)^2 g(x)\,dx < 0$$

unless $f_1(x)$ and $f_2(x)$ are equal. Thus it follows that $\sigma_1^2 < \sigma_2^2$.

The converse of these statements is not true. That is, if one is told that $\sigma_1^2 < \sigma_2^2$, he cannot conclude that the corresponding densities satisfy (7) for all values of a, although it can be shown that (7) must be true

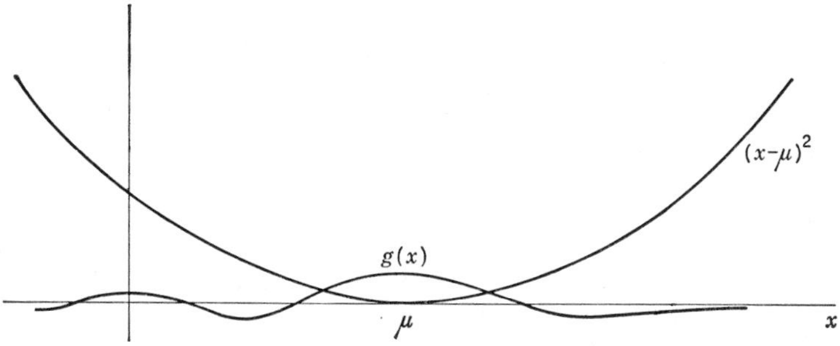

FIG. 5.2

for certain values of a. Thus the condition $\sigma_1^2 < \sigma_2^2$ does not give one any precise information about the nature of the corresponding distributions, but it is evidence that $f_1(x)$ has more area near the mean than $f_2(x)$, at least for certain intervals about the mean. The two densities in Fig. 5.3, for example, might have about equal variances, and one could alter either one slightly so as to make it have a smaller or larger variance than the other.

The third moment μ_3 about the mean is sometimes called a measure of asymmetry, or *skewness*. Symmetric distributions like those in Figs. 5.3 and 6.2 can be shown to have $\mu_3 = 0$. A curve shaped like $f_1(x)$ in Fig. 5.4 is said to be skewed to the left and can be shown to have a negative third moment about the mean; one shaped like $f_2(x)$ is called skewed to the right and can be shown to have a positive third moment about the mean. Actually, however, knowledge of the third moment gives almost no clue as to the shape of the distribution, and we mention it mainly to point out that fact. Thus, for example, the density $f_3(x)$ in Fig. 5.4 has $\mu_3 = 0$, but it is far from symmetric. By changing the curve slightly we could give it either a positive or negative third moment, as we pleased.

While a particular moment or a few of the moments give little information about a distribution, the whole set of moments (μ_1', μ_2', μ_3', $\cdots$) will ordinarily determine the distribution exactly, and for this reason we shall have occasion to use the moments in theoretical work.

In applied statistics, the first two moments are of great importance, as we shall see, but the third and higher moments are rarely useful. Ordinarily one does not know what distribution function he is working with in a practical problem, and often it makes little difference what

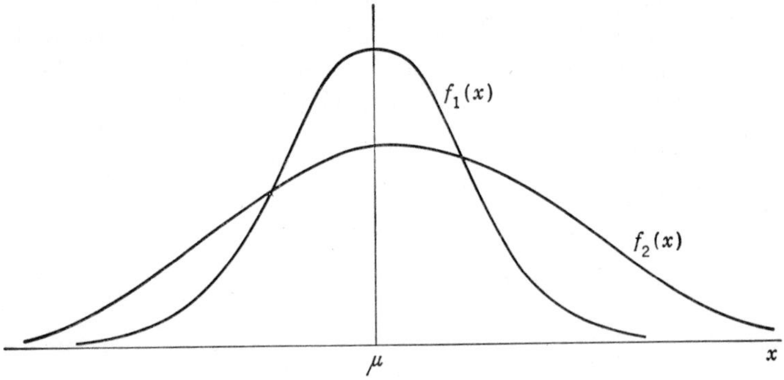

FIG. 5.3

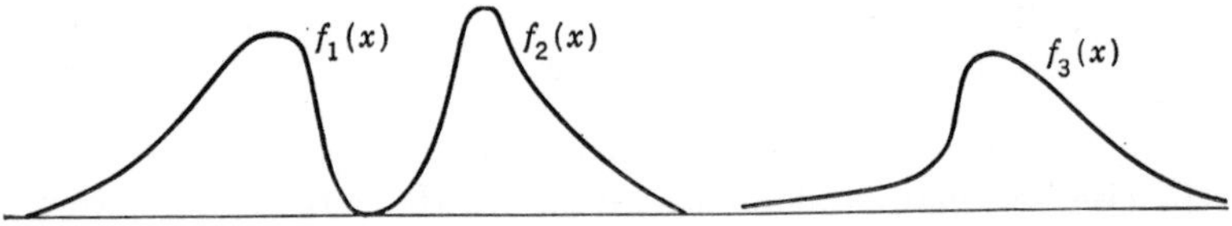

FIG. 5.4

the actual shape of the distribution is. But it is usually necessary to know at least the location of the distribution and to have some idea of its dispersion. These characteristics can be estimated by examining a sample drawn from a set of objects known to have the distribution in question. This estimation problem is probably the most important problem in applied statistics, and a large part of this book will be devoted to a study of it.

Example 5.6. Find the mean and variance of the hypergeometric distribution

$$f(x) = \frac{\binom{m}{x}\binom{n}{k-x}}{\binom{m+n}{k}} \qquad x = 0, 1, 2, \cdots, k \tag{8}$$

This problem will illustrate a technique that may be used to find the moments of a great many discrete distributions. The first step is to use the distribution to determine an identity in the parameters. Since $\Sigma f(x) = 1$, it follows that

$$\sum_{x=0}^{k} \binom{m}{x}\binom{n}{k-x} = \binom{m+n}{k} \tag{9}$$

for any positive integral values of m, n, and k. (Actually, as we have seen before, the limits depend on the relative sizes of m, n, and k, but we can avoid dealing with these details by defining the binomial coefficient $\binom{a}{b} = \frac{a!}{b!(a-b)!}$ to be zero when either b or $a - b$ is negative.)

The mean of the distribution is

$$\begin{aligned} \mu = E(\mathbf{x}) &= \sum_{x=0}^{k} xf(x) \\ &= \frac{\sum_{x=0}^{k} x\binom{m}{x}\binom{n}{k-x}}{\binom{m+n}{k}} \end{aligned} \tag{10}$$

In this expression x may be canceled with the x in the denominator of $\binom{m}{x}$ to get

$$x\binom{m}{x} = m\binom{m-1}{x-1}$$

and we have

$$\mu = \frac{\sum_{x=1}^{k} m\binom{m-1}{x-1}\binom{n}{k-x}}{\binom{m+n}{k}} \tag{11}$$

where we have written the sum to range from 1 to k because the first term in (10) vanishes and may be omitted. Actually, since we have defined a binomial coefficient to be 0 when its lower index is negative, there would be no objection to leaving the limits 0 to k. Now in this last expression let us substitute y for $x - 1$ and factor out factors which do not involve the summation index. We get

$$\mu = \frac{m}{\binom{m+n}{k}} \sum_{y=0}^{k-1} \binom{m-1}{y}\binom{n}{k-1-y} \tag{12}$$

This sum may be evaluated by means of the identity (9); we simply replace m by $m - 1$ and k by $k - 1$ in the right-hand side of (9) to get

$$\mu = \frac{m}{\binom{m+n}{k}} \binom{m-1+n}{k-1}$$

$$= \frac{mk}{m+n} \tag{13}$$

To get the variance, we shall need the second moment

$$\mu_2' = \sum_{x=0}^{k} x^2 f(x)$$

If we substitute directly for $f(x)$, we shall be able to cancel only one of the x's, and the other x will remain to prevent our using the identity to evaluate the sum. The trick here is to write x^2 in the form

$$x(x-1) + x$$

to get

$$\mu_2' = \Sigma x(x-1)f(x) + \Sigma x f(x) \tag{14}$$

We have already evaluated the second sum in obtaining the mean, and the same procedure used on the first sum gives

$$E[\mathbf{x}(\mathbf{x}-1)] = \frac{\sum_{x=0}^{k} x(x-1)\binom{m}{x}\binom{n}{k-x}}{\binom{m+n}{k}}$$

$$= \frac{\sum_{x=2}^{k} m(m-1)\binom{m-2}{x-2}\binom{n}{k-x}}{\binom{m+n}{k}}$$

$$= \frac{m(m-1)}{\binom{m+n}{k}} \sum_{y=0}^{k-2} \binom{m-2}{y}\binom{n}{k-2-y}$$

$$= \frac{m(m-1)}{\binom{m+n}{k}} \binom{m-2+n}{k-2}$$

$$= \frac{m(m-1)k(k-1)}{(m+n)(m+n-1)} \tag{15}$$

Adding (13) to this, we get μ_2' in accordance with (14); the variance is then obtained by substracting the square of (13) from μ_2' in accordance with (5). Thus the variance is

$$\begin{aligned}\sigma^2 &= \frac{m(m-1)k(k-1)}{(m+n)(m+n-1)} + \frac{mk}{m+n} - \left(\frac{mk}{m+n}\right)^2 \\ &= \frac{mnk(m+n-k)}{(m+n)^2(m+n-1)} \qquad (16)\end{aligned}$$

The general method for higher moments is now evident. To get the third moment, we would find the expected value of

$$\mathbf{x}(\mathbf{x}-1)(\mathbf{x}-2)$$

Since this is equal to $\mathbf{x}^3 - 3\mathbf{x}^2 + 2\mathbf{x}$, we have

$$\mu_3' - 3\mu_2' + 2\mu_1' = E[\mathbf{x}(\mathbf{x}-1)(\mathbf{x}-2)]$$

and, having evaluated the right-hand side of this expression, we could solve for μ_3', since μ_2' and μ_1' have already been determined. Having the third moment, we could obtain the fourth by finding the expected value of $\mathbf{x}(\mathbf{x}-1)(\mathbf{x}-2)(\mathbf{x}-3)$, then solving for μ_4' in

$$\mu_4' - 6\mu_3' + 11\mu_2' - 6\mu_1' = E[\mathbf{x}(\mathbf{x}-1)(\mathbf{x}-2)(\mathbf{x}-3)]$$

The right-hand side of this last expression is called the fourth *factorial moment* of the distribution. The rth factorial moment is

$$E[\mathbf{x}(\mathbf{x}-1)(\mathbf{x}-2)\cdots(\mathbf{x}-r+1)]$$

Example 5.7. Find the mean and standard deviation of the variate $\mathbf{x}$ with density $f(x) = 2(1-x)$, $0 < x < 1$. The rth moment is

$$\begin{aligned}\mu_r' = E(\mathbf{x}^r) &= \int_0^1 x^r 2(1-x)\,dx \\ &= 2\int_0^1 (x^r - x^{r+1})\,dx \\ &= \frac{2}{(\mathrm{r}+1)(r+2)}\end{aligned}$$

The mean is

$$\mu = \mu_1' = \frac{2}{2\times 3} = \frac{1}{3}$$

and the variance is

$$\sigma^2 = \mu_2' - \mu^2 = \frac{2}{3\times 4} - \frac{1}{9} = \frac{1}{18}$$

Hence

$$\sigma = \sqrt{\frac{1}{18}} = \frac{\sqrt{2}}{6}$$

5.3 Moment Generating Functions

The moments of a density function play a very important role in theoretical and applied statistics. In fact, in some cases, if all the moments are known, the density can be determined. This will be discussed briefly in Sec. 5.5. Since the moments of a density are so important, it will be very useful if a function can be found that will give us a representation of all the moments. Such a function is called a moment generating function. More precisely, this is defined in the following:

Definition 5.3. *Let* $\mathbf{x}$ *be a random variable with density* $f(x)$. *The expected value of* $e^{t\mathbf{x}}$ *is called the moment generating function of* $\mathbf{x}$ *if the expected value exists for every value of* t *in some interval* $-h^2 < t < h^2$. *The moment generating function (m.g.f.) is denoted by*

$$m(t) = E(e^{t\mathbf{x}}) = \int_{-\infty}^{\infty} e^{tx} f(x)\, dx \tag{1}$$

if the random variable is continuous and by

$$m(t) = E(e^{t\mathbf{x}}) = \sum_{x} e^{tx} f(x)$$

if the random variable is discrete.

Sometimes we shall use the notation $m_{\mathbf{x}}(t)$.

If a m.g.f. exists, then $m(t)$ is continuously differentiable in some neighborhood of the origin. If we differentiate the m.g.f. r times with respect to t, we have

$$\frac{d^r}{dt^r}\, m(t) = \int_{-\infty}^{\infty} x^r e^{xt} f(x)\, dx \tag{2}$$

and on putting $t = 0$, we find

$$\frac{d^r}{dt^r}\, m(0) = E(\mathbf{x}^r) = \mu_r' \tag{3}$$

where the symbol on the left is to be interpreted to mean the rth derivative of $m(t)$ evaluated at $t = 0$. Thus the moments of a distribution may be obtained from the m.g.f. by differentiation.

If in equation (1) we replace e^{xt} by its series expansion, we obtain the series expansion of $m(t)$ in terms of the moments of $f(x)$; thus

$$\begin{aligned} m(t) &= E\left(1 + \mathbf{x}t + \frac{1}{2!}(\mathbf{x}t)^2 + \frac{1}{3!}(\mathbf{x}t)^3 + \cdots\right) \\ &= 1 + \mu_1' t + \frac{1}{2!}\mu_2' t^2 + \cdots \\ &= \sum_{i=0}^{\infty} \frac{1}{i!}\mu_i' t^i \end{aligned} \tag{4}$$

from which it is again evident that μ'_r may be obtained by differentiating $m(t)$ r times and then putting $t = 0$.

We may illustrate this technique for finding moments by obtaining the mean and variance in the Poisson density:

$$f(x) = \frac{e^{-a}a^x}{x!} \qquad x = 0, 1, 2, \cdots$$

We find

$$\begin{aligned} m(t) = E(e^{\mathbf{x}t}) &= \sum_{x=0}^{\infty} \frac{e^{xt}e^{-a}a^x}{x!} \\ &= e^{-a} \sum_{x=0}^{\infty} \frac{(ae^t)^x}{x!} \\ &= e^{-a}e^{ae^t} \end{aligned}$$

The first two derivatives are

$$\begin{aligned} m'(t) &= e^{-a}ae^te^{ae^t} \\ m''(t) &= e^{-a}ae^te^{ae^t}(1 + ae^t) \end{aligned}$$

whence

$$\begin{aligned} \mu &= m'(0) = a \\ \mu'_2 &= m''(0) = a(1 + a) \\ \sigma^2 &= a(1 + a) - a^2 = a \end{aligned}$$

The *factorial moment generating function* is defined as $E(t^{\mathbf{x}})$, and the factorial moments are obtained from this function in the same way as the ordinary moments are obtained from $E(e^{\mathbf{x}t})$ except that t is put equal to 1 instead of 0. This function sometimes simplifies the problem of finding moments of discrete distributions. It is, however, of no help in the example used in the preceding section, because the sum $\Sigma t^x f(x)$ has no simple expression. For the Poisson distribution:

$$E(t^{\mathbf{x}}) = e^{a(t-1)}$$

whence

$$\begin{aligned} E(\mathbf{x}) &= ae^{a(t-1)}\Big]_{t=1} = a \\ E[\mathbf{x}(\mathbf{x} - 1)] &= a^2e^{a(t-1)}\Big]_{t=1} = a^2 \end{aligned}$$

giving the same moments as before.

Sometimes we shall have occasion to speak of the moments of a *function* of a random variable. Thus we may want the moments of $h(\mathbf{x})$, where $\mathbf{x}$ has the distribution $f(x)$. The rth moment of $h(\mathbf{x})$ is

$$E[h(\mathbf{x})]^r = \int_{-\infty}^{\infty} [h(x)]^r f(x)\, dx \tag{5}$$

and a function which will generate the moments is

$$E(e^{th(\mathbf{x})}) = \int_{-\infty}^{\infty} e^{th(x)}f(x)\,dx \tag{6}$$

5.4 Moments for Multivariate Distributions

The preceding ideas are readily extended to distributions of several variates. For the 3-dimensional random variable $(\mathbf{x}, \mathbf{y}, \mathbf{z})$ with density $f(x, y, z)$ the rth moment of $\mathbf{y}$, for example, is

$$E(\mathbf{y}^r) = \int_{-\infty}^{\infty}\int_{-\infty}^{\infty}\int_{-\infty}^{\infty} y^r f(x, y, z)\,dz\,dy\,dx \tag{1}$$

Besides the moments of the individual variates, there are various *joint moments* defined in general by

$$E(\mathbf{x}^q\mathbf{y}^r\mathbf{z}^s) = \int_{-\infty}^{\infty}\int_{-\infty}^{\infty}\int_{-\infty}^{\infty} x^q y^r z^s f(x, y, z)\,dz\,dy\,dx \tag{2}$$

where q, r, and s are any positive integers or zero. The most important joint moment is the *covariance*, which is the joint moment about the means of the product of two variates. Thus the covariance between $\mathbf{x}$ and $\mathbf{z}$ is

$$\sigma_{\mathbf{xz}} = \int_{-\infty}^{\infty}\int_{-\infty}^{\infty}\int_{-\infty}^{\infty} [x - E(\mathbf{x})][z - E(\mathbf{z})]f(x, y, z)\,dz\,dy\,dx \tag{3}$$

and there are two other covariances $\sigma_{\mathbf{xy}}$ and $\sigma_{\mathbf{yz}}$ defined analogously. The *correlation* between two variates, say $\mathbf{x}$ and $\mathbf{z}$, is denoted by $\rho_{\mathbf{xz}}$ and is defined by

$$\rho_{\mathbf{xz}} = \frac{\sigma_{\mathbf{xz}}}{\sigma_{\mathbf{x}}\sigma_{\mathbf{z}}} \tag{4}$$

where $\sigma_{\mathbf{x}}$ and $\sigma_{\mathbf{z}}$ are the standard deviations of $\mathbf{x}$ and $\mathbf{z}$.

A joint moment generating function of $(\mathbf{x}, \mathbf{y}, \mathbf{z})$ *is defined by*

$$m(t_1, t_2, t_3) = E(e^{t_1\mathbf{x}+t_2\mathbf{y}+t_3\mathbf{z}}) \tag{5}$$

if it exists for all values of t_1, t_2, t_3 *such that* $-h^2 < t_i < h^2$ *for some* h^2. It follows that the rth moment of $\mathbf{y}$, for example, may be obtained by differentiating the moment generating function r times with respect to t_2 and then putting all the t's equal to 0. Similarly the joint moment (2) would be obtained by differentiating the function q times with respect to t_1, r times with respect to t_2, s times with respect to t_3, and then putting all the t's equal to 0.

5.5 The Moment Problem

We have seen that, in general, a density function determines a set of moments $\mu_1', \mu_2', \cdots$ when they exist. One of the important problems in theoretical statistics is this: Given a set of moments, what is the density function from which these moments came, and is there only one density function which generates these particular moments? We shall state, without proof, a theorem which can be used to answer these questions.

Theorem 5.7. *Let* $\mathbf{x}$ *and* $\mathbf{y}$ *be two (continuous or discrete) random variables with densities* $f(x)$ *and* $g(y)$*, respectively. Suppose that the moment generating functions of* $\mathbf{x}$ *and* $\mathbf{y}$ *both exist and are equal for all* t *in the interval* $-h^2 < t < h^2$*. Then the two densities are equal (except possibly at points where they are not continuous if* $\mathbf{x}$ *and* $\mathbf{y}$ *are continuous random variables).*

A similar theorem holds for multivariate densities.

Example 5.8. Suppose that a random variable $\mathbf{x}$ has a moment generating function $m_{\mathbf{x}}(t) = 1/(1 - t)$. Now this exists for every t such that $-1 < t < 1$. Also we see that the density $g(y) = e^{-y}$, $0 < y < \infty$, has the moment generating function $m_{y}(t) = \int_0^\infty e^{yt}e^{-y}\,dy = 1/(1 - t)$. Hence, by Theorem 5.7, $\mathbf{x}$ has the density e^{-x}, $0 < x < \infty$.

To find the density of $\mathbf{x}$ in Example 5.8 we found a density which had $1/(1 - t)$ for a m.g.f. It is not always obvious what the density is. However, Laplace-transform theory can often be used to derive the density from a knowledge of the m.g.f. This technique is, however, beyond the scope of this book.

5.6 Conditional Expectations

In the following chapters we shall have occasion to find the expected value of random variables in conditional distributions.

Definition 5.4. *Let the two-dimensional random variable* $(\mathbf{x}, \mathbf{y})$ *have the joint density* $f(x, y)$*, let the conditional density of* $\mathbf{y}$*, given that* $\mathbf{x} = x$*, be* $g(y|x)$*, and let* $h(x)$ *be the marginal density of* $\mathbf{x}$*. The conditional expectation of* $\mathbf{y}$*, given* $\mathbf{x} = x$*, denoted by* $E(\mathbf{y}|x)$*, is defined to be*

$$E(\mathbf{y}|x) = \int_{-\infty}^{\infty} y g(y|x)\,dy = \int_{-\infty}^{\infty} y \frac{f(x, y)}{h(x)}\,dy$$

We note that $E(\mathbf{y}|x)$ is, in general, a function of x and is not a random variable, since x is a particular value of $\mathbf{x}$.

Example 5.9. Let the two-dimensional random variable $(\mathbf{x}, \mathbf{y})$ have the joint density $f(x, y) = 8xy$, $0 < y < x < 1$. Find $E(\mathbf{y}|x)$. The marginal density of $\mathbf{x}$ is

$$h(x) = \int_0^x 8xy\,dy = 4x^3 \qquad 0 < x < 1$$

Thus the conditional density of **y**, given **x**, is

$$g(y|x) = \frac{f(x, y)}{h(x)} = \frac{8xy}{4x^3} = \frac{2y}{x^2} \qquad 0 < y < x, 0 < x < 1$$

and

$$E(\mathbf{y}|x) = \int_0^x y \cdot g(y|x)\, dy = \int_0^x y \cdot \frac{2y}{x^2}\, dy = \frac{2}{3}x \qquad 0 < x < 1$$

As we stated above, $E(\mathbf{y}|x)$ is, in general, a function of x. Let us denote it by $u(x)$; that is, $E(\mathbf{y}|x) = u(x)$. Now we can evaluate the expected value of the random variable $u(\mathbf{x})$, where the random variable **x** has the density $h(x)$. This gives us

$$\begin{aligned} E[E(\mathbf{y}|\mathbf{x})] &= E[u(\mathbf{x})] = \int_{-\infty}^{\infty} u(x)h(x)\, dx = \int_{-\infty}^{\infty} E(\mathbf{y}|x)h(x)\, dx \\ &= \int_{-\infty}^{\infty} \left[\int_{-\infty}^{\infty} yg(y|x)\, dy\right] h(x)\, dx = \int_{-\infty}^{\infty}\int_{-\infty}^{\infty} yg(y|x)h(x)\, dy\, dx \\ &= \int_{-\infty}^{\infty}\int_{-\infty}^{\infty} yf(x, y)\, dy\, dx = E(\mathbf{y}) \end{aligned}$$

Thus we have proved the following theorem:

Theorem 5.8. *Let* $(\mathbf{x}, \mathbf{y})$ *be a two-dimensional random variable; then* $E(\mathbf{y}) = E[E(\mathbf{y}|\mathbf{x})]$.

We shall state without proof another theorem:

Theorem 5.9. *Let* $(\mathbf{y}, \mathbf{x}_1, \cdots, \mathbf{x}_k)$ *be a* $(k + 1)$*-dimensional random variable with density* $f(y, x_1, \cdots, x_k)$ *and with conditional density* $g(y|x_1, x_2, \cdots, x_k)$. *Then the expected value of a function u of* **y** *and the* $\mathbf{x}_i$*, given* $\mathbf{x}_1, \mathbf{x}_2, \cdots, \mathbf{x}_k$*, is*

$$E[u(\mathbf{y}, \mathbf{x}_1, \cdots, \mathbf{x}_k)|x_1, x_2, \cdots, x_k] = \int_{-\infty}^{\infty} u(y, x_1, \cdots, x_k)g(y|x_1, x_2, \cdots, x_k)\, dy$$

5.7 Problems

1. If 3000 lottery tickets are sold at $1 each on a $4000 car, what is the expected gain of a person who buys one ticket?

2. The density of a random variable **x** is given by

x	1	2	3
$f(x)$	½	⅓	⅙

Find $E(\mathbf{x})$.

3. A coin is tossed until a head appears; what is the expected number of tosses?

4. An event occurs with probability p and fails to occur with probability $q = 1 - p$. In a single trial, what are the mean and variance of $\mathbf{x}$, the number of successes?

5. If n independent trials are made of the event described in Prob. 4 and if $\mathbf{x}$ is the total number of successes, what are the mean and variance of $\mathbf{x}$?

6. Find the mean of the continuous variate $\mathbf{x}$ distributed by

$$f(x) = \frac{1}{\sqrt{2\pi}} e^{-(x-a)^2/2} \qquad -\infty < x < \infty$$

7. Find the mean and variance of $\mathbf{x}$ if $f(x) = 2$, $0 < x < \frac{1}{2}$.

8. Find the mean and variance of $2\mathbf{x}^2$ if $f(x) = 2$, $0 < x < \frac{1}{2}$.

9. Find the mean and variance of $\mathbf{x}$ if

$$f(x) = \frac{3}{(x+1)^4} \qquad 0 < x < \infty$$

10. Show that $E(\mathbf{xy}) = E(\mathbf{x})E(\mathbf{y})$ when $\mathbf{x}$ and $\mathbf{y}$ are independent.

11. Show that

$$\mu_r = \sum_{i=0}^{r} \binom{r}{i} (-1)^{r-i} \mu_i' (\mu_1')^{r-i}$$

12. What is the median of $\mathbf{x}$ if $f(x) = 2(1 - x)$, $0 < x < 1$?

13. Find the moment generating function of the variate $\mathbf{x}$ with density $f(x) = ae^{-ax}$, $x > 0$, and use it to obtain the mean and variance of $\mathbf{x}$.

14. Find the factorial moment generating function for the binomial distribution, and use it to obtain the third moment μ_3'.

15. If $\mathbf{x}$ has the density $f(x) = x/2$, $0 < x < 2$, find the rth moment of $\mathbf{x}^2$. Then show that $\mathbf{y} = \mathbf{x}^2$ has the distribution

$$g(y) = \tfrac{1}{4} \qquad 0 < y < 4$$

by showing that $\mathbf{y}$ has the same moments as $\mathbf{x}^2$.

16. If $f(x, y) = a^2e^{-a(x+y)}$, $x > 0$, $y > 0$, find the generating function of the variate $\mathbf{u}$ if $\mathbf{u} = \mathbf{x} + \mathbf{y}$. Deduce the distribution of $\mathbf{u}$ from the form of this generating function.

17. Show that if a density $f(x)$ is symmetric about a point, say b [that is, $f(b + c) = f(b - c)$ for every value of c] and if the mean exists, then that point must be the mean of $\mathbf{x}$. Show also in this case that all odd moments about the mean must be 0.

18. Given the moment generating function $m(t)$ for the moments μ_r' about the origin, how would one obtain the moment generating function for the moments μ_r about the mean?

19. In place of the moments μ'_r, another infinite set of constants γ_r called the *cumulants* of a distribution is often useful for characterizing the distribution function. The cumulants are defined by the generating function $c(t) = \log m(t)$, where $m(t)$ is the m.g.f. for the μ'_r, that is, $\gamma_r = d^r c(t)/dt^r$ evaluated at $t = 0$. Show that $\gamma_1 = \mu'_1$ and $\gamma_2 = \sigma^2$.

20. Find the rth cumulant γ_r for the density $f(x) = ae^{-ax}$, $x > 0$.

21. Show that if $M(t)$ generates the moments about an arbitrary point b, that is,

$$M(t) = \int_{-\infty}^{\infty} e^{t(x-b)} f(x)\, dx$$

then $C(t) = \log M(t)$ will correctly generate all the cumulants except the first. The cumulants of a distribution beyond γ_1 are thus said to be invariant under translations of the variate.

22. If **x** has cumulants γ_r, show that $\mathbf{y} = k\mathbf{x}$ has cumulants $k^r\gamma_r$.

23. Show that the correlation between two variates is 0 if they are independent. (The converse of this statement is not true, as the following problem shows.)

24. Let **x** have the marginal density $f_1(x) = 1$, $-\frac{1}{2} < x < \frac{1}{2}$, and let the conditional density of **y** be

$$\begin{aligned} f(y|x) &= 1 \qquad x < y < x + 1,\ -\tfrac{1}{2} < x < 0 \\ &= 1 \qquad -x < y < 1 - x,\ 0 < x < \tfrac{1}{2} \\ &= 0 \qquad \text{otherwise} \end{aligned}$$

Find the correlation between **x** and **y**.

25. Could the function $E[1/(1 + t\mathbf{x})]$ be used to generate the moments of a variate **x**?

26. In Prob. 16 find the joint m.g.f. of (**x**, **y**). Differentiate this m.g.f. to find $E(\mathbf{y}^2\mathbf{x})$.

27. If **x** and **y** are two independent random variables, show that $E(\mathbf{y}|x)$ does not depend on x.

28. Let the two-dimensional random variable (**x**, **y**) have the joint density

$$f(x, y) = \tfrac{1}{8}(6 - x - y) \qquad 0 < x < 2,\ 2 < y < 4$$

(*a*) Find $E(\mathbf{y}|x)$.
(*b*) Find $E(\mathbf{y}^2|x)$.
(*c*) Find var $(\mathbf{y}|x)$ defined by $E(\mathbf{y}^2|x) - [E(\mathbf{y}|x)]^2$.

29. The trinomial distribution of two variates **x** and **y** is

$$f(x, y) = \frac{n!}{x!y!(n - x - y)!} p^x q^y (1 - p - q)^{n-x-y} \qquad \begin{array}{l} x, y = 0, 1, \cdots, n \\ x + y \le n \end{array}$$

Find the marginal distribution of **y**.

30. Referring to Prob. 29, find the conditional distribution of $\mathbf{x}$, given $\mathbf{y}$, and obtain its expected value.

31. In Prob. 28, show that $E[E(\mathbf{y}|\mathbf{x})] = E(\mathbf{y})$.

32. Let the joint distribution of $\mathbf{x}$ and $\mathbf{y}$ be $f(x, y)$, and let $u(\mathbf{x})$ and $v(\mathbf{y})$ be functions of $\mathbf{x}$ and $\mathbf{y}$, respectively. Show that

$$E[u(\mathbf{x}) \cdot v(\mathbf{y})|x] = u(x)E[v(\mathbf{y})|x]$$

33. In Prob. 28, find $E(\mathbf{xy}|x)$.

34. If $\mathbf{x}$ and $\mathbf{y}$ are two random variables and $E(\mathbf{y}|x) = \mu$, where μ does not depend on x, show that var $(\mathbf{y}) = E[\text{var } (\mathbf{y}|\mathbf{x})]$.

35. Let the random variable $\mathbf{x}$ have the density $f(x)$ and m.g.f. $m_x(t)$.

(*a*) If c is a constant, show that the m.g.f. of $c + \mathbf{x}$ is $e^{ct}m_x(t)$.

(*b*) If c is a constant, show that the m.g.f. of $c\mathbf{x}$ is $m_x(ct)$, $c \neq 0$.

36. Let $\mathbf{x}_1, \mathbf{x}_2, \cdots, \mathbf{x}_n$ be a random sample from the density $f(x)$, and let $m_x(t)$ be the m.g.f. of $\mathbf{x}_i$.

(*a*) Show that the m.g.f. of $\mathbf{y}$ is $[m_x(t)]^n$, where $\mathbf{y} = \sum_{i=1}^{n} \mathbf{x}_i$.

(*b*) Show that the m.g.f. of $\bar{\mathbf{x}}$ is $[m_x(t/n)]^n$, where $\bar{\mathbf{x}} = \frac{1}{n}\sum_{i=1}^{n} \mathbf{x}_i$.

5.8 Bibliography

1. Brunk, H.: "An Introduction to Mathematical Statistics," Ginn & Company, Boston, 1960.
2. Feller, W.: "An Introduction to Probability Theory and Its Applications," 2d ed., Vol. I, John Wiley & Sons, Inc., New York, 1957.
3. Hoel, P. G.: "Introduction to Mathematical Statistics," 2d ed., John Wiley & Sons, Inc., New York, 1954.
4. Hogg, R., and A. Craig: "Introduction to Mathematical Statistics," The Macmillan Company, New York, 1959.
5. Kendall, M. G.: "The Advanced Theory of Statistics," Vol. I, Charles Griffin & Co., Ltd., London, 1948.

6

Special Continuous Distributions

6.1 Uniform Distribution

A very simple distribution for a continuous variate is the uniform density

$$f(x) = \frac{1}{\beta - \alpha} \qquad \alpha < x < \beta \tag{1}$$
$$= 0 \qquad \text{otherwise}$$

which is plotted in Fig. 6.1. The probability that an observation will fall in any interval within $\alpha < x < \beta$ is equal to $1/(\beta - \alpha)$ times the

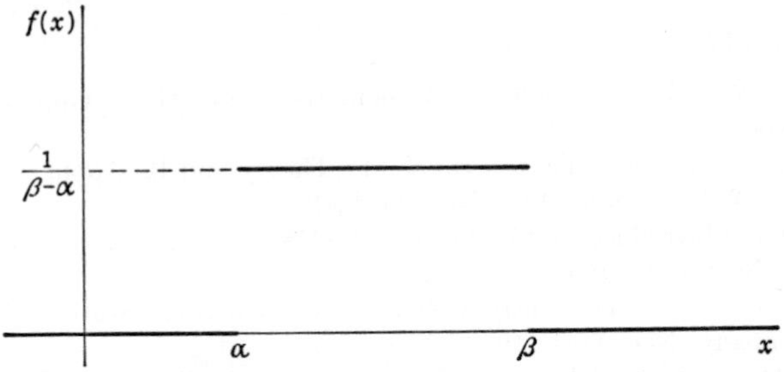

FIG. 6.1

length of the interval. The distribution is particularly useful in theoretical statistics because it is convenient to deal with mathematically.

We are enabled to deal with this simple distribution when discussing certain properties of distributions in general by the following theorem:

Theorem 6.1. *Any density for a continuous variate* $\mathbf{x}$ *may be transformed to the uniform density*

$$f(y) = 1 \qquad 0 < y < 1 \tag{2}$$

by letting $\mathbf{y} = G(\mathbf{x})$, *where* $G(x)$ *is the cumulative distribution of* $\mathbf{x}$.

The proof of this theorem will be left for the reader.

By means of this theorem it is possible to demonstrate many properties of continuous distributions in general by proving them merely for the uniform distribution over the unit interval.

6.2 The Normal Distribution

A great many of the techniques used in applied statistics are based upon the normal distribution, and much of the remainder of this book will be devoted to a study of this distribution.

Definition 6.1. *The random variable* **x** *is said to be normally distributed if its density function is given by*

$$n(x) = \frac{1}{\sqrt{2\pi}\,\sigma} e^{-(x-\mu)^2/2\sigma^2} \qquad -\infty < x < \infty \tag{1}$$

The function is plotted in Fig. 6.2 for several values of σ. Changing μ merely shifts the curves to the right or left without changing their

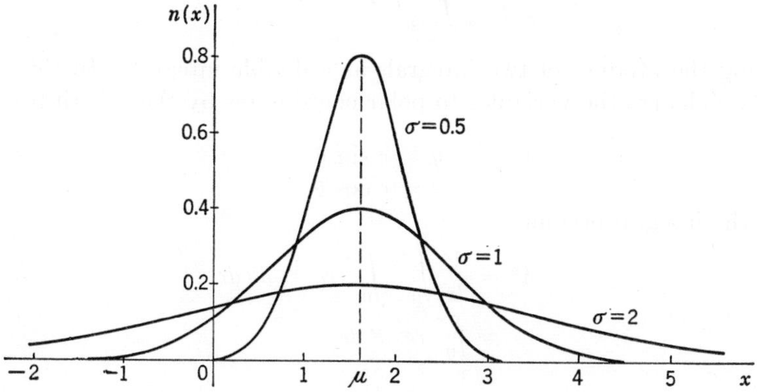

FIG. 6.2

shapes. The function given actually represents a two-parameter family of distributions, the parameters being μ and σ^2. We have used the symbols μ and σ^2 to represent the parameters because the parameters turn out, as we shall see, to be the mean and variance, respectively, of the distribution.

Since $n(x)$ is given to be a density function, it is implied that

$$\int_{-\infty}^{\infty} n(x)\,dx = 1$$

but we should satisfy ourselves that this is true. The verification is somewhat troublesome because this particular function does not integrate into a simple closed expression. Suppose that we represent the area under the curve by A; then

$$A = \frac{1}{\sqrt{2\pi}\,\sigma} \int_{-\infty}^{\infty} e^{-(x-\mu)^2/2\sigma^2}\,dx$$

and on making the substitution

$$y = \frac{x - \mu}{\sigma}$$

we find

$$A = \frac{1}{\sqrt{2\pi}} \int_{-\infty}^{\infty} e^{-\frac{1}{2}y^2}\, dy$$

We wish to show that $A = 1$, and this is most easily done by showing that A^2 is 1 and then reasoning that $A = 1$, since $f(x)$ is positive. We may put

$$\begin{aligned} A^2 &= \frac{1}{\sqrt{2\pi}} \int_{-\infty}^{\infty} e^{-\frac{1}{2}y^2}\, dy \frac{1}{\sqrt{2\pi}} \int_{-\infty}^{\infty} e^{-\frac{1}{2}z^2}\, dz \\ &= \frac{1}{2\pi} \int_{-\infty}^{\infty} \int_{-\infty}^{\infty} e^{-\frac{1}{2}(y^2+z^2)}\, dy\, dz \end{aligned}$$

writing the product of two integrals as a double integral. In this integral we change the variables to polar coordinates by the substitution

$$\begin{aligned} y &= r \sin \theta \\ z &= r \cos \theta \end{aligned}$$

and the integral becomes

$$\begin{aligned} A^2 &= \frac{1}{2\pi} \int_0^{\infty} \int_0^{2\pi} r e^{-\frac{1}{2}r^2}\, d\theta\, dr \\ &= \int_0^{\infty} r e^{-\frac{1}{2}r^2}\, dr \\ &= 1 \end{aligned}$$

Since the integral of $n(x)$ does not have a simple functional form, we can only exhibit the cumulative distribution formally as

$$N(x) = \frac{1}{\sqrt{2\pi}\,\sigma} \int_{-\infty}^{x} e^{-[(t-\mu)^2/2\sigma^2]}\, dt \tag{2}$$

and if we let

$$y = \frac{t - \mu}{\sigma}$$

we find

$$N(x) = \frac{1}{\sqrt{2\pi}} \int_{-\infty}^{(x-\mu)/\sigma} e^{-\frac{1}{2}y^2}\, dy \tag{3}$$

and, given a specific value for $(x - \mu)/\sigma$, the integral can be computed by numerical methods. A tabulation of this function may be found in Table II. Since the density is symmetric about μ, that is, since

$$n(\mu - a) = n(\mu + a)$$

it follows that $N(x)$ for $(x - \mu)/\sigma$ negative is equal to $1 - N(x')$, where $(x' - \mu)/\sigma = -(x - \mu)/\sigma$. The graph of $N(x)$ is given in Fig. 6.3.

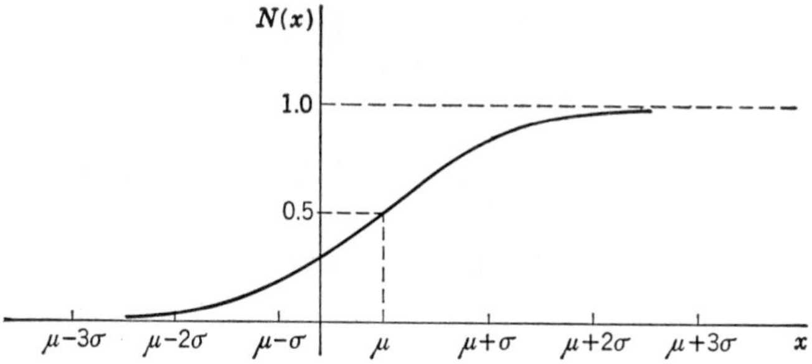

FIG. 6.3

To illustrate the use of the table, we shall find $P(-1 < \mathbf{x} < 4)$ when $\mathbf{x}$ has the density

$$n(x) = \frac{1}{4\sqrt{2\pi}} e^{-[(x-2)^2/32]} \tag{4}$$

We note that

$$\mu = 2 \qquad \sigma = 4$$

and thus that the values of $(x - \mu)/\sigma$ corresponding to -1 and 4 are

$$\frac{-1-2}{4} = -\frac{3}{4} \qquad \frac{4-2}{4} = \frac{1}{2}$$

Hence

$$\begin{aligned} P(-1 < \mathbf{x} < 4) &= N(4) - N(-1) \\ &= .6915 - (1 - .7734) \\ &= .4649 \end{aligned}$$

It is a great convenience that $N(x)$ is of such a form that it need not be tabulated for various combinations of values of μ and σ. The transformation $y = (x - \mu)/\sigma$ brings all normal distributions to the same form, called the *standard* or *normalized* form. We shall reserve the letters n and N henceforth to indicate the normal density and its cumulative form. This will be done by writing $n(x; \mu, \sigma^2)$ and $N(x; \mu, \sigma^2)$, separating the parameters from the variate by a semicolon. In this notation the distribution (4) would be symbolized by $n(x; 2, 16)$. The standard normal distribution is then

$$n(x; 0, 1) = \frac{1}{\sqrt{2\pi}} e^{-\frac{1}{2}x^2} \tag{5}$$

and its cumulative form is

$$N(x; 0, 1) = \int_{-\infty}^{x} n(t; 0, 1)\, dt \tag{6}$$

We shall now find the moments of $n(x; \mu, \sigma^2)$ by finding first the moment generating function. The computation is as follows:

$$\begin{aligned} m(t) &= E(e^{t\mathbf{x}}) = e^{t\mu}E(e^{t(\mathbf{x}-\mu)}) \\ &= e^{t\mu}\int_{-\infty}^{\infty} \frac{1}{\sqrt{2\pi}\,\sigma} e^{t(x-\mu)}\, e^{-(1/2\sigma^2)(x-\mu)^2}\, dx \\ &= e^{t\mu}\frac{1}{\sqrt{2\pi}\,\sigma}\int_{-\infty}^{\infty} e^{-(1/2\sigma^2)[(x-\mu)^2-2\sigma^2t(x-\mu)]}\, dx \end{aligned}$$

On completing the square inside the bracket, it becomes

$$\begin{aligned} (x-\mu)^2 - 2\sigma^2t(x-\mu) &= (x-\mu)^2 - 2\sigma^2t(x-\mu) + \sigma^4t^2 - \sigma^4t^2 \\ &= (x-\mu-\sigma^2t)^2 - \sigma^4t^2 \end{aligned}$$

and we have

$$m(t) = e^{t\mu}e^{\sigma^2t^2/2}\frac{1}{\sqrt{2\pi}\,\sigma}\int_{-\infty}^{\infty} e^{-(x-\mu-\sigma^2t)^2/2\sigma^2}\, dx$$

The integral together with the factor $1/\sqrt{2\pi}\,\sigma$ is necessarily 1, since it is the area under a normal distribution with mean $\mu + \sigma^2 t$ and variance σ^2. Hence, we have the following theorem:

Theorem 6.2. *If* $\mathbf{x}$ *has the density* $n(x; \mu, \sigma^2)$, *that is, the normal distribution, then the moment generating function of* $\mathbf{x}$ *is*

$$m(t) = e^{t\mu+(\sigma^2t^2)/2} \tag{7}$$

On differentiating this function twice and substituting $t = 0$ in the results, we find

$$\begin{aligned} \mu_1' &= \mu \\ \mu_2' &= \sigma^2 + \mu^2 \\ \text{Variance }(\mathbf{x}) &= \mu_2' - (\mu_1')^2 = \sigma^2 \end{aligned}$$

thus justifying our use of the moment symbols for the parameters.

6.3 The Gamma Distribution

Another distribution that plays an important role in statistics is the gamma distribution which we now define.

Definition 6.2. *A random variable* $\mathbf{x}$ *is said to be distributed as the gamma distribution if its density is*

$$\begin{aligned} f(x; \alpha, \beta) &= \frac{1}{\alpha!\beta^{\alpha+1}} x^\alpha e^{-x/\beta} & 0 < x < \infty \qquad (1) \\ &= 0 & \text{elsewhere} \end{aligned}$$

This is a two-parameter family of distributions, the parameters being α and β. β must be positive, and α must be greater than -1. The function is plotted in Fig. 6.4 for $\beta = 1$ and several values of α. Changing β

merely changes the scale on the two axes, as is evident on examining the form of the function.

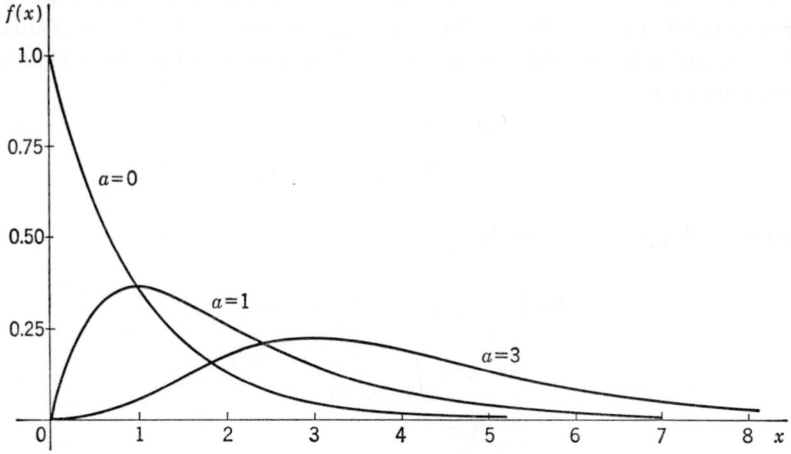

FIG. 6.4

To show that the function represents a density (has unit area), we shall evaluate the integral

$$A = \int_0^\infty \frac{1}{\beta^{\alpha+1}} x^\alpha e^{-x/\beta}\, dx$$

which becomes

$$A = A(\alpha) = \int_0^\infty y^\alpha e^{-y}\, dy$$

on substituting y for x/β; hence A is a function of α only. If $\alpha > 0$, we may integrate by parts to obtain

$$\begin{aligned} A(\alpha) &= -y^\alpha e^{-y}\Big]_0^\infty + \int_0^\infty \alpha y^{\alpha-1} e^{-y}\, dy \\ &= \alpha \int_0^\infty y^{\alpha-1} e^{-y}\, dy \end{aligned}$$

Whence it follows that

$$A(\alpha) = \alpha A(\alpha - 1) \tag{2}$$

If α is a positive integer, we may apply this recurrence formula (2) successively to obtain

$$A(\alpha) = \alpha(\alpha - 1)(\alpha - 2) \cdot \cdot \cdot (2)(1)A(0)$$

and since

$$A(0) = \int_0^\infty e^{-y}\, dy = 1$$

we have

$$A(\alpha) = \alpha!$$

The function $A(\alpha)$ is often denoted by $\Gamma(\alpha + 1)$ in mathematical literature, but we shall use the symbol $\alpha!$ whether or not α is an integer.

In most applications of the distribution, α is either a positive integer or a multiple of $\frac{1}{2}$. Hence for our purposes we need only to evaluate $(\frac{1}{2})!$ in order to be able to compute $\alpha!$ for many values of α that we may encounter.

$$\begin{aligned}(\tfrac{1}{2})! &= \tfrac{1}{2}(-\tfrac{1}{2})! \\ &= \tfrac{1}{2}\int_0^\infty y^{-\frac{1}{2}}e^{-y}\,dy\end{aligned}$$

and if we let $y = z^2/2$, we have

$$\begin{aligned}(\tfrac{1}{2})! &= \tfrac{1}{2}\int_0^\infty \sqrt{2}\,e^{-(z^2/2)}\,dz \\ &= \sqrt{\pi}\int_0^\infty \frac{1}{\sqrt{2\pi}}e^{-(z^2/2)}\,dz \\ &= \frac{\sqrt{\pi}}{2}\end{aligned}$$

since the integral is half the area under a normal density and is therefore $\frac{1}{2}$. Knowing this number, we can evaluate $\alpha!$ for any multiple of $\frac{1}{2}$ by using the relation (2); thus

$$\begin{aligned}(\tfrac{5}{2})! &= \tfrac{5}{2}(\tfrac{3}{2})! = \tfrac{5}{2} \times \tfrac{3}{2}(\tfrac{1}{2})! \\ &= \frac{15\sqrt{\pi}}{8}\end{aligned}$$

The cumulative distribution is

$$F(x) = \int_0^x \frac{1}{\alpha!\beta^{\alpha+1}}t^\alpha e^{-t/\beta}\,dt \qquad x > 0 \tag{3}$$

and is 0 when $x \leq 0$. It must be evaluated by numerical methods unless α is a positive integer, in which case the function can be found by successive integrations by parts to be

$$\begin{aligned}F(x) &= 1 - \left[1 + \frac{x}{\beta} + \frac{1}{2!}\left(\frac{x}{\beta}\right)^2 + \frac{1}{3!}\left(\frac{x}{\beta}\right)^3 + \cdots + \frac{1}{\alpha!}\left(\frac{x}{\beta}\right)^\alpha\right]e^{-x/\beta} \\ &\qquad\qquad x > 0 \quad (4) \\ &= 0 \qquad\qquad x \leq 0\end{aligned}$$

But in any case it is usually simpler to refer to tables of the function in dealing with specific problems. The function F is called the *incomplete gamma function* and has been extensively tabulated.

The moment generating function for this distribution is

$$m(t) = \int_0^\infty e^{tx} \frac{1}{\alpha!\beta^{\alpha+1}} x^\alpha e^{-x/\beta}\, dx$$
$$= \int_0^\infty e^{\beta t y} \frac{1}{\alpha!} y^\alpha e^{-y}\, dy$$

on substituting y for x/β. This may then be put in the form

$$m(t) = \frac{1}{\alpha!} \int_0^\infty y^\alpha e^{-y(1-\beta t)}\, dy$$
$$= \frac{1}{(1-\beta t)^{\alpha+1}} \int_0^\infty \frac{(1-\beta t)^{\alpha+1}}{\alpha!} y^\alpha e^{-y(1-\beta t)}\, dy$$
$$= \frac{1}{(1-\beta t)^{\alpha+1}} \tag{5}$$

provided that $t < 1/\beta$, since the last integral represents the area under a gamma distribution with parameters α and $\beta' = 1/(1 - \beta t)$ and is therefore 1. On differentiating $m(t)$ twice and putting $t = 0$ in the results, we find

$$\mu = \beta(\alpha + 1) \tag{6}$$
$$\mu_2' = \beta^2(\alpha + 1)(\alpha + 2) \tag{7}$$
$$\sigma^2 = \beta^2(\alpha + 1) \tag{8}$$

We have proved the following theorem:

Theorem 6.3. *Let the random variable* **x** *have a gamma distribution. The m.g.f. of* **x** *is*

$$m(t) = (1 - \beta t)^{-(\alpha+1)} \qquad t < \frac{1}{\beta}$$

6.4 The Beta Distribution

Another useful distribution in statistics is the beta distribution.

Definition 6.3. *A random variable* **x** *is said to have a beta distribution if its density is given by*

$$f(x; \alpha, \beta) = \frac{(\alpha + \beta + 1)!}{\alpha!\beta!} x^\alpha (1 - x)^\beta \qquad 0 < x < 1 \tag{1}$$
$$= 0 \qquad \text{elsewhere}$$

The function represents a two-parameter family of distributions, and a few examples are plotted in Fig. 6.5. The parameters α and β must both be greater than -1. The distribution becomes the uniform distribution over the unit interval when $\alpha = \beta = 0$.

To show that the area between $f(x)$ and the x axis is 1, we shall compute the integral

$$A(\alpha, \beta) = \int_0^1 x^\alpha (1 - x)^\beta\, dx \tag{2}$$

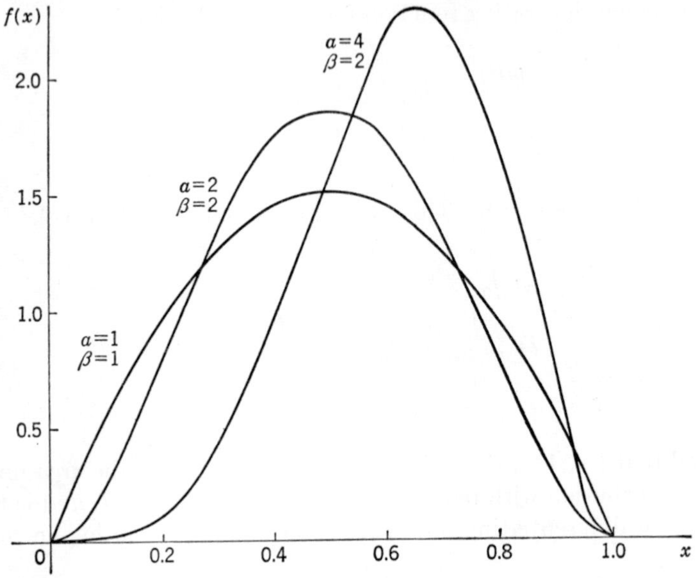

FIG. 6.5

Clearly A will be a function of α and β; we wish to show that it is the reciprocal of the constant multiplier in (1). Referring back to the gamma distribution, we may write

$$\alpha!\beta! = \left(\int_0^\infty x^\alpha e^{-x}\,dx\right)\left(\int_0^\infty y^\beta e^{-y}\,dy\right)$$
$$= \int_0^\infty \int_0^\infty x^\alpha y^\beta e^{-(x+y)}\,dx\,dy$$

and in this last integral we shall change the variable x to u by the substitution

$$u = \frac{x}{x+y}$$

or

$$x = \frac{uy}{1-u} \qquad dx = \frac{y\,du}{(1-u)^2}$$

Since u varies from 0 to 1, the integral becomes

$$\alpha!\beta! = \int_0^\infty \int_0^1 \left(\frac{uy}{1-u}\right)^\alpha y^\beta e^{-y/(1-u)} \frac{y}{(1-u)^2}\,du\,dy$$

In this integral we change y to v by the substitution

$$y = (1-u)v \qquad dy = (1-u)\,dv$$

to get

$$\begin{aligned}\alpha!\beta! &= \int_0^\infty \int_0^1 u^\alpha(1-u)^\beta v^{\alpha+\beta+1}e^{-v}\,du\,dv \\ &= \left(\int_0^\infty v^{\alpha+\beta+1}e^{-v}\,dv\right)\left[\int_0^1 u^\alpha(1-u)^\beta\,du\right] \\ &= (\alpha+\beta+1)!\int_0^1 u^\alpha(1-u)^\beta\,du\end{aligned}$$

which shows that $A(\alpha, \beta)$ has the stated value. $A(\alpha - 1, \beta - 1)$ is called the *beta function* of α and β in the literature and is usually denoted by $B(\alpha, \beta)$.

The cumulative distribution, often called the *incomplete beta*, is

$$\begin{aligned}F(x) &= 0 & x \le 0 \\ &= \int_0^x \frac{(\alpha+\beta+1)!}{\alpha!\beta!} t^\alpha(1-t)^\beta\,dt & 0 < x < 1 \\ &= 1 & x \ge 1\end{aligned} \tag{3}$$

and has also been extensively tabulated.

The moment generating function for this distribution does not have a simple form, but the moments are readily found:

$$\begin{aligned}\mu_r' = E(x^r) &= \frac{(\alpha+\beta+1)!}{\alpha!\beta!}\int_0^1 x^{r+\alpha}(1-x)^\beta\,dx \\ &= \frac{(\alpha+\beta+1)!(\alpha+r)!}{(\alpha+\beta+r+1)!\alpha!}\int_0^1 \frac{(\alpha+\beta+r+1)!}{(\alpha+r)!\beta!} x^{r+\alpha}(1-x)^\beta\,dx \\ &= \frac{(\alpha+\beta+1)!(\alpha+r)!}{(\alpha+\beta+r+1)!\alpha!}\end{aligned} \tag{4}$$

since the integral must be 1.

6.5 Other Distribution Functions

A distribution which we shall find useful for illustrative purposes is the Cauchy density

$$f(x) = \frac{1}{\pi}\frac{1}{1+(x-\mu)^2} \qquad -\infty < x < \infty \tag{1}$$

which has a mean only in a restricted sense and no higher moments. The cumulative distribution is

$$\begin{aligned}F(x) &= \frac{1}{\pi}\int_{-\infty}^x \frac{dt}{1+(t-\mu)^2} \\ &= \frac{1}{2} + \frac{1}{\pi}\arctan(x-\mu)\end{aligned}$$

Log Normal. Let $\mathbf{x}$ be a random variable, and let $\mathbf{y} = \log_e \mathbf{x}$. If $\mathbf{y}$ is a normal variable, then $\mathbf{x}$ is said to have a log normal distribution.

The density is

$$f(x) = \frac{1}{x\beta\sqrt{2\pi}} e^{-(1/2\beta^2)(\log x - \log \alpha)^2} \qquad x > 0$$
$$= 0 \qquad \text{elsewhere}$$

In this density there are two parameters α and β both of which are greater than 0.

6.6 Complete Density Functions

In this section we shall discuss a property of density functions which will be useful in developing the theory in later chapters. Throughout this section we shall denote a density by $f(x; \theta)$, where θ is the parameter. We shall assume that θ is in the interval $\alpha_0 < \theta < \alpha_1$. That is, each θ in the interval defines a different density $f(x; \theta)$. Thus as θ takes on all values in the interval, $\alpha_0 < \theta < \alpha_1$, a set of densities is defined; this is often referred to as a family of density functions. We shall further assume that $f(x; \theta)$ is greater than 0 for x in the interval $a < x < b$ and that $f(x; \theta)$ is equal to 0 elsewhere. We shall also assume that a and b do not depend on θ. More specifically,

1. $f(x; \theta) > 0$ for $a < x < b$ and for $\alpha_0 < \theta < \alpha_1$. If $f(x; \theta)$ is a discrete density, then $a < x < b$ will mean the integral values of x in the interval for which

$$f(x; \theta) > 0 \tag{1}$$

2. $f(x; \theta) = 0$ elsewhere, i.e., for x not in the interval $a < x < b$.
3. a and b do not depend on θ.

Before proceeding with the definition of a complete family of densities, we shall give two examples to illustrate the assumptions in (1).

Example 6.1. Let the random variable **x** have the normal density with mean θ and variance 1. This is given by

$$f(x; \theta) = \frac{1}{\sqrt{2\pi}} e^{-\frac{1}{2}(x-\theta)^2} \qquad -\infty < x < \infty$$

where in this problem θ can take on values in the interval $-\infty < \theta < \infty$. If we set $a = -\infty$, $b = \infty$, and $\alpha_0 = -\infty$, $\alpha_1 = \infty$, then $f(x; \theta) > 0$ if $a < x < b$ and $\alpha_0 < \theta < \alpha_1$, and so this density satisfies the assumptions in (1).

Example 6.2. Let the random variable **x** have the Poisson density with parameter θ. This is given by

$$f(x; \theta) = \frac{\theta^x e^{-\theta}}{x!} \qquad x = 0, 1, 2, \cdots$$
$$= 0 \qquad \text{elsewhere}$$

where θ takes on values in the interval $0 < \theta < 20$, say.

If we set $a = 0$, $b = \infty$, and $\alpha_0 = 0$, $\alpha_1 = 20$, we see that this discrete density satisfies the assumptions given in (1).

Actually the assumption that a and b be independent of θ is not essential for the definition of a complete density function, but it will simplify matters and will suffice for most of the densities that will be considered in this book.

We shall discuss the concept of *completeness* in more detail before giving the definition. Let u be *any* function of x which *does not depend on* θ, which is *not* identically equal to 0 for every x in the interval $a < x < b$, and which is continuous in the interval. Let u_0 be the zero function in the interval $a < x < b$; that is, let $u_0(x) = 0$ for all x in the interval $a < x < b$. Now $E[u_0(\mathbf{x})] = 0$ for all θ in the interval $\alpha_0 < \theta < \alpha_1$ since

$$E[u_0(\mathbf{x})] = \int_a^b 0 \cdot f(x; \theta)\, dx = 0$$

If u_0 is the *only* continuous function of x for $a < x < b$ whose expected value is 0 for every θ in $\alpha_0 < \theta < \alpha_1$, then $f(x; \theta)$ is said to be a *complete* family of densities.

This can be stated: Suppose that there exists no continuous function u of x for $a < x < b$ for which $E[u(\mathbf{x})] = 0$ for all θ in the interval $\alpha_0 < \theta < \alpha_1$, except the zero function u_0. Then $f(x; \theta)$ is *complete* (a complete family of densities). The following definition summarizes this.

Definition 6.4. *Let $f(x; \theta)$ be a family of densities, and let the assumptions in* (1) *apply. If there exists no function u, continuous in the interval $a < x < b$, for which $E[u(\mathbf{x})] = 0$ for all θ in the interval $\alpha_0 < \theta < \alpha_1$ except the zero function u_0, then $f(x; \theta)$ is defined to be a complete family of densities. If there exists at least one continuous function v such that $E[v(\mathbf{x})] = 0$ for every θ in the interval $\alpha_0 < \theta < \alpha_1$ and v is not the zero function, then $f(x; \theta)$ is not complete.*

To prove that a certain density function is complete generally requires mathematics which is beyond the scope of this book. For most of the density functions that we use in this book we shall merely state whether or not they are complete.

It can sometimes be shown that a density function is *not* complete by finding a nonzero function v for which $E[v(\mathbf{x})] = 0$ for all θ in the interval $\alpha_0 < \theta < \alpha_1$.

Example 6.3. Here we shall display a density function which is *not* complete. Let the random variable $\mathbf{x}$ have the normal density with mean 0 and variance σ^2; that is,

$$f(x; \sigma^2) = \frac{1}{\sigma\sqrt{2\pi}} e^{-(x^2)/2\sigma^2} \qquad -\infty < x < \infty$$

and let σ^2 take on values in the interval $0 < \sigma^2 < \infty$. Now we can easily show that $E(\mathbf{x}) = 0$ for every σ^2 in the interval $0 < \sigma^2 < \infty$. But obviously $v(\mathbf{x}) = \mathbf{x}$ is not the zero function, and so $f(x; \sigma^2)$ is *not* complete.

Below are some density functions which are complete:

$$f(x; \mu) = \frac{1}{\sqrt{2\pi}} e^{-\frac{1}{2}(x-\mu)^2} \qquad -\infty < x < \infty \qquad \alpha_0 < \mu < \alpha_1 \tag{2}$$

where α_0 and α_1 are $-\infty$ and $+\infty$, respectively, or any real numbers such that $-\infty < \alpha_0 < \alpha_1 < \infty$.

$$f(x; \mu, \sigma^2) = \frac{1}{\sigma\sqrt{2\pi}} e^{-(x-\mu)^2/2\sigma^2} \qquad -\infty < x < \infty \qquad \alpha_0 < \mu < \alpha_1 \qquad \beta_0 < \sigma^2 < \beta_1 \tag{3}$$

where $-\infty \le \alpha_0 < \alpha_1 \le \infty$, $0 < \beta_0 < \beta_1 \le \infty$.

$$f(x; p) = p^x(1-p)^{1-x} \qquad x = 0, 1;\ \alpha_0 \le p \le \alpha_1 \qquad 0 \le \alpha_0 < \alpha_1 \le 1 \tag{4}$$

$$f(x; \lambda) = \frac{\lambda^x e^{-\lambda}}{x!} \qquad x = 0, 1, 2, \cdots;\ \alpha_0 < \lambda < \alpha_1 \tag{5}$$

with $0 < \alpha_0 < \alpha_1 \le \infty$.

We shall now give an example of how the completeness property of a density can be used. Let the random variable $\mathbf{x}$ have the density

$$f(x; \mu) = \frac{1}{\sqrt{2\pi}} e^{-(x-\mu)^2/2} \qquad -\infty < x < \infty \qquad -\infty < \mu < \infty$$

Now $E(\mathbf{x}^2) = \mu^2 + 1$. We now pose the question, *Is there another continuous function of* $\mathbf{x}$, *say* $v(\mathbf{x})$, *besides* $\mathbf{x}^2$ *whose expected value is also* $\mu^2 + 1$? If there is another such function, let it be defined by $v(\mathbf{x})$; that is, let

$$E[v(\mathbf{x})] = \mu^2 + 1$$

Thus

$$E[v(\mathbf{x})] - E[(\mathbf{x}^2)] = (\mu^2 + 1) - (\mu^2 + 1) = 0$$

or

$$E[v(\mathbf{x}) - \mathbf{x}^2] = 0 \tag{6}$$

for all μ in the interval $-\infty < \mu < \infty$. Let us set $v(\mathbf{x}) - \mathbf{x}^2 = u(\mathbf{x})$. Now (6) can be written $E[u(\mathbf{x})] = 0$ for all μ in the interval $-\infty < \mu < \infty$. But since the density is complete [see (2)], this implies that $u(\mathbf{x}) \equiv 0$ for all x in the interval $-\infty < x < \infty$ or, in other words, $v(\mathbf{x}) \equiv \mathbf{x}^2$.

Thus $\mathbf{x}^2$ is the only continuous function whose expected value is $\mu^2 + 1$. We have stressed the fact that $u(x)$, $v(x)$, etc., be continuous in the interval $a < x < b$. This is not essential for the definition of completeness but will suffice for the work in this book. Definition 6.4 holds for densities of more than one random variable if x is replaced by $x, y, \cdots$, and for more than one parameter θ.

6.7 Problems

1. Find and plot the cumulative form of the uniform distribution.

2. What transformation will change the variate $\mathbf{x}$ to one which will have the uniform distribution over the unit interval if

$$f(x) = \frac{x - 1}{2}$$

$1 < x < 3$, and 0 elsewhere? What interval for the new variate corresponds to $1.1 < x < 2.9$?

3. Plot $n(x; 0, .25)$, $n(x; 1, .25)$, and $n(x; 1, 9)$ on the same graph. What would be the appearance of the distribution if σ were very small? (Use Table I.)

4. If $\mathbf{x}$ is normally distributed with unit mean and $\sigma = .6$, find $P(\mathbf{x} > 0)$ and $P(.2 < \mathbf{x} < 1.8)$.

5. Find the number k such that, for a normally distributed variate, $P(\mu - k\sigma < \mathbf{x} < \mu + k\sigma) = .95$. What would k be if $P = .90$? .99? For what value of k is $P(\mathbf{x} > \mu - k\sigma) = .95$?

6. Find the generating function $E(e^{t(\mathbf{x}-\mu)})$ for the moments about the mean for a normal distribution.

7. Find μ_r in terms of σ for a normal distribution for r even and r odd. (Expand the above generating function into an infinite series.)

8. What constant multiplier will change e^{-x^2+x} into a density? What are the mean and the variance of the resulting distribution?

9. Evaluate $\int_0^2 e^{-x^2}\,dx$.

10. Evaluate $\int_0^\infty x^{\frac{3}{2}}e^{-x/2}\,dx$.

11. Plot the gamma density for $\alpha = 1$, $\beta = 1$; $\alpha = 1$, $\beta = 2$; $\alpha = 2$, $\beta = 1$; $\alpha = 4$, $\beta = 1$.

12. Find the third moment, μ_3', of the gamma distribution.

13. If in the gamma distribution β is put equal to 2 and α is put equal to $(n - 2)/2$, the resulting distribution is called the chi-square distribution with n degrees of freedom. Find its moment generating function and its mean and variance.

14. Find k such that $P(\mathbf{x} > k) = .05$ for the chi-square distribution with two degrees of freedom.

15. Find the rth moment of the gamma distribution without using the moment generating function.

16. Find the rth moment of the gamma distribution using the generating function.

17. Plot the beta density for $\alpha = 0$, $\beta = 0$; $\alpha = 1$, $\beta = 1$; $\alpha = 3$, $\beta = 3$; $\alpha = 2$, $\beta = 3$; $\alpha = 3$, $\beta = 2$. What would be the appearance of the function if both α and β were large?

18. Find the mean and variance of the beta distribution.

19. Show that the beta density is symmetric about the point $x = \frac{1}{2}$ when $\alpha = \beta$.

20. Find the mean of the Cauchy distribution if

$$\frac{1}{\pi}\int_{-\infty}^{\infty} \frac{x\,dx}{1 + (x - \mu)^2}$$

is defined to be

$$\lim_{A\to\infty} \int_{\mu-A}^{\mu+A} \frac{1}{\pi}\,\frac{x\,dx}{1 + (x - \mu)^2}$$

Show that the distribution does not have any higher moments.

21. Let $\mathbf{x}$ and $\mathbf{y}$ be two random variables such that $g(y|x)$ is a normal density with mean μ and variance σ^2/x, where μ and σ^2 do not depend on x. Also we suppose that $x > 0$.

(*a*) Write out the density $g(y|x)$.

(*b*) Let the marginal density of $\mathbf{x}$ be a gamma with $\alpha = m/2 - 1$, $\beta = 2$; that is,

$$h(x) = 1/[\Gamma(m/2)2^{m/2}]x^{(m-2)/2}e^{-x/2} \qquad x > 0$$

Find the joint density of $\mathbf{x}$ and $\mathbf{y}$.

22. (*a*) Find the marginal density of $\mathbf{y}$ in Prob. 21.

(*b*) Find var ($\mathbf{y}$) from part (*a*).

23. Find var ($\mathbf{y}$) by using Prob. 34 in Chap. 5 without using the marginal density of $\mathbf{y}$.

24. Compare the Cauchy density and the normal density with $\sigma = 2$ by plotting them on the same graph both with mean 0. Notice that the variance is a poor criterion for comparing two distributions unless it is known that they have the same functional form.

25. What are the cumulants of the normal distribution?

26. Let $\mathbf{x}$ have the gamma distribution with parameters $\alpha = 10$, $\beta = 1$. How many moments does $\mathbf{y} = 1/\mathbf{x}$ have?

27. If $\mathbf{x}$ has the gamma distribution, find the moment generating function of $\mathbf{y} = \log \mathbf{x}$.

28. A variate **x** has the density

$$f(x) = 2\sqrt{\frac{2}{\pi}}\, xe^{-x^4/2} \qquad x > 0$$

Find its mean and variance.

29. A variate has moments $\mu'_r = r!$ Find its moment generating function and then deduce its distribution.

30. A variate **x** has the uniform distribution over the unit interval; what function of **x** has the gamma distribution with $\alpha = 0$, $\beta = 1$?

31. A variate **x** has the beta distribution with $\alpha = 0$, $\beta = 1$. What function of **x** has the gamma distribution with $\alpha = 0$, $\beta = 1$?

32. A variate has moments $\mu'_r = \dfrac{r!}{(r/2)!}$ when r is even and $\mu'_r = 0$ when r is odd. Deduce the distribution of the variate from its moment generating function.

33. Show how tables of the incomplete gamma $F(x; \alpha, \beta)$ may be used to evaluate the cumulative Poisson distribution, say,

$$\sum_{y=0}^{n} \frac{e^{-m}m^y}{y!}$$

34. If log **x** is normally distributed with $\mu = 1$, $\sigma^2 = 4$, find

$$P(\tfrac{1}{2} < \mathbf{x} < 2)$$

(log 2 = .693).

35. A variate **x** has the density

$$f(x) = 2\sqrt{\frac{2}{\pi}}\, xe^{-\frac{1}{2}x^4} \qquad x > 0$$

Find $P(\mathbf{x} < 4)$.

36. Determine the mean and variance of the normal distribution by differentiating the identity

$$\int_{-\infty}^{\infty} n(x; \mu, \sigma^2)\, dx = 1$$

with respect to μ and with respect to σ^2.

37. A variate **x** is said to be transformed to standard scale if it is divided by its standard deviation. Show that the cumulants of $\mathbf{x}/\sigma$ are equal to $\gamma_r/\gamma_2^{r/2}$, where γ_r is the rth cumulant of **x**.

38. Show that the gamma distribution is nearly normal when α is large, by comparing the cumulants of the two distributions on standard scale.

39. A variate $\mathbf{x}$ is normally distributed with mean μ and variance σ^2. Show that the mean of the conditional distribution of $\mathbf{x}$, given

$$a < \mathbf{x} < b$$

is

$$\mu + \frac{n(a) - n(b)}{N(b) - N(a)} \sigma^2$$

40. A variate $\mathbf{x}$ has density $f(x)$. How might one determine a function u given by $\mathbf{u} = u(\mathbf{x})$ such that $\mathbf{u}$ is distributed by $g(u)$?

41. Let the two-dimensional random variable $(\mathbf{x}, \mathbf{y})$ have the density

$$f(x, y) = p^{x+y}(1 - p)^{2-x-y} \qquad x = 0, 1; y = 0, 1; 0 < p < 1$$

(*a*) Show that $E(\mathbf{x}) = E(\mathbf{y})$.

(*b*) Use part (*a*) to show that the density is *not* complete by finding a nonzero function u such that $E[u(\mathbf{x}, \mathbf{y})] = 0$ for all p such that $0 < p < 1$.

42. Let the two-dimensional random variable $(\mathbf{x}, \mathbf{y})$ have the density

$$f(x, y) = \frac{1}{2\pi} \exp\left[-(\tfrac{1}{2})(x - \alpha)^2 - (\tfrac{1}{2})(y - \alpha)^2\right] \qquad \begin{matrix} -\infty < x < \infty \\ -\infty < y < \infty \\ 0 < \alpha < \infty \end{matrix}$$

Show that this density is not complete.

43. Let the discrete random variable $\mathbf{x}$ have the density

$$f(x) = p^x(1 - p)^{1-x} \quad x = 0, 1; 0 < p < 1$$

(*a*) Let u be *any* function of $\mathbf{x}$ (does not depend on p) except the zero function; that is, $u(1)$ and $u(0)$ are not both equal to 0. Find $E[u(\mathbf{x})]$.

(*b*) Show, by using part (*a*), that $E[u(\mathbf{x})]$ cannot be identically equal to 0 for all p in the interval $0 < p < 1$ unless u is the zero function.

(*c*) Use parts (*a*) and (*b*) to deduce that $f(x)$ is a complete density.

6.8 Bibliography

1. Anderson, T. W.: "An Introduction to Multivariate Statistical Analysis," John Wiley & Sons, Inc., New York, 1958.
2. Brunk, H.: "An Introduction to Mathematical Statistics," Ginn & Company, Boston, 1960.
3. Feller, W.: "An Introduction to Probability Theory and Its Applications," 2d ed., Vol. I, John Wiley & Sons, Inc., New York, 1957.
4. Hoel, P. G.: "Introduction to Mathematical Statistics," 2d ed., John Wiley & Sons, Inc., New York, 1954.
5. Hogg, R., and A. Craig: "Introduction to Mathematical Statistics," The Macmillan Company, New York, 1959.
6. Kendall, M. G.: "Advanced Theory of Statistics," Vol. I, Charles Griffin & Co., Ltd., London, 1948.

7

Sampling

7.1 Inductive Inference

Up to now we have been concerned with certain aspects of the theory of probability. The subject of sampling brings us to the theory of statistics proper, and we shall consider briefly here one important area of the theory of statistics and its relation to sampling.

Progress in science is ascribed to experimentation. The research worker performs an experiment and obtains some data. On the basis of the data, certain conclusions are drawn. The conclusions usually go beyond the materials and operations of the particular experiment. In other words, the scientist may generalize from a particular experiment to the class of all similar experiments. This sort of extension from the particular to the general is called *inductive inference.* It is one way in which new knowledge is found.

Inductive inference is well known to be a hazardous process. In fact, it is a theorem of logic that in inductive inference uncertainty is present. One simply cannot make perfectly certain generalizations. However, uncertain inferences can be made, and the degree of uncertainty can be measured if the experiment has been performed in accordance with certain principles. One function of statistics is the provision of techniques for making inductive inferences and for measuring the degree of uncertainty of such inferences. Uncertainty is measured in terms of probability, and that is the reason we have devoted so much time to the theory of probability.

Before proceeding further we shall say a few words about another kind of inference—*deductive inference.* While conclusions which are reached by inductive inference are only probable, those reached by deductive inference are conclusive. To illustrate deductive inference, consider the following two statements.

1. One of the interior angles of each right triangle equals 90°.
2. Triangle A is a right triangle.

If we accept these two statements, then we are forced to the conclusion

3. One of the angles of triangle A equals 90°.

This is an example of deductive inference which can be described as a method of deriving information (statement 3) from accepted facts (statements 1 and 2). Statement 1 is called the major premise, statement 2 the minor premise, and statement 3 the conclusion. For another example, consider the following:

Major premise:	1. All West Point graduates are over 18 years of age.
Minor premise:	2. John is a West Point graduate.
Conclusion:	3. John is over 18 years of age.

In deductive inference the conclusion is true if the premises are true. This can be pictured as in Fig. 7.1.

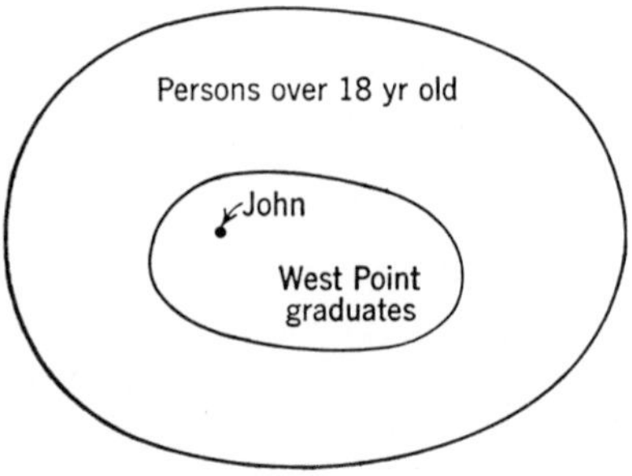

FIG. 7.1

West Point graduates is a subset of all persons over 18 years old, and John is an element in the subset of West Point graduates; hence John is also an element in the set of persons who are over 18 years old.

While deductive inference is extremely important, much of the new knowledge in the real world comes about by the process of inductive inference. In the science of mathematics, for example, *deductive* inference is used to *prove* theorems while in the empirical sciences *inductive* inference is used to find new knowledge.

Let us illustrate inductive inference by a simple example. Suppose that we have a storage bin which contains 10 million (let us say) flower seeds which we know will each produce either white or red flowers. The information which we want is, *How many (or what per cent) of these 10 million seeds will produce white flowers?* Now the only way in which we can be *sure* that this question is answered correctly is to plant every seed and observe the number producing white flowers. However, this is not feasible since we want to sell the seeds. Even if we did not want to sell the seeds, we would prefer to obtain an answer without expending so much effort. Of course, without planting each seed and observing the color of flower that each produces we cannot be *certain* of the number of seeds producing white flowers. Another thought which occurs is, *Can we plant a few of the seeds and, on the basis of the colors of these few flowers, make a statement as to how many of the 10 million seeds will produce white flowers?* The answer is that we cannot make an exact prediction as to how many white flowers the seeds will produce, but we can make a probabilistic statement if we select the few seeds in a certain fashion. This is inductive inference: We select a few of the 10 million seeds, plant them, observe the number which produce white flowers, and on the basis of these few we make a prediction as to how many of the 10 million will produce white flowers; from a knowledge of the color of a few we generalize to the whole 10 million. We cannot be certain of our answer but we can have confidence in it in a frequency-ratio–probability sense.

7.2 Populations and Samples

We have seen in the previous section that a central problem in discovering new knowledge in the real world consists of observing a few of the elements under discussion, and on the basis of these few we make a statement about the totality of elements. We shall now investigate this procedure in more detail.

Definition 7.1. Target Population. *The totality of elements which are under discussion and about which information is desired will be called the target population.*

In the example in the previous section the 10 million seeds in the storage bin form the target population. The target population may be all the dairy cattle in Wisconsin on a certain date, or the prices of bread in New York City on a certain date, or the hypothetical sequence of heads and tails obtained by tossing a certain coin an infinite number of times, or the hypothetical set of an infinite number of measurements of the velocity of light, and so forth. The important thing is that the target population must be capable of being quite well defined; it may be real or hypothetical.

The problem of inductive inference is regarded as follows from the point of view of statistics: The object of an investigation is to find out something about a certain target population. It is generally impossible or impractical to examine the entire population, but one may examine a part or sample of it and, on the basis of this limited investigation, make inferences regarding the target population.

The problem immediately arises as to how the sample of the population should be selected. We stated in the previous section that we could make probabilistic statements about the population if the sample is selected in a certain fashion. Of particular importance is the case of a *simple random sample,* sometimes called a *random sample.* This is given in the following definition:

Definition 7.2. Random Sample. *Let the random variables* $\mathbf{x}_1$, $\mathbf{x}_2$, $\cdots$, $\mathbf{x}_n$ *have joint density*

$$g(x_1, x_2, \cdots, x_n) = f(x_1)f(x_2) \cdots f(x_n)$$

where the density of each $\mathbf{x}_i$ *is* $f(x)$. *Then* $\mathbf{x}_1$, $\mathbf{x}_2$, $\cdots$, $\mathbf{x}_n$ *is said to be a random sample of size n from the population with density* $f(x)$.

Often it is not possible to select a random sample from the target population, but it is selected from some related population. To distinguish the two populations we define the following:

Definition 7.3. Sampled Population. *Let* $\mathbf{x}_1$, $\mathbf{x}_2$, $\cdots$, $\mathbf{x}_n$ *be a random sample from a population with density* $f(x)$; *then this population is called the sampled population.*

Valid probability statements can be made about sampled populations on the basis of random samples, but statements about the target populations are not valid in a relative-frequency–probability sense unless the target population is also the sampled population. We shall give some examples to bring out the distinction between the sampled population and the target population.

Example 7.1. Suppose that a sociologist desires to study the religious habits of 20-year-old males in the United States. He draws a sample from the 20-year-old males of a large city to make his study. In this case the target population is the 20-year-old males in the United States, and the sampled population is the 20-year-old males in the city which he sampled. He can draw valid probabilistic conclusions about his sampled population, but he must use his personal judgment to extrapolate to the target population, and the reliability of the extrapolation cannot be measured in relative-frequency–probability terms.

Example 7.2. A wheat researcher is studying the yield of a certain variety of wheat in the state of Colorado. He has at his disposal five farms scattered throughout the state on which he can plant the wheat and observe the yield. The sampled population consists of the yields on these five farms whereas the target population consists of the yields of wheat on every farm in the state.

This book will be concerned with the problem of selecting (drawing) a sample from a sampled population with density $f(x)$, and on the basis of these sample observations, probability statements will be made about $f(x)$. Thus we shall develop the ideas of sampling.

7.3 Sample Distributions

Suppose that a variate $\mathbf{x}$ has density $f(x)$ in some population. And suppose that a sample of two values of $\mathbf{x}$, say x_1 and x_2, is drawn at random. The pair of numbers (x_1, x_2) determines a point in a plane, and the population of all such pairs of numbers that might have been drawn forms a bivariate population. We are interested in finding the distribution of this bivariate population in terms of the original distribution $f(x)$.

The joint density function for $\mathbf{x}_1$ and $\mathbf{x}_2$ must be some function, say $g(x_1, x_2)$, such that for any a_1, a_2, b_1, b_2 we have

$$P(a_1 < \mathbf{x}_1 < b_1, a_2 < \mathbf{x}_2 < b_2) = \int_{a_1}^{b_1} \int_{a_2}^{b_2} g(x_1, x_2)\, dx_2\, dx_1 \tag{1}$$

Now by a random sample we shall mean that the value of the first observation has no effect whatever on the value of the second observation. In other words, for a random sample, $\mathbf{x}_1$ and $\mathbf{x}_2$ are independent in the probability sense. When the two variates of a bivariate distribution are independent in the probability sense, we have seen that the joint distribution is the product of the marginal distributions. In the present instance, the marginal distributions are simply $f(x_1)$ and $f(x_2)$, so that we have, by definition of randomness,

$$g(x_1, x_2) = f(x_1)f(x_2) \tag{2}$$

or, equivalently,

$$P(a_1 < \mathbf{x}_1 < b_1, a_2 < \mathbf{x}_2 < b_2) = P(a_1 < \mathbf{x}_1 < b_1)P(a_2 < \mathbf{x}_2 < b_2) \tag{3}$$

for all a_i and b_j.

As a simple example, suppose that $\mathbf{x}$ can have only two values, 0 and 1, with probabilities q and p, respectively. That is, $\mathbf{x}$ is a discrete variate which has the binomial distribution

$$f(x) = \binom{1}{x} p^x q^{1-x} \qquad x = 0, 1 \tag{4}$$

and since $\binom{1}{0} = \binom{1}{1} = 1$, we may write it as

$$f(x) = p^x q^{1-x}$$

The joint density for a random sample of two values from $f(x)$ is

$$g(x_1, x_2) = p^{x_1+x_2} q^{2-x_1-x_2} \qquad x_1 = 0, 1;\ x_2 = 0, 1 \tag{5}$$

which is defined at the four points $(0, 0)(0, 1)(1, 0)(1, 1)$ in the x_1x_2 plane. It is to be observed that this density is not what we should have obtained by drawing two elements from a binomial population and counting the number of successes, say $\mathbf{y}$; that density is

$$h(y) = \binom{2}{y} p^y q^{2-y} \qquad y = 0, 1, 2, \tag{6}$$

and it differs from (5) in that it is the distribution of the single variate $\mathbf{y} = \mathbf{x}_1 + \mathbf{x}_2$. Equation (5) gives us the joint distribution of the two random variables $\mathbf{x}_1$ and $\mathbf{x}_2$.

It is to be noted that $g(x_1, x_2)$ gives us the distribution of the sample in *the order drawn*. Thus in (5), $g(0, 1) = pq$, not $2pq$. $g(0, 1)$ refers to the probability of drawing first a 0, then a 1. In general, (1) represents the probability that the first observation drawn falls in the interval (a_1, b_1) and the second falls in (a_2, b_2). The opposite occurrence does not satisfy the specification unless, of course, the two intervals happen to be the same.

By reasoning exactly as before, we find that the joint density for a random sample of size n, $\mathbf{x}_1, \mathbf{x}_2, \cdots, \mathbf{x}_n$, from a population with distribution $f(x)$ is

$$g(x_1, x_2, \cdots, x_n) = f(x_1)f(x_2) \cdots f(x_n) \tag{7}$$

and this again gives the distribution of the sample in the order drawn.

Our definition of random sampling has automatically ruled out sampling from a finite population without replacement. If, for example, we draw two balls from an urn containing, say, two white and three black balls, the result of the first draw certainly affects the probability of the result of the second. The two drawings are not independent in the probability sense. In this case, another definition of sampling must be adopted (Probs. 26 and 32). Our present discussion in this and in the following chapters is thus concerned with sampling from continuous populations (where the question of drawing with or without replacement does not arise) and to sampling with replacement from discrete populations. We shall sometimes use the statement, "population $f(x)$" to mean "a population with density $f(x)$."

7.4 Sample Moments

One of the central problems in statistics is the following: It is desired to study a population which has a density $f(x; \theta)$, where the form of the density is known, but it contains an unknown parameter θ (if θ is known, then the density function is completely specified). Therefore, the procedure is to take a random sample $\mathbf{x}_1, \mathbf{x}_2, \cdots, \mathbf{x}_n$ of size n from this density and let some function, say $u(\mathbf{x}_1, \mathbf{x}_2, \cdots, \mathbf{x}_n)$, "represent" or "estimate" the unknown parameter θ. The problem is to determine which function will be the "best" one to estimate θ. This problem will be formulated in more detail in the next chapter. In this section we shall examine certain functions of the random samples, namely, the sample moments. First, however, we shall define what we shall mean by a statistic.

Definition 7.4. Statistic. *A statistic is a function of observable random variables which does not contain any unknown parameters.*

For example, if the random variable $\mathbf{x}$ has the density $n(x; \mu, \sigma^2)$, where

μ and σ^2 are unknown, then $\mathbf{x} - \mu$ is not a statistic; neither is $\mathbf{x}/\sigma$, but $\mathbf{x}$, $\mathbf{x} + 3$, $\mathbf{x}^2 + \log \mathbf{x}^2$ are statistics.

In the formulation above, one of the central problems in statistics is to find a suitable statistic (function of the random variables $\mathbf{x}_1, \mathbf{x}_2, \cdots, \mathbf{x}_n$) to "represent" θ.

Next we shall define and discuss some important statistics, the sample moments.

Definition 7.5. Sample Moments. *Let* $\mathbf{x}_1, \mathbf{x}_2, \cdots, \mathbf{x}_n$ *be a random sample from the density* $f(x)$. *Then the rth sample moment about zero is*

$$\mathbf{m}'_r = \frac{1}{n} \sum_{i=1}^{n} \mathbf{x}_i^r$$

In particular, if $r = 1$, *we get the sample mean which is usually denoted by* $\bar{\mathbf{x}}$; *that is,*

$$\bar{\mathbf{x}} = \frac{1}{n} \sum_{i=1}^{n} \mathbf{x}_i$$

In Chap. 5 we defined the rth moment of a density $f(x)$ to be $E(\mathbf{x}^r)$. We shall now show that the sample moments reflect the population moments in the sense that the expected values of the sample moments are equal to the population moments.

Theorem 7.1. *Let* $\mathbf{x}_1, \mathbf{x}_2, \cdots, \mathbf{x}_n$ *be a random sample from a population with density* $f(x)$. *The expected value of the rth sample moment is equal to the rth population moment; that is,* $E[\mathbf{m}'_r] = \mu'_r$.

Proof. First we notice that $\mathbf{m}'_r = \frac{1}{n} \sum \mathbf{x}_i^r$ and that $\mathbf{m}'_r$ is a random variable since it is a function of the random variables $\mathbf{x}_i$. Now, by Theorem 5.6, we get

$$E[\mathbf{m}'_r] = E\left[\frac{1}{n} \sum \mathbf{x}_i^r\right] = \frac{1}{n} E\left[\sum \mathbf{x}_i^r\right] = \frac{1}{n} \sum E[\mathbf{x}_i^r]$$

But by the definition of population moments we have $E(\mathbf{x}_i^r) = \mu'_r$; hence

$$E[\mathbf{m}'_r] = \frac{1}{n} \sum_{i=1}^{n} \mu'_r = \mu'_r$$

As a particular case when $r = 1$, we get the following:

Corollary 7.1.1. *Let* $\mathbf{x}_1, \mathbf{x}_2, \cdots, \mathbf{x}_n$ *be a random sample from a population with density* $f(x)$ *and let* μ *be the mean of the population. Then* $E(\bar{\mathbf{x}}) = \mu$.

Next we shall examine the variance of $\bar{\mathbf{x}}$, the mean of a random sample.

Theorem 7.2. *Let* $\mathbf{x}_1, \mathbf{x}_2, \ldots, \mathbf{x}_n$ *be a random sample of size* n *from the density* $f(x)$, *and let* $\bar{\mathbf{x}} = \frac{1}{n}\sum \mathbf{x}_i$. *We also assume that the density* $f(x)$ *has a finite variance* σ^2. *Then the variance of* $\bar{\mathbf{x}}$, *which we write as* $\sigma^2_{\bar{\mathbf{x}}}$, *is* σ^2/n.

Proof. By definition, we get

$$\sigma^2_{\bar{\mathbf{x}}} = E[\bar{\mathbf{x}} - E(\bar{\mathbf{x}})]^2 \tag{1}$$

or

$$\begin{aligned} \sigma^2_{\bar{\mathbf{x}}} &= E(\bar{\mathbf{x}} - \mu)^2 \\ &= E\left(\frac{1}{n}\sum \mathbf{x}_i - \mu\right)^2 \\ &= E\left[\frac{1}{n}\sum (\mathbf{x}_i - \mu)\right]^2 \\ &= \frac{1}{n^2} E\left[\sum (\mathbf{x}_i - \mu)\right]^2 \end{aligned} \tag{2}$$

On squaring the sum, we get n terms of the form $(\mathbf{x}_i - \mu)^2$ and $\binom{n}{2}$ terms of the form $2(\mathbf{x}_i - \mu)(\mathbf{x}_j - \mu)$ with $i < j$. The expected value of $(\mathbf{x}_i - \mu)^2$ depends only on the marginal distribution of $\mathbf{x}_i$, since in the integral

$$\int\int \cdots \int (x_i - \mu)^2 \prod_j [f(x_j)\,dx_j]$$

all factors not involving x_i become 1 and we are left with

$$\int (x_i - \mu)^2 f(x_i)\,dx_i = \sigma^2 \tag{3}$$

where σ^2 is the population variance. Similarly,

$$\begin{aligned} E[(\mathbf{x}_i - \mu)(\mathbf{x}_j - \mu)] &= \int\int (x_i - \mu)(x_j - \mu) f(x_i) f(x_j)\,dx_i\,dx_j \\ &= \int (x_i - \mu) f(x_i)\,dx_i \int (x_j - \mu) f(x_j)\,dx_j \\ &= 0 \end{aligned} \tag{4}$$

Equation (2) then becomes

$$\begin{aligned} \sigma^2_{\bar{\mathbf{x}}} &= \frac{1}{n^2} \sum_{i=1}^{n} E(\mathbf{x}_i - \mu)^2 \\ &= \frac{1}{n^2} \sum \sigma^2 \\ &= \frac{\sigma^2}{n} \end{aligned} \tag{5}$$

Thus the variance of the sample mean is equal to the population variance divided by the sample size.

This fact is of extreme importance in applied statistics. It implies that, whatever the population distribution (provided that it has a finite variance), the distribution of the sample mean becomes more and more concentrated near the population mean as the sample size increases. It follows that the larger the sample, the more certain we can be that the sample mean will be a good estimate of the population mean. This is essentially the law of large numbers. We shall obtain a more precise statement of it in the next section.

7.5 The Law of Large Numbers

Let $f(x; \theta)$ be the density of a random variable $\mathbf{x}$. We have discussed the fact that one way to get some information about the density function is to observe a random sample and make an inference from the sample to the population. If θ were known, the density function would be completely specified, and no inference from the sample to the population would be necessary. Therefore, it seems that we would like to have the random sample tell us something about the unknown parameter θ. This problem will be discussed in detail in the next chapter. In this section we shall discuss a related problem.

Let $E(\mathbf{x})$ be denoted by μ in the density $f(x)$. The problem is to estimate μ. In a loose sense, $E(\mathbf{x})$ is the average of an infinite number of values of the random variable $\mathbf{x}$. In any real-world problem we can observe only a finite number of values of the random variable $\mathbf{x}$. A very crucial question then is, *Using only a finite number of values of* $\mathbf{x}$ *(a random sample of size n, say), can any reliable inferences be made about* $E(\mathbf{x})$*, the "average" of an infinite number of values of* $\mathbf{x}$*?* The answer is "yes"; reliable inferences about $E(\mathbf{x})$ can be made by using only a finite sample, and we shall demonstrate this by proving what is called the weak law of large numbers. In words, the law states the following: An n can be determined such that, if a random sample of size n or larger is taken from a population with the density $f(x)$ [with $E(\mathbf{x}) = \mu$], the probability can be made to be as close to 1 as desired that the sample mean $\bar{\mathbf{x}}$ will deviate from μ by less than any arbitrarily specified small quantity. More precisely, the weak law of large numbers states that for any two chosen small numbers ϵ and δ, where $\epsilon > 0$, $0 < \delta < 1$, there exists an integer n such that if a random sample of size n or larger is obtained from $f(x)$, and the mean, denoted by $\bar{\mathbf{x}}_n$, computed, then the probability is greater than $1 - \delta$ (i.e., as close to 1 as desired) that $\bar{\mathbf{x}}_n$ deviates from μ by less than ϵ (i.e., is arbitrarily close to μ). In symbols this is written: For any $\epsilon > 0$ and δ between 0 and 1 there exists an integer n such that for all $m \geq n$

$$P(|\bar{\mathbf{x}}_m - \mu| < \epsilon) > 1 - \delta$$

Before proving the weak law of large numbers, we shall prove Tchebysheff's inequality.

Theorem 7.3. *Let $f(x)$ be a density with mean μ and finite variance σ^2. Let a be any positive number, and let $\bar{\mathbf{x}}_n$ be the mean of a random sample of size n from $f(x)$. Then*

$$P\left(-\frac{a\sigma}{\sqrt{n}} \leq \bar{\mathbf{x}}_n - \mu \leq \frac{a\sigma}{\sqrt{n}}\right) \geq 1 - \frac{1}{a^2}$$

Proof. In the proof we shall replace $\bar{\mathbf{x}}_n$ by $\bar{\mathbf{x}}$.

Suppose that the density of the sample mean is $g(\bar{x})$, where $\bar{\mathbf{x}}$ is the mean of a sample of size n from a population with density $f(x)$. We have

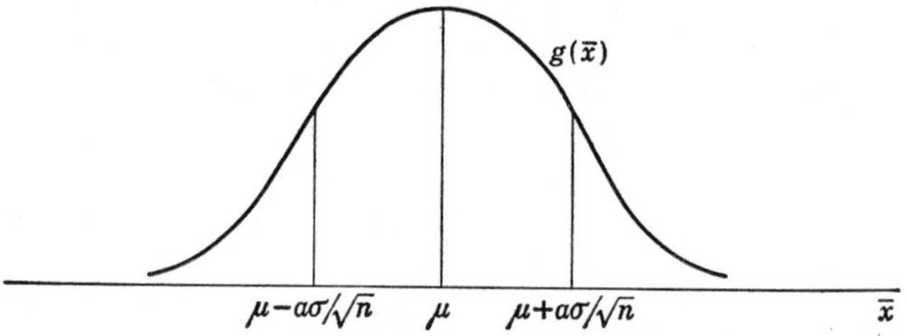

FIG. 7.2

found that the mean and variance of $\bar{\mathbf{x}}$ are μ and σ^2/n, where μ and σ^2 are the mean and variance in $f(x)$. It follows from the definition of the variance that

$$\sigma_{\bar{\mathbf{x}}}^2 = \frac{\sigma^2}{n} = \int_{-\infty}^{\infty} (\bar{x} - \mu)^2 g(\bar{x})\, d\bar{x} \tag{1}$$

Now let us break up the range of integration into three parts, as illustrated in Fig. 7.2:

$$\frac{\sigma^2}{n} = \int_{-\infty}^{\mu-(a\sigma/\sqrt{n})} (\bar{x} - \mu)^2 g(\bar{x})\, d\bar{x} + \int_{\mu-(a\sigma/\sqrt{n})}^{\mu+(a\sigma/\sqrt{n})} (\bar{x} - \mu)^2 g(\bar{x})\, d\bar{x} + \int_{\mu+(a\sigma/\sqrt{n})}^{\infty} (\bar{x} - \mu)^2 g(\bar{x})\, d\bar{x} \tag{2}$$

where a is any arbitrarily chosen positive number. We are going to obtain an inequality by changing the right-hand side of equation (2). We shall discard the second integral, and it is nonnegative so the right-hand side will not be increased. Also in the first integral we shall replace the factor $(\bar{x} - \mu)^2$ by $a^2\sigma^2/n$. This will clearly not increase the value of the integral, since in the range of integration

$$|\bar{x} - \mu| \geq \frac{a\sigma}{\sqrt{n}}$$

The same substitution will not increase the third integral. We shall have then

$$\frac{\sigma^2}{n} \geq \frac{a^2\sigma^2}{n} \int_{-\infty}^{\mu-(a\sigma/\sqrt{n})} g(\bar{x})\, d\bar{x} + \frac{a^2\sigma^2}{n} \int_{\mu+(a\sigma/\sqrt{n})}^{\infty} g(\bar{x})\, d\bar{x} \tag{3}$$

or, what is the same thing,

$$\frac{1}{a^2} \geq P\left(|\bar{\mathbf{x}} - \mu| \geq \frac{a\sigma}{\sqrt{n}}\right) \tag{4}$$

since the two integrals in (3) give exactly the probability that $\bar{\mathbf{x}}$ lies outside the interval $\mu - (a\sigma/\sqrt{n})$ to $\mu + (a\sigma/\sqrt{n})$.

Rewriting (4) completes the proof.

Now we shall consider the weak law of large numbers.

Theorem 7.4. *Let $f(x)$ be a density with mean μ and finite variance σ^2. Let $\bar{\mathbf{x}}_n$ be the mean of a random sample of size n from $f(x)$. Let ϵ and δ be two specified small numbers such that $\epsilon > 0$, $0 < \delta < 1$. If n is any integer greater than $\sigma^2/\epsilon^2\delta$, then*

$$P(-\epsilon < \bar{\mathbf{x}}_n - \mu < \epsilon) \geq 1 - \delta \tag{5}$$

Proof. In Theorem 7.3, choose the positive number a so that $1/a^2 = \delta$ or, in other words, choose a such that $a = 1/\sqrt{\delta}$. Then choose n such that $a\sigma/\sqrt{n} < \epsilon$, that is, $n > \sigma^2/\delta\epsilon^2$. Substitute these into the probability statement in Theorem 7.3, and equation (5) is verified.

To consider an example, suppose that some distribution with an unknown mean has a variance equal to 1. How large a sample must be taken in order that the probability will be at least .95 that the sample mean $\bar{\mathbf{x}}_n$ will lie within .5 of the population mean? We have $\sigma^2 = 1$, $\epsilon = .5$, $\delta = .05$. Thus

$$n > \frac{\sigma^2}{\delta\epsilon^2} = \frac{1}{.05(.5)^2} = 80$$

We have shown that, by the use of a random sample, inductive inferences to populations can be made and the reliability of the inference can be measured in terms of probability.

7.6 The Central-limit Theorem

The central-limit theorem is one of the most important theorems in statistics. It justifies the effort which we have expended in studying the normal density function. It is also one of the most remarkable theorems in the whole of mathematics.

Theorem 7.5. *Let $f(x)$ be a density with mean μ and finite variance σ^2. Let $\bar{\mathbf{x}}_n$ be the mean of a random sample of size n from $f(x)$. Let the random* *variable* $\mathbf{y}_n$ *be defined by*

$$\mathbf{y}_n = \frac{\bar{\mathbf{x}}_n - \mu}{\sigma}\sqrt{n}$$

The density of $\mathbf{y}_n$ *approaches the normal with mean* 0 *and variance* 1, *as n increases without bound.*

The astonishing thing about this theorem is the fact that nothing is said about the form of the original density function. Whatever the distribution function, provided only that it have a finite variance, the sample mean will have approximately the normal distribution for large samples. The condition that the variance be finite is not a critical restriction so far as applied statistics is concerned, because in almost any practical situation the range of the variate will be finite, in which case the variance must necessarily be finite.

The importance of this theorem, as far as practical applications are concerned, is the fact that the mean $\bar{\mathbf{x}}_n$ of a random sample from *any* distribution with finite variance σ^2 and mean μ is approximately distributed as a normal variate with mean μ and variance σ^2/n.

We shall not be able to prove this theorem, because it requires rather advanced mathematical techniques. However, in order to make the theorem plausible, we shall outline a proof for the more restricted situation in which the distribution has a moment generating function. The argument will be essentially a matter of showing that the moment generating function for the sample mean approaches the moment generating function for the normal distribution. We shall first obtain the moment generating function for

$$\mathbf{y} = \frac{\mathbf{x}' - \mu'}{\sigma'}$$

when $\mathbf{x}'$ is normally distributed. The generating function is

$$m_1(t) = \int_{-\infty}^{\infty} e^{ty} n(x'; \mu', \sigma'^2)\, dx' \tag{1}$$

$$= \int_{-\infty}^{\infty} \frac{1}{\sqrt{2\pi}\,\sigma'} e^{t(x'-\mu')/\sigma'} e^{-\frac{1}{2}(x'-\mu')^2/\sigma'^2}\, dx' \tag{2}$$

and, as in Sec. 6.2, we find

$$m_1(t) = e^{\frac{1}{2}t^2} \tag{3}$$

Now suppose that $\mathbf{x}$ has some arbitrary density $f(x)$ with mean μ and variance σ^2 which has a moment generating function. The moment generating function of $(\mathbf{x} - \mu)/\sigma$, say $m_2(t)$, is defined as

$$m_2(t) = \int_{-\infty}^{\infty} e^{t(x-\mu)/\sigma} f(x)\, dx \tag{4}$$

A sample of size n will have a mean $\mathbf{\bar{x}}$ with some distribution, say $g(\bar{x})$, which we have seen must have mean μ and variance σ^2/n. The moment generating function for

$$\mathbf{z} = \frac{\mathbf{\bar{x}} - \mu}{\sigma/\sqrt{n}} \tag{5}$$

say $m_3(t)$, is defined as

$$m_3(t) = \int_{-\infty}^{\infty} \exp\left(t\,\frac{\bar{x} - \mu}{\sigma/\sqrt{n}}\right) g(\bar{x})\,d\bar{x} \tag{6}$$

It is our purpose to show that $m_3(t)$ must approach $m_1(t)$ when n, the sample size, becomes large.

We can determine $m_3(t)$ in terms of $m_2(t)$. $m_3(t)$ is the expected value,

$$E\left[\exp\left(t\,\frac{\mathbf{\bar{x}} - \mu}{\sigma/\sqrt{n}}\right)\right] = E\left[\exp\left(\frac{t}{n}\sum\frac{\mathbf{x}_i - \mu}{\sigma/\sqrt{n}}\right)\right]$$

and since we know that the joint distribution of the $\mathbf{x}_1, \mathbf{x}_2, \cdots, \mathbf{x}_n$ is $\prod_{i=1}^{n} f(x_i)$, we may write

$$\begin{aligned} m_3(t) &= \int_{-\infty}^{\infty} \cdots \int_{-\infty}^{\infty} e^{\frac{t}{\sqrt{n}}\sum\frac{x_i-\mu}{\sigma}} \prod_{i=1}^{n} f(x_i)\,dx_i \\ &= \prod_{i=1}^{n}\left[\int_{-\infty}^{\infty} e^{\frac{t}{\sqrt{n}}\frac{x_i-\mu}{\sigma}} f(x_i)\,dx_i\right] \end{aligned} \tag{7}$$

and, by virtue of (4), each factor in this product is simply $m_2(t/\sqrt{n})$; hence

$$m_3(t) = \left[m_2\left(\frac{t}{\sqrt{n}}\right)\right]^n \tag{8}$$

The rth derivative of $m_2(t/\sqrt{n})$ evaluated at $t = 0$ obviously gives us the rth moment about the mean divided by $(\sigma\sqrt{n})^r$. We may write

$$m_2\left(\frac{t}{\sqrt{n}}\right) = 1 + \frac{\mu_1}{\sigma}\frac{t}{\sqrt{n}} + \frac{1}{2!}\frac{\mu_2}{\sigma^2}\left(\frac{t}{\sqrt{n}}\right)^2 + \frac{1}{3!}\frac{\mu_3}{\sigma^3}\left(\frac{t}{\sqrt{n}}\right)^3 + \cdots \tag{9}$$

and since $\mu_1 = 0$, $\mu_2 = \sigma^2$, this may be written

$$m_2\left(\frac{t}{\sqrt{n}}\right) = 1 + \frac{1}{n}\left(\frac{1}{2}t^2 + \frac{1}{3!\sqrt{n}}\frac{\mu_3}{\sigma^3}t^3 + \frac{1}{4!n}\frac{\mu_4}{\sigma^4}t^4 + \cdots\right) \tag{10}$$

If we recall that the definition of e^u is

$$e^u = \lim_{n\to\infty}\left(1 + \frac{u}{n}\right)^n$$

we see that $m_3(t)$, as n becomes infinite, becomes of exactly this form, where u represents the parenthesis in (10), and when n becomes infinite, all terms in u vanish except the first, so that we have

$$\lim_{n\to\infty} m_3(t) = e^{\frac{1}{2}t^2} \tag{11}$$

Hence, in the limit, **z** has the same moment generating function as **y** and, by a theorem similar to 5.7, has the same distribution. Thus for large n, we may say that the sample mean is approximately normally distributed whatever the distribution $f(x)$, provided that $f(x)$ has a moment generating function or, more generally, provided that $f(x)$ has a second moment.

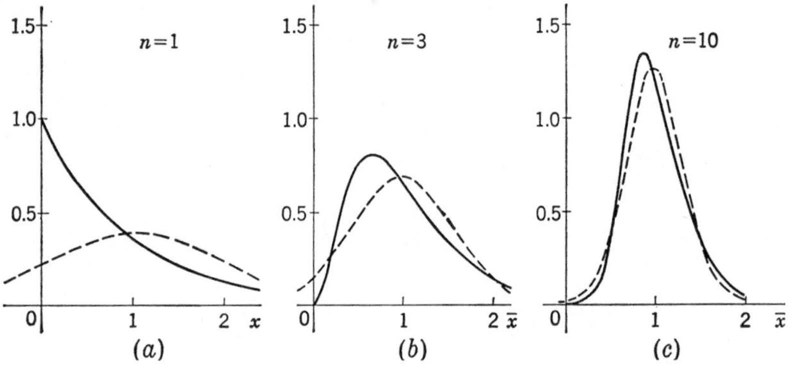

FIG. 7.3

The degree of approximation depends, of course, on the sample size and on the particular density $f(x)$. The approach to normality is illustrated in Fig. 7.3 for the particular function defined by $f(x) = e^{-x}$, $x > 0$. The solid curves give the actual distributions, while the dashed curves give the normal approximations. Figure 7.3*a* gives the original distribution which corresponds to samples of one; Fig. 7.3*b* shows the distribution of sample means for $n = 3$; Fig. 7.3*c* gives the distribution of sample means for $n = 10$. The curves rather exaggerate the approach to normality because they cannot show what happens on the tails of the distribution. Ordinarily distributions of sample means approach normality fairly rapidly with the sample size in the region of the mean, but more slowly at points distant from the mean; usually the greater the distance of a point from the mean, the more slowly the normal approximation approaches the actual distribution.

The central-limit theorem applies to discrete as well as to continuous distributions. The moment generating functions used in this section could have been moment generating functions for discrete distributions, and the argument would have been just the same except that the integrals would have been replaced by sums. We shall investigate the nature of this approximation in the next section for a particular discrete distribution.

7.7 Normal Approximation to the Binomial Distribution

We shall consider the density

$$f(x) = p^x q^{1-x} \qquad x = 0, 1 \tag{1}$$

which has

$$\mu = p \qquad \sigma^2 = pq \tag{2}$$

and suppose that a sample, $\mathbf{x}_1, \mathbf{x}_2, \cdots, \mathbf{x}_n$, of size n is drawn. The sample will simply be a sequence of 0's and 1's in this instance, 1 denoting a success, say, and 0 a failure. And

$$\bar{\mathbf{x}} = \frac{1}{n} \sum \mathbf{x}_i$$

is the proportion of successes in the sample. We have seen that the mean and variance of $\bar{\mathbf{x}}$ are

$$E(\bar{\mathbf{x}}) = \mu = p \tag{3}$$

$$\sigma_{\bar{\mathbf{x}}}^2 = \frac{\sigma^2}{n} = \frac{pq}{n} \tag{4}$$

The distribution of $\bar{\mathbf{x}}$ is discrete; in fact, $\bar{\mathbf{x}}$ can take on only the values

$$0, \frac{1}{n}, \frac{2}{n}, \cdots, \frac{j}{n}, \cdots, 1$$

and we know that the density of $\mathbf{j} = n\bar{\mathbf{x}}$ is

$$\binom{n}{j} p^j q^{n-j} \qquad j = 0, 1, 2, \cdots, n \tag{5}$$

Thus, the density of $\bar{\mathbf{x}}$ is

$$h(\bar{x}) = \binom{n}{n\bar{x}} p^{n\bar{x}} q^{n(1-\bar{x})} \qquad \bar{x} = 0, \frac{1}{n}, \frac{2}{n}, \cdots, 1 \tag{6}$$

The way in which this discrete density is approximated by a continuous density is illustrated in Fig. 7.4.

Suppose that we construct rectangles of heights $h(\bar{x})$ and widths $1/n$ with mid-points of the bases at j/n, $j = 0, 1, 2, \cdots, n$. The tops of these rectangles form a broken curve which we may represent by $g(\bar{x})$. Since $\Sigma h(\bar{x}) = 1$, the area under $g(\bar{x})$ will be $1/n$. It is clear that

$$P\left(\frac{a}{n} \le \bar{\mathbf{x}} \le \frac{b}{n}\right) = n \int_{(a-\frac{1}{2})/n}^{(b+\frac{1}{2})/n} g(\bar{x})\, d\bar{x} \tag{7}$$

for any integers a and b ($b > a$) which j can assume, since the integral is simply the area under the tops of the rectangles over the points a to b and is therefore

$$\sum_{\bar{x}=a/n}^{b/n} h(\bar{x})\,\frac{1}{n} = \frac{1}{n}\sum_{j=a}^{b}\binom{n}{j}p^j q^{n-j} \tag{8}$$

As n becomes large, the width of the rectangles decreases and the steps in $ng(\bar{x})$ become closer together so that it has the appearance, say,

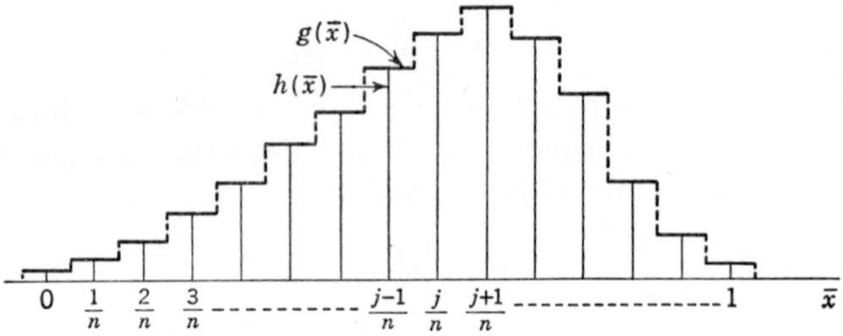

Fig. 7.4

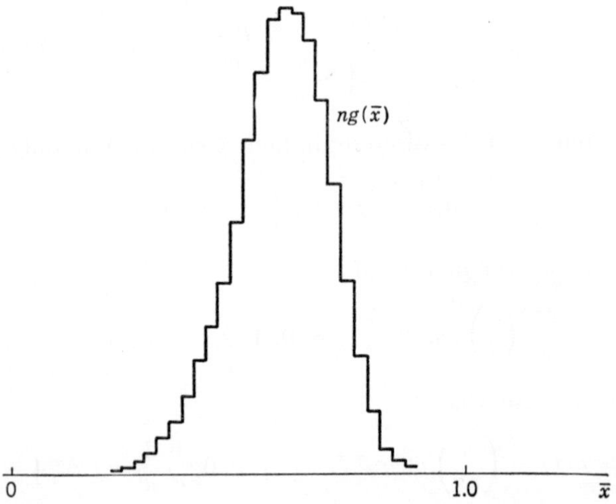

Fig. 7.5

of the function in Fig. 7.5. The normal approximation to the binomial distribution may be regarded as the limiting form of this broken curve as n becomes infinite.

This normal approximation is of particular interest because it provides a method of computing easily the approximate value of sums of the binomial distribution. As an illustration, let us suppose that a true die is cast and a one or a two counted as a success. Then $p = \frac{1}{3}$,

$q = \frac{2}{3}$. For a sample of 300 trials, the total number of successes, $\mathbf{j}$, has the density

$$f(j) = \binom{300}{j}\left(\frac{1}{3}\right)^j\left(\frac{2}{3}\right)^{300-j} \qquad j = 0, 1, \cdots, 300$$

Suppose that we wanted the probability that the number of successes will not deviate from 100 by more than 15; we should have to sum $f(j)$ over the values 85 to 115, a very tedious calculation. We can approximate the sum by using the fact that

$$P(85 \leq \mathbf{j} \leq 115) = P\left(\frac{85}{300} \leq \frac{\mathbf{j}}{300} \leq \frac{115}{300}\right)$$

and since $\bar{\mathbf{x}} = \mathbf{j}/300$ is approximately normally distributed with mean $\frac{1}{3}$ and variance $\frac{1}{3} \times \frac{2}{3} \times \frac{1}{300}$, we have

$$P(\tfrac{85}{300} \leq \bar{\mathbf{x}} \leq \tfrac{115}{300}) \cong \int_{\frac{85}{300}}^{\frac{115}{300}} n(\bar{x}; \tfrac{1}{3}, \tfrac{2}{2700})\, d\bar{x}$$
$$\cong \int_{\frac{85}{300}}^{\frac{115}{300}} \frac{1}{\sqrt{2\pi}} \frac{1}{\sqrt{\frac{2}{2700}}} \exp\left[-\frac{\frac{1}{2}(\bar{x} - \frac{1}{3})^2}{\frac{2}{2700}}\right] d\bar{x}$$

and letting $t = (\bar{\mathbf{x}} - \frac{1}{3})/\sqrt{\frac{2}{2700}}$, we have

$$P\left(\frac{85}{300} \leq \bar{\mathbf{x}} \leq \frac{115}{300}\right) \cong \int_{-1.84}^{1.84} \frac{1}{\sqrt{2\pi}} e^{-\frac{1}{2}t^2}\, dt$$

since

$$\frac{\frac{85}{300} - \frac{1}{3}}{\sqrt{\frac{2}{2700}}} \cong -1.84 \qquad \frac{\frac{115}{300} - \frac{1}{3}}{\sqrt{\frac{2}{2700}}} \cong 1.84$$

Using tables of the normal distribution, we find

$$P(85 \leq \mathbf{j} \leq 115) \cong .934 \tag{9}$$

The approximation could be slightly improved by using $85 - \frac{1}{2}$ and $115 + \frac{1}{2}$ in computing limits on the integral as indicated by (7).

In general, for the binomial distribution, it is now evident that

$$P(a \leq \mathbf{j} \leq b) = \sum_{j=a}^{b} \binom{n}{j} p^j q^{n-j} \tag{10}$$
$$\cong \int_{a'}^{b'} \frac{1}{\sqrt{2\pi}} e^{-\frac{1}{2}t^2}\, dt \tag{11}$$

where

$$a' = \frac{[(a - \frac{1}{2})/n] - p}{\sqrt{pq/n}} \qquad b' = \frac{[(b + \frac{1}{2})/n] - p}{\sqrt{pq/n}} \tag{12}$$

A more detailed investigation would show that the error in this approximation is less than

$$\frac{.15}{\sqrt{npq}} \tag{13}$$

provided that $npq > 25$. Thus in the above example our maximum error is measured by

$$\frac{.15}{\sqrt{300 \times \frac{1}{3} \times \frac{2}{3}}} = .018$$

so that the approximation (9) does not quite have two-place accuracy in so far as we can judge by (13). More accurate approximations are provided by Uspensky ("Introduction to Mathematical Probability," Chap. VII, McGraw-Hill Book Company, Inc., New York, 1937, and Ref. 5).

7.8 Role of the Normal Distribution in Statistics

It will be found in the ensuing chapters that the normal distribution plays a very predominant part. Of course, the central-limit theorem alone ensures that this will be the case, but there are other almost equally important reasons.

In the first place, many populations encountered in the course of research in many fields seem to have a normal distribution to a good degree of approximation. It has often been argued that this phenomenon is quite reasonable in view of the central-limit theorem. We may consider the firing of a shot at a target as an illustration. The course of the projectile is affected by a great many factors, all admittedly with small effect. The net deviation is the net effect of all these factors. Suppose that the effect of each factor is an observation from some population; then the total effect is essentially the mean of a set of observations from a set of populations. Being of the nature of means, the actual observed deviations might therefore be expected to be approximately normally distributed. We do not intend to imply here that most distributions encountered in practice are normal, for such is not the case at all, but nearly normal distributions are encountered quite frequently.

Another consideration which favors the normal distribution is the fact that sampling distributions based on a parent normal distribution are fairly manageable analytically. In making inferences about populations from samples, it is necessary to have the distributions for various functions of the sample observations. The mathematical problem of obtaining these distributions is often easier for samples from a normal population than from any other.

In applying statistical methods based on the normal distribution, the experimenter must know, at least approximately, the general form of the distribution function which his data follow. If it is normal, he may use the methods directly; if it is not, he may transform his data so that the transformed observations follow a normal distribution. When the experimenter does not know the form of his population distribution, then he must use other more general but usually less powerful methods of analysis called *nonparametric* methods. Some of these methods will be presented in the final chapter of the book.

7.9 Problems

1. Give an example where the target population and the sampled population are the same.

2. Give an example where the target population and the sampled population are not the same.

3. A company manufactures transistors in three different plants A, B, and C whose manufacturing methods are very similar. It is decided to inspect those transistors that are manufactured in plant A since plant A is the largest plant and statisticians are available there. In order to inspect a week's production, 100 transistors will be selected at random and tested for defects. Define the sampled population and target population.

4. In Prob. 3, it is decided to use the results in plant A to draw conclusions about plants B and C. Define the target population.

5. Let $(\mathbf{x}_1, \mathbf{x}_2)$ be a two-dimensional random variable with joint distribution $p^{x_1+x_2}q^{2-x_1-x_2}$, $x_1 = 0, 1;\ x_2 = 0, 1$.

(*a*) List the points (x_1, x_2) in the two-dimensional space that the random variable assumes.

(*b*) Let $\mathbf{x}_1 = \mathbf{y} - \mathbf{x}_2$, and list the values that the random variable $(\mathbf{y}, \mathbf{x}_2)$ can assume.

6. In Prob. 5, find the joint distribution of $\mathbf{y}$ and $\mathbf{x}_2$. Put the answer in the form of a two-way table.

7. Find the marginal distribution of $\mathbf{y}$ from the results of the above problem.

8. What is the probability that the two observations of a sample of two from a population with a rectangular distribution over the unit interval will not differ by more than $\frac{1}{2}$?

9. What is the probability that the mean of a sample of two observations from a rectangular distribution (over the unit interval) will be between $\frac{1}{4}$ and $\frac{3}{4}$?

10. Balls are drawn, with replacement, from an urn containing one white and two black balls. Let $\mathbf{x} = 0$ for a white ball and $\mathbf{x} = 1$ for a black ball. For samples $\mathbf{x}_1, \mathbf{x}_2, \cdots, \mathbf{x}_9$ of size 9, what is the joint distribution of the observations? The distribution of the sum of the observations?

11. Referring to Prob. 10, find the expected values of the sample mean $\bar{\mathbf{x}}$ and sample variance $(1/n) \sum_{i=1}^{n} (\mathbf{x}_i - \bar{\mathbf{x}})^2$.

12. For samples of size 2 from a population with variance σ^2, show that the expected value of the sample variance is $\sigma^2/2$.

13. Generalize the result of Prob. 12 to samples of size n.

14. What value of y minimizes $\sum_{1}^{n} (x_i - y)^2$?

15. If $\bar{x} = (1/n) \sum_{1}^{n} x_i$, show that

$$\sum_{1}^{n} (x_i - \mu)^2 = \sum_{1}^{n} (x_i - \bar{x})^2 + n(\bar{x} - \mu)^2$$

Use this result and that of Prob. 14 to prove that the expected value of the sample variance is not equal to the population variance.

16. Find $E(\mathbf{m}_3)$ for a random sample of size 2 from a population with a finite third moment where $\mathbf{m}_3 = (1/n) \sum_{i=1}^{n} (\mathbf{x}_i - \bar{\mathbf{x}})^3$.

17. Show that $E[(1/n)\Sigma(\mathbf{x}_i - \mu)^r] = \mu_r$ for a random sample of size n from a population with mean μ and rth moment μ_r.

18. Use Tchebysheff's inequality to find how many times a coin must be tossed in order that the probability will be at least .90 that $\bar{\mathbf{x}}$ will lie between .4 and .6. (Assume that the coin is true.)

19. How could one determine the number of tosses required in Prob. 18 more accurately, i.e., make the probability very nearly equal to .90? What is the number of tosses?

20. If a population has $\sigma = 2$ and $\bar{\mathbf{x}}$ is the mean of samples of size 100, find limits between which $\bar{\mathbf{x}} - \mu$ will lie with probability .90. Use both Tchebysheff's inequality and the central-limit theorem. Why do the two results differ?

21. Suppose that $\bar{\mathbf{x}}_1$ and $\bar{\mathbf{x}}_2$ are means of two samples of size n from a population with variance σ^2. Determine n so that the probability will be about .01 that the two sample means will differ by more than σ. (Consider the variate $\mathbf{y} = \bar{\mathbf{x}}_1 - \bar{\mathbf{x}}_2$.)

22. Suppose that light bulbs made by a standard process have an average life of 2000 hours with a standard deviation of 250 hours. And suppose that it is considered worth while to replace the process if the mean life can be increased by at least 10 per cent. An engineer wishes to test a proposed new process, and he is willing to assume that the standard deviation of the distribution of lives is about the same as for the standard process. How large a sample should he examine if he wishes the probability to be about .01 that he will fail to adopt the new process if in fact it produces bulbs with a mean life of 2250 hours?

23. A research worker wishes to estimate the mean of a population, using a sample large enough that the probability will be .95 that the sample mean will not differ from the population mean by more than 25 per cent of the standard deviation. How large a sample should he take?

24. A polling agency wishes to take a sample of voters in a given state large enough that the probability is only .01 that they will find the proportion favoring a certain candidate to be less than 50 per cent when in fact it is 52 per cent. How large a sample should be taken?

25. A standard drug is known to be effective in about 80 per cent of the cases in which it is used to treat infections. A new drug has been found effective in 85 of the first 100 cases tried. Is the superiority of the new drug well established? (If the new drug were equally effective as the old, what would be the probability of obtaining 85 or more successes in a sample of 100?)

26. A bowl contains five chips numbered from one to five. A sample of two drawn without replacement from this finite population is said to be random if all possible pairs of the five chips have an equal chance to be drawn. What is the expected value of the sample mean? What is the variance of the sample mean?

27. Suppose that the two chips of Prob. 26 were drawn with replacement, what would be the variance of the sample mean? Why might one guess that this variance would be larger than the one obtained before?

28. If a density $f(x)$ has a moment generating function $m(t)$, show that the mean of a random sample of size n has the moment generating function $[m(t/n)]^n$.

29. Use the result of Prob. 28 to show that the mean and variance of the sample mean are μ and σ^2/n.

30. Find the third moment about the mean of the sample mean for samples of size n from a binomial population. Show that it approaches zero as n becomes large (as it must if the normal approximation is to be valid).

31. Suppose that the life of a certain part of a machine is distributed by $.01e^{-.01t}$, where t is measured in days. The machine comes supplied with one spare. What is the density of the combined life of the part and its spare?

32. Generalize Prob. 26, considering N chips and samples of size n. The variance of the sample mean is

$$\frac{\sigma^2}{n}\frac{N-n}{N-1}$$

where σ^2 is the population variance,

$$\sigma^2 = \frac{1}{N}\sum_{i=1}^{N}\left(i - \frac{N+1}{2}\right)^2$$

7.10 Bibliography

1. Bross, I. D. J.: "Design for Decision," The Macmillan Company, New York, 1953.
2. Brunk, H.: "An Introduction to Mathematical Statistics," Ginn & Company, Boston, 1960.
3. Cochran, W.: "Sampling Techniques," John Wiley & Sons, Inc., New York, 1953.
4. Dixon, W. J., and F. J. Massey, Jr.: "Introduction to Statistical Analysis," McGraw-Hill Book Company, Inc., New York, 1957.
5. Feller, W.: "An Introduction to Probability Theory and Its Applications," 2d ed., Vol. I, John Wiley & Sons, Inc., New York, 1957.
6. Fraser, D. A. S.: "Statistics—An Introduction," John Wiley & Sons, Inc., New York, 1958.
7. Hogg, R., and A. Craig: "Introduction to Mathematical Statistics," The Macmillan Company, New York, 1959.
8. Neyman, J.: "First Course in Probability and Statistics," Holt, Rinehart and Winston, New York, 1950.
9. Wallis, W. A., and H. V. Roberts: "Statistics—A New Approach," Free Press, Glencoe, Ill., 1956.
10. Wilks, S. S.: "Elementary Statistical Analysis," Princeton University Press, Princeton, N.J., 1948.
11. Youden, W. J.: "Statistical Methods for Chemists," John Wiley & Sons, Inc., New York, 1951.

8

Point Estimation

8.1 Decision Theory

In this chapter we shall discuss one of the important problems in statistics, point estimation, but first we shall discuss the general decision problem. Suppose that a statistician or scientist must select an action from a certain number of available actions. Suppose also that the appropriate action depends upon an unknown parameter θ which determines the density $f(x; \theta)$ of the population to be sampled. If θ were known, the density function would be known and so would the appropriate action.

The method to be used is to select a random sample $\mathbf{x}_1, \mathbf{x}_2, \cdots, \mathbf{x}_n$ from $f(x; \theta)$ and to decide on an action on the basis of the sample values. The procedure is as follows:

1. Define the set of *all* possible values that θ can assume in the problem. This space of all values of θ is the parameter space and is denoted by Ω. (In this book Ω will be either an interval or a finite number of points.)

2. Define the set of *all* possible actions which can be taken in the particular problem. This set is called the *action* space (or decision space) and is denoted by A. These actions are sometimes referred to as *terminal actions.*

3. Select a function d of the random sample; i.e., let

$$\mathbf{a} = d(\mathbf{x}_1, \mathbf{x}_2, \cdots, \mathbf{x}_n)$$

where $\mathbf{a}$ is in the action space A. That is to say, we plan or decide to take the action a, where $a = d(x_1, x_2, \cdots, x_n)$, if we observe $x_1, x_2, \cdots, x_n$. The function d is called a *decision function* or strategy. Before proceeding we shall give some examples to help explain these ideas.

Example 8.1. Let $f(x; \theta)$ be a normal density with mean μ and variance 1. Hence θ is the parameter μ. Now suppose that we assume that μ can be any real number. Then Ω, the parameter space, is the real line; that is, $\Omega = \{\mu: -\infty < \mu < \infty\}$. Suppose that there is a distinct action for each μ. Then we can represent an action by an *estimate* $\hat{\mu}$ of μ and the action space A is also the real line. This is denoted by $A = \{\hat{\mu}: -\infty < \hat{\mu} < \infty\}$. For the decision function, suppose that we use d_1, which assigns $\hat{\boldsymbol{\mu}} = \bar{\mathbf{x}}$. This means that a random sample

$\mathbf{x}_1, \mathbf{x}_2, \cdots, \mathbf{x}_n$ is selected from a normal distribution and the action $\hat{\mathbf{u}} = \bar{\mathbf{x}} = d_1(\mathbf{x}_1, \mathbf{x}_2, \cdots, \mathbf{x}_n)$ is taken as the estimate of μ. Other decision functions could be used. For example, one could use d_2, defined by $d_2(\mathbf{x}_1, \mathbf{x}_2, \cdots, \mathbf{x}_n) = \sum_{i=1}^{n} \mathbf{x}_i^2$, or d_3 defined by $d_3(\mathbf{x}_1, \mathbf{x}_2, \cdots, \mathbf{x}_n) = \sum_{i=1}^{n} \mathbf{x}_i^5$, or many other functions. Of course we want to use a decision function which gives "good" estimates. This will be discussed later. These types of decision problems are called point-estimation problems and will be discussed in detail later in this chapter.

Example 8.2. Let $f(x; \mu)$ be the normal density with mean μ and variance 1. Suppose that we want to take one of two possible actions: action 1, call it a_1, will be the statement that $\mu < 0$; action 2, call it a_2, will be the statement that $\mu \geq 0$. Now the parameter space is the same as in Example 8.1; that is, $\Omega = \{\mu: -\infty < \mu < \infty\}$, but the action space A consists of only two elements: $A = \{a: a = a_1, a_2\}$. Now suppose that our decision function d is such that action a_1 is taken, for example, if $\bar{\mathbf{x}} < 0$ and that action a_2 is taken if $\bar{\mathbf{x}} \geq 0$. Thus a random sample $\mathbf{x}_1, \mathbf{x}_2, \cdots, \mathbf{x}_n$ is observed, $\bar{\mathbf{x}}$ computed, and the statement $\mu < 0$ made if $\bar{\mathbf{x}} < 0$, and the statement $\mu \geq 0$ made if $\bar{\mathbf{x}} \geq 0$. Again we remark that other decision functions could be used. We shall discuss criteria for "good" decision functions for this problem later. These types of decision problems are called testing hypotheses and will be discussed in Chap. 12.

Example 8.3. A seed manufacturer has a storage bin full of seeds of a certain variety of flowers. He knows that every seed will not grow when planted, and so he wants to get an estimate as to what fraction will germinate. He conducts an experiment, in which 1000 seeds are selected at random from the storage bin. He puts them in a germination oven, and on the basis of the outcome of this experiment he will make a decision as to the value of p, the fraction of the population (seeds in the bin) that will germinate. Now the parameter space is $\Omega = \{p: 0 \leq p \leq 1\}$. The action space is $A = \{\hat{p}: 0 \leq \hat{p} \leq 1\}$, where $\hat{p}$ is the estimate of p. Let $f(x; p) = p^x(1-p)^{1-x}$, $x = 0, 1$, be the density of the population of seeds. Let $\mathbf{x}_1, \mathbf{x}_2, \cdots, \mathbf{x}_{1000}$ be a random sample of size 1000 from this density, so that $\mathbf{x}_i = 1$ if the ith seed germinates. A decision function which we could use in this problem is defined by $\hat{\mathbf{p}} = \bar{\mathbf{x}} =$ the fraction of the 1000 seeds that germinate.

Since in every problem there are actually many different functions which could be used as the decision function, we need to develop some theory that will enable us to evaluate decision functions and to select good ones. To evaluate a decision function, it is necessary first to evaluate the consequences of the terminal actions. To do this we introduce a *loss function* denoted by $l(a; \theta)$. This is a real-valued nonnegative function which reflects the loss in taking action a when θ is the parameter. This loss is zero when a is the best action for θ. For a statistical problem where θ is not known, we do not know the best action. Instead we apply a strategy d which yields the action

$$\mathbf{a} = d(\mathbf{x}_1, \mathbf{x}_2, \cdots, \mathbf{x}_n)$$

and the corresponding loss $l(\mathbf{a}; \theta) = l[d(\mathbf{x}_1, \mathbf{x}_2, \cdots, \mathbf{x}_n); \theta]$ which depends on the sample values; i.e., even though the functions l and d are prescribed, the actual loss depends on the particular observations $\mathbf{x}_i$ obtained in the random sample. Because the loss is random, we shall define the *risk* which is the expected value of the loss function. The risk for the decision function d when the parameter is θ is denoted by $R(d; \theta)$ and depends on the decision function d, the loss function l, and the value of the parameter θ. It does not depend on the particular random sample which is chosen. Hence we have

$$\begin{aligned} R(d; \theta) &= E[l(\mathbf{a}; \theta)] \\ &= \int_{-\infty}^{\infty} \int_{-\infty}^{\infty} \cdots \int_{-\infty}^{\infty} l[d(x_1, x_2, \cdots, x_n); \theta] f(x_1; \theta) f(x_2; \theta) \\ &\qquad \cdots f(x_n; \theta)\, dx_1 \cdots dx_n \end{aligned}$$

Then a "good" decision function is one that will in some fashion minimize the risk for every value of θ in the parameter space Ω.

One of the difficulties in using decision theory in applied problems is that of specifying a realistic loss function. It is impossible, for instance, to specify accurately the loss incurred in making an erroneous decision in asserting a scientific hypothesis or in failing to recommend a new variety of wheat when it is really superior to one which is currently being planted. In some gambling problems the loss function could reflect actual numerical loss, but even then it is questionable whether the mathematical expectation of loss is an appropriate measure of the random losses when the statistical problem is faced only once. These difficulties may be partially resolved as follows: First, experience with statistical problems shows that "good" procedures are insensitive to small changes in the loss function, especially when considerable data are available. Thus precise values of the loss are not absolutely necessary. Second, one can measure the random loss by taking expectation just so long as these losses are themselves measured in terms of a *utility function*. The reader is referred to the bibliography for a discussion of this concept.

The types of problems which we shall discuss are the following, where

$f(x; \theta)$ is a density with parameter θ (the symbol θ may represent more than one parameter):

1. Point estimation of θ: to be presented in this chapter
2. Testing hypotheses about θ: to be presented in Chap. 12

Next we shall give some examples of loss functions and risk functions for some particular problems; then we shall put these concepts into formal definitions.

Example 8.4. Consider the density given in Example 8.1. We desire an estimate for the mean μ. Suppose that the loss function for this particular problem is given by

$$l(a; \mu) = (a - \mu)^2$$

If we use the decision function d defined by $\mathbf{a} = \bar{\mathbf{x}} = d(\mathbf{x}_1, \mathbf{x}_2, \cdots, \mathbf{x}_n)$, then the loss is given by

$$l(\bar{\mathbf{x}}; \mu) = (\bar{\mathbf{x}} - \mu)^2$$

In this case the risk is $R(d; \mu) = E[(\bar{\mathbf{x}} - \mu)^2] = 1/n$. Other loss functions which could be appropriate are

$$l(a; \mu) = |a - \mu|$$

or

$$l(a; \mu) = (a - \mu)^4$$

or many others.

Example 8.5. Let $\mathbf{x}$ be distributed $n(x; 0, \sigma^2)$, where σ^2 can take on any value greater than 0; that is, $\Omega = \{\sigma^2 : \sigma^2 > 0\}$. Suppose that we want to find an estimate of σ^2. Then the action space A is $A = \{\hat{\sigma}^2 : \hat{\sigma}^2 > 0\}$. Suppose that $\mathbf{x}_1, \mathbf{x}_2, \cdots, \mathbf{x}_n$ is a random sample from $n(x; 0, \sigma^2)$ and the decision function defined by $\hat{\boldsymbol{\sigma}}^2 = \dfrac{1}{n-1} \Sigma(\mathbf{x}_i - \bar{\mathbf{x}})^2$ is used. A typical loss function could be $l(\hat{\sigma}^2; \sigma^2) = (\hat{\sigma}^2 - \sigma^2)^2$, or we could use $(\log \hat{\sigma}^2/\sigma^2)^2$, or many others.

Later we shall exhibit a reasonable loss function for many point-estimation problems, but now we shall formalize the definitions of loss and risk functions.

Definition 8.1. Loss Functions. *Let θ be a parameter which can take values in the parameter space Ω. Let a be a terminal action which can take values in the action space A. Then l is a loss function if it is a real-valued function of a and θ which satisfies the two conditions:*

(*a*) $l(a; \theta) \geq 0$ *for all a in A and all θ in Ω.*

(*b*) *For each θ in Ω there is at least one a in A for which* $l(a; \theta) = 0$.

These values of a for which the loss is 0 are called the correct decision or action when the parameter is θ. These two conditions state that the loss function must be nonnegative, and the loss is equal to 0 if the correct decision is made.

Definition 8.2. Risk Function. *The risk function (sometimes referred to simply as "the risk") for the decision function d and loss function l is*

$$\begin{aligned} R(d; \theta) &= E[l(\mathbf{a}; \theta)] \\ &= \int_{-\infty}^{\infty} \int_{-\infty}^{\infty} \cdots \int_{-\infty}^{\infty} l[d(x_1, x_2, \cdots, x_n); \theta] f(x_1; \theta) \\ &\qquad \cdots f(x_n; \theta)\, dx_1, \cdots dx_n \end{aligned}$$

if $\mathbf{a} = d(\mathbf{x}_1, \mathbf{x}_2, \cdots, \mathbf{x}_n)$ *is the action resulting from applying the strategy d to a random sample* $\mathbf{x}_1, \mathbf{x}_2, \cdots, \mathbf{x}_n$ *from the population with density* $f(x; \theta)$.

Of course the risk depends on the decision function d which we choose for the problem, on the loss function l, and on the unknown parameter θ.

8.2 Point Estimation

If the action labeled $\hat{\theta}$ consists of acting as though $\hat{\theta}$ were θ, then $l(\hat{\theta}; \theta) = 0$ for $\hat{\theta} = \theta$. Suppose that we are given a loss function l such that $l(\hat{\theta}; \theta) = 0$ if and only if $\hat{\theta} = \theta$. Then this loss function specifies a *point-estimation* problem. The decision function d, where

$$\hat{\boldsymbol{\theta}} = d(\mathbf{x}_1, \mathbf{x}_2, \cdots, \mathbf{x}_n)$$

is then called an *estimator* of θ. The statistician is interested in finding an estimator with relatively small risk. In many decision-making problems, a good argument can be presented for using a loss function of the form

$$l(\hat{\theta}; \theta) = c(\theta)(\hat{\theta} - \theta)^2 \tag{1}$$

where $c(\theta) > 0$ for all values of θ. This function implies that the loss increases, the further that $\hat{\theta}$ is from the true value θ. It may be quite difficult to find a $c(\theta)$ which will make this loss realistic, but $c(\theta)$ plays a minor role in determining the relative merit of two decision functions.

Essentially, a major argument in favor of a loss function of the form (1) is that many reasonably smooth functions of $\hat{\theta}$ which assume a minimum value of 0 at $\hat{\theta} = \theta$ can be approximated by quadratic functions for $\hat{\theta}$ close to θ. Experience has indicated that a loss function of the form given in (1) is not unrealistic for many applied problems. Throughout the rest of this chapter we shall assume a loss function of this form or with $c(\theta) = 1$, in which case (1) is called a squared-error loss function.

The problem that we face now is finding a suitable decision function d of the observed random sample $\mathbf{x}_1, \mathbf{x}_2, \cdots, \mathbf{x}_n$ from the density $f(x; \theta)$, which will minimize the risk function

$$R(d; \theta) = E[c(\theta)(\hat{\boldsymbol{\theta}} - \theta)^2] = c(\theta)E[(\hat{\boldsymbol{\theta}} - \theta)^2] \tag{2}$$

For the remainder of this chapter we shall use the term "estimators" instead of decision functions and the word "estimate" in place of "action." If θ is the parameter being estimated, we shall use the symbol $\hat{\boldsymbol{\theta}}$ to represent the estimate (action). However, when there is no chance for ambiguity, we shall also call $\hat{\boldsymbol{\theta}}$ an estimator. When we call $\hat{\boldsymbol{\theta}}$ an estimator, we shall mean the decision function d such that $\hat{\boldsymbol{\theta}} = d(\mathbf{x}_1, \cdots, \mathbf{x}_n)$.

Suppose that we want to choose between two estimators

$$\hat{\boldsymbol{\theta}}_1 = d_1(\mathbf{x}_1, \mathbf{x}_2, \cdots, \mathbf{x}_n)$$

and $\hat{\boldsymbol{\theta}}_2 = d_2(\mathbf{x}_1, \mathbf{x}_2, \cdots, \mathbf{x}_n)$. We want to know how $R(d_1; \theta)$ compares with $R(d_2; \theta)$ for specified values of θ. If

$$R(d_1; \theta) > R(d_2; \theta)$$

we can also write

$$E[l(\hat{\boldsymbol{\theta}}_1; \theta)] > E[l(\hat{\boldsymbol{\theta}}_2; \theta)]$$

If we use the loss function in (1), this gives us

$$c(\theta)E[(\hat{\boldsymbol{\theta}}_1 - \theta)^2] > c(\theta)E[(\hat{\boldsymbol{\theta}}_2 - \theta)^2]$$

or, since $c(\theta)$ is positive, this reduces to

$$E[(\hat{\boldsymbol{\theta}}_1 - \hat{\theta})^2] > E[(\hat{\boldsymbol{\theta}}_2 - \theta)^2]$$

We have thus shown that, if a loss function of the form (1) is used, $\hat{\boldsymbol{\theta}}_1$ has larger risk than $\hat{\boldsymbol{\theta}}_2$ if and only if $E[(\hat{\boldsymbol{\theta}}_1 - \theta)^2] > E[(\hat{\boldsymbol{\theta}}_2 - \theta)^2]$. To compare *two* estimators $\hat{\boldsymbol{\theta}}_1 = d_1(\mathbf{x}_1, \mathbf{x}_2, \cdots, \mathbf{x}_n)$ and

$$\hat{\boldsymbol{\theta}}_2 = d_2(\mathbf{x}_1, \mathbf{x}_2, \cdots, \mathbf{x}_n)$$

when the loss function is of the form given in (1), the quantity *relative efficiency* of $\hat{\boldsymbol{\theta}}_1$ to $\hat{\boldsymbol{\theta}}_2$, or more accurately of d_1 to d_2, is equal to

$$r(d_1, d_2) = \frac{R(d_2; \theta)}{R(d_1; \theta)}$$

If $r(d_1, d_2)$ is greater than 1 (for certain values of θ, say θ in a region C), then $\hat{\boldsymbol{\theta}}_1$ might reasonably be regarded as a "better" estimator than $\hat{\boldsymbol{\theta}}_2$ (for θ in C). In summary, if the loss function which we employ is of the form given in (1), then the problem of finding an estimator with minimum risk is equivalent to the problem of finding an estimator $\hat{\boldsymbol{\theta}}$ which minimizes the quantity $E[(\hat{\boldsymbol{\theta}} - \theta)^2]$, which is called *mean-squared error*.

Unfortunately, for most densities $f(x; \theta)$ there does *not* exist an estimator which minimizes the mean-squared error for all values of θ, but one estimator may produce a minimum mean-squared error for some values of θ and another estimator may produce a minimum mean-squared error for other values of θ. Since θ is unknown, this situation complicates the problem. That is to say, except in trivial cases, there is no estimator whose mean-squared error is a minimum for all values of θ in Ω. Therefore, it seems as if we must settle for some arbitrariness in our search for minimum-risk estimators. We shall, however, use mean-squared error as our guide. For instance, if $\hat{\boldsymbol{\theta}}_1$, $\hat{\boldsymbol{\theta}}_2$, $\hat{\boldsymbol{\theta}}_3$ are different estimators of θ with densities $g_1(\hat{\theta}; \theta)$, $g_2(\hat{\theta}; \theta)$, $g_3(\hat{\theta}; \theta)$, as illustrated in Fig. 8.1, then, roughly speaking, it appears that $\hat{\boldsymbol{\theta}}_2$ is a "better" estimator than $\hat{\boldsymbol{\theta}}_1$ or $\hat{\boldsymbol{\theta}}_3$, and $\hat{\boldsymbol{\theta}}_3$ is "better" than $\hat{\boldsymbol{\theta}}_1$.

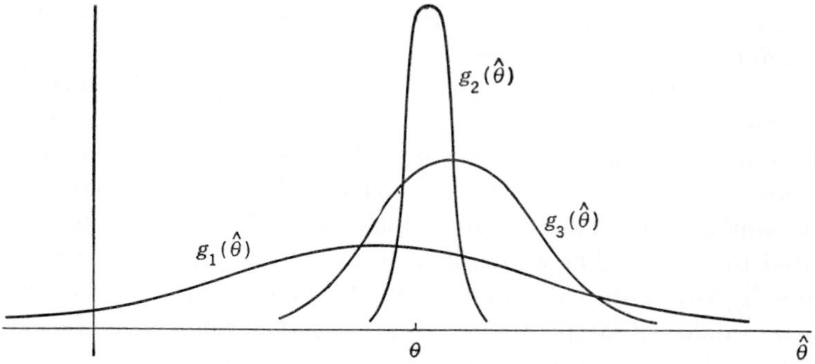

FIG. 8.1

Criteria other than minimum mean-squared error which seem to be valuable for estimators to possess are listed below. We shall examine each of them to show in what manner they are useful. In an applied problem an estimator with minimum mean-squared error for all values of θ is not likely to exist, so that the experimenter should select estimators that possess properties from the list below which seem desirable in his particular situation.

List of Properties for an Estimator

1. Unbiased
2. Consistent (simple consistency and squared-error consistency)
3. Asymptotically efficient and BAN (best asymptotically normal)
4. Minimum variance unbiased

These will be discussed in turn but first we shall discuss an important property of density functions, *sufficiency*.

8.3 Sufficient Statistics; Single-parameter Case

In this section we shall consider a density $f(x; \theta)$ with a single parameter θ, where θ is in the set Ω, and, on the basis of a random sample of n values $\mathbf{x}_1, \mathbf{x}_2, \cdots, \mathbf{x}_n$, a statistic $\hat{\boldsymbol{\theta}} = d(\mathbf{x}_1, \mathbf{x}_2, \cdots, \mathbf{x}_n)$ is used as an estimator of θ. Now $\hat{\boldsymbol{\theta}}$ is a random variable, and since we started with n random variables $\mathbf{x}_1, \mathbf{x}_2, \cdots, \mathbf{x}_n$ and condensed by the use of $d(\mathbf{x}_1, \cdots, \mathbf{x}_n)$ to a *single* random variable $\hat{\boldsymbol{\theta}}$, we shall be interested in seeing if we lost any "information" by this condensing process. For example, a possible choice of $d(\mathbf{x}_1, \cdots, \mathbf{x}_n)$ is $\mathbf{x}_1$, and so we would have $\hat{\boldsymbol{\theta}} = \mathbf{x}_1$. In this case it seems apparent that all the "information" in the sample has not been utilized.

In many cases, knowing only the statistic $\hat{\boldsymbol{\theta}}$ may give all the "information" about the parameter θ that the sample contains. If this is the case, we prefer to work with $\hat{\boldsymbol{\theta}}$ rather than the n random variables $\mathbf{x}_1, \mathbf{x}_2, \cdots, \mathbf{x}_n$ for the simple reason that one random variable is easier to manage than n random variables are. We must examine what we mean by a statistic $\hat{\boldsymbol{\theta}}$ containing all the "information" about a parameter that is in the n sample values.

The only "information" about θ in the density $f(x; \theta)$ is contained in the sample values $\mathbf{x}_1, \mathbf{x}_2, \cdots, \mathbf{x}_n$. We can obtain no information about θ by sampling from a density $g(x)$ which does not contain θ or parameters related to θ. In other words, if we want to find the average height of people in New York City, we would *not* sample fish from Lake Ontario, and we would *not* sample from a table of random numbers and expect to get the desired information.

In case a statistic $\hat{\boldsymbol{\theta}}$ does exist which contains all the "information" about θ that is in the sample, we call $\hat{\boldsymbol{\theta}}$ a sufficient statistic. Now we shall formalize the definition.

Definition 8.3 Sufficient Statistic. *Let $\mathbf{x}_1, \mathbf{x}_2, \cdots, \mathbf{x}_n$ be a random sample from the density $f(x; \theta)$, and let $\hat{\boldsymbol{\theta}} = d(\mathbf{x}_1, \cdots, \mathbf{x}_n)$ be a statistic (function of the $\mathbf{x}_i$ only). Let $\boldsymbol{\theta}^* = d^*(\mathbf{x}_1, \cdots, \mathbf{x}_n)$ be any other statistic which is not a function of $\hat{\boldsymbol{\theta}}$. If, for each of the statistics $\boldsymbol{\theta}^*$, the conditional density of $\boldsymbol{\theta}^*$, given $\hat{\boldsymbol{\theta}}$, does not involve θ, then $\hat{\boldsymbol{\theta}}$ is called a sufficient statistic for θ; that is, if $p(\theta^*|\hat{\theta})$ does not contain θ, then $\hat{\boldsymbol{\theta}}$ is a sufficient statistic for θ.*

Let $\hat{\boldsymbol{\theta}}_1$ be any statistic which is not a function of the sufficient statistic $\hat{\boldsymbol{\theta}}$. Then, by the definition of a sufficient statistic, the conditional distribution of $\hat{\boldsymbol{\theta}}_1$, given $\hat{\boldsymbol{\theta}}$, does not involve θ. Hence $\hat{\boldsymbol{\theta}}_1$ can give us no information about θ that the sufficient statistic has not already given us. The concept of a sufficient statistic was first discussed in a series of papers by R. A. Fisher.

In many cases, a relatively easy criterion for examining a statistic $\hat{\boldsymbol{\theta}}$ for sufficiency has been developed by J. Neyman. This is given in the next theorem, the proof of which is omitted.

Theorem 8.1. *Let $\mathbf{x}_1, \mathbf{x}_2, \cdots, \mathbf{x}_n$ be a random sample of size n from the density $f(x; \theta)$, $a < x < b$, where a and b do not involve θ, and let the joint density of these n random variables be*

$$g(x_1, x_2, \cdots, x_n; \theta) = f(x_1; \theta)f(x_2; \theta) \cdots f(x_n; \theta)$$

If this density factors as

$$g(x_1, x_2, \cdots, x_n; \theta) = h(\hat{\theta}; \theta)k(x_1, x_2, \cdots, x_n)$$

where $k(x_1, x_2, \cdots, x_n)$ *does not involve the parameter* θ, *then* $\hat{\boldsymbol{\theta}}$ *is a sufficient statistic for* θ.

This theorem gives us a relatively easy method for judging whether a certain statistic is sufficient. It will be noticed that we have refrained from using the word sufficient estimator but have used the term sufficient statistic. As we noted before, we are attempting only to reduce n random variables to one random variable for ease of handling; however, since we have shown that all the information that is in the sample is in the sufficient statistic, it seems plausible that we might want to use some function of the sufficient statistic for the estimator of θ. We might then wonder, if we use some function of the sufficient statistic as an estimator, whether this function still contains all the "information" that is in the sample. The answer is given without proof in the following theorem:

Theorem 8.2. *Let* $\hat{\boldsymbol{\theta}} = d(\mathbf{x}_1, \mathbf{x}_2, \cdots, \mathbf{x}_n)$ *be a sufficient statistic for* θ *from a random sample of size* n *in the density* $f(x; \theta)$. *If* u *is a function of* θ *with a single-valued inverse, then* $\tilde{\boldsymbol{\theta}} = u(\hat{\boldsymbol{\theta}})$ *is also a sufficient statistic for* θ, *and* $\hat{\boldsymbol{\theta}}$ *is a sufficient statistic for* $u(\theta)$.

Now we shall give some examples to illustrate these theorems and definitions.

Example 8.6. Let $\mathbf{x}_1, \mathbf{x}_2, \cdots, \mathbf{x}_n$ be a random sample from the normal distribution $n(x; \mu, 1)$, $-\infty < x < \infty$. The joint density of $\mathbf{x}_1, \mathbf{x}_2, \cdots, \mathbf{x}_n$ is given by

$$\begin{aligned} g(x_1, x_2, \cdots, x_n; \mu) &= n(x_1; \mu, 1) \cdot n(x_2; \mu, 1) \cdots n(x_n; \mu, 1) \\ &= \frac{1}{(2\pi)^{\frac{1}{2}}} e^{-\frac{1}{2}(x_1-\mu)^2} \cdot \frac{1}{(2\pi)^{\frac{1}{2}}} e^{-\frac{1}{2}(x_2-\mu)^2} \cdots \frac{1}{(2\pi)^{\frac{1}{2}}} e^{-\frac{1}{2}(x_n-\mu)^2} \\ &= \frac{1}{(2\pi)^{n/2}} e^{-\frac{1}{2}\sum_{i=1}^{n}(x_i-\mu)^2} \qquad (1) \end{aligned}$$

But

$$\begin{aligned} \Sigma(x_i - \mu)^2 &= \Sigma[(x_i - \bar{x}) - (\mu - \bar{x})]^2 \\ &= \Sigma(x_i - \bar{x})^2 + \Sigma(\bar{x} - \mu)^2 \\ &= \Sigma(x_i - \bar{x})^2 + n(\bar{x} - \mu)^2 \end{aligned}$$

Substituting into (1) gives

$$g(x_1, x_2, \cdots, x_n; \mu) = \frac{1}{(2\pi)^{n/2}} \exp\left[-\tfrac{1}{2} n(\bar{x} - \mu)^2\right] \cdot \exp\left[-\tfrac{1}{2} \sum (x_i - \bar{x})^2\right]$$

If we let $\hat{\boldsymbol{\theta}} = \bar{\mathbf{x}}$, we can use Theorem 8.1, and it follows that $\bar{\mathbf{x}}$ is a sufficient statistic for μ. Now, by Theorem 8.2, each of the quantities

$\bar{\mathbf{x}} + 8$, $6\bar{\mathbf{x}}$, $n\bar{\mathbf{x}}$, $\Sigma(\mathbf{x}_i - 4)$, etc., is also a sufficient statistic for μ; and $\bar{\mathbf{x}}$ is a sufficient statistic for 16μ, $3\mu + 5$, etc.

Example 8.7. Let $\mathbf{x}_1, \mathbf{x}_2, \cdots, \mathbf{x}_n$ be a random sample from $n(x; 0, \sigma^2)$. The joint density is

$$g(x_1, x_2, \cdots, x_n; \sigma^2) = \frac{1}{(2\pi\sigma^2)^{n/2}} e^{-\frac{1}{2\sigma^2}\sum x_i^2}$$

If we let

$$h(\hat{\sigma}^2; \sigma^2) = \frac{1}{(2\pi\sigma^2)^{n/2}} e^{-\frac{\hat{\sigma}^2}{2\sigma^2}}$$

and $k(x_1, x_2, \cdots, x_n) = 1$, then, by Theorem 8.1, the statistic $\hat{\boldsymbol{\sigma}}^2 = \Sigma\mathbf{x}_i^2$ is a sufficient statistic for σ^2. Now, by Theorem 8.2, each of the quantities $\Sigma\mathbf{x}_i^2/n$, $\Sigma\mathbf{x}_i^2 + 8$, $1/(2 + \Sigma\mathbf{x}_i^2)$, etc., is also a sufficient statistic for σ^2, and $\hat{\boldsymbol{\sigma}}^2$ is a sufficient statistic for $3\sigma^2$, $\sigma^2 + 18$, etc.

8.4 Sufficient Statistics; More than One Parameter

In this section we shall assume that $f(x; \theta_1, \theta_2, \cdots, \theta_k)$ is a density with k unknown parameters, and let $\mathbf{x}_1, \mathbf{x}_2, \cdots, \mathbf{x}_n$ be a random sample of size n. Again we are interested in condensing the n random variables to fewer than n statistics. However, in this case the density contains k unknown parameters, and we may not be able to condense the n random variables into a *single* statistic and retain all the "information." However, we may be able to condense to m statistics, where $m < n$, without losing "information." These will be called a *set* of sufficient statistics, and the definition is given below.

Definition 8.4. Sufficient Statistics; Multiparameter Case. *Let* $\mathbf{x}_1, \mathbf{x}_2, \cdots, \mathbf{x}_n$ *be a random sample of size n from the density*

$$f(x; \theta_1, \theta_2, \cdots, \theta_k)$$

Let $\hat{\boldsymbol{\theta}}_1 = d_1(\mathbf{x}_1, \mathbf{x}_2, \cdots, \mathbf{x}_n)$,

$$\hat{\boldsymbol{\theta}}_2 = d_2(\mathbf{x}_1, \mathbf{x}_2, \cdots, \mathbf{x}_n), \cdots, \hat{\boldsymbol{\theta}}_m = d_m(\mathbf{x}_1, \mathbf{x}_2, \cdots, \mathbf{x}_n)$$

be m statistics. If the conditional distribution of $\mathbf{x}_1, \mathbf{x}_2, \cdots, \mathbf{x}_n$, *given* $\hat{\boldsymbol{\theta}}_1, \hat{\boldsymbol{\theta}}_2, \cdots, \hat{\boldsymbol{\theta}}_m$, is independent of $\theta_1, \theta_2, \cdots, \theta_k$, *then* $\hat{\boldsymbol{\theta}}_1, \hat{\boldsymbol{\theta}}_2, \cdots, \hat{\boldsymbol{\theta}}_m$ *is a set of m sufficient statistics for the parameters* $\theta_1, \cdots, \theta_k$.

The integer m can be less than, greater than, or equal to k; that is, the number of sufficient statistics in a set of sufficient statistics may be less than, greater than, or equal to the number of parameters in the density function. In general, in this book we shall study densities where $m = k$. Notice that there always exists a set of n sufficient statistics since, by Theorem 8.3, which will be stated below, the n sample random variables

$\mathbf{x}_1, \mathbf{x}_2, \cdots, \mathbf{x}_n$ is a sufficient set. In fact, in any density there will exist many sets of sufficient statistics, but we are interested in a "smallest" set in the sense that this set is a function of all other sets of sufficient statistics and is called a *minimal set* of sufficient statistics.

As in the one-parameter case, we have a criterion in the multiparameter case to aid in testing a set of statistics for sufficiency. The proof will not be given.

Theorem 8.3. *Let $f(x; \theta_1, \cdots, \theta_k)$, $a < x < b$, be a density, where a and b do not involve the θ's. If the joint density of a random sample from this distribution can be factored as*

$$g(x_1, \cdots, x_n; \theta_1, \theta_2, \cdots, \theta_k) = h(\hat{\theta}_1, \cdots, \hat{\theta}_m; \theta_1, \cdots, \theta_k)q(x_1, \cdots, x_n)$$

where $q(x_1, \cdots, x_n)$ does not contain the θ_i, then $\hat{\boldsymbol{\theta}}_1, \cdots, \hat{\boldsymbol{\theta}}_m$ is a set of m sufficient statistics.

Theorem 8.4. *Let $\hat{\boldsymbol{\theta}}_1, \hat{\boldsymbol{\theta}}_2, \cdots, \hat{\boldsymbol{\theta}}_m$ be a set of sufficient statistics. Suppose that a one-to-one transformation on these m statistics yields $\hat{\boldsymbol{\alpha}}_1, \cdots, \hat{\boldsymbol{\alpha}}_m$. Then the set $\hat{\boldsymbol{\alpha}}_1, \hat{\boldsymbol{\alpha}}_2, \cdots, \hat{\boldsymbol{\alpha}}_m$ is also a sufficient set.*

We shall illustrate this with an example.

Example 8.8. Let $\mathbf{x}_1, \mathbf{x}_2, \cdots, \mathbf{x}_n$ be a random sample from $n(x; \mu, \sigma^2)$, where $-\infty < \mu < \infty$, $0 < \sigma^2 < \infty$. The joint density is

$$\begin{aligned}
g(x_1, \cdots, x_n; \mu, \sigma^2) &= n(x_1; \mu, \sigma^2) \cdots n(x_n; \mu, \sigma^2) \\
&= \frac{1}{(\sigma\sqrt{2\pi})^n} \exp\left[-\frac{1}{2\sigma^2}\sum (x_i - \mu)^2\right] \\
&= \frac{1}{(\sigma\sqrt{2\pi})^n} \exp\left\{-\frac{1}{2\sigma^2}\left[\sum (x_i - \bar{x})^2 \right.\right. \\
&\qquad\qquad \left.\left. + n(\bar{x} - \mu)^2\right]\right\} \\
&= \frac{1}{(\sigma\sqrt{2\pi})^n} \exp\left\{-\frac{1}{2\sigma^2}[(n-1)\hat{\sigma}^2 \right. \\
&\qquad\qquad \left. + n(\hat{\mu} - \mu)^2]\right\} \cdot 1 \\
&= h(\hat{\sigma}^2, \hat{\mu}; \sigma^2, \mu) \cdot q(x_1, \cdots, x_n)
\end{aligned}$$

where

$$\hat{\sigma}^2 = \frac{1}{n-1}\sum (x_i - \bar{x})^2 \qquad \hat{\mu} = \bar{x} \qquad q(x_1, \cdots, x_n) = 1$$

By Theorem 8.3, $\hat{\boldsymbol{\sigma}}^2$ and $\hat{\boldsymbol{\mu}}$ are a set of two sufficient statistics. By Theorem 8.4, $\Sigma(\mathbf{x}_i - \bar{\mathbf{x}})^2$ and $\Sigma\mathbf{x}_i$ are also a set of sufficient statistics as is the set $\Sigma\mathbf{x}_i^2$ and $\Sigma\mathbf{x}_i$.

Next we shall examine the properties of estimators which were listed in Sec. 8.2.

8.5 Unbiased

The mean-squared error can be written as

$$\begin{aligned} E[(\hat{\theta} - \theta)^2] &= E[\{\hat{\theta} - E(\hat{\theta})\} - \{\theta - E(\hat{\theta})\}]^2 \\ &= E[\hat{\theta} - E(\hat{\theta})]^2 + [\theta - E(\hat{\theta})]^2 \\ &= \text{var}\,(\hat{\theta}) + [\theta - E(\hat{\theta})]^2 \end{aligned} \tag{1}$$

Thus the mean-squared error is the sum of two nonnegative quantities. The term $\theta - E(\hat{\theta})$ is called the bias of the estimator and can be either positive, negative, or zero.

If an estimator can be found with bias close to zero and such that var $(\hat{\theta})$ is small, the mean-squared error will be small. Thus it seems that it may be desirable to have an estimator whose bias is 0. We shall now define unbiased estimator.

Definition 8.5. Unbiased Estimator. *An estimator $\hat{\theta}$ is called an unbiased estimator of θ if the expected value of $\hat{\theta}$ equals θ; that is, if $E(\hat{\theta}) = \theta$ for all values of θ in Ω.*

Example 8.9. Let $\mathbf{x}_1, \mathbf{x}_2, \cdots, \mathbf{x}_n$ be a random sample from a density whose mean is μ; then $E(\bar{\mathbf{x}}) = \mu$; also $E(\mathbf{x}_i) = \mu$, and so $\bar{\mathbf{x}}$ and $\mathbf{x}_i$ are both unbiased estimators of μ. Let $\mathbf{y} = \sum_{i=1}^{n} a_i\mathbf{x}_i$, where the a_i are constants such that $\Sigma a_i = 1$. Then

$$\begin{aligned} E(\mathbf{y}) &= E(\Sigma a_i\mathbf{x}_i) \\ &= \Sigma a_i E(\mathbf{x}_i) \\ &= \Sigma a_i \mu \\ &= \mu \end{aligned}$$

and so $\mathbf{y}$ is also an unbiased estimator of μ.

8.6 Consistent Estimator

It seems that a "good" estimator should be one for which the risk becomes small as the sample size increases. That is, the estimator ought to be better when it is based on twenty observations than when it is based on two observations, say. To put this idea more explicitly, let $\hat{\theta}_1 = d_1(\mathbf{x}_1)$ be an estimator of θ based on a sample of size 1 from $f(x; \theta)$; let $\hat{\theta}_2 = d_2(\mathbf{x}_1, \mathbf{x}_2)$ be an estimator of θ based on a sample of size 2; and in general let $\hat{\theta}_n = d_n(\mathbf{x}_1, \mathbf{x}_2, \cdots, \mathbf{x}_n)$ be an estimator of θ based on a sample of size n. That is to say, let $\hat{\theta}_1, \hat{\theta}_2, \cdots, \hat{\theta}_n, \cdots$, sometimes written $\{\hat{\theta}_n\}$ or, interchangeably, $\{d_n\}$, be a sequence of estimators of θ.

The condition suggested above is that

$$\lim_{n\to\infty} R(\theta; d_n) = 0 \qquad \text{for all } \theta \text{ in } \Omega$$

In the case of squared-error loss, the formal definition is as follows:

Definition 8.6a. Squared-error Consistency. *Let* $\hat{\theta}_1, \hat{\theta}_2, \cdots, \hat{\theta}_n, \cdots$ *be a sequence of estimators of* θ *(more accurately let* $d_1, d_2, \cdots, d_n, \cdots$ *be a sequence of estimators for* θ*). This sequence is a squared-error consistent estimator of* θ *if*

$$\lim_{n\to\infty} E[(\hat{\theta}_n - \theta)^2] = 0 \qquad \textit{for all } \theta \textit{ in } \Omega$$

Since $R(\theta; d_n) = E[(\hat{\theta}_n - \theta)^2] = \text{var}(\hat{\theta}_n) + [\theta - E(\hat{\theta}_n)]^2$, it follows that squared-error consistency implies that both the bias and variance of $\hat{\theta}_n$ approach zero. As in the derivation of the law of large numbers, an application of Tchebysheff's inequality will show that if the bias and variance of $\hat{\theta}_n$ approach zero the following definition of (simple) *consistency* is satisfied.

Definition 8.6b. Consistency. *Let* $\hat{\theta}_1, \hat{\theta}_2, \cdots, \hat{\theta}_n, \cdots$ *be a sequence of estimators of* θ. *This sequence is a simple consistent estimator of* θ if *for every* $\epsilon > 0$ *the following is satisfied:*

$$\lim_{n\to\infty} P(\theta - \epsilon < \hat{\theta}_n < \theta + \epsilon) = 1 \qquad \textit{for every } \theta \textit{ in } \Omega$$

Loosely speaking, the condition of consistency (we shall henceforth generally use the term consistency for simple consistency), which is weaker than squared-error consistency, states that, for large samples, $\hat{\theta}_n$ tends to be close to θ. (We shall sometimes say that $\hat{\theta}$ is consistent to mean $\{\hat{\theta}_n\}$ is consistent.)

Because squared-error is not necessarily a good approximation to the loss when $\hat{\theta}$ is far from θ, a rather involved argument can be advanced to indicate that simple consistency is often more fundamental than squared-error consistency.

8.7 Asymptotically Efficient Estimators

We remarked before that, generally, there do not exist estimators which minimize mean-squared error for all θ. This is due to the fact that the estimator $\hat{\theta} = \theta_0$, which consists of ignoring the data and guessing that θ is equal to θ_0, is better than any other estimator when θ is actually equal to θ_0 and is quite good when θ is close to θ_0. The existence of consistent estimators implies that the range of values of θ for which our guess is "better" than a consistent estimator shrinks as the sample size increases. This suggests that there may exist estimators which are efficient in an appropriate limiting sense as $n \to \infty$.

For the case of squared-error loss, we state the following definition:

Definition 8.7a. Squared-error Asymptotically Efficient Estimators. *Let* $\hat{\boldsymbol{\theta}}_1, \hat{\boldsymbol{\theta}}_2, \cdots, \hat{\boldsymbol{\theta}}_n, \cdots$ *be a squared-error consistent estimator of* θ. *This sequence is called a squared-error asymptotically efficient estimator (from here on we shall generally use the term efficient estimator) if there is no other squared-error consistent estimator* $\boldsymbol{\theta}_1^*, \boldsymbol{\theta}_2^*, \cdots, \boldsymbol{\theta}_n^*, \cdots$ *for which*

$$\overline{\lim_{n\to\infty}} \frac{E[(\hat{\boldsymbol{\theta}}_n - \theta)^2]}{E[(\boldsymbol{\theta}_n^* - \theta)^2]} > 1$$

for all θ *in some open interval.*

The upper limit $c = \overline{\lim_{n\to\infty}} c_n$ is the greatest number (possibly $+\infty$) such that, for every $\epsilon > 0$, $c_n \geq c - \epsilon$ for infinitely many n.

It is interesting that, in many problems, there exist estimators which satisfy the above definition. For technical reasons related to those which led to the definition of (simple) consistency, we sometimes find more appropriate another definition involving the limiting distribution of $\sqrt{n}\,(\hat{\boldsymbol{\theta}}_n - \theta)$. To this end we confine attention to alternative estimators $\hat{\boldsymbol{\theta}}_n$ for which $\sqrt{n}\,(\hat{\boldsymbol{\theta}}_n - \theta)$ has a limiting *normal* distribution with mean 0 and variance $\sigma^2(\theta)$. The symbol $\sigma^2(\theta)$ indicates that the variance depends on θ.

Definition 8.7b. Best Asymptotically Normal Estimators (BAN Estimators). *The sequence of estimators* $\hat{\boldsymbol{\theta}}_1, \hat{\boldsymbol{\theta}}_2, \cdots, \hat{\boldsymbol{\theta}}_n, \cdots$ *is a best asymptotically normal (BAN) estimator of* θ *if the following three conditions are satisfied:*

(*a*) *The distribution of* $\sqrt{n}\,(\hat{\boldsymbol{\theta}}_n - \theta)$ *approaches the normal distribution with mean* 0 *and variance* $\sigma^2(\theta)$ *as* n *approaches infinity.*

(*b*) *For every* $\epsilon > 0$,

$$\lim_{n\to\infty} P\{|\hat{\boldsymbol{\theta}}_n - \theta| > \epsilon\} = 0 \qquad \text{for each } \theta \text{ in } \Omega$$

(*c*) *There is no other sequence of consistent estimators* $\boldsymbol{\theta}_1^*, \boldsymbol{\theta}_2^*, \cdots, \boldsymbol{\theta}_n^*, \cdots$ *for which the distribution of* $\sqrt{n}\,(\boldsymbol{\theta}_n^* - \theta)$ *approaches the normal distribution with mean* 0 *and variance* $\sigma^{*2}(\theta)$ *and such that*

$$\frac{\sigma^2(\theta)}{\sigma^{*2}(\theta)} > 1$$

for all θ *in some open interval.*

The usefulness of this definition derives partially from theorems proving the existence of BAN estimators and from the fact that ordinarily reasonable estimators are approximately normally distributed.

It can be shown that, for samples drawn from a normal density with mean μ and variance σ^2, the sequence $\hat{\theta}_n = \frac{1}{n}\sum_{i=1}^{n} \mathbf{x}_i = \bar{\mathbf{x}}_n$ for $n = 1, 2, \cdots$ is an efficient estimator and a BAN estimator of μ. In fact, the limiting distribution of $\sqrt{n}\,(\bar{\mathbf{x}}_n - \mu)$ is normal with zero mean and variance σ^2, and no other estimator can have smaller limiting variance in any interval of μ values. However, there are many other estimators for this problem which are also efficient estimators and BAN estimators of μ, that is, estimators with the same normal distribution in the limit. For example,

$$\mathbf{y}_n = \frac{1}{n+1}\sum_{i=1}^{n} \mathbf{x}_i \qquad n = 1, 2, \cdots$$

is an efficient estimator and a BAN estimator of μ. Efficient estimators and BAN estimators are necessarily consistent.

8.8 Minimum-variance Unbiased Estimators

Since estimators with minimum mean-squared error rarely exist, a reasonable procedure is to restrict the class of estimating functions and look for estimators with minimum mean-squared error in the restricted class. For example, we might consider only unbiased estimators and then among the class of unbiased estimators we shall see if we can find an estimator with minimum mean-squared error. According to (8.5.1) the mean-squared error can be written

$$\begin{aligned} E\{(\hat{\theta} - \theta)^2\} &= E\{[\hat{\theta} - E(\hat{\theta})]^2\} + [\theta - E(\hat{\theta})]^2 \\ &= \text{var}\,(\hat{\theta}) + [\theta - E(\hat{\theta})]^2 \end{aligned} \tag{1}$$

If we consider only estimators which are unbiased, then $E(\hat{\theta}) = \theta$, and we see that the mean-squared error of an unbiased estimator is equal to the variance of the estimator; thus (1) becomes

$$E\{(\hat{\theta} - \theta)^2\} = \text{var}\,(\hat{\theta})$$

if $\hat{\theta}$ is unbiased. Now we shall formalize the definition.

Definition 8.8. Minimum-variance Unbiased Estimators. *Let* $\mathbf{x}_1, \mathbf{x}_2, \cdots, \mathbf{x}_n$ *be a random sample from* $f(x; \theta)$. *Let* $\hat{\theta} = d(\mathbf{x}_1, \cdots, \mathbf{x}_n)$ *be an estimator of* θ *such that*

(*a*) $E(\hat{\theta}) = \theta$; *that is,* $\hat{\theta}$ *is unbiased.*

(*b*) *var* $(\hat{\theta})$ *is less than the variance of any other estimator satisfying* (*a*); *that is, var* $(\hat{\theta})$ *is less than the variance of any other unbiased estimator.*

Then $\hat{\theta}$ *is the minimum-variance unbiased estimator of* θ.

Instead of estimating θ, if we are interested in estimating some function of θ, say $u(\theta)$, we look for an unbiased estimator of $u(\theta)$ with minimum variance. Minimum-variance unbiased estimators can be found for many of the parameters that play an important role in applied statistics.

Consistent estimators, BAN estimators, and efficient estimators have optimum properties when the sample size is large, but the property minimum variance unbiased is optimum for any sample size. Even though minimum-variance unbiased estimators are not as desirable as minimum mean-squared-error estimators, they frequently exist, whereas minimum mean-squared-error estimators rarely do.

Next we shall show that the concept of sufficient statistics and complete density functions aids us greatly in finding minimum-variance unbiased estimators. Loosely speaking, an unbiased estimator which is a function of the sufficient statistics has smaller variance than an unbiased estimator which is not based on a sufficient statistic. In fact, let $f(x; \theta)$ be a density, and suppose that we want to estimate $u(\theta)$. Let us assume that $\mathbf{t} = t(\mathbf{x}_1, \cdots, \mathbf{x}_n)$ is an unbiased estimator of $u(\theta)$ and that $\hat{\boldsymbol{\theta}} = d(\mathbf{x}_1, \cdots, \mathbf{x}_n)$ is a sufficient statistic for θ. It can be shown that there is a function of $\hat{\boldsymbol{\theta}}$, say $v(\hat{\boldsymbol{\theta}})$, such that $E[v(\hat{\boldsymbol{\theta}})] = u(\theta)$; that is, there is a function of the sufficient statistic $\hat{\boldsymbol{\theta}}$ which is also an unbiased estimator of $u(\theta)$. Also the variance of $v(\hat{\boldsymbol{\theta}})$ is less than or equal to the variance of $\mathbf{t}$. Therefore, in our search for minimum-variance unbiased estimators we need to consider only estimators that are functions of sufficient statistics. We shall formalize these ideas in the following theorem.

Theorem 8.5. *Let $\mathbf{x}_1, \mathbf{x}_2, \cdots, \mathbf{x}_n$ be a random sample from the density $f(x; \theta)$, and let $\hat{\boldsymbol{\theta}} = d(\mathbf{x}_1, \mathbf{x}_2, \cdots, \mathbf{x}_n)$ be a sufficient statistic for θ. Let the statistic $\mathbf{t} = t(\mathbf{x}_1, \mathbf{x}_2, \cdots, \mathbf{x}_n)$ be an unbiased estimator of $u(\theta)$, and suppose that $\mathbf{t}$ is not a function of $\hat{\boldsymbol{\theta}}$. Let us denote the conditional expectation of $\mathbf{t}$, given $\hat{\boldsymbol{\theta}}$, by $v(\hat{\boldsymbol{\theta}})$; that is, let $E(\mathbf{t}|\hat{\boldsymbol{\theta}}) = v(\hat{\boldsymbol{\theta}})$. Then*

(*a*) $E[v(\hat{\boldsymbol{\theta}})] = u(\theta)$; *that is, if the expectation of $\mathbf{t}$ is equal to $u(\theta)$, then the expectation of $v(\hat{\boldsymbol{\theta}})$ is also equal to $u(\theta)$.*

(*b*) *var* $[v(\hat{\boldsymbol{\theta}})] <$ *var* $(\mathbf{t})$.

(*c*) $v(\hat{\boldsymbol{\theta}})$ *does not involve θ and hence is a statistic and can be computed from observed sample values.*

Proof. From Chap. 5 we have that $E(\mathbf{t}|\hat{\boldsymbol{\theta}})$ is a function of $\hat{\boldsymbol{\theta}}$, which we have denoted by $v(\hat{\boldsymbol{\theta}})$. First we shall prove part (*c*) of the theorem. Let us denote the joint density function of $\mathbf{t}$ and $\hat{\boldsymbol{\theta}}$ by $g(t, \hat{\theta}; \theta)$ and the conditional distribution of $\mathbf{t}$, given $\hat{\boldsymbol{\theta}}$, by $p(t|\hat{\theta})$. But by the definition of a sufficient statistic, $p(t|\hat{\theta})$ does not involve θ; hence the expected value of $\mathbf{t}$, given $\hat{\boldsymbol{\theta}}$, which is $v(\hat{\boldsymbol{\theta}})$ cannot involve θ. Next we shall prove part (*a*). Now since $\mathbf{t}$ is an unbiased estimator of $u(\theta)$, we get

$$E(\mathbf{t}) = \int_{-\infty}^{\infty} \int_{-\infty}^{\infty} t \cdot g(t, \hat{\theta}; \theta)\, dt\, d\hat{\theta} = u(\theta) \tag{2}$$

But we can write

$$g(t, \hat{\theta}; \theta) = p(t|\hat{\theta})h(\hat{\theta}; \theta) \tag{3}$$

where $h(\hat{\theta}; \theta)$ is the marginal density of $\hat{\boldsymbol{\theta}}$. Substituting (3) in (2) gives

$$\begin{aligned} u(\theta) = E(\mathbf{t}) &= \int_{-\infty}^{\infty}\int_{-\infty}^{\infty} t \cdot g(t, \hat{\theta}; \theta)\, dt\, d\hat{\theta} = \int_{-\infty}^{\infty}\int_{-\infty}^{\infty} t \cdot p(t|\hat{\theta})h(\hat{\theta}; \theta)\, dt\, d\hat{\theta} \\ &= \int_{-\infty}^{\infty}\left[\int_{-\infty}^{\infty} tp(t|\hat{\theta})\, dt\right] h(\hat{\theta}; \theta)\, d\hat{\theta} \end{aligned} \tag{4}$$

But the integral in brackets, namely,

$$\int_{-\infty}^{\infty} tp(t|\hat{\theta})\, dt = v(\hat{\theta}) \tag{5}$$

is, by definition, equal to $E(\mathbf{t}|\hat{\theta})$, and it is a function of $\hat{\theta}$ only; it does not depend on θ since $p(t|\hat{\theta})$ does not contain θ. Substituting (5) in (4) gives us

$$u(\theta) = E(\mathbf{t}) = \int_{-\infty}^{\infty} v(\hat{\theta})h(\hat{\theta}; \theta)\, d\hat{\theta} = E[v(\hat{\boldsymbol{\theta}})]$$

and part (*a*) is proved. To prove part (*b*) we have

$$\begin{aligned} \text{var}\ (\mathbf{t}) &= E[\mathbf{t} - u(\theta)]^2 = E\{[\mathbf{t} - v(\hat{\boldsymbol{\theta}})] + [v(\hat{\boldsymbol{\theta}}) - u(\theta)]\}^2 \\ &= E[v(\hat{\boldsymbol{\theta}}) - u(\theta)]^2 + E[\mathbf{t} - v(\hat{\boldsymbol{\theta}})]^2 \\ &\qquad + 2E\{[\mathbf{t} - v(\hat{\boldsymbol{\theta}})][v(\hat{\boldsymbol{\theta}}) - u(\theta)]\} \end{aligned} \tag{6}$$

We shall show that the third term in (6) is equal to 0. We get

$$\begin{aligned} E\{[\mathbf{t} - v(\hat{\boldsymbol{\theta}})][v(\hat{\boldsymbol{\theta}}) - u(\theta)]\} &= \int_{-\infty}^{\infty}\int_{-\infty}^{\infty} [t - v(\hat{\theta})][v(\hat{\theta}) - u(\theta)]g(t, \hat{\theta}; \theta)\, dt\, d\hat{\theta} \\ &= \int_{-\infty}^{\infty}\left\{\int_{-\infty}^{\infty} [t - v(\hat{\theta})]p(t|\hat{\theta})\, dt\right\} [v(\hat{\theta}) \\ &\qquad - u(\theta)]h(\hat{\theta}; \theta)\, d\hat{\theta} \end{aligned}$$

But, by (5), the term in braces is equal to 0. Now we have shown that (6) reduces to

$$\text{var}\ (\mathbf{t}) = \text{var}\ [v(\hat{\boldsymbol{\theta}})] + E[\mathbf{t} - v(\hat{\boldsymbol{\theta}})]^2$$

or

$$\text{var}\ (\mathbf{t}) > \text{var}\ [v(\hat{\boldsymbol{\theta}})]$$

since

$$E[\mathbf{t} - v(\hat{\boldsymbol{\theta}})]^2 > 0$$

This proves part (*b*).

The ideas in Theorem 8.5 were first discussed by C. R. Rao and D. Blackwell.

This theorem helps us a great deal in our search for minimum-variance unbiased estimators since it essentially tells us that we need to look only at unbiased estimators that are functions of sufficient statistics. However, this theorem does not give the final answer since there may possibly be many estimators, each based on sufficient statistics, and each unbiased. The theorem does not tell us which of *these* has minimum variance. However, Theorem 8.6 can often be used. This theorem states that, if the density of the sufficient statistic is *complete*, then there is only *one* unbiased estimator of $u(\theta)$ which is based on the sufficient statistic. If there is only one unbiased estimator which is based on the sufficient statistic, then it must be *the* minimum-variance unbiased estimator.

Theorem 8.6. *Let* $\mathbf{x}_1, \mathbf{x}_2, \cdots, \mathbf{x}_n$ *be a random sample from* $f(x; \theta)$, *and let* $\hat{\boldsymbol{\theta}} = d(\mathbf{x}_1, \mathbf{x}_2, \cdots, \mathbf{x}_n)$ *be a sufficient statistic. Let the density of* $\hat{\boldsymbol{\theta}}$ *be complete. If a function of* $\hat{\boldsymbol{\theta}}$, *say* $v(\hat{\boldsymbol{\theta}})$, *exists such that* $E[v(\hat{\boldsymbol{\theta}})] = u(\theta)$, *then* $v(\hat{\boldsymbol{\theta}})$ *is the minimum-variance unbiased estimator of* $u(\theta)$.

Example 8.10. Let $\mathbf{x}_1, \mathbf{x}_2, \cdots, \mathbf{x}_n$ be a random sample from $n(x; \mu, 1)$. Now $\bar{\mathbf{x}}$ is a sufficient statistic for μ, and the density function of $\bar{\mathbf{x}}$ is complete. Suppose that we want to find the minimum-variance unbiased estimators for (*a*) μ; (*b*) μ^2; (*c*) 3μ; (*d*) $\mu^2 + 6\mu$. By Theorem 8.6, if we can find for each (*a*), (*b*), (*c*), (*d*) an unbiased estimator which is a function of the sufficient complete statistic $\bar{\mathbf{x}}$, then it will be the minimum-variance unbiased estimator. The reader can verify that the following estimators are unbiased: (*a*) $\bar{\mathbf{x}}$; (*b*) $\bar{\mathbf{x}}^2 - 1/n$; (*c*) $3\bar{\mathbf{x}}$; (*d*) $\bar{\mathbf{x}}^2 + 6\bar{\mathbf{x}} - 1/n$.

Theorems similar to the above on minimum-variance unbiased estimators hold for densities with more than one parameter.

Example 8.11. Let $\mathbf{x}_1, \mathbf{x}_2, \cdots, \mathbf{x}_n$ be a random sample from $n(x; \mu, \sigma^2)$. $\bar{\mathbf{x}}$ and $\Sigma \mathbf{x}_i^2$ are a set of sufficient statistics, and the joint density of $\bar{\mathbf{x}}$ and $\Sigma \mathbf{x}_i^2$ is complete. Suppose that we want to find the minimum-variance unbiased estimators for (*a*) μ; (*b*) σ^2; (*c*) $\mu + \sigma^2$; (*d*) $6\mu + 8\sigma^2$. By the multiparameter extension of Theorem 8.6, we need only find unbiased estimators (based on the sufficient statistics) of the function of the parameters in (*a*), (*b*), (*c*), and (*d*), and they are the *minimum-variance unbiased* estimators. The reader can verify that the following are unbiased estimators for the parameters in (*a*), (*b*), (*c*), and (*d*) above:

$$(a)\ \bar{\mathbf{x}};\quad (b)\ \frac{1}{n-1}\left(\sum \mathbf{x}_i^2 - n\bar{\mathbf{x}}^2\right);\quad (c)\ \bar{\mathbf{x}} + \frac{1}{n-1}\sum \mathbf{x}_i^2 - \frac{n}{n-1}\bar{\mathbf{x}}^2;$$

$$(d)\ 6\bar{\mathbf{x}} + \frac{8}{n-1}\sum \mathbf{x}_i^2 - \frac{8n}{n-1}\bar{\mathbf{x}}^2.$$

8.9 Principle of Maximum Likelihood

Even though an experimenter decides on the properties which he wants an estimator to have, he still faces the problem of how to obtain the estimator. There are several methods available which will produce estimators with some of the various properties listed in previous sections. The only methods which we shall discuss are (1) *method of maximum likelihood;* (2) *method of moments;* (3) *method of Bayes.* In a later chapter we shall discuss another method which is used for certain types of estimation problems: *the method of least squares.* In this section we shall discuss the principle of maximum likelihood.

To introduce the idea, we shall consider a very simple estimation problem. Suppose that an urn contains a number of black and white balls, and suppose that it is known that the ratio of the numbers is 3/1 but that it is not known whether the black or the white balls are more numerous. That is, the probability of drawing a black ball is either $\frac{1}{4}$ or $\frac{3}{4}$. If n balls are drawn, with replacement, from the urn, the distribution of $\mathbf{x}$, the number of black balls, is given by the binomial

$$f(x; p) = \binom{n}{x} p^x q^{n-x} \qquad x = 0, 1, 2, \cdots, n \qquad (1)$$
$$p = \tfrac{1}{4}, \tfrac{3}{4}$$

where $q = 1 - p$ and p is the probability of drawing a black ball.

We shall draw a sample of three balls, that is, $n = 3$, with replacement, and attempt to estimate the unknown parameter p of the distribution. The estimation problem is particularly simple in this case because we have only to choose between the two numbers .25 and .75. Let us anticipate the result of the drawing of the sample. The possible outcomes and their probabilities are given below:

x	0	1	2	3
$f(x; \frac{3}{4})$	$\frac{1}{64}$	$\frac{9}{64}$	$\frac{27}{64}$	$\frac{27}{64}$
$f(x; \frac{1}{4})$	$\frac{27}{64}$	$\frac{27}{64}$	$\frac{9}{64}$	$\frac{1}{64}$

In the present example, if we found $\mathbf{x} = 0$ in a sample of three, the estimate .25 for p would be preferred over .75 because the probability $\frac{27}{64}$ is greater than $\frac{1}{64}$, i.e., because a sample with $\mathbf{x} = 0$ is more likely to arise from a population with $p = \frac{1}{4}$ than from one with $p = \frac{3}{4}$. And in general we should estimate p by .25 when $\mathbf{x} = 0$ or 1, and by .75 when $\mathbf{x} = 2$ or 3. The estimator may be defined as

$$\begin{aligned} \hat{\mathbf{p}}(x) &= .25 \qquad x = 0, 1 \\ &= .75 \qquad x = 2, 3 \end{aligned} \qquad (2)$$

The estimator thus selects for every $\mathbf{x}$ the value of p, say $\hat{p}$, such that

$$f(\mathbf{x}; \hat{p}) > f(\mathbf{x}; p')$$

where p' is the alternative value of p.

More generally, if several alternative values of p were possible, we might reasonably proceed in the same manner. Thus if we found $\mathbf{x} = 6$ in a sample of 25 from a binomial population, we should substitute all possible values of p in the expression

$$f(6; p) = \binom{25}{6} p^6(1 - p)^{19} \qquad 0 \le p \le 1 \tag{3}$$

and choose as our estimate that value of p which maximized $f(6; p)$. For the given possible values of p we should find our estimate to be $6/25$. The position of its maximum value can be found by putting the derivative of the function defined in (3) with respect to p equal to 0 and solving the resulting equation for p. Thus,

$$\frac{d}{dp} f(6; p) = \binom{25}{6} p^5(1 - p)^{18}[6(1 - p) - 19p] \tag{4}$$

and on putting this equal to 0 and solving for p, we find that $p = 0, 1, 6/25$ are the roots. The first two roots give a minimum, and so our estimate is therefore $\hat{\mathbf{p}} = 6/25$. This estimate has the property that

$$f(6; \hat{p}) > f(6; p') \tag{5}$$

where p' is any other value of p in the interval $0 \le p \le 1$.

Definition 8.9. Likelihood Function. *The likelihood function of n random variables $\mathbf{x}_1, \mathbf{x}_2, \cdots, \mathbf{x}_n$ is the joint density of the n random variables $g(\mathbf{x}_1, \cdots, \mathbf{x}_n; \theta)$ which is considered to be a function of θ. In particular, if $\mathbf{x}_1, \cdots, \mathbf{x}_n$ is a random sample from the density $f(x; \theta)$, then the likelihood function is $g(\mathbf{x}_1, \mathbf{x}_2, \cdots, \mathbf{x}_n; \theta) = f(\mathbf{x}_1; \theta)\, f(\mathbf{x}_2; \theta) \cdots f(\mathbf{x}_n; \theta)$.*

The likelihood function $g(\mathbf{x}_1, \cdots, \mathbf{x}_n; \theta)$ gives the relative likelihood that the random variables assume a particular value $x_1, x_2, \cdots, x_n$. Suppose for a moment that θ is *known;* denote the value by θ_0. The particular value of the random variables which is "most likely to occur" is that value $x_1', x_2', \cdots, x_n'$ such that $g(x_1, x_2, \cdots, x_n; \theta_0)$ is a maximum. For example, for simplicity, let us assume that $n = 1$ and $\mathbf{x}_1$ has the normal density with mean 6 and variance 1. Then the value of the random variable which is "most likely to occur" is $\mathbf{x}_1 = 6$. By "most likely to occur" we mean the value x_1' of $\mathbf{x}_1$ such that $n(x_1'; 6, 1) > n(x_1; 6, 1)$. Now let us suppose that the joint density of n random variables is $g(x_1, x_2, \cdots, x_n; \theta)$, where θ is *unknown.* Let the particular values which are observed be represented by $x_1', x_2', \cdots, x_n'$. We want to know from which density is this particular set of values "most likely" to have come. In other words, as θ takes on different values in Ω, a family of densities is defined. We want to know from which density (what value of θ) is the likelihood largest that the set $x_1', \cdots, x_n'$ was obtained. In other words, we want to find the value of θ in Ω, denoted by $\hat{\boldsymbol{\theta}}$, which maximizes the likelihood function $g(\mathbf{x}_1, \mathbf{x}_2, \cdots, \mathbf{x}_n; \theta)$. The value $\hat{\boldsymbol{\theta}}$ which maximizes the likelihood function is, in general, a function of $\mathbf{x}_1, \cdots, \mathbf{x}_n$, say $\hat{\boldsymbol{\theta}} = d(\mathbf{x}_1, \mathbf{x}_2, \cdots, \mathbf{x}_n)$. When this is the case, the random variable $\hat{\boldsymbol{\theta}} = d(\mathbf{x}_1, \mathbf{x}_2, \cdots, \mathbf{x}_n)$ is called the maximum-likelihood estimator of θ. (We are assuming throughout that the maximum of the likelihood function exists.) We shall now formalize the definition of a maximum-likelihood estimator.

Definition 8.10. Maximum-likelihood Estimator. *Let*

$$L(\theta) = g(\mathbf{x}_1, \mathbf{x}_2, \cdots, \mathbf{x}_n; \theta)$$

be the likelihood function for the random variables $\mathbf{x}_1, \mathbf{x}_2, \cdots, \mathbf{x}_n$. *If* $\hat{\boldsymbol{\theta}}$ [*where* $\hat{\boldsymbol{\theta}} = d(\mathbf{x}_1, \mathbf{x}_2, \cdots, \mathbf{x}_n)$] *is the value of* θ *in* Ω *which maximizes* $L(\theta)$, *then* $\hat{\boldsymbol{\theta}}$, *or, more accurately,* $d(\mathbf{x}_1, \mathbf{x}_2, \cdots, \mathbf{x}_n)$, *is the maximum-likelihood estimator of* θ.

The most important cases which we shall consider are those in which $\mathbf{x}_1, \mathbf{x}_2, \cdots, \mathbf{x}_n$ is a random sample from some density $f(x; \theta)$, so that the likelihood function is

$$L(\theta) = f(\mathbf{x}_1; \theta) f(\mathbf{x}_2; \theta) \cdots f(\mathbf{x}_n; \theta)$$

Many likelihood functions satisfy regularity conditions so that the maximum-likelihood estimator is the solution of the equation

$$\frac{dL(\theta)}{d\theta} = 0$$

Also $L(\theta)$ and $\log [L(\theta)]$ have their maximum at the same value of θ, and it is sometimes easier to find the maximum of the logarithm of the likelihood.

If the likelihood function contains k parameters, i.e., if

$$L(\theta_1, \theta_2, \cdots, \theta_k) = \prod_{i=1}^{n} f(\mathbf{x}_i; \theta_1, \theta_2, \cdots, \theta_k)$$

then the maximum-likelihood estimators of the parameters $\theta_1, \theta_2, \cdots, \theta_k$ are the random variables $\hat{\boldsymbol{\theta}}_1 = d_1(\mathbf{x}_1, \cdots, \mathbf{x}_n)$; $\hat{\boldsymbol{\theta}}_2 = d_2(\mathbf{x}_1, \mathbf{x}_2, \cdots, \mathbf{x}_n)$; $\cdots$; $\hat{\boldsymbol{\theta}}_k = d_k(\mathbf{x}_1, \mathbf{x}_2, \cdots, \mathbf{x}_n)$, where $\hat{\boldsymbol{\theta}}_1, \hat{\boldsymbol{\theta}}_2, \cdots, \hat{\boldsymbol{\theta}}_k$ are the values in Ω which maximize $L(\theta_1, \theta_2, \cdots, \theta_k)$.

If certain regularity conditions are satisfied, the point where the likelihood is a maximum is a solution of the k equations

$$\frac{\partial L(\theta_1, \cdots, \theta_k)}{\partial \theta_1} = 0$$
$$\frac{\partial L(\theta_1, \cdots, \theta_k)}{\partial \theta_2} = 0$$
$$\cdots\cdots\cdots\cdots$$
$$\frac{\partial L(\theta_1, \cdots, \theta_k)}{\partial \theta_k} = 0$$

In this case it may also be easier to work with the logarithm of the likelihood.

In the next section we shall illustrate these definitions with some examples.

8.10 Some Maximum-likelihood Estimators

In this section we shall obtain maximum-likelihood estimators for the parameters of some of the common distributions. Often the likelihood function satisfies regularity conditions so that the maximum value may be obtained by putting the derivatives of the likelihood function equal to 0 and solving for the parameters in the resulting equations.

Example 8.12. Suppose that a random sample of size n is drawn from the point binomial distribution

$$f(x; p) = p^x q^{1-x} \qquad x = 0, 1; 0 \leq p \leq 1 \tag{1}$$

The sample values, $\mathbf{x}_1, \mathbf{x}_2, \cdots, \mathbf{x}_n$, will be a sequence of 0's and 1's, and the likelihood function is

$$L(p) = \prod_{i=1}^{n} p^{\mathbf{x}_i} q^{1-\mathbf{x}_i} = p^{\Sigma \mathbf{x}_i} q^{n-\Sigma \mathbf{x}_i} \tag{2}$$

If we let

$$\mathbf{y} = \Sigma \mathbf{x}_i \tag{3}$$

we obtain

$$L^* = \log L\,(p) = \mathbf{y} \log p + (n - \mathbf{y}) \log q \tag{4}$$
$$\frac{dL^*}{dp} = \frac{\mathbf{y}}{p} - \frac{n - \mathbf{y}}{q} \tag{5}$$

remembering that $q = 1 - p$. On putting this last expression equal to 0 and solving for p, we find the estimator

$$\hat{\mathbf{p}} = \frac{\mathbf{y}}{n} = \frac{1}{n} \sum \mathbf{x}_i = \bar{\mathbf{x}} \tag{6}$$

which is the obvious estimator for this parameter.

We shall show that this estimator is sufficient, and since it is also unbiased and complete, it is the unique minimum-variance unbiased estimator of p. We need to show that the conditional distribution of the $\mathbf{x}_i$, given $\bar{\mathbf{x}}$, is independent of p. Since the marginal distribution of $n\bar{\mathbf{x}} = \mathbf{y}$ is given by

$$\binom{n}{y} p^y q^{n-y} \tag{7}$$

the conditional distribution of the $\mathbf{x}_i$, given y, is obtained by dividing (2) by (7) to get, say,

$$g(x_1, x_2, \cdots, x_n|\hat{p}) = \frac{1}{\binom{n}{n\hat{p}}} \qquad x_i = 0, 1; \Sigma x_i = n\hat{p} \tag{8}$$

a distribution which is independent of the parameter p.

Example 8.13. A random sample of size n from the normal distribution has the density

$$\prod_{i=1}^{n} \frac{1}{\sqrt{2\pi}\,\sigma} e^{-(1/2\sigma^2)(x_i-\mu)^2} = \left(\frac{1}{2\pi\sigma^2}\right)^{n/2} e^{-(1/2\sigma^2)\Sigma(x_i-\mu)^2} \tag{9}$$

The logarithm of the likelihood function is

$$L^* = -\frac{n}{2}\log 2\pi - \frac{n}{2}\log\sigma^2 - \frac{1}{2\sigma^2}\sum(\mathbf{x}_i - \mu)^2 \tag{10}$$

To find the location of its maximum, we compute

$$\frac{\partial L^*}{\partial\mu} = \frac{1}{\sigma^2}\sum(\mathbf{x}_i - \mu) \tag{11}$$

$$\frac{\partial L^*}{\partial\sigma^2} = -\frac{n}{2}\frac{1}{\sigma^2} + \frac{1}{2\sigma^4}\sum(\mathbf{x}_i - \mu)^2 \tag{12}$$

and on putting these derivatives equal to 0 and solving the resulting equations for μ and σ^2, we find the estimators

$$\hat{\boldsymbol{\mu}} = \frac{1}{n}\sum\mathbf{x}_i = \bar{\mathbf{x}} \tag{13}$$

$$\hat{\boldsymbol{\sigma}}^2 = \frac{1}{n}\sum(\mathbf{x}_i - \bar{\mathbf{x}})^2 \tag{14}$$

which turn out to be the sample moments corresponding to μ and σ^2. The estimator $\hat{\boldsymbol{\mu}}$ is unbiased, but $\hat{\boldsymbol{\sigma}}^2$ is not, since

$$E(\hat{\boldsymbol{\sigma}}^2) = \frac{n-1}{n}\sigma^2 \tag{15}$$

This pair of estimators is sufficient for the parameters; the sample distribution for given values of $\hat{\mu}$ and $\hat{\sigma}^2$ does not involve μ and σ^2. We note in this case that it is possible to estimate μ without estimating σ^2 but not possible to estimate σ^2 without first estimating μ.

Example 8.14. Let the random variable $\mathbf{x}$ have a uniform density given by

$$\begin{aligned} f(x) &= \frac{1}{\beta - \alpha} \qquad \alpha < x < \beta \\ &= 0 \qquad \text{elsewhere} \end{aligned} \tag{16}$$

where α and β are two numbers such that $\alpha < \beta$. The likelihood function for a random sample of size n is

$$\begin{aligned} L(\alpha, \beta) &= g(\mathbf{x}_1, \cdots, \mathbf{x}_n; \alpha, \beta) = \frac{1}{(\beta - \alpha)^n} \qquad \alpha < \mathbf{x}_i < \beta \\ &= 0 \qquad \text{otherwise} \end{aligned} \tag{17}$$

If we put the derivatives of this expression with respect to α and β equal to 0 and attempt to solve for α and β, we find that at least one of α, β must be infinite, a nonsensical result. The trouble here is that the likelihood does not have zero slope at its maximum value, so that we must locate its maximum by other means. It is evident from (17) that the likelihood will be made as large as possible when $\beta - \alpha$ is made as small as possible. Given a sample of n observations $\mathbf{x}_1, \mathbf{x}_2, \cdots, \mathbf{x}_n$, suppose that we denote the smallest of the observations by $\mathbf{x}'$ and the largest by $\mathbf{x}''$. Clearly α can be no larger than $\mathbf{x}'$ and β can be no smaller than $\mathbf{x}''$; hence the smallest possible value for $\beta - \alpha$ is $\mathbf{x}'' - \mathbf{x}'$. The maximum-likelihood estimators are obviously

$$\begin{aligned} \hat{\alpha} &= \mathbf{x}' \\ \hat{\beta} &= \mathbf{x}'' \end{aligned} \tag{18}$$

a somewhat curious result because no use is made of the intervening observations.

These three examples are sufficient to illustrate the application of the method of maximum likelihood. The last example shows that one must not always rely on the differentiation process to locate the maximum. The function $L(\theta)$ may, for example, be represented by the curve in Fig. 8.2, where the actual maximum is at $\hat{\theta}$, but the differentiation process would locate θ' as the maximum. One must also remember that the equation $\partial L/\partial\theta = 0$ locates minima as well as maxima, and hence one must avoid using a root of the equation which actually locates a minimum.

We have not illustrated the estimation of a parameter which appears as a factorial in the distribution function. This may be done in any given problem with the aid of tables of the derivative of the factorial function.

However, such a problem arises so rarely that it is not worth while to study it here. The parameters—n in the binomial distribution, α in the gamma distribution, and α and β in the beta distribution—are usually

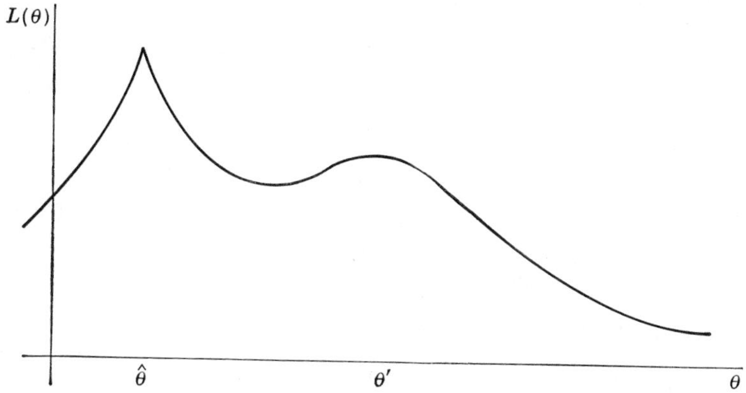

FIG. 8.2

determined by the sample size, and we are considering the case where the sample size is known.

8.11 Properties of Maximum-likelihood Estimators

In many of the problems which are of importance in applied statistics, maximum-likelihood estimators are quite easy to obtain, and often they have some of the optimum properties discussed in the previous sections. In fact, under quite general regularity conditions on the density function $f(x; \theta)$, maximum-likelihood estimators are (1) (asymptotically) efficient estimators and BAN estimators; (2) (simple) consistent estimators and squared-error consistent estimators; (3) a function of the minimal sufficient statistics. In addition to these properties, the maximum-likelihood estimators possess a property which is called invariance. That is, let $\hat{\boldsymbol{\theta}} = d(\mathbf{x}_1, \mathbf{x}_2, \cdots, \mathbf{x}_n)$ be the maximum-likelihood estimator of θ in the density $f(x; \theta)$. If $u(\theta)$ is a function of θ with a single-valued inverse, then the maximum-likelihood estimator of $u(\theta)$ is $u(\hat{\boldsymbol{\theta}})$. For example, in the normal density the maximum-likelihood estimator of σ^2 is

$$\hat{\boldsymbol{\sigma}}^2 = \frac{1}{n} \sum_{i=1}^{n} (\mathbf{x}_i - \bar{\mathbf{x}})^2$$

By the invariance property of maximum-likelihood estimators, the maximum-likelihood estimator of σ is

$$\hat{\boldsymbol{\sigma}} = \sqrt{\frac{1}{n} \sum (\mathbf{x}_i - \bar{\mathbf{x}})^2}$$

Similarly, the maximum-likelihood estimator of, say, $\log \sigma^2$ is

$$\log \left[\frac{1}{n} \sum (\mathbf{x}_i - \bar{\mathbf{x}})^2 \right]$$

etc.

The maximum-likelihood estimator is not always unbiased, but many times it can be modified so that it becomes unbiased. For example,

$$\hat{\boldsymbol{\sigma}}^2 = \frac{1}{n} \sum (\mathbf{x}_i - \bar{\mathbf{x}})^2$$

is a biased estimator of σ^2, but $[n/(n-1)]\hat{\boldsymbol{\sigma}}^2$ is unbiased. For a more general discussion of maximum likelihood the reader is referred to the references in the bibliography.

8.12 Estimation by the Method of Moments

Let $f(x; \theta_1, \cdots, \theta_k)$ be a density which has k parameters. Let $\mu_1', \mu_2', \cdots, \mu_k'$ be the first k moments about zero; i.e.,

$$\mu_t' = \int_{-\infty}^{\infty} x^t f(x; \theta_1, \cdots, \theta_k)\, dx \qquad t = 1, 2, \cdots, k$$

In general, μ_t' will be a function of the k parameters $\theta_1, \cdots, \theta_k$, and we denote this by writing $\mu_t' = \mu_t'(\theta_1, \theta_2, \cdots, \theta_k)$. Let $\mathbf{x}_1, \mathbf{x}_2, \cdots, \mathbf{x}_n$ be a random sample of size n from the density $f(x; \theta_1, \cdots, \theta_k)$. From this sample let us form the first k sample moments $\mathbf{m}_1', \mathbf{m}_2', \cdots, \mathbf{m}_k'$, where

$$\mathbf{m}_t' = \frac{1}{n} \sum_{i=1}^{n} \mathbf{x}_i^t$$

Let $\hat{\boldsymbol{\theta}}_1, \hat{\boldsymbol{\theta}}_2, \cdots, \hat{\boldsymbol{\theta}}_k$ be the solution for θ_i of the k equations

$$\mathbf{m}_t' = \mu_t' \qquad t = 1, 2, \cdots, k$$

These solutions are the estimators obtained by the method of moments. For example, let $\mathbf{x}$ be distributed $n(x; \mu, \sigma^2)$. In Chap. 6 we found that $\mu_1' = \mu$; $\mu_2' = \sigma^2 + \mu^2$. Now let $\mathbf{x}_1, \mathbf{x}_2, \cdots, \mathbf{x}_n$ be a random sample of size n from this distribution. Then the sample moments are $\mathbf{m}_1' = \frac{1}{n} \sum \mathbf{x}_i$; $\mathbf{m}_2' = \frac{1}{n} \sum \mathbf{x}_i^2$. Equating the population and sample moments gives us

$$\hat{\boldsymbol{\mu}} = \bar{\mathbf{x}} \qquad \hat{\boldsymbol{\sigma}}^2 + \hat{\boldsymbol{\mu}}^2 = \frac{1}{n} \sum \mathbf{x}_i^2$$

or

$$\hat{\boldsymbol{\mu}} = \bar{\mathbf{x}} \qquad \hat{\boldsymbol{\sigma}}^2 = \frac{1}{n} \left(\sum \mathbf{x}_i^2 - n\bar{\mathbf{x}}^2 \right)$$

In this density the estimators obtained by the method of moments are the same as the maximum-likelihood estimators.

Under quite general conditions it can be shown that estimators derived by the method of moments are (1) (simple) consistent estimators and squared-error consistent estimators and (2) asymptotically normal but not, in general, (asymptotically) efficient nor BAN.

8.13 Bayes Estimators

In the previous sections we have been discussing a density, say $f(x; \theta)$, of a random variable $\mathbf{x}$, where θ is the unknown parameter which can take values in the space Ω. In some real-world situations which the density $f(x; \theta)$ represents, there is often some additional information about θ (the only assumption which we heretofore have made about θ is that it can take on values in Ω). For example, the experimenter may have evidence that θ itself acts as a random variable, for which he may be able to postulate a realistic density function. For instance, suppose that a machine which stamps out parts for automobiles is to be examined to see what fraction p of defectives are being made. On a certain day, 10 pieces of the machine's output are examined, with the observations denoted by $\mathbf{x}_1, \mathbf{x}_2, \cdots, \mathbf{x}_{10}$, where $\mathbf{x}_i = 1$ if the ith piece is defective and $\mathbf{x}_i = 0$ if it is nondefective. These can be viewed as a random sample of size 10 from the point binomial density

$$f(x; p) = p^x(1 - p)^{1-x} \qquad x = 0, 1; 0 \leq p \leq 1$$

which indicates that the probability that a given part is defective is equal to the unknown number p. The joint density of the 10 random variables $\mathbf{x}_1, \mathbf{x}_2, \cdots, \mathbf{x}_{10}$ is

$$g(x_1, x_2, \cdots, x_{10}; p) = p^{\Sigma x_i}(1 - p)^{10-\Sigma x_i} \qquad x_i = 0, 1; 0 \leq p \leq 1$$

The maximum-likelihood estimator of p, as explained in previous sections, is $\hat{\mathbf{p}} = \bar{\mathbf{x}}$. The method of moments gives the same estimator.

Suppose, however, that the experimenter has some additional information about p; suppose that he has observed that on various days the value of p changes and it appears that the change can be represented as a random variable with the density

$$h(p) = 6p(1 - p) \qquad 0 \leq p \leq 1$$

An important question is, How can this *additional* information about p be used to estimate p? In many problems it may be unrealistic to assume that p acts as a random variable; in other problems, even though it seems reasonable to assume that p acts as a random variable, it may not be known what the density function of p is. However, in some problems the assumptions are realistic, and so we shall examine this situation in this section. Heretofore we have used the notation $f(x; \theta)$ to indicate the density of a random variable $\mathbf{x}$ for each value of θ in Ω. Whenever we want to indicate that the *parameter* is also a random variable, we shall write the density of $\mathbf{x}$ as $f(x|\theta)$ instead of $f(x; \theta)$.

Let $\mathbf{x}_1, \cdots, \mathbf{x}_n$ be a random sample of size n from the density $f(x|\theta)$. Suppose that we want to estimate the θ that determined the density from which the random sample was taken. Suppose that $p(\theta)$ is the marginal density of $\boldsymbol{\theta}$ and $l(\hat{\theta}; \theta)$ is the loss. Remember that, even though we are assuming that $\boldsymbol{\theta}$ is a random variable, we desire to estimate a particular value of $\boldsymbol{\theta}$—that value, call it θ, that determined the density $f(x|\theta)$ from which the particular random sample was selected. In other words, as $\boldsymbol{\theta}$ varies, it determines different densities. From one of these densities the random sample is taken. We desire to estimate the value of θ that determines this density. The risk is $E[l(\hat{\boldsymbol{\theta}}; \boldsymbol{\theta})] = R(d, \boldsymbol{\theta})$. Since $\boldsymbol{\theta}$ is a random variable, we shall be interested in finding the function d which will minimize the *expected* risk. The expected risk can be written

$$B(d) = E[R(d, \boldsymbol{\theta})] = \int_{-\infty}^{\infty} R(d, \theta)p(\theta)\, d\theta \tag{1}$$

$$= \int_{-\infty}^{\infty} \left\{ \int_{-\infty}^{\infty} \cdots \int_{-\infty}^{\infty} l[d(x_1, \cdots, x_n); \theta] g(x_1, \cdots, x_n|\theta)\, dx_1 \cdots dx_n \right\} p(\theta)\, d\theta \tag{2}$$

A "good" estimator will be a function d of the x_i which minimizes $B(d)$; this function will be called the *Bayes estimator*. If we interchange the order of integration of the x's and θ in (2), we get

$$B(d) = \int_{-\infty}^{\infty} \cdots \int_{-\infty}^{\infty} \left\{ \int_{-\infty}^{\infty} l[d(x_1, \cdots, x_n); \theta] g(x_1, \cdots, x_n|\theta) p(\theta)\, d\theta \right\} dx_1 \cdots dx_n \tag{3}$$

Now $B(d)$ will be minimized if a function d of the x_i can be found which minimizes the quantity in braces in (3) for every set of the x's. That is, we want to find $d(x_1, \cdots, x_n)$ which minimizes

$$\int_{-\infty}^{\infty} l[d(x_1, \cdots, x_n); \theta] g(x_1, \cdots, x_n|\theta) p(\theta)\, d\theta \tag{4}$$

The quantity $g(x_1, \cdots, x_n|\theta) \cdot p(\theta)$ in (4) is the joint distribution of $\mathbf{x}_1, \cdots, \mathbf{x}_n, \boldsymbol{\theta}$. We shall denote this by $q(x_1, \cdots, x_n, \theta)$. The marginal distribution of the x's is given by

$$k(x_1, \cdots, x_n) = \int_{-\infty}^{\infty} q(x_1, \cdots, x_n, \theta)\, d\theta = \int_{-\infty}^{\infty} g(x_1, \cdots, x_n|\theta) \cdot p(\theta)\, d\theta \tag{5}$$

and the conditional distribution of $\boldsymbol{\theta}$, given $\mathbf{x}_1, \mathbf{x}_2, \cdots, \mathbf{x}_n$, is

$$h(\theta|x_1, \cdots, x_n) = \frac{q(x_1, \cdots x_n, \theta)}{k(x_1, \cdots, x_n)} = \frac{g(x_1, \cdots, x_n|\theta)p(\theta)}{k(x_1, \cdots, x_n)} \tag{6}$$

and is called the a posteriori density. Thus we can write (4) as

$$k(x_1, \cdots, x_n) \int_{-\infty}^{\infty} l[d(x_1, \cdots, x_n); \theta] h(\theta|x_1, \cdots, x_n)\, d\theta \tag{7}$$

Thus a Bayes estimator is *the value of* $\hat{\theta}$ which minimizes for each possible sample $\mathbf{x}_1, \mathbf{x}_2, \cdots, \mathbf{x}_n$ the quantity

$$v(\hat{\theta}; x_1, \cdots, x_n) = \int_{-\infty}^{\infty} l(\hat{\theta}; \theta) h(\theta|x_1, \cdots, x_n)\, d\theta \tag{8}$$

The function v represents the *a posteriori risk* for estimating $\boldsymbol{\theta}$, given that $\mathbf{x}_1 = x_1, \cdots, \mathbf{x}_n = x_n$. This will be summarized in the following definition.

Definition 8.11. *Let $\mathbf{x}_1, \cdots, \mathbf{x}_n$ be a random sample from the density $f(x|\theta)$, let $p(\theta)$ be the density of $\boldsymbol{\theta}$, and let $g(x_1, \cdots, x_n|\theta)$ be the conditional density of the* $\mathbf{x}$*'s, given $\boldsymbol{\theta}$. Further, let $h(\theta|x_1, \cdots, x_n)$ be the conditional density of $\boldsymbol{\theta}$, given the* $\mathbf{x}$*'s, and let $l(\hat{\boldsymbol{\theta}}; \boldsymbol{\theta})$ be the loss. Then the Bayes estimator of $\boldsymbol{\theta}$ is a function defined by $\hat{\boldsymbol{\theta}} = d(\mathbf{x}_1, \cdots, \mathbf{x}_n)$ which minimizes $B(d)$ given in* (1).

By (2) to (8) above we have the following theorem:

Theorem 8.7. *The value of $\hat{\theta}$ as a function of the x's which minimizes the a posteriori risk $v[\hat{\theta}; x_1, \cdots, x_n]$ in equation* (8) *is the Bayes estimator of θ for the densities and the loss function given in Definition* 8.11.

If the densities in Definition 8.11 are discrete rather than continuous, the integrals in this section are replaced by summation signs.

Example 8.15. Let $\mathbf{x}_1, \cdots, \mathbf{x}_n$ be a random sample from the density $f(x|\theta) = \theta^x(1-\theta)^{1-x}$; $x = 0, 1$; $0 \le \theta \le 1$. Therefore the conditional density of the $\mathbf{x}$'s, given $\boldsymbol{\theta}$, is

$$g(x_1, \cdots, x_n|\theta) = \theta^{\Sigma x_i}(1-\theta)^{n-\Sigma x_i}$$

Suppose that the loss is squared-error; that is, $l(\hat{\boldsymbol{\theta}}; \boldsymbol{\theta}) = (\hat{\boldsymbol{\theta}} - \boldsymbol{\theta})^2$. Further suppose that the density of $\boldsymbol{\theta}$ is uniform, so that $p(\theta) = 1, 0 \le \theta \le 1$. Then

$$q(x_1, \cdots, x_n, \theta) = \theta^{\Sigma x_i}(1-\theta)^{n-\Sigma x_i} \cdot 1$$

and

$$k(x_1, \cdots, x_n) = \int_0^1 \theta^{\Sigma x_i}(1-\theta)^{n-\Sigma x_i}\, d\theta$$

which, by Sec. 6.4, is equal to

$$\frac{[(\Sigma x_i)!][(n - \Sigma x_i)!]}{(n + 1)!}$$

so that

$$h(\theta|x_1, \cdots, x_n) = (n + 1)! \frac{\theta^{\Sigma x_i}(1 - \theta)^{n - \Sigma x_i}}{[(\Sigma x_i)!][(n - \Sigma x_i)!]} \qquad 0 \leq \theta \leq 1$$

By (8), we want to find a function d defined by $\hat{\boldsymbol{\theta}} = d(\mathbf{x}_1, \cdots, \mathbf{x}_n)$ which will minimize

$$v(\hat{\theta}; x_1, \cdots, x_n) = \int_0^1 (\hat{\theta} - \theta)^2 \frac{(n + 1)!\theta^{\Sigma x_i}(1 - \theta)^{n - \Sigma x_i}}{[(\Sigma x_i)!][(n - \Sigma x_i)!]} \, d\theta$$

By Sec. 6.4, we get

$$\begin{aligned} v(\hat{\theta}; x_1, \cdots, x_n) &= \hat{\theta}^2 - 2\hat{\theta} \frac{[(n + 1)!][(\Sigma x_i + 1)!]}{[(n + 2)!][(\Sigma x_i)!]} \\ &\qquad + \frac{[(n + 1)!][(\Sigma x_i + 2)!]}{[(n + 3)!][(\Sigma x_i)!]} \\ &= \hat{\theta}^2 - 2\hat{\theta} \frac{\Sigma x_i + 1}{n + 2} + \frac{(\Sigma x_i + 2)(\Sigma x_i + 1)}{(n + 2)(n + 3)} \end{aligned}$$

The value of $\hat{\theta}$ as a function of the x's which minimizes $v(\hat{\theta}; x_1, \cdots, x_n)$ is obtained by setting the derivative of v with respect to $\hat{\theta}$ equal to 0. The solution is

$$\hat{\theta} = \frac{\Sigma x_i + 1}{n + 2}$$

and so the Bayes estimator of θ for this problem is

$$\hat{\boldsymbol{\theta}} = \frac{\Sigma \mathbf{x}_i + 1}{n + 2}$$

Example 8.16. Let $\mathbf{x}_1, \cdots, \mathbf{x}_n$ be a random sample from the normal density with variance 1:

$$f(x|\mu) = \frac{1}{\sqrt{2\pi}} e^{-\frac{1}{2}(x - \mu)^2}$$

Then

$$g(x_1, \cdots, x_n|\mu) = \frac{1}{(2\pi)^{n/2}} e^{-\frac{1}{2}\Sigma(x_i - \mu)^2} = \frac{1}{(2\pi)^{n/2}} e^{-\frac{1}{2}(\Sigma x_i^2 - 2\mu\Sigma x_i + n\mu^2)}$$

Suppose that $\boldsymbol{\mu}$ is a random variable and the density of $\boldsymbol{\mu}$ is

$$p(\mu) = \frac{1}{\sqrt{2\pi}} e^{-\mu^2/2} \qquad -\infty < \mu < \infty$$

Then

$$q(x_1, \cdots, x_n, \mu) = \frac{1}{(2\pi)^{(n+1)/2}} \exp\left\{-\frac{1}{2}\left[\sum x_i^2 + (n+1)\mu^2 - 2\mu n\bar{x}\right]\right\}$$

and

$$k(x_1, \cdots, x_n) = \frac{1}{(2\pi)^{(n+1)/2}} \exp\left(-\frac{1}{2}\sum x_i^2\right) \int_{-\infty}^{\infty} \exp\left\{-\frac{1}{2}[(n+1)\mu^2 - 2\mu n\bar{x}]\right\} d\mu$$

By completing the square in the exponent under the integral, this becomes

$$\frac{1}{(2\pi)^{n/2}} \exp\left[-\frac{1}{2}\left(\sum x_i^2 - \frac{n^2\bar{x}^2}{n+1}\right)\right] \left\{\frac{1}{(2\pi)^{\frac{1}{2}}} \int_{-\infty}^{\infty} \exp\left[-\frac{1}{2}(n+1)\left(\mu - \frac{n\bar{x}}{n+1}\right)^2\right] d\mu\right\}$$

By Sec. 6.2 , the quantity in braces is $(n + 1)^{-\frac{1}{2}}$ and so

$$k(x_1, \cdots, x_n) = \frac{1}{(n+1)^{\frac{1}{2}}(2\pi)^{n/2}} \exp\left[-\frac{1}{2}\left(\sum x_i^2 - \frac{n^2\bar{x}^2}{n+1}\right)\right]$$

and

$$h(\mu|x_1, \cdots, x_n) = \frac{(2\pi)^{-(n+1)/2} \exp\left\{-\frac{1}{2}\left[\sum x_i^2 + (n+1)\mu^2 - 2n\bar{x}\mu\right]\right\}}{(2\pi)^{-(n/2)}(n+1)^{-\frac{1}{2}} \exp\left[-\frac{1}{2}\left(\sum x_i^2 - \frac{n^2\bar{x}^2}{n+1}\right)\right]}$$

$$= \frac{(n+1)^{\frac{1}{2}}}{(2\pi)^{\frac{1}{2}}} \exp\left\{-\frac{1}{2}(n+1)\left[\mu^2 - \frac{2n\bar{x}\mu}{n+1} + \frac{n^2\bar{x}^2}{(n+1)^2}\right]\right\}$$

$$= \frac{(n+1)^{\frac{1}{2}}}{(2\pi)^{\frac{1}{2}}} \exp\left\{-\frac{1}{2}(n+1)\left[\mu - \frac{n\bar{x}}{n+1}\right]^2\right\}$$

Thus the conditional distribution of $\boldsymbol{\mu}$, given $\mathbf{x}_1, \cdots, \mathbf{x}_n$, is normal with mean $\bar{x}n/(n + 1)$ and variance $(n + 1)^{-1}$. Suppose that the loss function that we want to consider is the squared-error loss function

$$l(\hat{\boldsymbol{\mu}}; \boldsymbol{\mu}) = (\hat{\boldsymbol{\mu}} - \boldsymbol{\mu})^2$$

Then the Bayes estimator is the value of $\hat{\mu}$ as a function of the x's which minimizes $v(\hat{\mu}; x_1, \cdots, x_n)$, where

$$v(\hat{\mu}; x_1, \cdots, x_n) = \int_{-\infty}^{\infty} (\hat{\mu} - \mu)^2 \cdot h(\mu|x_1, \cdots, x_n)\, d\mu$$

$$= \frac{(n+1)^{\frac{1}{2}}}{(2\pi)^{\frac{1}{2}}} \int_{-\infty}^{\infty} (\hat{\mu} - \mu)^2 \exp\left\{-\frac{1}{2}(n+1)\left[\mu - \frac{n\bar{x}}{n+1}\right]^2\right\} d\mu$$

$$= \hat{\mu}^2 - \frac{2\hat{\mu}\bar{x}n}{n+1} + \frac{1}{n+1} + \frac{\bar{x}^2n^2}{(n+1)^2}$$

To find the value of $\hat{\mu}$ that minimizes $v(\hat{\mu}; x_1, \cdots, x_n)$, we solve the equation

$$\frac{\partial[v(\hat{\mu}; x_1, \cdots, x_n)]}{\partial\hat{\mu}} = 2\hat{\mu} - \frac{2\bar{x}n}{n+1} = 0$$

which gives $\hat{\mu} = \Sigma x_i/(n + 1)$. Thus the Bayes estimator for μ is

$$\hat{\mathbf{u}} = \frac{\Sigma \mathbf{x}_i}{n+1}$$

Under quite general conditions it can be shown that the Bayes estimator corresponding to an arbitrary a priori probability distribution with positive density is (1) consistent; (2) (asymptotically) efficient and a BAN estimator; and (3) a function of the minimal sufficient statistic. In addition, it can be shown that the Bayes estimator differs from the maximum-likelihood estimator by an amount which is small compared with $1/\sqrt{n}$.

8.14 Problems

1. Let $\mathbf{x}_1$, $\mathbf{x}_2$ be a random sample of size 2 from a normal distribution with unknown mean μ and variance 1, where μ can vary between $-\infty$ and $+\infty$. We want to find a point estimate of μ. We shall consider three estimators

$$\hat{\mathbf{u}}_1 = d_1(\mathbf{x}_1, \mathbf{x}_2) = \tfrac{2}{3}\mathbf{x}_1 + \tfrac{1}{3}\mathbf{x}_2 \qquad \hat{\mathbf{u}}_2 = d_2(\mathbf{x}_1, \mathbf{x}_2) = \tfrac{1}{4}\mathbf{x}_1 + \tfrac{3}{4}\mathbf{x}_2$$

$$\hat{\mathbf{u}}_3 = d_3(\mathbf{x}_1, \mathbf{x}_2) = \tfrac{1}{2}\mathbf{x}_1 + \tfrac{1}{2}\mathbf{x}_2$$

and the loss function

$$l(\hat{\mathbf{u}}; \mu) = 3\mu^2(\hat{\mathbf{u}} - \mu)^2$$

Find $R(d_1; \mu)$.

2. In Prob. 1, define the action space and the parameter space.

3. In Prob. 1, find $R(d_2; \mu)$ and $R(d_3; \mu)$.

4. How does d_1, d_2, or d_3 compare as far as minimum risk for every value of μ?

5. Prove that all three estimators in Prob. 1 are unbiased.

6. In Prob. 1, find the relative efficiencies (*a*) d_1 to d_2; (*b*) d_1 to d_3; (*c*) d_2 to d_3.

7. Find the maximum-likelihood estimator for μ, the population mean, given a sample of size n from a population with $f(x) = 1/\beta$, $0 < x < \beta$. Estimate β by the method of moments.

8. The sample 1.3, .6, 1.7, 2.2, .3, 1.1 was drawn from a population with the density $f(x) = 1/\beta$, $0 < x < \beta$. What are the maximum-likelihood estimates of the mean and variance of the population?

9. What is the maximum-likelihood estimator for α in the density $f(x) = (\alpha + 1)x^\alpha$, $0 < x < 1$? Estimate α by the method of moments.

10. Assuming α known, find the maximum-likelihood estimator for β for a random sample of size n in the gamma distribution. Is it a sufficient statistic? Unbiased?

11. For a random sample of size n find the maximum-likelihood estimator for the parameter of the Poisson distribution. Is it a sufficient statistic? Unbiased?

12. For a random sample of size n find the maximum-likelihood estimator for the variance of a normal population, assuming that the mean is known. Is it a sufficient statistic? Unbiased?

13. For a random sample of size 1 find the maximum-likelihood estimator for the variance of the gamma distribution, assuming that α is known.

14. If $\mathbf{x}$ is distributed by $f(x) = 1/\beta$, $0 < x < \beta$, and one considers samples consisting of only one observation $\mathbf{x}$, then since $E(\mathbf{x}) = \beta/2$, the estimator for β based on the method of moments is $\hat{\boldsymbol{\beta}}_1 = 2\mathbf{x}$. On the other hand, the maximum-likelihood estimator for β is $\hat{\boldsymbol{\beta}}_2 = \mathbf{x}$. Is there any choice between these two estimators on grounds of relative efficiency?

15. Let $\mathbf{x}_1, \cdots, \mathbf{x}_n$ be a random sample of size n from a normal density with mean μ and variance σ^2, where $-\infty < \mu < \infty$ and $0 < \sigma^2 < \infty$. If $\hat{\boldsymbol{\sigma}}^2 = \frac{1}{n-1} \sum (\mathbf{x}_i - \bar{\mathbf{x}})^2$, it can be shown that

$$\text{var}\,(\hat{\boldsymbol{\sigma}}^2) = \frac{2\sigma^2}{n-1}$$

Show that $\hat{\boldsymbol{\sigma}}^2$ is a squared-error consistent estimator of σ^2.

16. Let $\mathbf{x}_1, \cdots, \mathbf{x}_n$ be a random sample from the density $f(x; \theta)$ which is either discrete or continuous, and let $\{\hat{\boldsymbol{\theta}}_n\}$ be a sequence of estimators which is a squared-error consistent estimator for θ. Use Tchebysheff's inequality to show that $\{\hat{\boldsymbol{\theta}}_n\}$ is also a (simple) consistent estimator for θ.

17. If $\mathbf{x}$ is normally distributed with mean μ and variance σ^2, find, for a random sample of size k, the maximum-likelihood estimator of the point A such that $\int_A^\infty n(x; \mu, \sigma^2)\,dx = .05$. Find the minimum-variance unbiased estimator of A.

18. It is shown in Chap. 10 that the mean of a sample from a normal population is exactly normally distributed. Use this fact to show that the sample mean is sufficient for the population mean when σ is known.

19. In genetic investigations one frequently samples from a binomial $f(x) = \binom{m}{x} p^x q^{m-x}$ except that observations of $x = 0$ are impossible, so that, in fact, the sampling is from the conditional distribution

$$g(x|x > 0) = \binom{m}{x} \frac{p^x q^{m-x}}{1 - q^m} \qquad x = 1, 2, \cdots, m$$

Find the maximum-likelihood estimator of p in the case $m = 2$ for samples of size n. Is the estimator unbiased?

20. Find the estimator for α in the density

$$f(x; \alpha) = \frac{2}{\alpha^2}(\alpha - x) \qquad 0 < x < \alpha$$

for samples of size 2. Is it a sufficient statistic? Estimate α by the method of moments.

21. Referring to Prob. 20, what is the maximum-likelihood estimator of the population mean?

22. An urn contains black and white balls. A sample of size n is drawn, with replacement. What is the maximum-likelihood estimator of the ratio R of black to white balls in the urn?

23. Referring to Prob. 22, suppose that one draws balls one by one, with replacement, until a black ball appears. Let $\mathbf{x}$ be the number of draws required (not counting the last draw). This operation is repeated n times to obtain a sample $\mathbf{x}_1, \mathbf{x}_2, \cdots, \mathbf{x}_n$. What is the maximum-likelihood estimator of R on the basis of this sample?

24. Let $\mathbf{x}_1, \mathbf{x}_2, \cdots, \mathbf{x}_n$ be a random sample of size n from a normal density with mean μ and variance σ^2. The estimators $\bar{\mathbf{x}} = \hat{\boldsymbol{\mu}}$ and $\hat{\boldsymbol{\sigma}}^2 = (n - 1)^{-1}\Sigma(\mathbf{x}_i - \bar{\mathbf{x}})^2$ are sufficient and complete. Find the minimum-variance unbiased estimator for (*a*) $6\mu + 4\sigma^2$ and (*b*) $\mu^2 - 5\sigma^2$.

25. Let $\mathbf{x}_1, \mathbf{x}_2, \cdots, \mathbf{x}_n$ be a random sample of size n from the point binomial density $p^x(1 - p)^{1-x}$, $x = 0, 1$. The estimator $\hat{\mathbf{p}} = \bar{\mathbf{x}}$ is sufficient and complete. Find the minimum-variance unbiased estimator for (*a*) $3p$ and (*b*) $5p - 1$.

26. Suppose that n cylindrical shafts made by a machine are selected at random from the production of the machine and their diameters and lengths measured. It is found that $\mathbf{n}_{11}$ have both measurements within the tolerance limits, $\mathbf{n}_{12}$ have satisfactory lengths but unsatisfactory diameters, $\mathbf{n}_{21}$ have satisfactory diameters but unsatisfactory lengths, and $\mathbf{n}_{22}$ are unsatisfactory as to both measurements. $\Sigma\mathbf{n}_{ij} = n$. Each shaft may be regarded as a drawing from a multinomial population with density

$$p_{11}{}^{x_{11}}p_{12}{}^{x_{12}}p_{21}{}^{x_{21}}(1 - p_{11} - p_{12} - p_{21})^{x_{22}} \qquad x_{ij} = 0, 1; \Sigma x_{ij} = 1$$

having three parameters. What are the maximum-likelihood estimates of the parameters if $\mathbf{n}_{11} = 90$, $\mathbf{n}_{12} = 6$, $\mathbf{n}_{21} = 3$, $\mathbf{n}_{22} = 1$?

27. Referring to the above problem, suppose that there is no reason to believe that defective diameters can in any way be related to defective lengths. Then the distribution of the $\mathbf{x}_{ij}$ can be set up in terms of two parameters: p_1, the probability of a satisfactory length, and q_1, the probability of a satisfactory diameter. The density of the $\mathbf{x}_{ij}$ is then

$$(p_1q_1)^{x_{11}}[p_1(1 - q_1)]^{x_{12}}[(1 - p_1)q_1]^{x_{21}}[(1 - p_1)(1 - q_1)]^{x_{22}} \qquad x_{ij} = 0, 1; \Sigma x_{ij} = 1$$

What are the maximum-likelihood estimates for these parameters? Are the probabilities for the four classes different under this model from those obtained in the above problem?

28. A sample of size n_1 is to be drawn from a normal population with mean μ_1 and variance σ_1^2. A second sample of size n_2 is to be drawn from a normal population with mean μ_2 and variance σ_2^2. What is the maximum-likelihood estimator of $\alpha = \mu_1 - \mu_2$? Assuming that the total sample size $n = n_1 + n_2$ is fixed, how should the n observations be divided between the two populations in order to minimize the variance of $\hat{\alpha}$?

29. A sample of size n is drawn from each of four normal populations, all of which have the same variance σ^2. The means of the four populations are $a + b + c$, $a + b - c$, $a - b + c$, $a - b - c$. What are the maximum-likelihood estimators of a, b, c, and σ^2? (The sample observations may be denoted by $\mathbf{x}_{ij}$, $i = 1, 2, 3, 4$, and $j = 1, 2, \cdots, n$.)

30. Observations $\mathbf{x}_1, \mathbf{x}_2, \cdots, \mathbf{x}_n$ are drawn from normal populations with the same mean μ but with different variances $\sigma_1^2, \sigma_2^2, \cdots, \sigma_n^2$. Is it possible to estimate all the parameters? Assuming that the σ_i^2 are known, what is the maximum-likelihood estimator of μ?

31. Is $\hat{\sigma}$, the square root of the expression in equation (8.10.14), an unbiased estimate of σ?

32. Let μ be the true I.Q. of a certain student. To measure his I.Q., he takes a test, and it is known that his test scores are normally distributed with mean μ and standard deviation 5. This student takes the I.Q. test and gets a score of 130. What is the maximum-likelihood estimator of μ?

33. In Prob. 32, suppose that it is known that the true I.Q.'s of students of a certain age are distributed normally with mean 100 and variance 225; i.e., assume that $\boldsymbol{\mu}$ is distributed normally with mean 100 and variance 225. Thus $f(x|\mu)$ in Prob. 32 is $n(x; \mu, 25)$ and $p(\mu)$ is $n(\mu; 100, 225)$. Find $q(x, \mu)$ and $k(x)$ in Sec. 8.13.

34. In Prob. 33, show that the conditional density $h(\mu|x)$ is normal with mean $.9x + 10$ and variance $45/2$.

35. Using the loss $l(\hat{\boldsymbol{\mu}}; \boldsymbol{\mu}) = (\hat{\boldsymbol{\mu}} - \boldsymbol{\mu})^2$ in Prob. 34, find the Bayes estimator of μ, the student's I.Q., if the student's test score is $\mathbf{x} = 130$. Note that it is not the same as the maximum-likelihood estimator in Prob. 32.

36. The fraction defective in a day's production of a certain product is θ. Let $\mathbf{x}$ be an observation on one of the items of a given day's production. The distribution of $\mathbf{x}$ is

$$f(x|\theta) = \theta^x(1-\theta)^{1-x} \qquad x = 0, 1; 0 \le \theta \le 1$$

where $\mathbf{x} = 1$ is identified with a defective item and $\mathbf{x} = 0$ is identified with the item if it is not defective. While the proportion defective remains constant for a given day, it is noticed that θ varies from day to day and θ acts as a random variable with density function

$$p(\theta) = 6\theta(1-\theta) \qquad 0 \le \theta \le 1$$

Consider the loss $l(\hat{\boldsymbol{\theta}}; \boldsymbol{\theta}) = 2(\hat{\boldsymbol{\theta}} - \boldsymbol{\theta})^2$, where $\hat{\boldsymbol{\theta}}$ is the estimator for θ. If no observations $\mathbf{x}$ are available, the value of $\hat{\boldsymbol{\theta}}$ that minimizes

$$E[l(\hat{\boldsymbol{\theta}}; \boldsymbol{\theta})] = \int_0^1 2(\hat{\boldsymbol{\theta}} - \theta)^2 p(\theta)\, d\theta$$

could be used to estimate θ. Find this value of $\hat{\boldsymbol{\theta}}$.

37. If one observation $\mathbf{x}$ is available in Prob. 36, find $q(x, \theta)$ and $k(x)$ in Sec. 8.13.

38. In Prob. 37, find $h(\theta|x)$ in Sec. 8.13.

39. In Prob. 37, find $v(\hat{\theta}; x)$ in Sec. 8.13.

40. In Prob. 37, find the Bayes estimator of θ.

41. If

$$f(x|\theta) = \frac{2x}{\theta^2} \qquad 0 < x < \theta$$

and

$$p(\theta) = 1 \qquad 0 < \theta < 1$$

find the Bayes estimator for θ, using the loss $l(\hat{\boldsymbol{\theta}}; \boldsymbol{\theta}) = \boldsymbol{\theta}^2(\hat{\boldsymbol{\theta}} - \boldsymbol{\theta})^2$.

42. Show that for the loss $(\hat{\boldsymbol{\theta}} - \boldsymbol{\theta})^2$ the Bayes estimator is given by $\hat{\boldsymbol{\theta}}^*$, where

$$\hat{\boldsymbol{\theta}}^* = E(\boldsymbol{\theta}|\mathbf{x}) = \int_{-\infty}^{\infty} \theta h(\theta|\mathbf{x})\, d\theta$$

43. Let $\mathbf{x}_1, \cdots, \mathbf{x}_n$ be a random sample of size n from the Poisson density

$$f(x|\lambda) = \frac{\lambda^x e^{-\lambda}}{x!} \qquad x = 0, 1, \cdots$$

Let $\boldsymbol{\lambda}$ have the density

$$p(\lambda) = e^{-\lambda} \qquad 0 < \lambda < \infty$$

Find the a posteriori density $h(\lambda|x_1, \cdots, x_n)$.

44. In Prob. 43, find $E(\boldsymbol{\lambda}|x_1, \cdots, x_n)$ and show that this is the Bayes estimator for the loss

$$l(\hat{\boldsymbol{\lambda}}; \boldsymbol{\lambda}) = (\hat{\boldsymbol{\lambda}} - \boldsymbol{\lambda})^2$$

8.15 Bibliography

1. Blackwell, D.: "Conditional expectation and unbiased sequential estimation," *Annals of Mathematical Statistics,* Vol. 18(1947), pp. 105–110.
2. Chernoff, Herman: "Remarks on a rational selection of a decision function," Cowles Commission Discussion Paper 326, Statistics, Jan. 10, 1949. Unpublished.
3. Chernoff, H., and L. E. Moses: "Elementary Decision Theory," John Wiley & Sons, Inc., New York, 1959.
4. Cramér, Harald: "Mathematical Methods of Statistics," Princeton University Press, Princeton, N.J., 1946.
5. Doob, J.: "Statistical estimation," *Transactions of the American Mathematical Society,* Vol. 39(1936), pp. 410–421.
6. Fisher, R. A.: "On the mathematical foundations of theoretical statistics," *Philosophical Transactions of the Royal Society of London,* Series A, Vol. 222(1922).
7. Fisher, R. A.: "Statistical Methods for Research Workers," Oliver & Boyd, Ltd., Edinburgh and London, 1925.
8. Fisher, R. A.: "Theory of statistical estimation," *Proceedings of the Cambridge Philosophical Society,* Vol. 22(1925).
9. Fisher, R. A.: "The Design of Experiments," Oliver & Boyd, Ltd., Edinburgh and London, 1935.
10. Lehmann, E. L.: "Testing Statistical Hypotheses," John Wiley & Sons, Inc., New York, 1959.
11. Lehmann, E. L., and H. Scheffé: "Completeness, similar regions and unbiased estimation," *Sankhyā,* Vol. 10(1950), pp. 305–340.
12. Neyman, Jerzy: "Contributions to the theory of the χ^2 test," *Proceedings of the Berkeley Symposium on Mathematical Statistics and Probability,* University of California Press, Berkeley, Calif., 1949, pp. 239–273.
13. Pitman, E. J. G.: "The 'closest' estimate of statistical parameters," *Proceedings of the Cambridge Philosophical Society,* Vol. 33(1937), pp. 212–222.
14. Rao, C. R.: "Information and accuracy attainable in the estimation of statistical parameters," *Bulletin of the Calcutta Mathematical Society,* Vol. 37(1945), p. 81.
15. Rao, C. R.: "Minimum variance and the estimation of several parameters," *Proceedings of the Cambridge Philosophical Society,* Vol. 43(1947), p. 280.
16. Rao, C. R.: "Sufficient statistics and minimum variance estimates," *Proceedings of the Cambridge Philosophical Society,* Vol. 45(1948), p. 213.
17. Thrall, Robert M., Clyde H. Coombs, and Robert L. Davis (eds.): "Decision Processes," John Wiley & Sons, Inc., New York, 1954.
18. Wald, Abraham: "On the Principles of Statistical Inference," University of Notre Dame Press, Notre Dame, Ind., 1942.
19. Wald, Abraham: "Statistical Decision Functions," John Wiley & Sons, Inc., New York, 1950.
20. Weiss, Lionel: "Statistical Decision Theory," McGraw-Hill Book Company, Inc., New York, 1961.
21. Wolfowitz, J.: "On Wald's proof of the consistency of the maximum-likelihood estimates," *Annals of Mathematical Statistics,* Vol. 20(1949), pp. 601–602.

9

The Multivariate Normal Distribution

9.1 The Bivariate Normal Distribution

One of the important multivariate densities is the multivariate normal, which is a generalization of the normal distribution for a single variate. In this section we shall discuss a special case, the case of a two-variate (bivariate) normal. To discuss more than two variates is very tedious without the use of matrices and vectors. Therefore Sec. 9.2 will provide the necessary elements of matrix theory, and the remainder of the chapter will be devoted to a study of the multivariate normal by employing matrices. Those readers who are not familiar with matrices and who do not wish to take the time to study Sec. 9.2 can study the bivariate normal in this section and then go directly to Chap. 10.

Definition 9.1. The Bivariate Normal. *Let the two-dimensional random variable* $(\mathbf{x}, \mathbf{y})$ *have the joint density*

$$f(x, y) = \frac{1}{2\pi\sigma_x\sigma_y\sqrt{1-\rho^2}} e^{-\frac{1}{2(1-\rho^2)}\left[\left(\frac{x-\mu_x}{\sigma_x}\right)^2 - 2\rho\frac{x-\mu_x}{\sigma_x}\frac{y-\mu_y}{\sigma_y} + \left(\frac{y-\mu_y}{\sigma_y}\right)^2\right]} \tag{1}$$

$-\infty < x < \infty$, $-\infty < y < \infty$, *where* σ_y, σ_x, μ_x, μ_y, ρ *are constants such that* $-1 < \rho < 1$; $0 < \sigma_y$; $0 < \sigma_x$; $-\infty < \mu_x < \infty$; $-\infty < \mu_y < \infty$. *Then the random variable is said to have a bivariate normal distribution.*

The density in (1) may be represented by a bell-shaped surface $z = f(x, y)$ as in Fig. 9.1. Any plane parallel to the xy plane which cuts the surface will intersect it in an elliptical curve, while any plane perpendicular to the xy plane will cut the surface in a curve of the normal form. The probability that a point $(\mathbf{x}, \mathbf{y})$ drawn at random will lie in any region R of the xy plane is obtained by integrating the density over that region,

$$P[(\mathbf{x}, \mathbf{y}) \text{ is in } R] = \iint_R f(x, y)\, dy\, dx \tag{2}$$

The density might, for example, represent the distribution of hits on a vertical target (Chap. 4) where x and y represent the horizontal and vertical deviations from the central lines. And in fact the distribution closely approximates the distribution of this as well as many other bivariate populations encountered in practice.

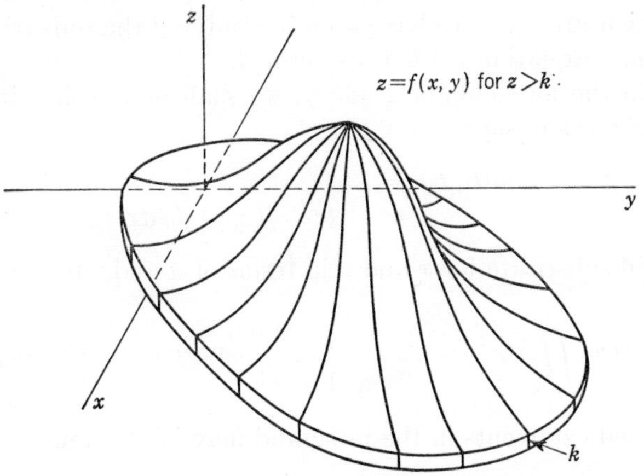

FIG. 9.1

We must first show that the function actually represents a density by showing that its integral over the whole plane is 1, i.e.,

$$\int_{-\infty}^{\infty} \int_{-\infty}^{\infty} f(x, y)\, dy\, dx = 1 \tag{3}$$

The density is, of course, positive. To simplify the integral, we shall substitute

$$u = \frac{x - \mu_x}{\sigma_x} \tag{4}$$

$$v = \frac{y - \mu_y}{\sigma_y}$$

so that it becomes

$$\int_{-\infty}^{\infty} \int_{-\infty}^{\infty} \frac{1}{2\pi \sqrt{1 - \rho^2}} e^{-[1/2(1-\rho^2)](u^2 - 2\rho uv + v^2)}\, dv\, du$$

On completing the square on u in the exponent, we have

$$\int_{-\infty}^{\infty} \int_{-\infty}^{\infty} \frac{1}{2\pi \sqrt{1 - \rho^2}} e^{-[1/2(1-\rho^2)][(u-\rho v)^2 + (1-\rho^2)v^2]}\, dv\, du$$

and on substituting

$$w = \frac{u - \rho v}{\sqrt{1 - \rho^2}} \qquad dw = \frac{du}{\sqrt{1 - \rho^2}}$$

the integral may be written as the product of two simple integrals,

$$\int_{-\infty}^{\infty} \frac{1}{\sqrt{2\pi}} e^{-(w^2/2)}\, dw \int_{-\infty}^{\infty} \frac{1}{\sqrt{2\pi}} e^{-(v^2/2)}\, dv \tag{5}$$

both of which are 1, as we have seen in studying the univariate normal distribution. Equation (3) is thus verified.

To obtain the moments of **x** and **y**, we shall find their joint moment generating function, say,

$$\begin{aligned} m(t_1, t_2) &= E(e^{t_1\mathbf{x}+t_2\mathbf{y}}) &(6)\\ &= \iint e^{t_1x+t_2y} f(x, y)\, dy\, dx &(7)\end{aligned}$$

Let us again substitute for x and y in terms of u and v to obtain $m(t_1, t_2) =$

$$e^{t_1\mu_x+t_2\mu_y} \iint e^{t_1\sigma_x u+t_2\sigma_y v} \frac{1}{2\pi\sqrt{1-\rho^2}} e^{-[1/2(1-\rho^2)](u^2-2\rho uv+v^2)}\, dv\, du \tag{8}$$

The combined exponents in the integrand may be written

$$-\frac{1}{2(1-\rho^2)}[u^2 - 2\rho uv + v^2 - 2(1-\rho^2)t_1\sigma_x u - 2(1-\rho^2)t_2\sigma_y v]$$

and on completing the square first on u and then on v, we find this expression becomes

$$-\frac{1}{2(1-\rho^2)}\{[u - \rho v - (1-\rho^2)t_1\sigma_x]^2 + (1-\rho^2)(v - \rho t_1\sigma_x - t_2\sigma_y)^2 - (1-\rho^2)(t_1^2\sigma_x^2 + 2\rho t_1t_2\sigma_x\sigma_y + t_2^2\sigma_y^2)\}$$

which, on substituting

$$w = \frac{u - \rho v - (1-\rho^2)t_1\sigma_x}{\sqrt{1-\rho^2}}$$
$$z = v - \rho t_1\sigma_x - t_2\sigma_y$$

becomes

$$-\tfrac{1}{2}w^2 - \tfrac{1}{2}z^2 + \tfrac{1}{2}(t_1^2\sigma_x^2 + 2\rho t_1t_2\sigma_x\sigma_y + t_2^2\sigma_y^2)$$

and the integral in (8) may be written

$$\begin{aligned} m(t_1, t_2) &= e^{t_1\mu_x+t_2\mu_y} e^{\frac{1}{2}(t_1^2\sigma_x^2+2\rho t_1t_2\sigma_x\sigma_y+t_2^2\sigma_y^2)} \int_{-\infty}^{\infty}\int_{-\infty}^{\infty} \frac{1}{2\pi} e^{-(w^2/2)-(z^2/2)}\, dw\, dz\\ &= e^{t_1\mu_x+t_2\mu_y+\frac{1}{2}(t_1^2\sigma_x^2+2\rho t_1t_2\sigma_x\sigma_y+t_2^2\sigma_y^2)} \end{aligned} \tag{9}$$

since the integral is obviously 1. Thus we have the following theorem.

Theorem 9.1. *The moment generating function of the bivariate normal distribution is*

$$m(t_1, t_2) = e^{t_1\mu_x+t_2\mu_y+\frac{1}{2}(t_1^2\sigma_x^2+2\rho t_1t_2\sigma_x\sigma_y+t_2^2\sigma_y^2)}$$

The moments may be obtained by evaluating the derivatives of $m(t_1, t_2)$ at $t_1 = 0$, $t_2 = 0$. Thus,

$$E(\mathbf{x}) = \frac{\partial m}{\partial t_1}\bigg]_{t_1,t_2=0} = \mu_x \tag{10}$$

$$E(\mathbf{x}^2) = \frac{\partial^2 m}{\partial t_1^2}\bigg]_{t_1,t_2=0} = \mu_x^2 + \sigma_x^2 \tag{11}$$

Hence the variance of **x** is

$$E(\mathbf{x} - \mu_x)^2 = E(\mathbf{x}^2) - \mu_x^2 = \sigma_x^2 \tag{12}$$

Similarly, on differentiating with respect to t_2, one finds the mean and variance of **y** to be μ_y and σ_y^2. We can also obtain joint moments

$$E(\mathbf{x}^r\mathbf{y}^s)$$

by differentiating $m(t_1, t_2)$ r times with respect to t_1 and s times with respect to t_2, then putting t_1 and t_2 equal to 0. The *covariance* of **x** and **y** is

$$\begin{aligned} E[(\mathbf{x} - \mu_x)(\mathbf{y} - \mu_y)] &= E(\mathbf{xy} - \mathbf{x}\mu_y - \mathbf{y}\mu_x + \mu_x\mu_y) \\ &= E(\mathbf{xy}) - \mu_x\mu_y \\ &= \rho\sigma_x\sigma_y \end{aligned} \tag{13}$$

The parameter ρ is called the *correlation* between **x** and **y**. When the correlation is 0, it will be observed in (1) that $f(x, y)$ becomes the product of two univariate normal distributions; hence in this case ($\rho = 0$), **x** and **y** will be independent in the probability sense.

The marginal density of one of the variables, **x**, for example, is, by definition,

$$f_1(x) = \int_{-\infty}^{\infty} f(x, y)\, dy \tag{14}$$

and again substituting

$$v = \frac{y - \mu_y}{\sigma_y}$$

and completing the square on v, one finds

$$f_1(x) = \int_{-\infty}^{\infty} \frac{1}{2\pi\sigma_x\sqrt{1-\rho^2}} e^{-\frac{1}{2}\left(\frac{x-\mu_x}{\sigma_x}\right)^2 - \frac{1}{2(1-\rho^2)}\left(v - \rho\frac{x-\mu_x}{\sigma_x}\right)^2} dv$$

Then the substitution

$$w = \frac{v - \rho[(x - \mu_x)/\sigma_x]}{\sqrt{1-\rho^2}} \qquad dw = \frac{dv}{\sqrt{1-\rho^2}}$$

shows at once that

$$f_1(x) = \frac{1}{\sqrt{2\pi}\,\sigma_x} e^{-\frac{1}{2}\left(\frac{x-\mu_x}{\sigma_x}\right)^2} \tag{15}$$

the univariate normal density. Similarly the marginal density of **y** may be found to be

$$f_2(y) = \frac{1}{\sqrt{2\pi}\,\sigma_y} e^{-\frac{1}{2}\left(\frac{y-\mu_y}{\sigma_y}\right)^2} \tag{16}$$

We have the following theorem.

Theorem 9.2. *Let the two-dimensional random variable* (**x**, **y**) *have the bivariate density given in Definition* 9.1. *The marginal density of* **x** *is normal with mean* μ_x *and variance* σ_x^2. *The marginal density of* **y** *is normal with mean* μ_y *and variance* σ_y^2.

Having the marginal distributions, it is possible to determine the conditional distributions. Thus the conditional density of **x** for fixed values of **y** is

$$f(x|y) = \frac{f(x, y)}{f_2(y)}$$

and, after substituting, the expression may be put in the form

$$f(x|y) = \frac{1}{\sqrt{2\pi}\,\sigma_x\sqrt{1-\rho^2}} e^{-\frac{1}{2\sigma_x^2(1-\rho^2)}\left[x-\mu_x-\frac{\rho\sigma_x}{\sigma_y}(y-\mu_y)\right]^2} \tag{17}$$

which is a univariate normal density with mean $\mu_x + (\rho\sigma_x/\sigma_y)(y - \mu_y)$ and with variance $\sigma_x^2(1 - \rho^2)$. The conditional distribution of **y** may be obtained by interchanging x and y throughout (17) to get

$$f(y|x) = \frac{1}{\sqrt{2\pi}\,\sigma_y\sqrt{1-\rho^2}} e^{-\frac{1}{2\sigma_y^2(1-\rho^2)}\left[y-\mu_y-\frac{\rho\sigma_y}{\sigma_x}(x-\mu_x)\right]^2} \tag{18}$$

Thus we have the following theorem.

Theorem 9.3. *Let the two-dimensional random variable* (**x**, **y**) *have the bivariate density given in Definition* 9.1. *The conditional density of* **x**, *given* **y** $= y$, *is normal with mean* $\mu_x + (\rho\sigma_x/\sigma_y)(y - \mu_y)$ *and variance* $\sigma_x^2(1 - \rho^2)$. *The conditional density of* **y**, *given* **x** $= x$, *is normal with mean* $\mu_y + (\rho\sigma_y/\sigma_x)(x - \mu_x)$ *and variance* $\sigma_y^2(1 - \rho^2)$.

The mean value of a variate in a conditional distribution is called a *regression* when regarded as a function of the fixed variates in the conditional distribution. Thus the regression for **x** in (17) is $\mu_x + (\rho\sigma_x/\sigma_y)(y - \mu_y)$, which is a linear function of y in the present case. For bivariate distributions in general, the mean of **x** in the conditional density of **x** given **y** $= y$ will be some function of y, say g, and the equation

$$x = g(y)$$

when plotted in the xy plane gives the *regression curve* for **x**. It is simply a curve which gives the location of the mean of **x** for various values of **y** in the conditional density of **x** given **y**.

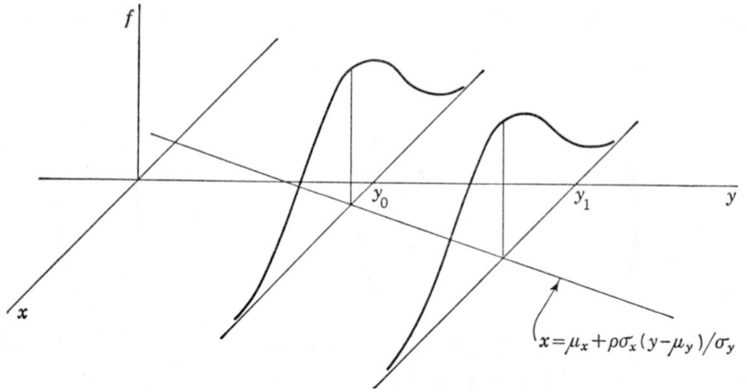

FIG. 9.2

For the bivariate normal distribution, the regression curve is the straight line obtained by plotting

$$x = \mu_x + \frac{\rho\sigma_x}{\sigma_y}(y - \mu_y) \tag{19}$$

as shown in Fig. 9.2. The conditional density of **x**, $f(x|y)$, is also plotted in the figure for two particular values, y_0 and y_1, of **y**.

The cumulative bivariate normal distribution

$$F(x, y) = \int_{-\infty}^{x} \int_{-\infty}^{y} f(s, t)\, dt\, ds$$

may be reduced to a form involving only the parameter ρ by the substitution (4).

9.2 Matrices and Determinants

In this section we shall give some theorems on matrices and determinants which will be necessary for developing the general p-variate normal distribution. We shall not give the proofs for the theorems in this section, but we assume that the reader is acquainted with the elementary concepts of matrices. Throughout this chapter we shall use the capital letters V, R, R_{11}, R_{12}, R_{21}, R_{22}, V_{11}, V_{12}, V_{21}, and A to represent matrices and the letters Y, μ, U_2, Y_2^*, Y_1^*, U_1, X^* to represent vectors. This section and the remaining ones in this chapter can be omitted without interrupting the continuity of the book, except for a few sections which are starred. Chapter 14 and a portion of Chap. 13 will make extensive use of matrices and vectors.

Definition 9.2. *A matrix V with p rows and q columns is a rectangular array of elements σ_{ij}. The elements σ_{ij} may be numbers, functions, random variables, etc. The quantity σ_{ij} denotes the element in the ith row and jth column of V.*

For example, let

$$V = \begin{pmatrix} \sigma_{11} & \sigma_{12} & \cdots & \sigma_{1p} \\ \sigma_{21} & \sigma_{22} & \cdots & \sigma_{2p} \\ \cdot & \cdot & & \cdot \\ \cdot & \cdot & & \cdot \\ \cdot & \cdot & & \cdot \\ \sigma_{p1} & \sigma_{p2} & \cdots & \sigma_{pp} \end{pmatrix} \quad \text{and} \quad Y = \begin{pmatrix} y_1 \\ y_2 \\ \cdot \\ \cdot \\ \cdot \\ y_p \end{pmatrix} \tag{1}$$

Then V is a $p \times p$ matrix whose ijth element is σ_{ij}, and it is sometimes written $V = (\sigma_{ij})$. Y is a $p \times 1$ matrix whose ith element is y_i. (If a matrix has a single row or a single column, it is called a vector.)

We shall use **0** for the zero matrix; i.e., every element is 0. I will represent the identity matrix, i.e., a square matrix such that $\sigma_{ii} = 1$ and $\sigma_{ij} = 0$ if $i \neq j$. V' will represent the transpose of a matrix V; that is, the rows and columns are interchanged. V^{-1} will represent the inverse of the matrix V; that is, V^{-1} is a square matrix such that $VV^{-1} = V^{-1}\, V = I$. $|V|$ will denote the determinant of the square matrix V. If $V = V'$, the matrix is called symmetric.

We shall make extensive use of quadratic forms.

Definition 9.3. *Let Y be a $p \times 1$ vector with elements y_i, and let V be a $p \times p$ symmetric matrix with elements σ_{ij}; then $Y'VY$ is a quadratic form in the elements y_i, and V is called the matrix of the quadratic form, where*

$$Y'VY = \sum_{i=1}^{p} \sum_{j=1}^{p} y_i y_j \sigma_{ij} \tag{2}$$

For a general matrix V, the quadratic form can be positive, negative, or zero. However, we shall be interested in a class of matrices for which the quadratic form is always positive except when Y is the zero vector.

Definition 9.4. *If the quadratic form $Y'VY$ is positive for every nonzero vector Y, then $Y'VY$ is called a positive definite quadratic form, and V is called a positive definite (symmetric) matrix.*

To determine whether a quadratic form is positive definite, the following theorem can be used.

Theorem 9.4. *Let a $p \times p$ symmetric matrix V be represented by* (1). *A necessary and sufficient condition that V is a positive definite symmetric matrix is that the following p determinants be positive.*

$$\sigma_{11}; \quad \begin{vmatrix} \sigma_{11} & \sigma_{12} \\ \sigma_{21} & \sigma_{22} \end{vmatrix}; \quad \begin{vmatrix} \sigma_{11} & \sigma_{12} & \sigma_{13} \\ \sigma_{21} & \sigma_{22} & \sigma_{23} \\ \sigma_{31} & \sigma_{32} & \sigma_{33} \end{vmatrix}; \quad \cdots; \quad \begin{vmatrix} \sigma_{11} & \sigma_{12} & \cdots & \sigma_{1p} \\ \sigma_{21} & \sigma_{22} & \cdots & \sigma_{2p} \\ \cdot & \cdot & & \cdot \\ \cdot & \cdot & & \cdot \\ \cdot & \cdot & & \cdot \\ \sigma_{p1} & \sigma_{p2} & \cdots & \sigma_{pp} \end{vmatrix} \tag{3}$$

For example, if

$$V = \begin{pmatrix} 3 & 2 & 0 \\ 2 & 2 & 1 \\ 0 & 1 & 2 \end{pmatrix}$$

then

$$\sigma_{11} = 3 > 0 \qquad \begin{vmatrix} \sigma_{11} & \sigma_{12} \\ \sigma_{21} & \sigma_{22} \end{vmatrix} = \begin{vmatrix} 3 & 2 \\ 2 & 2 \end{vmatrix} = 2 > 0 \qquad \text{and} \qquad |V| = 1 > 0$$

and so V is positive definite.

Also let $Y' = (y_1, y_2, y_3)$. Then

$$\begin{aligned} Y'VY &= (y_1, y_2, y_3) \begin{pmatrix} 3 & 2 & 0 \\ 2 & 2 & 1 \\ 0 & 1 & 2 \end{pmatrix} \begin{pmatrix} y_1 \\ y_2 \\ y_3 \end{pmatrix} \\ &= 3y_1^2 + 2y_2^2 + 2y_3^2 + 4y_1y_2 + 2y_2y_3 \end{aligned}$$

It can be shown that

$$V^{-1} = \begin{pmatrix} 3 & -4 & 2 \\ -4 & 6 & -3 \\ 2 & -3 & 2 \end{pmatrix}$$

It is often useful to partition a matrix into submatrices such as

$$V = \begin{pmatrix} V_{11} & V_{12} \\ V_{21} & V_{22} \end{pmatrix} \tag{4}$$

where V is $p \times p$, V_{11} is $k \times k$, V_{12} is $k \times (p - k)$, V_{21} is $(p - k) \times k$, and V_{22} is $(p - k) \times (p - k)$. Notice also, if V is symmetric, then $V'_{12} = V_{21}$. If V is positive definite symmetric, then V_{11} is also positive definite symmetric, as is V_{22}, and so V_{11}^{-1} and V_{22}^{-1} exist. In general, V_{12} has no inverse. Let R be another $p \times p$ matrix, which we shall partition into submatrices of the same size as V. Then to multiply we have

$$VR = \begin{pmatrix} V_{11} & V_{12} \\ V_{21} & V_{22} \end{pmatrix} \begin{pmatrix} R_{11} & R_{12} \\ R_{21} & R_{22} \end{pmatrix} = \begin{pmatrix} V_{11}R_{11} + V_{12}R_{21} & V_{11}R_{12} + V_{12}R_{22} \\ V_{21}R_{11} + V_{22}R_{21} & V_{21}R_{12} + V_{22}R_{22} \end{pmatrix} \tag{5}$$

Let us assume that R is the inverse of V, and so $R^{-1} = V$ and $VR = I$. If V is positive definite symmetric, then R is also positive definite symmetric and R_{11}^{-1} and R_{22}^{-1} exist, but in general R_{12} has no inverse. Now partition the $p \times p$ identity so that $VR = I$ becomes

$$\begin{pmatrix} V_{11}R_{11} + V_{12}R_{21} & V_{11}R_{12} + V_{12}R_{22} \\ V_{21}R_{11} + V_{22}R_{21} & V_{21}R_{12} + V_{22}R_{22} \end{pmatrix} = \begin{pmatrix} I & \mathbf{0} \\ \mathbf{0} & I \end{pmatrix}$$

which gives $V_{11}R_{11} + V_{12}R_{21} = I$ and $V_{11}R_{12} + V_{12}R_{22} = \mathbf{0}$ so that $V_{12} = -V_{11}R_{12}R_{22}^{-1}$ and substituting gives $V_{11}R_{11} - V_{11}R_{12}R_{22}^{-1}R_{21} = I$. Multiplication by V_{11}^{-1} gives

$$V_{11}^{-1} = R_{11} - R_{12}R_{22}^{-1}R_{21}$$

By using other equations we get the following theorem.

Theorem 9.5. *Let $V^{-1} = R$, and let the two positive definite symmetric matrices be partitioned as in* (5); *then the following matrix equations are obtained:*

$$\begin{array}{ll} (a)\ V_{11}^{-1} = R_{11} - R_{12}R_{22}^{-1}R_{21} & (b)\ V_{22}^{-1} = R_{22} - R_{21}R_{11}^{-1}R_{12} \\ (c)\ R_{11}^{-1} = V_{11} - V_{12}V_{22}^{-1}V_{21} & (d)\ R_{22}^{-1} = V_{22} - V_{21}V_{11}^{-1}V_{12} \\ (e)\ V_{11}^{-1}V_{12} = -R_{12}R_{22}^{-1} & (f)\ V_{22}^{-1}V_{21} = -R_{21}R_{11}^{-1} \end{array} \tag{6}$$

If V is symmetric positive definite, then the determinant of V can be written as

$$\begin{aligned} |V| &= |V_{22}|\,|V_{11} - V_{12}V_{22}^{-1}V_{21}| \\ &= |V_{11}|\,|V_{22} - V_{21}V_{11}^{-1}V_{12}| \end{aligned}$$

Also

$$\begin{aligned} |R| &= |R_{11}|\,|R_{22} - R_{21}R_{11}^{-1}R_{12}| \\ &= |R_{22}|\,|R_{11} - R_{12}R_{22}^{-1}R_{21}| \end{aligned} \tag{7}$$

Let the matrix in the example above be partitioned so that

$$V_{11} = 3$$

Then

$$V_{12} = (2, 0) \qquad V_{21} = \begin{pmatrix} 2 \\ 0 \end{pmatrix} \qquad V_{22} = \begin{pmatrix} 2 & 1 \\ 1 & 2 \end{pmatrix}$$

Let $R = V^{-1}$, and partition it so that

$$R_{11} = 3$$

$$R_{12} = (-4, 2) \qquad R_{21} = \begin{pmatrix} -4 \\ 2 \end{pmatrix} \qquad R_{22} = \begin{pmatrix} 6 & -3 \\ -3 & 2 \end{pmatrix}$$

Since $RV = I$, we can demonstrate part (a) of Theorem 9.5 as

$$\begin{aligned} R_{11} - R_{12}R_{22}^{-1}R_{21} &= 3 - (-4, 2)\begin{pmatrix} 6 & -3 \\ -3 & 2 \end{pmatrix}^{-1}\begin{pmatrix} -4 \\ 2 \end{pmatrix} \\ &= 3 - (-4, 2)\begin{pmatrix} 2/3 & 1 \\ 1 & 2 \end{pmatrix}\begin{pmatrix} -4 \\ 2 \end{pmatrix} = 3 - 8/3 = 1/3 \end{aligned}$$

But $V_{11} = 3$, so that $V_{11}^{-1} = \frac{1}{3}$, and this demonstrates part (*a*) of Theorem 9.5.

Also $|R| = 1$ but $R_{11} - R_{12}R_{22}^{-1}R_{21} = \frac{1}{3}$ and

$$|R_{22}| = 12 - 9 = 3$$

and so
$$|R_{22}| \cdot |R_{11} - R_{12}R_{22}^{-1}R_{21}| = 3 \cdot \tfrac{1}{3} = 1$$

The student can demonstrate other relations in Theorem 9.5.

Another important result of determinants is: If $V^{-1} = R$, then $R = 1/|V|$.

*9.3 Multivariate Normal

Let $(\mathbf{y}_1, \mathbf{y}_2, \cdots, \mathbf{y}_p)$ be a p-dimensional random variable which we shall designate as elements of a vector $\mathbf{Y}$ by

$$\mathbf{Y} = \begin{pmatrix} \mathbf{y}_1 \\ \mathbf{y}_2 \\ \cdot \\ \cdot \\ \cdot \\ \mathbf{y}_p \end{pmatrix} \tag{1}$$

$\mathbf{Y}$ will be called a random $p \times 1$ vector.

Definition 9.5. *The random vector* $\mathbf{Y}$ *is distributed as the p-variate normal if the joint density of* $\mathbf{y}_1, \mathbf{y}_2, \cdots, \mathbf{y}_p$ *is*

$$f(Y) = f(y_1, y_2, \cdots, y_p) = \frac{|R|^{\frac{1}{2}}}{(2\pi)^{p/2}} e^{-\frac{1}{2}(Y-\mu)'R(Y-\mu)} \qquad \begin{matrix} -\infty < y_i < \infty \\ i = 1, 2, \cdots, p \end{matrix} \tag{2}$$

where

(*a*) *R is a positive definite symmetric matrix whose elements* r_{ij} *are constants (not random variables).*

(*b*) μ *is a* $p \times 1$ *vector whose elements* μ_i *are constants.*

We notice that, if $p = 1$, then $R = r_{11}$ which, by part (*a*), must be positive. If we set $r_{11} = 1/\sigma^2$, it is clear that the density in (2) is the normal distribution defined in Chap. 6. The quantity $Q = (Y - \mu)'R(Y - \mu)$ is called the quadratic form of the p-variate normal. It is a quadratic form in the elements $y_i - \mu_i$. It can be written as

$$Q = \sum_{j=1}^{p} \sum_{i=1}^{p} (y_i - \mu_i)(y_j - \mu_j)r_{ij} \tag{3}$$

To prove that (2) satisfies the properties that qualify it to be a density, we must show (1) that $f(Y) \geq 0$, which is obvious since R, the determinant of

* See explanation in Sec. 9.2.

a positive definite matrix, is positive and (2) that the integral of $f(Y)$ is equal to 1. We shall not prove condition 2, but a consequence of this fact is

$$\int_{-\infty}^{\infty} \cdots \int_{-\infty}^{\infty} e^{-\frac{1}{2}(Y-\mu)'R(Y-\mu)}\, dy_1, dy_2, \cdots, dy_p = \frac{(2\pi)^{p/2}}{|R|^{\frac{1}{2}}} \tag{4}$$

which gives us the following theorem.

Theorem 9.6. *The multiple integral*

$$\int_{-\infty}^{\infty} \cdots \int_{-\infty}^{\infty} e^{-\frac{1}{2}(Y-\mu)'R(Y-\mu)}\, dy_1 \cdots dy_p \tag{5}$$

is equal to $(2\pi)^{p/2}|R|^{-\frac{1}{2}}$ *and does not depend on the vector* μ.

To find the marginal distribution of one of the random variables in $\mathbf{Y}$, say $\mathbf{y}_1$, we get

$$g(y_1) = \int_{-\infty}^{\infty} \cdots \int_{-\infty}^{\infty} |R|^{\frac{1}{2}}(2\pi)^{-p/2}e^{-\frac{1}{2}(Y-\mu)'R(Y-\mu)}\, dy_2\, dy_3 \cdots dy_p$$

If we partition the vectors and the matrix in the exponent we get

$$(Y-\mu)'R(Y-\mu) = \begin{pmatrix} y_1-\mu_1 \\ Y_2-U_2 \end{pmatrix}' \begin{pmatrix} r_{11} & R_{12} \\ R_{21} & R_{22} \end{pmatrix} \begin{pmatrix} y_1-\mu_1 \\ Y_2-U_2 \end{pmatrix} \tag{6}$$

where Y_2 and U_2 are $(p-1) \times 1$ vectors, R_{12} is $1 \times (p-1)$, and R_{22} is $(p-1) \times (p-1)$. Multiplying gives us

$$\begin{aligned}(Y-\mu)'R(Y-\mu) &= (y_1-\mu_1)r_{11}(y_1-\mu_1) + (y_1-\mu_1)R_{12}(Y_2-U_2) \\ &\quad + (Y_2-U_2)'R_{21}(y_1-\mu_1) + (Y_2-U_2)'R_{22}(Y_2-U_2)\end{aligned} \tag{7}$$

Since R is positive definite symmetric, it follows that $R_{12}' = R_{21}$, R_{22}^{-1} exists and is symmetric, and $r_{11} > 0$. We can write (7) as

$$\begin{aligned}(Y-\mu)'R(Y-\mu) &= (y_1-\mu_1)(r_{11} - R_{12}R_{22}^{-1}R_{21})(y_1-\mu_1) \\ &\quad + [(Y_2-U_2) + R_{22}^{-1}R_{21}(y_1-\mu_1)]'R_{22}[(Y_2-U_2) + R_{22}^{-1}R_{21}(y_1-\mu_1)]\end{aligned} \tag{8}$$

Equation (8) can be verified by multiplication and comparing term by term with (7). Using (8), we can write the marginal of $\mathbf{y}_1$ as

$$g(y_1) = |R|^{\frac{1}{2}}(2\pi)^{-p/2}e^{-(y_1-\mu_1)^2/2\sigma^2}.F \tag{9}$$

where F is the multiple integral

$$F = \int_{-\infty}^{\infty} \cdots \int_{-\infty}^{\infty} e^{-\frac{1}{2}(Y_2-h)'R_{22}(Y_2-h)}\, dy_2 \cdots dy_p$$

where $1/\sigma^2 = r_{11} - R_{12}R_{22}^{-1}R_{21}$ and $h = U_2 - R_{22}^{-1}R_{21}(y_1-\mu_1)$.

By (4) we get

$$F = \int_{-\infty}^{\infty} \cdots \int_{-\infty}^{\infty} e^{-1/2(Y_2-h)'R_{22}(Y_2-h)}\, dy_2\, dy_3 \cdots dy_p = (2\pi)^{(p-1)/2}|R_{22}|^{-\frac{1}{2}}$$

and so

$$g(y_1) = \frac{|R|^{\frac{1}{2}}}{|R_{22}|^{\frac{1}{2}}(2\pi)^{\frac{1}{2}}} e^{-(y_1-\mu_1)^2/2\sigma^2}$$

By equation (9.2.7), $|R| = |R_{22}| \cdot |r_{11} - R_{12}R_{22}^{-1}R_{21}|$ and so

$$g(y_1) = \frac{1}{\sigma\sqrt{2\pi}} e^{-(y_1-\mu_1)^2/2\sigma^2}$$

which, by Sec. 6.2, indicates that $\mathbf{y}_1$ is a normal variable with mean μ_1 and variance $\sigma^2 = (r_{11} - R_{12}R_{22}^{-1}R_{21})^{-1}$. We have used the variable $\mathbf{y}_1$, but a similar proof follows for any variable $\mathbf{y}_t$. We have proved the following theorem.

Theorem 9.7. *Let* $\mathbf{Y}$ *be distributed as the p-variate normal with density given by* (2). *Then the marginal density of* $\mathbf{y}_1$ *is normal with mean* μ_1 *and variance* $(r_{11} - R_{12}R_{22}^{-1}R_{21})^{-1}$.

Instead of the marginal density of a single random variable $\mathbf{y}_1$, the joint density of k random variables in $\mathbf{Y}$ can be obtained by replacing $\mathbf{y}_1$ by the $k \times 1$ vector $\mathbf{Y}_1$, μ_1 by U_1, and r_{11} by R_{11} in the above proof.

Corollary 9.7.1. *Let the* $p \times 1$ *random vector* $\mathbf{Y}$ *be normal with density given by* (2). *Let* $\mathbf{Y}_1$ *be the first k components of* $\mathbf{Y}$, *let* U_1 *be the first k components of* μ, *and let R be partitioned as follows:*

$$R = \begin{pmatrix} R_{11} & R_{12} \\ R_{21} & R_{22} \end{pmatrix}$$

where R_{11} *is* $k \times k$. *Then* $\mathbf{Y}_1$ *is distributed as the k-variate normal with density*

$$f(Y_1) = \frac{|R_{11} - R_{12}R_{22}^{-1}R_{21}|^{\frac{1}{2}}}{(2\pi)^{k/2}} e^{-\frac{1}{2}(Y_1-U_1)'(R_{11}-R_{12}R_{22}{}^{-1}R_{21})(Y_1-U_1)}$$

Next we shall examine the moments of the p-variate normal, and in particular we shall be interested in the first and second moments, but first we shall define the expected value of a matrix.

Definition 9.6. *The expected value of a matrix or vector* $\mathbf{A}$, *which we shall write as* $E(\mathbf{A})$, *will be defined as the expected value of each element of* $\mathbf{A}$.

For example, if

$$\mathbf{A} = \begin{pmatrix} \mathbf{y}_{11} & \mathbf{y}_{12} \\ \mathbf{y}_{21} & \mathbf{y}_{22} \end{pmatrix}$$

then

$$E(\mathbf{A}) = \begin{pmatrix} E(\mathbf{y}_{11}) & E(\mathbf{y}_{12}) \\ E(\mathbf{y}_{21}) & E(\mathbf{y}_{22}) \end{pmatrix} \tag{10}$$

The first moments of the p-variate normal, $E(\mathbf{y}_i)$, are the moments of the respective marginal distributions. We can write

$$E(\mathbf{Y}) = \begin{pmatrix} E(\mathbf{y}_1) \\ E(\mathbf{y}_2) \\ \cdot \\ \cdot \\ \cdot \\ E(\mathbf{y}_p) \end{pmatrix} \tag{11}$$

and thus examine the first moments of every component simultaneously.

Theorem 9.8. *Let the $p \times 1$ random vector $\mathbf{Y}$ be distributed as the p-variate normal; then $E(\mathbf{Y}) = \mu$.*

Proof. By virtue of (11), we must show that $E(\mathbf{y}_i) = \mu_i$. The definition of the expected value of the random variable $\mathbf{y}_1$ gives (again we shall use $\mathbf{y}_1$ instead of $\mathbf{y}_i$, but the proof is general)

$$\begin{aligned} E(\mathbf{y}_1) &= \frac{|R|^{\frac{1}{2}}}{(2\pi)^{p/2}} \int_{-\infty}^{\infty} \cdots \int_{-\infty}^{\infty} y_1 e^{-\frac{1}{2}(Y-\mu)'R(Y-\mu)}\, dy_1\, dy_2 \cdots dy_p \\ &= \int_{-\infty}^{\infty} y_1 \left[\frac{|R|^{\frac{1}{2}}}{(2\pi)^{p/2}} \int_{-\infty}^{\infty} \cdots \int_{-\infty}^{\infty} e^{-\frac{1}{2}(Y-\mu)'R(Y-\mu)}\, dy_2 \cdots dy_p \right] dy_1 \end{aligned}$$

But by Theorem 9.7 the bracketed term is the marginal of $\mathbf{y}_1$ so that

$$E(\mathbf{y}_1) = \int_{-\infty}^{\infty} \frac{y_1}{\sigma \sqrt{2\pi}} e^{-\frac{1}{2\sigma^2}(y_1 - \mu_1)^2}\, dy_1 = \mu_1$$

and the proof is complete.

The variance of the random variable $\mathbf{y}_i$ is, by definition, $E[\mathbf{y}_i - E(\mathbf{y}_i)]^2$ which is $E(\mathbf{y}_i - \mu_i)^2$, and the covariance of the two random variables $\mathbf{y}_i$ and $\mathbf{y}_j$ is $E(\mathbf{y}_i - \mu_i)(\mathbf{y}_j - \mu_j)$, $i \neq j$. In a p-variate normal there will be p variances, one for each random variable $\mathbf{y}_i$, and $p(p-1)/2$ covariances. We shall define a $p \times p$ matrix which will have the covariance of $\mathbf{y}_i$ and $\mathbf{y}_j$ as its ijth element, if $i \neq j$, and the variance of $\mathbf{y}_i$ as its ith diagonal element. Thus

$$V = \begin{pmatrix} \sigma_{11} & \sigma_{12} & \cdots & \sigma_{1p} \\ \sigma_{21} & \sigma_{22} & \cdots & \sigma_{2p} \\ \cdot & \cdot & & \cdot \\ \cdot & \cdot & & \cdot \\ \cdot & \cdot & & \cdot \\ \sigma_{p1} & \sigma_{p2} & \cdots & \sigma_{pp} \end{pmatrix} \tag{12}$$

where $\sigma_{ij} = \sigma_{ji} = E(\mathbf{y}_i - \mu_i)(\mathbf{y}_j - \mu_j)$. This can also be written

$$V = E(\mathbf{Y} - \mu)(\mathbf{Y} - \mu)' \tag{13}$$

V will be called the covariance matrix of the vector $\mathbf{Y}$, and a remarkable relationship exists between the matrix R and the matrix V in the p-variate normal.

Theorem 9.9. *In the p-variate normal the matrix R is the inverse of the covariance matrix V; that is,* $V^{-1} = R$; *also, of course,* $R^{-1} = V$.

We shall omit the proof of this theorem, but it is a very important result, and we shall hereafter generally write the p-variate normal as

$$\frac{1}{|V|^{\frac{1}{2}}(2\pi)^{p/2}} e^{-\frac{1}{2}(Y-\mu)'V^{-1}(Y-\mu)}$$

If the ijth ($i \neq j$) element of the covariance matrix is 0, then the two random variables $\mathbf{y}_i$ and $\mathbf{y}_j$ are independent. We shall not prove this statement but it will be very useful later. Clearly the ijth element is 0 if and only if the correlation between the two random variables $\mathbf{y}_i$ and $\mathbf{y}_j$ is 0, since by definition the correlation is

$$\rho_{ij} = \frac{\sigma_{ij}}{\sqrt{\sigma_{ii}\sigma_{jj}}}$$

Theorem 9.10. *Let* $\mathbf{Y}$ *have a p-variate normal density with mean* μ *and covariance matrix* V, *and let* $\alpha_1, \cdots, \alpha_p$ *be a set of constants. Then* $\mathbf{z} = \sum_{i=1}^{p} \alpha_i \mathbf{y}_i$ *is distributed as the univariate normal with mean* $\Sigma\alpha_i\mu_i$ *and variance* $\Sigma\alpha_i^2\sigma_i^2 + \sum_{i}\sum_{j \atop i \neq j} \alpha_i\alpha_j\sigma_{ij}$.

Example 9.1. For an example to illustrate the foregoing theorems and definitions, let the 3×1 vector $\mathbf{Y}$ have a p-variate normal density, where

$$\mu = \begin{pmatrix} 3 \\ -1 \\ 0 \end{pmatrix} \qquad R = \begin{pmatrix} 2 & 0 & 3 \\ 0 & 1 & 0 \\ 3 & 0 & 5 \end{pmatrix}$$

The covariance matrix is

$$R^{-1} = V = \begin{pmatrix} 5 & 0 & -3 \\ 0 & 1 & 0 \\ -3 & 0 & 2 \end{pmatrix}$$

The mean of, say, $\mathbf{y}_2$ is -1, and the variance of $\mathbf{y}_2$ is 1. The covariance of $\mathbf{y}_1$ and $\mathbf{y}_3$ is -3, and $\mathbf{y}_1$ and $\mathbf{y}_2$ are independent. The mean of

$$\mathbf{z} = \mathbf{y}_1 - 3\mathbf{y}_2 + 2\mathbf{y}_3$$

is $1(3) - 3(-1) + 2(0) = 6$. The variance of $\mathbf{z}$ is

$$(1)^2(5) + (-3)^2(1) + (2)^2 2 + 2[(1)(-3)(0) + (1)(2)(-3) + (-3)(2)(0)] = 10$$

By Theorem 9.9 and (12), the variance of $\mathbf{y}_1$ is $\sigma_{11} = 5$. But by Theorem 9.7 the variance of $\mathbf{y}_1$ is $(r_{11} - R_{12}R_{22}^{-1}R_{21})^{-1}$. This gives

$$r_{11} - R_{12}R_{22}^{-1}R_{21} = 2 - (0, 3)\begin{pmatrix}1 & 0\\ 0 & \tfrac{1}{5}\end{pmatrix}\begin{pmatrix}0\\ 3\end{pmatrix} = 2 - \tfrac{9}{5} = \tfrac{1}{5}$$

and so $\sigma_{11} = 5$, the same as before.

Let the $p \times 1$ vector $\mathbf{Y}$, the $p \times 1$ vector μ, the matrix V, and the matrix R be partitioned as follows:

$$\mathbf{Y} = \begin{pmatrix}\mathbf{Y}_1^*\\ \mathbf{Y}_2^*\end{pmatrix} \qquad \mu = \begin{pmatrix}U_1\\ U_2\end{pmatrix} \qquad R = \begin{pmatrix}R_{11} & R_{12}\\ R_{21} & R_{22}\end{pmatrix} \qquad V = \begin{pmatrix}V_{11} & V_{12}\\ V_{21} & V_{22}\end{pmatrix} \tag{14}$$

where

$$\mathbf{Y}_1^* = \begin{pmatrix}\mathbf{y}_1\\ \cdot\\ \cdot\\ \cdot\\ \mathbf{y}_k\end{pmatrix} \qquad U_1 = \begin{pmatrix}\mu_1\\ \cdot\\ \cdot\\ \cdot\\ \mu_k\end{pmatrix}$$

R_{11} and V_{11} are each $k \times k$, and the sizes of the other matrices and vectors are determined. The conditional distribution of $\mathbf{y}_1, \mathbf{y}_2, \cdots, \mathbf{y}_k$, given $\mathbf{y}_{k+1}, \cdots, \mathbf{y}_p$, is, by definition,

$$h(y_1, \cdots, y_k | y_{k+1}, \cdots, y_p) = \frac{f(y_1, \cdots, y_p)}{g(y_{k+1}, \cdots, y_p)}$$

This will sometimes be written

$$h(Y_1^* | Y_2^*) = \frac{f(Y)}{g(Y_2^*)} \tag{15}$$

By Corollary 9.7.1, $\mathbf{Y}_2^*$ is a $(p - k)$-variate normal with mean U_2 and covariance V_{22}. Thus (15) becomes

$$h(Y_1^* | Y_2^*) = \frac{|V|^{-1/2}(2\pi)^{-p/2}e^{-\frac{1}{2}(Y-\mu)'V^{-1}(Y-\mu)}}{|V_{22}|^{-1/2}(2\pi)^{-(p-k)/2}e^{-\frac{1}{2}(Y_2^*-U_2)'V_{22}^{-1}(Y_2^*-U_2)}}$$
$$= |V_{11} - V_{12}V_{22}^{-1}V_{21}|^{-\frac{1}{2}}(2\pi)^{-k/2}e^{-\frac{1}{2}[(Y-\mu)'V^{-1}(Y-\mu)-(Y_2^*-U_2)'V_{22}^{-1}(Y_2^*-U_2)]}$$

By using (14), the quadratic form in the exponent can be written

$$\begin{aligned}
&(Y - \mu)'R(Y - \mu) - (Y_2^* - U_2)'V_{22}^{-1}(Y_2^* - U_2)\\
&\quad = \begin{pmatrix}Y_1^* - U_1\\ Y_2^* - U_2\end{pmatrix}'\begin{pmatrix}R_{11} & R_{12}\\ R_{21} & R_{22}\end{pmatrix}\begin{pmatrix}Y_1^* - U_1\\ Y_2^* - U_2\end{pmatrix}\\
&\qquad\qquad - (Y_2^* - U_2)'(R_{22} - R_{21}R_{11}^{-1}R_{12})(Y_2^* - U_2)\\
&\quad = [Y_1^* - U_1 - V_{12}V_{22}^{-1}(Y_2^* - U_2)]'R_{11}[Y_1^* - U_1 - V_{12}V_{22}^{-1}(Y_2^* - U_2)]\\
&\quad = (Y_1^* - U_1^*)'(R_{11}^{-1})^{-1}(Y_1^* - U_1^*)
\end{aligned} \tag{16}$$

where $U_1^* = U_1 + V_{12}V_{22}^{-1}(Y_2^* - U_2)$.

We have proved the following theorem.

Theorem 9.11. *Let $p \times 1$ vector* $\mathbf{Y}$ *be distributed as the p-variate normal with mean* μ *and covariance matrix* V, *and let these be partitioned as in* (14). *The conditional distribution of* $\mathbf{Y}_1^*$, *given* $\mathbf{Y}_2^*$, *is the k-variate normal with mean* $U_1^* = U_1 + V_{12} V_{22}^{-1}(Y_2^* - U_2)$ *and covariance matrix*

$$R_{11}^{-1} = V_{11} - V_{12}V_{22}^{-1}V_{21}$$

We shall sometimes denote R_{11}^{-1} by $V_{11.2}$. Notice that the covariance matrix of $\mathbf{Y}_1^*$, given $\mathbf{Y}_2^*$, does not depend on what value $\mathbf{Y}_2^*$ is. The iith element of $V_{11.2}$ is called the variance of $\mathrm{y}_i (i \le k)$, given $\mathrm{y}_{k+1}, \cdots, \mathrm{y}_p$, and is denoted by $\sigma_{ii.(k+1)\cdots p}$. Similarly the ijth element $(i \neq j)$ of $V_{11.2}$ will be denoted by $\sigma_{ij.(k+1)\cdots p}$, where the subscripts after the dot are those in $\mathbf{Y}_2^*$. The partial correlation of y_i and y_j $(i, j < k)$, given $\mathrm{y}_{k+1}, \cdots, \mathrm{y}_p$, is defined as

$$\rho_{ij.(k+1)\cdots p} = \frac{\sigma_{ij.(k+1)\cdots p}}{\sqrt{\sigma_{ii.(k+1)\cdots p}\sigma_{jj.(k+1)\cdots p}}} \tag{17}$$

Some rules will be given which will be useful in finding the various marginal and conditional distributions.

μ and V given:

Rule 1. To find the marginal of $\mathbf{Y}_1^{*\prime} = (\mathrm{y}_1, \mathrm{y}_2, \cdots, \mathrm{y}_k)$, cross out the last $p - k$ rows and columns of V and the last $p - k$ elements of μ. The resulting vector U_1 and matrix V_{11} are the vector mean and covariance of the random variable $(\mathrm{y}_1, \cdots, \mathrm{y}_k)$. If other than the first k are involved, permute the elements in $\mathbf{Y}$ until the desired random variables are the first k, and proceed as above.

Rule 2. To find the conditional density of $\mathbf{Y}_1^*$, given $\mathbf{Y}_2^*$, compute $V_{12}V_{22}^{-1}$ and $V_{12}V_{22}^{-1}V_{21}$. Then $U_1^* = U_1 + V_{12}V_{22}^{-1}(Y_2^* - U_2)$ and $V_{11.2} = V_{11} - V_{12}V_{22}^{-1}V_{21}$. Then the conditional distribution of $\mathbf{Y}_1^*$, given $\mathbf{Y}_2^*$, is the k-variate normal with mean vector U_1^* and covariance matrix $V_{11.2}$.

Example 9.2. Suppose that the 4×1 vector $\mathbf{Y}$ has mean vector μ and covariance matrix V, where

$$\mu = \begin{pmatrix} 1 \\ 0 \\ -2 \\ 3 \end{pmatrix} \qquad V = \begin{pmatrix} 2 & 0 & 1 & 0 \\ 0 & 5 & 0 & -3 \\ 1 & 0 & 1 & 0 \\ 0 & -3 & 0 & 2 \end{pmatrix}$$

To find the marginal density of $\mathbf{Y}_1^{*\prime} = (\mathrm{y}_1, \mathrm{y}_2)$, we get

$$U_1 = \begin{pmatrix} 1 \\ 0 \end{pmatrix} \qquad V_{11} = \begin{pmatrix} 2 & 0 \\ 0 & 5 \end{pmatrix}$$

Thus $\mathbf{Y}_1^*$ is distributed as the bivariate normal with mean U_1 and covariance V_{11}. Notice that $\mathbf{y}_1$ and $\mathbf{y}_2$ are independent since the element in the first row and second column of V is 0. This is, of course, also true in V_{11}. To find the conditional of $\mathbf{y}_1, \mathbf{y}_4$, given $\mathbf{y}_2, \mathbf{y}_3$, we first permute $\mathbf{y}_2, \mathbf{y}_3$, and $\mathbf{y}_4$ to get a new vector $\mathbf{Y}' = (\mathbf{y}_1, \mathbf{y}_4, \mathbf{y}_2, \mathbf{y}_3)$ which has mean and covariance

$$\mu = \begin{pmatrix} 1 \\ 3 \\ 0 \\ -2 \end{pmatrix} \qquad V = \begin{pmatrix} 2 & 0 & 0 & 1 \\ 0 & 2 & -3 & 0 \\ 0 & -3 & 5 & 0 \\ 1 & 0 & 0 & 1 \end{pmatrix} \tag{18}$$

and

$$U_1 = \begin{pmatrix} 1 \\ 3 \end{pmatrix} \qquad U_2 = \begin{pmatrix} 0 \\ -2 \end{pmatrix} \qquad V_{11} = \begin{pmatrix} 2 & 0 \\ 0 & 2 \end{pmatrix}$$

$$V_{22}^{-1} = \begin{pmatrix} 1/5 & 0 \\ 0 & 1 \end{pmatrix} \qquad V_{12} = \begin{pmatrix} 0 & 1 \\ -3 & 0 \end{pmatrix}$$

and

$$V_{11.2} = V_{11} - V_{12}V_{22}^{-1}V_{21} = \begin{pmatrix} 1 & 0 \\ 0 & 1/5 \end{pmatrix}$$

$$U_1^* = U_1 + V_{12}V_{22}^{-1}(Y_2^* - U_2) = \begin{pmatrix} y_3 + 3 \\ -3/5 y_2 + 3 \end{pmatrix}$$

So the conditional density of $(\mathbf{y}_1, \mathbf{y}_4)$ given $(\mathbf{y}_2, \mathbf{y}_3)$ is the bivariate normal with mean U_1^* and covariance $V_{11.2}$.

μ and R given:

Rule 3. To find marginal distributions, find $V = R^{-1}$ and proceed by Rule 1, or find V_{11} by equation $V_{11} = (R_{11} - R_{12}R_{22}^{-1}R_{21})^{-1}$, whichever is easier.

Rule 4. To find conditional distributions, we can use the equation $V_{12}V_{22}^{-1} = -R_{11}^{-1}R_{12}$ to evaluate U_1^*. The covariance matrix is R_{11}^{-1}.

Example 9.3. In the previous example, find the conditional distribution of $\mathbf{y}_1, \mathbf{y}_4$, given $\mathbf{y}_2, \mathbf{y}_3$, when we are given μ and R. We get

$$\mu = \begin{pmatrix} 1 \\ 3 \\ 0 \\ -2 \end{pmatrix} \qquad R = \begin{pmatrix} 1 & 0 & 0 & -1 \\ 0 & 5 & 3 & 0 \\ 0 & 3 & 2 & 0 \\ -1 & 0 & 0 & 2 \end{pmatrix} \tag{19}$$

$$R_{11} = \begin{pmatrix} 1 & 0 \\ 0 & 5 \end{pmatrix}$$

and so

$$V_{11.2} = R_{11}^{-1} = \begin{pmatrix} 1 & 0 \\ 0 & 1/5 \end{pmatrix}$$

and

$$U_1^* = U_1 - R_{11}^{-1}R_{12}(Y_2^* - U_2) = \begin{pmatrix} y_3 + 3 \\ -\frac{3}{5}y_2 + 3 \end{pmatrix}$$

the same as when Rule 2 is used. Notice also from $V_{11.2}$ that $\sigma_{11.23} = 1$, $\sigma_{44.23} = \frac{1}{5}$, $\sigma_{14.23} = 0$, and $\rho_{14.23} = 0$. Also from V in (18), $\sigma_{11} = 2$ and $\sigma_{44} = 2$ and so $\sigma_{11.23} < \sigma_{11}$ and $\sigma_{44.23} < \sigma_{44}$. This result will be the next theorem.

Theorem 9.12. *In the conditional distribution of* $\mathbf{y}_1, \cdots, \mathbf{y}_k$, *given* $\mathbf{y}_{k+1}, \cdots, \mathbf{y}_p$, *the conditional variances are less than or equal to the marginal variances; that is,* $\sigma_{ii.(k+1)\cdots p} \le \sigma_{ii}$, *where* $i = 1, 2, \cdots, k$.

The moment generating function of the p-variate normal is

$$m(t_1, t_2, \cdots, t_p) = E(e^{t_1\mathbf{y}_1 + t_2\mathbf{y}_2 + \cdots + t_p\mathbf{y}_p})$$
$$= |V|^{-\frac{1}{2}}(2\pi)^{-p/2} \int_{-\infty}^{\infty} \cdots \int_{-\infty}^{\infty} e^{\Sigma t_i y_i} e^{-\frac{1}{2}(Y-\mu)'V^{-1}(Y-\mu)} \, dy_1 dy_2 \cdots dy_p \quad (20)$$

The exponent can be written [let the $1 \times p$ vector $T' = (t_1, \cdots, t_p)$]

$$-\tfrac{1}{2}\{[Y - (\mu + VT)]'V^{-1}[Y - (\mu + VT)] - 2T'\mu - T'VT\}$$

Thus (20) can be written

$$m(T) = e^{T'\mu + \frac{1}{2}T'VT}\left[|V|^{-\frac{1}{2}}(2\pi)^{-p/2} \int_{-\infty}^{\infty} \cdots \int_{-\infty}^{\infty} e^{-\frac{1}{2}(Y-\mu-VT)'V^{-1}(Y-\mu-VT)} \, dy_1 \cdots dy_p\right] = e^{T'\mu + \frac{1}{2}T'VT}$$

Theorem 9.13. *Let* $\mathbf{Y}$ *be distributed normally with mean* μ *and covariance* V. *The m.g.f. of* $\mathbf{Y}$ *is*

$$m(T) = m(t_1, \cdots, t_p) = e^{T'\mu + \frac{1}{2}T'VT} = e^{\sum \mu_i t_i + \frac{1}{2}\sum_i \sum_j t_i t_j \sigma_{ij}}$$

The reader can refer to item 2 in the bibliography for proofs and extensions of the material presented in this section.

9.4 Problems

1. Show that the contour lines for the bivariate normal density [i.e., curves for which $f(x, y) = \text{const}$] are ellipses.

2. Show that any plane perpendicular to the xy plane intersects the normal surface in a curve of the normal form.

3. If the quadratic form of a bivariate normal density is given as $\frac{1}{3}[6(x + 1)^2 - 2(x + 1)(y - 2) + (y - 2)^2]$, what are the means, variances, and covariance of the variates?

4. What is the moment generating function for the distribution specified in Prob. 3?

5. What is the moment generating function for moments about the means for the bivariate normal distribution?

***6.** Find the inverse of the matrix $\begin{pmatrix} 3 & 1 & 0 & 0 \\ 1 & 2 & 0 & 0 \\ 0 & 0 & 2 & 0 \\ 0 & 0 & 0 & 4 \end{pmatrix}$.

***7.** Find the variances and covariances of normal variates which have the quadratic form $2y_1^2 + y_2^2 + 4y_3^2 - y_1y_2 - 2y_1y_3$ in their distribution.

***8.** What is the marginal density of $\mathbf{y}_2$ in Prob. 7?

***9.** What is the conditional density of $\mathbf{y}_1$, given $\mathbf{y}_2$, $\mathbf{y}_3$, in Prob. 7?

***10.** If the matrix of Prob. 6 is the matrix R of a normal distribution of $\mathbf{y}_1$, $\mathbf{y}_2$, $\mathbf{y}_3$, $\mathbf{y}_4$, show that the conditional distribution of $\mathbf{y}_1$ and $\mathbf{y}_2$ is the same as the marginal distribution of $\mathbf{y}_1$ and $\mathbf{y}_2$, hence that the pair $(\mathbf{y}_1, \mathbf{y}_2)$ is distributed independently of the pair $(\mathbf{y}_3, \mathbf{y}_4)$.

***11.** Let the 4×1 vector $\mathbf{Y}$ be distributed normally with mean μ and covariance V, where

$$\mu = \begin{pmatrix} 6 \\ -1 \\ 0 \\ 3 \end{pmatrix} \qquad V = \begin{pmatrix} 2 & 0 & 3 & 0 \\ 0 & 5 & 0 & 2 \\ 3 & 0 & 5 & 0 \\ 0 & 2 & 0 & 1 \end{pmatrix}$$

Find

(*a*) $\sigma_{11.34}$
(*b*) $\sigma_{12.34}$
(*c*) $\rho_{12.34}$
(*d*) σ_{11}
(*e*) ρ_{12}
(*f*) The mean in the conditional of $\mathbf{y}_3$, given $\mathbf{y}_4$

***12.** Show that the determinant with k rows and columns

$$\begin{vmatrix} a & b & b & \cdots & b \\ b & a & b & \cdots & b \\ \cdot & \cdot & \cdot & & \cdot \\ \cdot & \cdot & \cdot & & \cdot \\ \cdot & \cdot & \cdot & & \cdot \\ b & b & b & \cdots & a \end{vmatrix}$$

which has a's in the main diagonal and b's everywhere else, has the value

$$(a - b)^{k-1}[a + (k - 1)b]$$

Before expanding the determinant, subtract the second row from the first, the third from the second, and so on; then add the first column to the second, the second to the third, and so on.

* Starred problems depend on Secs. 9.2 and 9.3.

13. Let (**x**, **y**) have a bivariate normal density with means μ_x and μ_y and covariance matrix

$$V = \begin{pmatrix} \sigma_{11} & \sigma_{12} \\ \sigma_{21} & \sigma_{22} \end{pmatrix}$$

Find R and the quadratic form in the exponent and show that it is equal to the exponent in equation (9.1.1).

14. In Prob. 13, show that $|V|^{-\frac{1}{2}}$ is equal to 2π times the coefficient in equation (9.1.1), that is, $1/\sigma_x\sigma_y(1 - \rho^2)^{\frac{1}{2}}$.

15. Given the random sample $(\mathbf{x}_1, \mathbf{y}_1)$; $(\mathbf{x}_2, \mathbf{y}_2)$; $\cdots$; $(\mathbf{x}_n, \mathbf{y}_n)$ from the bivariate normal in Prob. 13, find the maximum-likelihood estimators of $\mu_x, \mu_y, \sigma_x^2, \sigma_y^2, \rho$.

16. Given the sample (2.5, 7.0), (4.0, 9.0), (.4, 1.7), (1.2, 2.0), (.3, .0), (1.5, 3.7) from a normal bivariate population, find the maximum-likelihood estimate of the regression function for the conditional distribution of $\mathbf{y}_2$, given $\mathbf{y}_1$. Plot the sample observations and the regression function.

***17.** Consider any multivariate density $f(y_1, y_2, \cdots, y_k)$. If we use the symbols

$$\begin{aligned} \text{The means:} \quad & \mu_i = E(\mathbf{y}_i) \\ \text{The variances:} \quad & \sigma_{ii} = E[(\mathbf{y}_i - \mu_i)^2] \\ \text{The covariances:} \quad & \sigma_{ij} = E[(\mathbf{y}_i - \mu_i)(\mathbf{y}_i - \mu_i)] \\ \text{The correlations:} \quad & \rho_{ij} = \frac{\sigma_{ij}}{\sqrt{\sigma_{ii}\,\sigma_{jj}}} \end{aligned}$$

what is the mean and variance of the linear function $\mathbf{x} = \Sigma\alpha_i\mathbf{y}_i$ of the y's if $\alpha_i = 1/n$?

***18.** Let α' be the $1 \times p$ vector $\alpha' = (\alpha_1, \alpha_2, \cdots, \alpha_p)$. In Prob. 17, $\mathbf{x} = \sum_{i=1}^{p} \alpha_i\mathbf{y}_i$ becomes $\mathbf{x} = \alpha'\mathbf{Y}$. Show that $E(\mathbf{x}) = \alpha'\mu$ and $\text{var}(\mathbf{x}) = \alpha'V\alpha$, where $V = (\sigma_{ij})$ and $\mu = (\mu_i)$.

***19.** Referring to Prob. 17, what is the correlation between two linear functions $\mathbf{x} = \Sigma\alpha_i\mathbf{y}_i = \alpha'\mathbf{Y}$ and $\mathbf{z} = \Sigma b_i\mathbf{y}_i = b'\mathbf{Y}$, where $\mathbf{x} \neq k\mathbf{z}$, $b' = (b_1, \cdots, b_p)$ and k is any constant.

***20.** Let **Y** be distributed as a p-variate normal with mean **O** and covariance I. Show that the density of **Y** is the same as the joint density of a random sample $\mathbf{y}_1, \cdots, \mathbf{y}_p$ from a normal density with mean 0 and variance 1.

***21.** Let the $p \times 1$ vector **Y** be distributed as a p-variate normal with mean **O** and covariance I. Let A be a $q \times p$ matrix of rank $q \leq p$. Prove that the $q \times 1$ vector $\mathbf{X}^* = A\mathbf{Y}$ is a q-variate normal with mean **O** and covariance AA'. HINT: Find the m.g.f. of $\mathbf{X}^*$ and use Theorems 9.13 and 5.7.

***22.** Show that Theorem 9.10 is a special case of the theorem in Prob. 21.

***23.** Let the $p \times 1$ vector $\mathbf{Y}$ be distributed as a p-variate normal with mean μ and covariance V. Let A be a $q \times p$ matrix of rank $q \leq p$. Prove that the $q \times 1$ vector $\mathbf{X}^* = A\mathbf{Y}$ is a q-variate normal with mean $A\mu$ and covariance AVA'.

***24.** An orthogonal $p \times p$ matrix P is such that $P'P = I$; that is, $P' = P^{-1}$. In Prob. 21, if $p = q$ and $A = P$, show that $\mathbf{X}^*$ and $\mathbf{Y}$ have the same distribution.

***25.** Let the two $p \times 1$ vectors α and b be defined as in Probs. 18 and 19. Let $\mathbf{Y}$ be distributed as a p-variate normal with mean μ and covariance I. Prove that a necessary and sufficient condition for $\mathbf{x} = \alpha'\mathbf{Y}$ and $\mathbf{z} = b'\mathbf{Y}$ to be independent is $\alpha'b = 0$.

26. Let $\mathbf{y}_1, \mathbf{y}_2, \cdots, \mathbf{y}_{2k}$ denote scores on $2k$ questions in an aptitude test. Let the scores be normally distributed, each with the same mean and variance (μ and σ^2) and such that the correlation between any pair of questions is $\rho > 0$. If $\mathbf{y}_1 = \sum_1^k \mathbf{y}_{2i-1}$ and $\mathbf{y}_2 = \sum_1^k \mathbf{y}_{2i}$ are total scores on the odd and even questions, find the correlation between $\mathbf{y}_1$ and $\mathbf{y}_2$ and show that it can be made as near unity as one pleases by making the test sufficiently long.

***27.** Let the $p \times 1$ vector $\mathbf{Y}$ be distributed as a p-variate normal with mean μ and covariance V, and let $\mathbf{Y}_1^*$ and U_1 be a $k \times 1$ partition of $\mathbf{Y}$ and μ, respectively, and V_{11} be a $k \times k$ partition of V. Show that the elements of the $k \times 1$ vector $\mathbf{X}^*$, where

$$\mathbf{X}^* = \mathbf{Y}_1^* - U_1 - V_{12}V_{22}^{-1}(\mathbf{Y}_2^* - U_2)$$

are independent of the elements of the $(p - k) \times k$ vector $\mathbf{Y}_2^*$. Hint: Notice that $E(\mathbf{Y}_1^* - U_1)(\mathbf{Y}_2^* - U_2)' = V_{12}$.

***28.** Let $\mathbf{y}_{1.23\cdots r}$ represent the deviation of $\mathbf{y}_1$ from its regression function in the conditional distribution of $\mathbf{y}_1$, given $\mathbf{y}_2, \mathbf{y}_3, \cdots, \mathbf{y}_r$. Show for a trivariate normal distribution that $\mathbf{y}_1, \mathbf{y}_{2.1}, \mathbf{y}_{3.21}$ are independently normally distributed.

***29.** Generalize the result of Prob. 28 to k variates.

***30.** Let the $p \times 1$ vector $\mathbf{Y}$ be distributed as a p-variate normal with mean μ and covariance V. Partition $\mathbf{Y}$, μ, and V as in equation (9.3.14) with $k = 1$. In the conditional distribution of $\mathbf{y}_1$, given $\mathbf{Y}_2^*$, the regression function is $\mu_1 + V_{12}V_{22}^{-1}(Y_2^* - U_2)$. Let

$$\mathbf{z} = V_{12}V_{22}^{-1}(\mathbf{Y}_2^* - U_2)$$

The correlation between $\mathbf{z}$ and $\mathbf{y}_1$ is called the multiple correlation coefficient of $\mathbf{y}_1$ on $\mathbf{y}_2, \cdots, \mathbf{y}_p$ and is denoted by $R_{1.23\cdots p}$. Show that $E(\mathbf{z}) = 0$ and $E(\mathbf{z}^2) = E(\mathbf{z}\mathbf{y}_1)$.

***31.** In Prob. 30 and for $p = 3$, show that

$$\sigma_{11.23} = \sigma_{11}(1 - R^2_{1.23})$$

***32.** Referring to Prob. 30, show that

$$\sigma_{11.23\cdots k} = \sigma_{11}(1 - R^2_{1.23\cdots k})$$

***33.** Show, for the trivariate normal distribution, that

$$\rho_{12.3} = \frac{\rho_{12} - \rho_{13}\rho_{23}}{[(1 - \rho^2_{13})(1 - \rho^2_{23})]^{\frac{1}{2}}}$$

9.5 Bibliography

1. Anderson, T. W.: "An Introduction to Multivariate Statistical Analysis," John Wiley & Sons, Inc., New York, 1958.
2. Graybill, F. A.: "An Introduction to Linear Statistical Models," Vol. I, McGraw-Hill Book Company, Inc., New York, 1961.
3. Hald, A.: "Statistical Theory with Engineering Applications," John Wiley & Sons, Inc., New York, 1952.
4. Rao, C. R.: "Advanced Statistical Methods in Biometric Research," John Wiley & Sons, Inc., New York, 1952.
5. Roy, S. N.: "Some Aspects of Multivariate Analysis," John Wiley & Sons, Inc., New York, 1957.
6. Wilks, S. S.: "Mathematical Statistics," Princeton University Press, Princeton, N.J., 1947.

10

Sampling Distributions

10.1 Distributions of Functions of Random Variables

In order to study further the problem of estimation, it is necessary to have the distributions of the estimators. In this section we shall consider methods of obtaining such distributions, and then in the remaining sections of the chapter the methods will be employed to obtain certain distributions of particular interest.

A variate $\mathbf{x}$ may be transformed by some function u to define a new variate $\mathbf{u}$. The density of $\mathbf{u}$, say $g(u)$, will be determined by the transformation $u(x)$ together with the density $f(x)$ of $\mathbf{x}$.

If $\mathbf{x}$ is a discrete variate, the distribution of $u(\mathbf{x})$ is determined directly by the laws of probability. If $\mathbf{x}$ takes on the values $0, 1, 2, \cdots, r$, for example, with probabilities $f(0), f(1), \cdots, f(r)$, then the possible values of $\mathbf{u}$, say $u_0, u_1, \cdots, u_s$, are determined by substituting the successive values of $\mathbf{x}$ in $u(\mathbf{x})$. It may be that several values of $\mathbf{x}$ give rise to the same value of $\mathbf{u}$. The probability that $\mathbf{u}$ takes on a given value, say u_i, is

$$g(u_i) = \Sigma' f(x) \tag{1}$$

where the sum, Σ', is taken over all values of $\mathbf{x}$ such that $u(\mathbf{x}) = u_i$.

Example 10.1. Suppose that $\mathbf{x}$ takes on the values 0, 1, 2, 3, 4, 5 with probabilities $p_0, p_1, p_2, p_3, p_4, p_5$; the density of $\mathbf{u} = (\mathbf{x} - 2)^2$ is

$$\begin{aligned} g(0) &= p_2 \\ g(1) &= p_1 + p_3 \\ g(4) &= p_0 + p_4 \\ g(9) &= p_5 \end{aligned}$$

and 0, 1, 4, 9 are all the possible values of $\mathbf{u}$.

Similarly, if u is a function of several discrete variates $\mathbf{x}_1, \mathbf{x}_2, \cdots, \mathbf{x}_k$ with a joint density $f(x_1, x_2, \cdots, x_k)$, the probability that $u(\mathbf{x}_1, \mathbf{x}_2, \cdots, \mathbf{x}_k)$ takes on a particular one of its values u_i is

$$g(u_i) = \Sigma f(x_1, x_2, \cdots, x_k) \tag{2}$$

where Σ is taken over all sets of values of the $\mathbf{x}$'s so that

$$u(\mathbf{x}_1, \mathbf{x}_2, \cdots, \mathbf{x}_k) = u_i$$

The basic and often the simplest method for finding distributions of functions of continuous random variables was given in Chap. 4.

Suppose that $\mathbf{x}$ has a density $f(x)$ for $a < x < b$, and 0 elsewhere, and we want the density of $\mathbf{y} = u(\mathbf{x})$, where $u'(x)$ is continuous and positive for $a \leq x \leq b$. Then the density of $\mathbf{y}$ is 0 if $\mathbf{y}$ is not in the interval $u(a) < y < u(b)$. Let $\mathbf{x} = v(\mathbf{y})$ be the solution of $\mathbf{y} = u(\mathbf{x})$ for $\mathbf{x}$. Let the density of $\mathbf{y}$ be denoted by $g(y)$. We shall find the cumulative distribution $G(y)$ of $\mathbf{y}$ and differentiate it at points where the derivative exists in order to find $g(y)$. If $u'(x)$ is negative and continuous, a similar proof holds.

$$\begin{aligned} G(y) &= P(\mathbf{y} \leq y) = P[u(\mathbf{x}) \leq y] = P[\mathbf{x} \leq v(y)] = \int_a^{v(y)} f(x)\,dx \\ &= F[v(y)] - F(a) \qquad \text{if } u(a) < y < u(b) \\ G(y) &= 0 \qquad \text{if } y \leq u(a) \\ G(y) &= 1 \qquad \text{if } y \geq u(b) \end{aligned} \tag{3}$$

Thus

$$\begin{aligned} g(y) = G'(y) &= \frac{d}{dy}\{F[v(y)] - F(a)\} \qquad u(a) < y < u(b) \\ &= 0 \qquad \text{elsewhere} \end{aligned} \tag{4}$$

Example 10.2. Let $\mathbf{x}$ have the density $f(x) = 2x$, $0 < x < 1$, and let $f(x)$ be 0 elsewhere, and suppose that we want the density of $\mathbf{y} = \mathbf{x}^3 - 2$. In the interval $0 \leq x \leq 1$, $y'(x)$ is continuous and positive and $x = (y + 2)^{\frac{1}{3}}$. Now

$$\begin{aligned} G(y) &= P(\mathbf{y} \leq y) = P(\mathbf{x}^3 - 2 \leq y) = P(\mathbf{x}^3 \leq y + 2) \\ &= P(\mathbf{x} \leq \sqrt[3]{y+2}) = \int_0^{\sqrt[3]{y+2}} 2x\,dx = (y+2)^{\frac{2}{3}} \\ &\qquad\qquad -2 < y < -1 \end{aligned} \tag{5}$$

$$\begin{aligned} G(y) &= 0 \qquad \text{for } y \leq -2 \\ G(y) &= 1 \qquad \text{for } y \geq -1 \end{aligned}$$

Thus

$$\begin{aligned} g(y) &= (2/3)(y+2)^{-\frac{1}{3}} \qquad -2 < y < -1 \\ &= 0 \qquad \text{elsewhere} \end{aligned} \tag{6}$$

It will be instructive to consider another approach to this problem of finding the distributions of functions of continuous variates.

We shall first investigate functions of a single random variable $\mathbf{x}$.

Let $f(x)$ be the density of a continuous random variable $\mathbf{x}$ such that

$$f(x) > 0 \qquad \text{for } a < x < b$$

and

$$f(x) = 0 \qquad \text{elsewhere}$$

Let u be a function of x given by $u = u(x)$, and suppose that $u(x)$ has a continuous derivative at every point x in the interval $a \leq x \leq b$ and that the derivative is 0 only at the points $a_1, a_2, \cdots, a_{n-1}$, where $a = a_0 < a_1 < \cdots < a_{n-1} < a_n = b$. Let the interval $a_0 < x < a_n$ be partitioned into n disjoint intervals, $I_1, I_2, \cdots, I_n$, denoted by

$$a_0 < x < a_1; \, a_1 < x < a_2; \, \cdots; \, a_{n-1} < x < a_n$$

such that u is either monotonic increasing or monotonic decreasing in the ith interval $a_{i-1} < x < a_i$ for each i (see Fig. 10.1), and let $x = x_i(u)$ be the solution of $u = u(x)$ for x in the ith interval, where the inverse is $u = u_i(x)$. We can write

$$u(x) = \begin{cases} u_1(x), & a_0 < x < a_1; & \text{inverse} \quad x = x_1(u), & u \text{ in } A_1 \\ u_2(x), & a_1 < x < a_2; & \text{inverse} \quad x = x_2(u), & u \text{ in } A_2 \\ \cdot & \cdot & \cdot \qquad \cdot & \cdot \\ \cdot & \cdot & \cdot \qquad \cdot & \cdot \\ \cdot & \cdot & \cdot \qquad \cdot & \cdot \\ u_n(x), & a_{n-1} < x < a_n; & \text{inverse} \quad x = x_n(u), & u \text{ in } A_n \end{cases}$$

where

$$A_i = \{u \colon u_i(a_{i-1}) < u < u_i(a_i)\}$$

if u is a monotonic increasing function of x in the ith interval and

$$A_i = \{u \colon u_i(a_i) < u < u_i(a_{i-1})\}$$

if u is a monotonic decreasing function of x in the ith interval. By the

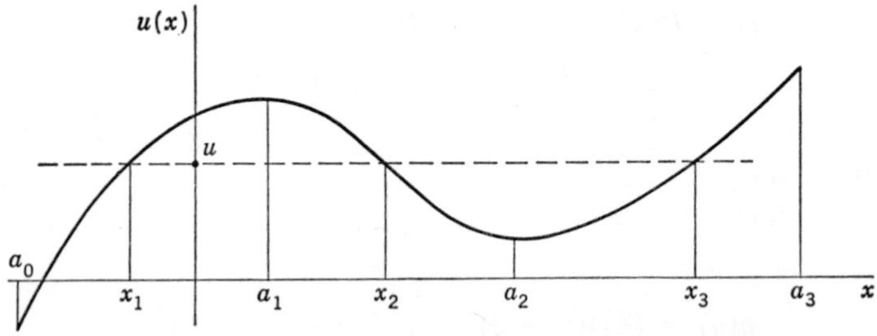

FIG. 10.1

above assumptions on u, the derivative $d[x_i(u)]/du$ exists for u in A_i. If **u** is a random variable, then the density of **u** at the point $\mathbf{u} = u$ is

$$g(u) = 0 \tag{7}$$

if there are no points x in I_i for any i such that $u = u(x)$; and

$$g(u) = \sum f[x_i(u)] \frac{d[x_i(u)]}{du+} \tag{8}$$

where the summation is over those values of i for which $u_i(x) = u$ for some value of x in the ith interval I_i. We define $d[x_i(u)]/du+$ as the absolute value of $d[x_i(u)]/du$.

Example 10.3. Consider the random variable $\mathbf{x}$ with density

$$f(x) = \tfrac{2}{9}(x+1) \qquad -1 < x < 2$$
$$= 0 \qquad \text{elsewhere}$$

See Fig. 10.2.

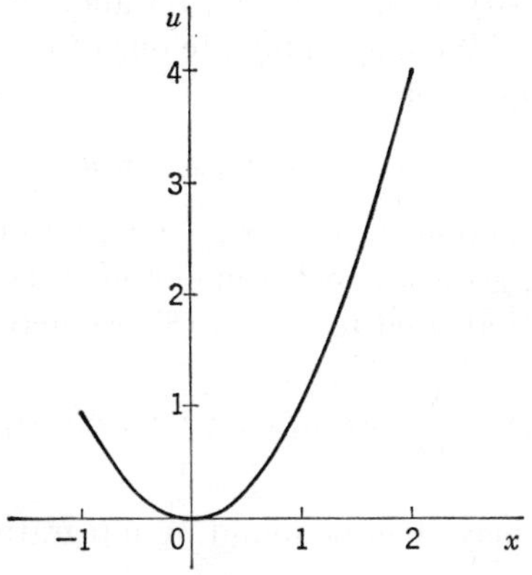

FIG. 10.2

We want the density of $\mathbf{u}$, where $\mathbf{u} = \mathbf{x}^2$. We obtain $a = a_0 = -1$; $a_1 = 0$; $a_2 = b = 2$.

$$u(x) = \begin{cases} u = x^2; & -1 < x < 0: \text{ inverse } x = -\sqrt{u};\ 0 < u < 1 \\ u = x^2; & 0 < x < 2: \text{ inverse } x = +\sqrt{u};\ 0 < u < 4 \end{cases}$$

$$\frac{dx}{du+} = \frac{1}{2\sqrt{u}}$$

For u in the interval $0 < u < 1$, from (8) we get

$$g(u) = f(-\sqrt{u})\frac{1}{2\sqrt{u}} + f(\sqrt{u})\frac{1}{2\sqrt{u}} \qquad 0 < u < 1$$

For u in the interval $1 < u < 4$, from (8) we get

$$g(u) = f(\sqrt{u})\frac{1}{2\sqrt{u}} \qquad 1 < u < 4$$

and

$$g(u) = 0 \qquad \text{elsewhere}$$

This gives

$$g(u) = \frac{2}{9\sqrt{u}} \qquad 0 < u < 1$$

$$g(u) = \frac{\sqrt{u} + 1}{9\sqrt{u}} \qquad 1 < u < 4$$

$$g(u) = 0 \qquad \text{elsewhere}$$

When $\mathbf{u}$ is a function of several random variables, the density of $\mathbf{u}$ may be obtained as a marginal distribution. Suppose that $\mathbf{x}_1, \mathbf{x}_2, \cdots, \mathbf{x}_k$ have a density $f(x_1, x_2, \cdots, x_k)$ and the density of $u(\mathbf{x}_1, \mathbf{x}_2, \cdots, \mathbf{x}_k)$ is required. We may eliminate one of the x's, say x_1, in terms of u by solving the equation

$$u(x_1, x_2, \cdots, x_k) = u$$

for x_1 to obtain a function $x_1(u, x_2, x_3, \cdots, x_k)$ or several such functions $x_{1i}(u, x_2, \cdots, x_k)$ if u is not a monotone function of x_1. Using a similar argument to that used to obtain (8), we may obtain a density

$$g(u, x_2, \cdots, x_k) = \sum_i f(x_{1i}(u, x_2, \cdots, x_k), x_2, \cdots, x_k) \frac{\partial x_{1i}}{\partial u_+} \tag{9}$$

and the density of $\mathbf{u}$ may then be found by integrating out $x_2, x_3, \cdots, x_k$ in g.

The procedure described above may be generalized to determine the joint distribution of several functions $u_1(\mathbf{x}_1, \cdots, \mathbf{x}_k), u_2(\mathbf{x}_1, \cdots, \mathbf{x}_k), \cdots, u_r(\mathbf{x}_1, \cdots, \mathbf{x}_k) (r \leq k)$ of k random variables. We may put

$$\begin{aligned} u_1(x_1, \cdots, x_k) &= u_1 \\ u_2(x_1, \cdots, x_k) &= u_2 \\ \cdots\cdots&\cdots\cdots \\ u_r(x_1, \cdots, x_k) &= u_r \end{aligned} \tag{10}$$

and solve the resulting set of equations for $x_1, x_2, \cdots, x_r$ to obtain a set of r functions $x_j^*(u_1, u_2, \cdots, u_r, x_{r+1}, \cdots, x_k)$, or if the solution is not unique, we may have several such sets of r functions. The joint density of the $\mathbf{u}$'s and the remaining $\mathbf{x}$'s can be shown to be

$$g(u_1, \cdots, u_r, x_{r+1}, \cdots, x_k) = \sum f(x_1^*, \ldots, x_r^*, x_{r+1}, \cdots, x_k) \left| \frac{\partial x_i}{\partial u_j} \right|_+ \tag{11}$$

where the sum is taken over all sets of solutions of (10).

The quantity $\left| \frac{\partial x_i}{\partial u_j} \right|_+$ is the absolute value of the Jacobian which is the determinant

$$\begin{vmatrix} \frac{\partial x_1}{\partial u_1} & \frac{\partial x_1}{\partial u_2} & \cdots & \frac{\partial x_1}{\partial u_k} \\ \frac{\partial x_2}{\partial u_1} & \frac{\partial x_2}{\partial u_2} & \cdots & \frac{\partial x_2}{\partial u_k} \\ \cdot & \cdot & & \cdot \\ \cdot & \cdot & & \cdot \\ \cdot & \cdot & & \cdot \\ \frac{\partial x_k}{\partial u_1} & \frac{\partial x_k}{\partial u_2} & \cdots & \frac{\partial x_k}{\partial u_k} \end{vmatrix}$$

We omit the proof of (11); it is essentially the same as the derivation of the formulas for transforming variables in multiple integrals, which may be found in any textbook on advanced calculus.

Use of Moment Generating Functions. There is another method of determining distributions of functions of random variables which we shall find to be particularly useful. If $u(\mathbf{x}_1, \mathbf{x}_2, \cdots, \mathbf{x}_k)$ is a function of random variables $\mathbf{x}_i$ which have the density $f(x_1, x_2, \cdots, x_k)$, the m.g.f. of $\mathbf{u}$, if it exists, is

$$\begin{aligned} m(t) &= E(e^{t\mathbf{u}}) \\ &= \int \cdots \int e^{tu(x_1,x_2,\cdots,x_k)} f(x_1, x_2, \cdots, x_k) \, \Pi \, dx_i \end{aligned} \tag{12}$$

If the resulting function of t can be recognized as the moment generating function of some known distribution, it will follow that $\mathbf{u}$ has that distribution by virtue of Theorem 5.7.

This method is quite powerful in connection with certain techniques of advanced mathematics (the theory of Laplace transforms) which enable one to determine the distribution associated with many moment generating functions. The method can also be generalized to determine the joint distribution of several functions of random variables.

10.2 Distribution of the Sample Mean for Normal Densities

Let $\mathbf{x}_1, \mathbf{x}_2, \cdots, \mathbf{x}_n$ be a random sample of size n from the normal density with mean μ and variance σ^2. To find the density of $\bar{\mathbf{x}} = \frac{1}{n} \sum_{i=1}^{n} \mathbf{x}_i$, we shall find the m.g.f. of $\bar{\mathbf{x}}$ and use Theorem 5.7. The m.g.f. of $\mathbf{x}_i$ is, by Theorem 6.2,

$$m_{\mathbf{x}_i}(t) = e^{\mu t + (\sigma^2 t^2)/2} \qquad i = 1, 2, \cdots, n$$

To find the m.g.f. of $\bar{\mathbf{x}}$, we shall use the results of Probs. 5.35 and 5.36. Since $\bar{\mathbf{x}} = \mathbf{x}_1/n + \mathbf{x}_2/n + \cdots + \mathbf{x}_n/n$, we need the m.g.f. of $\mathbf{x}_i/n$. By

Prob. 5.35 and the above, this is

$$m_{\mathbf{x}_i/n}(t) = m_{\mathbf{x}_i}\left(\frac{t}{n}\right) = e^{\mu t/n + \sigma^2 t^2/2n^2}$$

By Prob. 5.36, the m.g.f. of $\bar{\mathbf{x}}$ is

$$m_{\bar{\mathbf{x}}}(t) = (e^{\mu t/n + \sigma^2 t^2/2n^2})^n = e^{\mu t + \sigma^2 t^2/2n}$$

but this is the m.g.f. of a normal density with mean μ and variance σ^2/n; hence, by Theorem 5.7, we have proved the following theorem.

Theorem 10.1. *If $\mathbf{x}_1, \cdots, \mathbf{x}_n$ is a random sample from a normal distribution with mean μ and variance σ^2, then $\bar{\mathbf{x}}$ is a normal variable with mean μ and variance σ^2/n.*

10.3 The Chi-square Distribution

We shall obtain the distribution of

$$\mathbf{u} = \sum_{i=1}^{k} \left(\frac{\mathbf{x}_i - \mu_i}{\sigma_i}\right)^2 \tag{1}$$

where the $\mathbf{x}_i$ are normally and independently distributed with means μ_i and variances σ_i^2. In the joint distribution of the $\mathbf{x}_i$ we again transform the variates to

$$\mathbf{y}_i = \frac{\mathbf{x}_i - \mu_i}{\sigma_i}$$

in order to simplify the equations; $\mathbf{u}$ is then simply $\Sigma \mathbf{y}_i^2$. The method of moment generating functions will be employed to obtain its distribution.

The moment generating function of $\mathbf{u}$ is

$$m(t) = \left(\frac{1}{2\pi}\right)^{k/2} \iint \cdots \int e^{t\Sigma y_i^2} e^{-\frac{1}{2}\Sigma y_i^2} \prod dy_i \tag{2}$$

and the multiple integral may be written as the product of k integrals of the form

$$\frac{1}{\sqrt{2\pi}} \int_{-\infty}^{\infty} e^{-\frac{1}{2}(1-2t)y_i^2}\, dy_i \tag{3}$$

The integral (3) has the value $1/\sqrt{1-2t}$ since multiplication of the integral by $\sqrt{1-2t}$ makes it represent the area under a normal curve with variance $1/(1-2t)$. It follows that

$$m(t) = \left(\frac{1}{1-2t}\right)^{k/2} \qquad t < \frac{1}{2} \tag{4}$$

The moment generating function is of the form of the moment generating function for a gamma distribution (Sec. 6.3) with $\alpha = (k/2) - 1$ and $\beta = 2$. We may conclude therefore that the density of $\mathbf{u}$ is

$$f(u) = \frac{1}{[(k/2) - 1]!} \frac{1}{2^{k/2}} u^{(k/2)-1} e^{-\frac{1}{2}u} \qquad u > 0 \tag{5}$$

This particular form of the gamma distribution is usually referred to as a chi-square distribution with k *degrees of freedom*. The variate $\mathbf{u}$ is commonly designated by the square of the Greek letter chi,

$$\chi^2 = \sum_i^k \left(\frac{\mathbf{x}_i - \mu_i}{\sigma_i} \right)^2 \tag{6}$$

hence the name for this distribution. The phrase *degrees of freedom* refers to the number of independent squares in the sum in (6); we may think of it, however, as merely a name for the parameter k in the density (5).

Theorem 10.2. *Let* $\mathbf{y}_1, \ldots, \mathbf{y}_n$ *be a random sample from a normal distribution with mean* 0 *and variance* 1. *Then* $\mathbf{u} = \sum_{i=1}^{n} \mathbf{y}_i^2$ *has a chi-square distribution with n degrees of freedom.*

We may notice here that (5) gives essentially the distribution of the maximum-likelihood estimator for σ^2 in normal populations when μ is known. If one considers samples of size n from a normal population with known mean μ, the maximum-likelihood estimator for σ^2 is found to be

$$\hat{\boldsymbol{\sigma}}^2 = \frac{1}{n} \sum_{i=1}^{n} (\mathbf{x}_i - \mu)^2 = \frac{\sigma^2}{n} \mathbf{u}$$

where $\mathbf{u} = \sum_{i=1}^{n} [(\mathbf{x}_i - \mu)/\sigma]^2$ has the chi-square distribution with n degrees of freedom. The density for the estimator is therefore

$$f(\hat{\sigma}^2) = \frac{1}{[(n/2) - 1]!} \left(\frac{n}{2\sigma^2} \right)^{n/2} (\hat{\sigma}^2)^{(n/2)-1} e^{-n\hat{\sigma}^2/2\sigma^2} \qquad \hat{\sigma}^2 > 0 \tag{7}$$

since

$$\frac{du}{d\hat{\sigma}^2} = \frac{n}{\sigma^2}$$

This is a gamma density with $\alpha = (n/2) - 1$ and $\beta = 2\sigma^2/n$.

The chi-square distribution is partially tabulated in Table III.

*10.4 Independence of the Sample Mean and Variance for Normal Densities

Ordinarily the mean of a population is unknown, and we are generally more interested in the estimator $(1/n)\Sigma(\mathbf{x}_i - \bar{\mathbf{x}})^2$ for σ^2 than in the estimator $(1/n)\Sigma(\mathbf{x}_i - \mu)^2$ considered in the preceding section. We shall now derive the distribution of this estimator and show incidentally that it is distributed independently of the sample mean.

We shall let

$$\mathbf{y}_i = \frac{\mathbf{x}_i - \mu}{\sigma} \tag{1}$$

$$\mathbf{u} = n\bar{\mathbf{y}}^2 = \frac{1}{n}\left(\sum \mathbf{y}_i\right)^2 \tag{2}$$

$$\mathbf{v} = \sum_1^n (\mathbf{y}_i - \bar{\mathbf{y}})^2 \tag{3}$$

and find the joint moment generating function for $\mathbf{u}$ and $\mathbf{v}$, say,

$$m(t_1, t_2) = E(e^{t_1\mathbf{u}+t_2\mathbf{v}}) \tag{4}$$

$$= \iint \cdots \int \left(\frac{1}{2\pi}\right)^{n/2} e^{(t_1/n)(\Sigma y_i)^2 + t_2\Sigma(y_i - \bar{y})^2 - \frac{1}{2}\Sigma y_i^2} \prod_1^n dy_i$$

$$= \iint \cdots \int \left(\frac{1}{2\pi}\right)^{n/2} e^{-\frac{1}{2}[\Sigma y_i^2 - (2t_1/n)(\Sigma y_i)^2 - 2t_2\Sigma(y_i - \bar{y})^2]} \prod_1^n dy_i \tag{5}$$

The quadratic form may be written

$$\sum y_i^2 - \frac{2t_1}{n}\left(\sum y_i\right)^2 - 2t_2 \sum (y_i - \bar{y})^2$$

$$= \sum y_i^2 - \frac{2t_1}{n}\left(\sum y_i\right)^2 - 2t_2 \sum y_i^2 + 2nt_2\bar{y}^2 \tag{6}$$

$$= (1 - 2t_2) \sum y_i^2 - \frac{2(t_1 - t_2)}{n}\left(\sum y_i\right)^2$$

$$= \sum r_{ij} y_i y_j \tag{7}$$

where

$$r_{ii} = 1 - 2t_2 - \frac{2(t_1 - t_2)}{n} = a$$

$$r_{ij} = -\frac{2(t_1 - t_2)}{n} = b \qquad i \neq j$$

* If the reader omitted Secs. 9.2 and 9.3, then Theorem 10.3 in this section may be studied but the proofs omitted.

A determinant of order n with a's in the main diagonal and b's elsewhere has the value

$$(a - b)^{n-1}[a + (n - 1)b]$$

Hence

$$|R| = \left[1 - 2t_2 - \frac{2(t_1 - t_2)}{n} + \frac{2(t_1 - t_2)}{n}\right]^{n-1} \left[1 - 2t_2 - \frac{2(t_1 - t_2)}{n} - \frac{n-1}{n} 2(t_1 - t_2)\right]$$
$$= (1 - 2t_2)^{n-1}(1 - 2t_1) \tag{8}$$

From the multivariate normal distribution it follows that

$$\int_{-\infty}^{\infty} \cdots \int_{-\infty}^{\infty} \left(\frac{1}{2\pi}\right)^{n/2} e^{-\frac{1}{2}\Sigma\Sigma r_{ij}y_i y_j} \prod dy_i = \frac{1}{\sqrt{|R|}} \tag{9}$$

Hence the integral in (5) has the value

$$m(t_1, t_2) = \left(\frac{1}{1 - 2t_1}\right)^{\frac{1}{2}} \left(\frac{1}{1 - 2t_2}\right)^{(n-1)/2} \qquad t_1 < \tfrac{1}{2},\ t_2 < \tfrac{1}{2} \tag{10}$$

The fact that the joint moment generating function factors into a function of t_1 alone and a function of t_2 alone implies that **u** and **v** are independently distributed. We shall not prove this rigorously but merely indicate the argument. Similar reasoning to that employed in Sec. 5.5 will show that, if two distributions of several variates have the same joint moment generating function, the two distributions are the same. We have a density, say $f(u, v)$, with joint moment generating function (10). Given the marginal distributions $f_1(u)$ and $f_2(v)$, we may form the bivariate density

$$g(u, v) = f_1(u)f_2(v) \tag{11}$$

which is clearly a density function. Furthermore, its moment generating function must be

$$m(t_1, 0)m(0, t_2) \tag{12}$$

where

$$m(t_1, t_2) = \int\int e^{t_1 u + t_2 v} f(u, v)\, du\, dv \tag{13}$$

Since (12) and (13) are identical by (10), it follows that $g(u, v)$ and $f(u, v)$ are the same density and hence that $f(u, v)$ is equal to the product of its marginal densities.

The two factors of equation (10) are each of the form of the moment generating function for a chi-square distribution; hence it follows that **u** and **v** are each independently distributed by chi-square distributions, the first having one degree of freedom, and the second $n - 1$ degrees of freedom. The fact that $\mathbf{u} = n\bar{\mathbf{y}}^2$ is distributed as chi-square with one degree of freedom is in accord with the results of Secs. 10.2 and 10.3. For we have seen that $\bar{\mathbf{y}}$ is normally distributed with zero mean and variance $1/n$, and from the result of Sec. 10.3 with $k = 1$ it follows that

$$\mathbf{u} = \frac{(\bar{\mathbf{y}} - 0)^2}{1/n} = n\bar{\mathbf{y}}^2 = n\left(\frac{\bar{\mathbf{x}} - \mu}{\sigma}\right)^2 \tag{14}$$

must have the chi-square distribution with one degree of freedom. The quantity

$$\mathbf{v} = \sum_1^n (\mathbf{y}_i - \bar{\mathbf{y}})^2 = \sum_1^n \left(\frac{\mathbf{x}_i - \bar{\mathbf{x}}}{\sigma}\right)^2 \tag{15}$$

has the distribution given by equation (10.3.5) with k replaced by $n - 1$ instead of n, as would be the case if the deviations were measured from the population mean. It is sometimes said that one degree of freedom is lost by taking the sum of squares of deviations from the sample mean rather than the population mean, or that one degree of freedom is used in estimating the mean. While $\mathbf{v}$ in equation (15) is the sum of n squares, the squares are not all functionally independent. The relation $\Sigma\mathbf{y}_i = n\bar{\mathbf{y}}$ enables one to compute any one of the deviations $\mathbf{y}_i - \bar{\mathbf{y}}$, given the other $n - 1$ of them.

Theorem 10.3. *Let $\mathbf{y}_1, \mathbf{y}_2, \cdots, \mathbf{y}_n$ be a random sample from a normal distribution with mean 0 and variance 1; then*

(*a*) $\sum_{i=1}^n (\mathbf{y}_i - \bar{\mathbf{y}})^2$ *is a chi-square variate with* $n - 1$ d.f.

(*b*) $\bar{\mathbf{y}}$ *has a normal distribution with mean* 0 *and variance* $1/n$.

(*c*) $\bar{\mathbf{y}}$ *and* $\sum_{i=1}^n (\mathbf{y}_i - \bar{\mathbf{y}})^2$ *are independent.*

In terms of $\mathbf{v}$ of (15), the estimator

$$\hat{\boldsymbol{\sigma}}^2 = \frac{1}{n}\sum (\mathbf{x}_i - \bar{\mathbf{x}})^2 \tag{16}$$

can be written

$$\hat{\boldsymbol{\sigma}}^2 = \frac{\sigma^2\mathbf{v}}{n}$$

The density for this estimator is therefore

$$f(\hat{\sigma}^2) = \frac{1}{[(n-3)/2]!}\left(\frac{n}{2\sigma^2}\right)^{(n-1)/2} (\hat{\sigma}^2)^{(n-3)/2} \exp\left(-\frac{n\hat{\sigma}^2}{2\sigma^2}\right) \qquad \hat{\sigma}^2 > 0 \tag{17}$$

All the results of this section apply only to normal populations. It can be proved that for no other distributions are (1) the sample mean and sample variance independently distributed or (2) the sample mean exactly normally distributed.

10.5 The F Distribution

A distribution which we shall later find to be of considerable practical interest is that of the ratio of two quantities independently distributed by chi-square laws. Suppose that **u** and **v** are independently distributed by chi-square distributions with m and n degrees of freedom, respectively. Their joint density is, by (10.3.5),

$$f(u, v) = \frac{1}{[(m-2)/2]![(n-2)/2]!2^{(m+n)/2}} u^{(m-2)/2}v^{(n-2)/2}e^{-\frac{1}{2}(u+v)} \qquad (1)$$

$$u > 0, v > 0$$

We shall find the distribution of the quantity

$$\mathbf{F} = \frac{\mathbf{u}/m}{\mathbf{v}/n} = \frac{n\mathbf{u}}{m\mathbf{v}} \qquad (2)$$

which is sometimes referred to as the *variance ratio*. We shall find the density of **F** by eliminating u in terms of F in (1) and then integrating out v from the resulting density. Since

$$\frac{\partial u}{\partial F} = \frac{mv}{n} \qquad (3)$$

and since $\frac{\partial u}{\partial F}$ is continuous and positive, the joint density of **F** and **v** is,

$$g(F, v) = \frac{1}{[(m-2)/2]![(n-2)/2]!2^{(m+n)/2}} v^{(n-2)/2}\left(\frac{mvF}{n}\right)^{(m-2)/2} e^{-\frac{1}{2}[v+(mvF/n)]}\frac{mv}{n} \qquad (4)$$

To integrate out v, we must evaluate the integral

$$\int_0^\infty v^{(m+n-2)/2}e^{-\frac{1}{2}[1+(mF/n)]v}\,dv \qquad (5)$$

of the factors in (4) which involve v. We observe that the integrand is, apart from certain constants, the integral of a gamma density. In fact, if the integral were multiplied by

$$\frac{\{\frac{1}{2}[1+(mF/n)]\}^{(m+n)/2}}{[(m+n-2)/2]!} \qquad (6)$$

it would be exactly the area under the gamma density with

$$\alpha = \frac{m + n - 2}{2}$$

and

$$\beta = \frac{1}{\frac{1}{2}[1 + (mF/n)]}$$

and would have the value 1. Hence the value of (5) is the reciprocal of expression (6). The density of **F** is therefore

$$\begin{aligned} h(F) &= \int_0^\infty g(F, v)\, dv \\ &= \frac{1}{\left(\frac{m-2}{2}\right)!\left(\frac{n-2}{2}\right)!\,2^{\frac{m+n}{2}}} \left(\frac{m}{n}\right)^{\frac{m}{2}} F^{\frac{m-2}{2}} \int_0^\infty v^{\frac{m+n-2}{2}} e^{-\frac{1}{2}\left(1+\frac{mF}{n}\right)v}\, dv \\ &= \frac{\left(\frac{m+n-2}{2}\right)!}{\left(\frac{m-2}{2}\right)!\left(\frac{n-2}{2}\right)!} \left(\frac{m}{n}\right)^{\frac{m}{2}} \frac{F^{\frac{m-2}{2}}}{\left(1 + \frac{mF}{n}\right)^{\frac{m+n}{2}}} \qquad F > 0 \end{aligned} \tag{7}$$

a function with two parameters m and n. These parameters are also called *degrees of freedom;* thus (7) is called the F density with *m and n degrees of freedom;* the number of degrees of freedom of the variate **u** in the numerator of **F** is always quoted first.

Theorem 10.4. *Let* **u** *be a chi-square variate with m degrees of freedom, let* **v** *be a chi-square variate with n degrees of freedom, and let* **u** *and* **y** *be independent. Then the random variable*

$$\mathbf{F} = \frac{\mathbf{u}/m}{\mathbf{v}/n}$$

is distributed as F with m and n degrees of freedom. The density is given in (7).

Five points on the upper tail of the cumulative distribution of **F** are given in Table V. The reciprocals of the numbers in Table V provide five points on the lower tail of the cumulative distribution. To evaluate in general an integral of the form

$$P(a < \mathbf{F} < b) = \int_a^b h(F)\, dF$$

one may transform to the beta distribution. The required transformation is

$$w = \frac{mF/n}{1 + (mF/n)} \tag{8}$$

which changes (7) to a beta density with parameters $\alpha = (m - 2)/2$ and $\beta = (n - 2)/2$.

10.6 "Student's" t Distribution

Another distribution of considerable practical importance is that of the ratio of a normally distributed variate to the square root of a variate independently distributed by the chi-square distribution. More precisely, if $\mathbf{x}$ is normally distributed with mean μ and variance σ^2, if $\mathbf{u}$ has the chi-square distribution with k degrees of freedom, and if $\mathbf{x}$ and $\mathbf{u}$ are independently distributed, we seek the distribution of

$$\mathbf{t} = \frac{(\mathbf{x} - \mu)/\sigma}{\sqrt{\mathbf{u}/k}} \tag{1}$$

and letting

$$\mathbf{y} = \frac{\mathbf{x} - \mu}{\sigma}$$

$\mathbf{t}$ becomes $\dfrac{\mathbf{y}}{\sqrt{\mathbf{u}/k}}$. The joint density of $\mathbf{y}$ and $\mathbf{u}$ is

$$f(y, u) = \frac{1}{\sqrt{2\pi}} e^{-\frac{1}{2}y^2} \frac{1}{[(k-2)/2]!2^{k/2}} u^{(k-2)/2} e^{-\frac{1}{2}u} \tag{2}$$

and we find the distribution of $\mathbf{t}$ by the same procedure as was used in the preceding section. We substitute for y in terms of t $(y = t\sqrt{u/k})$ in (2) and then integrate out u from the resulting function. The final result is

$$h(t) = \frac{[(k-1)/2]!}{\sqrt{k\pi}\,[(k-2)/2]!} \frac{1}{[1 + (t^2/k)]^{(k+1)/2}} \qquad -\infty < t < \infty \tag{3}$$

a distribution with one parameter k, which is also referred to as the number of degrees of freedom of the distribution. Since $[(\mathbf{x} - \mu)/\sigma]^2$ has the chi-square distribution with one degree of freedom, it is evident from (1) that $\mathbf{t}^2$ has the F distribution with one and k degrees of freedom. The cumulative form of the distribution is partially tabulated in Table IV.

Theorem 10.5. *Let $\mathbf{y}$ be a normal variate with mean 0 and variance 1. Let $\mathbf{u}$ be a chi-square variate with k degrees of freedom and let $\mathbf{u}$ and $\mathbf{y}$ be independent. Then the random variable*

$$\mathbf{t} = \frac{\mathbf{y}\sqrt{k}}{\sqrt{\mathbf{u}}}$$

is distributed as Student's t with k degrees of freedom. The density is given in (3).

10.7 Distribution of Sample Means for Binomial and Poisson Densities

In the preceding sections we have illustrated two methods of finding distributions of functions of continuous random variables described in the first section. Here we shall illustrate the technique for discrete variates in two cases of particular interest.

If $\mathbf{x}_1, \mathbf{x}_2, \cdots, \mathbf{x}_n$ is a random sample of size n from the point binomial density

$$f(x) = p^x q^{1-x} \quad x = 0, 1; \quad 0 \le p \le 1 \tag{1}$$

the joint density of the x's is

$$f(x_1, x_2, \cdots, x_n) = p^{\Sigma x_i} q^{n-\Sigma x_i} \qquad x_i = 0, 1 \tag{2}$$

The sample mean

$$\bar{\mathbf{x}} = \frac{1}{n} \sum \mathbf{x}_i$$

is a function of the random variates, and it is evident that the only possible values of $\bar{\mathbf{x}}$ are $0, 1/n, 2/n, \cdots, 1$. The probability, $g(j/n)$, that $\bar{\mathbf{x}}$ takes on the value j/n is obtained by summing (2) over all sets $(x_1, x_2, \cdots, x_n)$ so that $(1/n)\ \Sigma x_i = j/n$, or so that $\Sigma x_i = j$. For all such sets, $f(x_1, x_2, \cdots, x_n)$ has the same value $p^j q^{n-j}$; hence the sum may be evaluated by multiplying this value by the number of sets $(x_1, x_2, \cdots, x_n)$ with the required specification. The number of such sets is the number of arrangements of j 1's and $n - j$ 0's, which is $\binom{n}{j}$; hence

$$g\left(\frac{j}{n}\right) = \binom{n}{j} p^j q^{n-j} \qquad \frac{j}{n} = 0, \frac{1}{n}, \frac{2}{n}, \cdots, 1 \tag{3}$$

as we have found already in Sec. 7.7.

Theorem 10.6. *Let $\mathbf{x}_1, \mathbf{x}_2, \cdots, \mathbf{x}_n$ be a random sample from the point binomial*

$$f(x) = p^x q^{1-x} \qquad x = 0, 1; \qquad 0 \le p \le 1$$

The density of $\bar{\mathbf{x}} = \frac{1}{n} \sum \mathbf{x}_i$ is

$$g(\bar{x}) = \binom{n}{n\bar{x}} p^{n\bar{x}} q^{n-n\bar{x}} \qquad \bar{x} = 0, \frac{1}{n}, \frac{2}{n}, \cdots, \frac{n-1}{n}, 1$$

In a similar manner we may find the distribution of the mean of a random sample, $\mathbf{x}_1, \mathbf{x}_2, \cdots, \mathbf{x}_n$, from a Poisson population. The joint density of the observations is

$$f(x_1, x_2, \cdots, x_n) = \frac{e^{-n\mu} \mu^{\Sigma x_i}}{\prod_i x_i!} \qquad x_i = 0, 1, 2, \cdots \tag{4}$$

using μ for the parameter of the distribution. The sample mean $\bar{\mathbf{x}}$ can obviously have any of the values j/n, where $j = 0, 1, 2, \cdots$. For a particular value j/n, the x's must be such that $\Sigma x_i = j$; hence

$$g\left(\frac{j}{n}\right) = \sum_{\Sigma x_i = j} \frac{e^{-n\mu}\mu^j}{\Pi\, x_i!} = e^{-n\mu}\mu^j \sum_{\Sigma x_i = j} \frac{1}{\prod x_i!} \qquad (5)$$

The sum can be performed with the aid of the multinomial theorem which, on putting all $x_i = 1$ in equation (2.11.2), states that

$$\sum \frac{j!}{\Pi\, x_i!} = n^j$$

The sum is therefore $n^j/j!$, and the required density is

$$g\left(\frac{j}{n}\right) = \frac{e^{-n\mu}(n\mu)^j}{j!} \qquad \bar{x} = \frac{j}{n} = 0, \frac{1}{n}, \frac{2}{n}, \cdots \qquad (6)$$

The function may be written explicitly as a function of $\bar{x}$:

$$g(\bar{x}) = \frac{e^{-n\mu}(n\mu)^{n\bar{x}}}{(n\bar{x})!} \qquad (7)$$

We may notice that, since there is a unique correspondence between $\bar{x} = j/n$ and $j = \Sigma x_i$, the density of $\mathbf{j}$ is

$$h(j) = \frac{e^{-n\mu}(n\mu)^j}{j!} \qquad j = 0, 1, 2, \cdots$$

Theorem 10.7. *Let* $\mathbf{x}_1, \mathbf{x}_2, \ldots, \mathbf{x}_n$ *be a random sample from the Poisson with parameter* μ. *Then the density of* $\bar{\mathbf{x}}$ *is*

$$g(\bar{x}) = \frac{e^{-n\mu}(n\mu)^{n\bar{x}}}{(n\bar{x})!} \qquad \bar{x} = 0, \frac{1}{n}, \frac{2}{n}, \cdots$$

*10.8 Large-sample Distribution of Maximum-likelihood Estimators

We have investigated several special problems in sampling theory not only to illustrate the methods of finding sampling distributions but because the particular distributions that we have obtained are important in applied statistics. They are sometimes referred to as "small-sample distributions," although of course they hold for large or small samples and the term is merely meant to indicate that they are valid for small samples. In this section we shall consider a distribution much more general, in the sense that it is more or less independent of the form of the population distribution, but valid only for large samples.

* If the reader omitted Secs. 9.2 and 9.3, this section may be omitted also.

For a wide class of distributions, the maximum-likelihood estimator is approximately normally distributed about the true parameter value as a mean for large samples. This is a powerful tool for solving many important problems of applied statistics, as we shall see in the following chapters. The following theorem is applicable to discrete and continuous distributions if the density satisfies certain regularity conditions.

Theorem 10.8. *The maximum-likelihood estimators* $\hat{\boldsymbol{\theta}}_1, \hat{\boldsymbol{\theta}}_2, \cdots, \hat{\boldsymbol{\theta}}_k$ *for the parameters of a density* $f(x; \theta_1, \theta_2, \cdots, \theta_k)$ *from samples of size* n *are, for large samples, approximately distributed by the multivariate normal distribution with means* $\theta_1, \theta_2, \cdots, \theta_k$ *and with matrix* nR *in the quadratic form, where*

$$r_{ij} = -E\left[\frac{\partial^2}{\partial\theta_i\,\partial\theta_j}\log f(\mathbf{x}; \theta_1, \theta_2, \cdots, \theta_k)\right]$$

The variances and covariances of the estimators are $(1/n)V$, *where*

$$V = R^{-1}$$

The theorem obviously depends in no way on the fact that we have used univariate distributions. The variate $\mathbf{x}$ in all the statements of this section may be replaced by a set of variates $(\mathbf{x}, \mathbf{y}, \mathbf{z}, \cdots)$.

Example 10.4. To illustrate the use of the theorem just given, we may find the large-sample distribution for the estimators of the two parameters of the normal distribution. We shall write it in the form

$$f(x; \theta_1, \theta_2) = \frac{1}{\sqrt{2\pi\theta_2}}\, e^{-(1/2\theta_2)(x-\theta_1)^2} \tag{1}$$

For samples of size n we have seen that the maximum-likelihood estimators are

$$\hat{\boldsymbol{\theta}}_1 = \frac{1}{n}\sum \mathbf{x}_i \tag{2}$$

$$\hat{\boldsymbol{\theta}}_2 = \frac{1}{n}\sum (\mathbf{x}_i - \hat{\boldsymbol{\theta}}_1)^2 \tag{3}$$

In accordance with the theorem, these estimators will be approximately normally distributed for large samples with means θ_1 and θ_2 and matrix $nR = (nr_{ij})$ in the quadratic form, where

$$r_{ij} = -E\left(\frac{\partial^2 \log \mathbf{f}}{\partial\theta_i\partial\theta_j}\right) \tag{4}$$

Since

$$\log f = -\frac{1}{2}\log 2\pi - \frac{1}{2}\log\theta_2 - \frac{1}{2\theta_2}(x - \theta_1)^2 \tag{5}$$

the required derivatives are

$$\frac{\partial^2 \log f}{\partial \theta_1^2} = -\frac{1}{\theta_2}$$
$$\frac{\partial^2 \log f}{\partial \theta_1\,\partial \theta_2} = -\frac{x-\theta_1}{\theta_2^2}$$
$$\frac{\partial^2 \log f}{\partial \theta_2^2} = \frac{1}{2\theta_2^2} - \frac{(x-\theta_1)^2}{\theta_2^3}$$

and because

$$E(\mathbf{x}) = \theta_1 \qquad E(\mathbf{x}-\theta_1)^2 = \theta_2$$

the r_{ij} are readily seen to be

$$R = \begin{pmatrix} \dfrac{1}{\theta_2} & 0 \\ 0 & \dfrac{1}{2\theta_2^2} \end{pmatrix} \tag{6}$$

The large-sample distribution of the estimators is, therefore, say,

$$g(\hat{\theta}_1, \hat{\theta}_2) = \frac{1}{2\pi}\frac{n}{\sqrt{2\theta_2^3}}\, e^{-\frac{n}{2}\left[\frac{(\hat{\theta}_1-\theta_1)^2}{\theta_2}+\frac{(\hat{\theta}_2-\theta_2)^2}{2\theta_2^2}\right]} \tag{7}$$

with large-sample variances and covariances given by

$$\left(\frac{1}{n}\sigma_{ij}\right) = \begin{pmatrix} \dfrac{\theta_2}{n} & 0 \\ 0 & \dfrac{2\theta_2^2}{n} \end{pmatrix} \tag{8}$$

Since $\sigma_{12} = 0$, the estimators are shown to be independently distributed for large samples; we have already seen, of course, in Sec. 10.4 that they are actually independent for any sample size. The large-sample distribution of $\hat{\boldsymbol{\theta}}_1$ is exactly the normal distribution as given in (7). But the exact distribution of $\hat{\boldsymbol{\theta}}_2$ is given by the gamma distribution for any sample size, and this appears to conflict with the normal distribution indicated in (7). However, it can be shown that the exact distribution of $\hat{\boldsymbol{\theta}}_2$ does approach the normal form

$$\frac{1}{\sqrt{2\pi}}\sqrt{\frac{n}{2}}\,\frac{1}{\theta_2}\, e^{-\frac{n}{2}\frac{(\hat{\theta}_2-\theta_2)^2}{2\theta_2^2}}$$

as n becomes large.

Example 10.5. As a second illustration, we shall obtain the large-sample distribution of the estimators of the parameters of a multinomial distribution.

Suppose that the elements of a population may be classified into $k + 1$ categories, say $A_1, A_2, \cdots, A_{k+1}$. We shall describe an element by the set of variables $(\mathbf{x}_1, \mathbf{x}_2, \cdots, \mathbf{x}_{k+1})$ where, if the element belongs to A_i, $\mathbf{x}_i = 1$ and all the other $\mathbf{x}$'s are 0. If the probability is p_i that an element drawn at random belongs to A_i, then the joint density of the $\mathbf{x}$'s is

$$f(x_1, x_2, \cdots, x_{k+1}) = p_1^{x_1} p_2^{x_2} \cdots p_{k+1}^{x_{k+1}} \qquad x_i = 0, 1; \Sigma x_i = 1 \quad (9)$$

where $\Sigma p_i = 1$. Summing $f(x_1, \cdots, x_{k+1})$ over all possible sets of x's, namely, $(1, 0, 0, \cdots, 0)$, $(0, 1, 0, 0, \cdots, 0)$, $(0, 0, 1, 0, \cdots, 0)$, and so on, we have

$$\sum f(x_1, \cdots, x_{k+1}) = \sum_{i=1}^{k+1} p_i = 1$$

The distribution (9) is a multivariate distribution with k functionally independent parameters; we shall take them to be $p_1, p_2, \cdots, p_k$ and think of p_{k+1} as a symbol for $1 - p_1 - p_2 - \cdots - p_k$.

Let a sample of size n be drawn, and let $\mathbf{n}_i$ be the number of sample elements in A_i; then $\Sigma \mathbf{n}_i = n$ and the likelihood of the sample is

$$L(p_1, \cdots, p_k) = \prod_{i=1}^{k+1} p_i^{\mathbf{n}_i}$$

the logarithm of which is

$$L^* = \log L(p_1, p_2, \cdots, p_k) = \sum_{i=1}^{k+1} \mathbf{n}_i \log p_i \quad (10)$$

The estimators are found by putting the first derivatives of L^* equal to 0 and solving for the parameters. The equations are

$$\begin{aligned} \frac{\partial L^*}{\partial p_1} &= \frac{\mathbf{n}_1}{\hat{\mathbf{p}}_1} - \frac{\mathbf{n}_{k+1}}{\hat{\mathbf{p}}_{k+1}} = 0 \\ \frac{\partial L^*}{\partial p_2} &= \frac{\mathbf{n}_2}{\hat{\mathbf{p}}_2} - \frac{\mathbf{n}_{k+1}}{\hat{\mathbf{p}}_{k+1}} = 0 \end{aligned} \quad (11)$$

and so on, remembering that $\hat{\mathbf{p}}_{k+1}$ represents $1 - \hat{\mathbf{p}}_1 - \hat{\mathbf{p}}_2 - \cdots - \hat{\mathbf{p}}_k$. On multiplying the first equation by $\hat{\mathbf{p}}_1\hat{\mathbf{p}}_{k+1}$, the second by $\hat{\mathbf{p}}_2\hat{\mathbf{p}}_{k+1}$, and so on, and adding the results, one finds $\hat{\mathbf{p}}_{k+1} = \mathbf{n}_{k+1}/n$, and then that

$$\hat{\mathbf{p}}_i = \frac{\mathbf{n}_i}{n} \qquad i = 1, 2, \cdots, k + 1 \quad (12)$$

We wish to find the approximate distribution of the estimators in (12) for large samples. Applying Theorem 10.8, we know that the distribution is approximately normal with means p_i. We need only to find the coefficients nr_{ij} of the quadratic form. By Theorem 10.8,

$$r_{ij} = -E\left(\frac{\partial^2}{\partial p_i \, \partial p_j} \log \mathbf{f}\right) \tag{13}$$

Differentiating log f, we have

$$\begin{aligned} \frac{\partial^2}{\partial p_i \, \partial p_j} \log f &= -\frac{x_{k+1}}{p_{k+1}^2} && \text{if } i \neq j \\ &= -\frac{x_i}{p_i^2} - \frac{x_{k+1}}{p_{k+1}^2} && \text{if } i = j \end{aligned} \tag{14}$$

and taking expected values,

$$E(\mathbf{x}_i) = \sum_{x_i} x_i \prod_{1}^{k+1} p_i^{x_i} = p_i \qquad i = 1, 2, \cdots, k \tag{15}$$

$$E(\mathbf{x}_{k+1}) = \sum_{x_i} x_{k+1} \prod_{1}^{k+1} p_i^{x_i} = p_{k+1}$$

Thus

$$\begin{aligned} r_{ij} &= \frac{1}{p_{k+1}} && \text{if } i \neq j \\ &= \frac{1}{p_i} + \frac{1}{p_{k+1}} && \text{if } i = j \end{aligned} \tag{16}$$

and we may write these two relations as one, using the symbol δ_{ij},

$$r_{ij} = \frac{\delta_{ij}}{p_i} + \frac{1}{p_{k+1}} \qquad i, j = 1, 2, \cdots, k \tag{17}$$

The value of the determinant $|R|$ can be shown to be $1 \Big/ \prod_{1}^{k+1} p_i$; hence the approximate large-sample distribution of the estimators is, say,

$$g(\hat{p}_1, \hat{p}_2, \cdots, \hat{p}_k) = \left(\frac{1}{2\pi}\right)^{\frac{k}{2}} \sqrt{\frac{1}{\prod_{1}^{k+1} p_i}} \; n^{\frac{k}{2}} e^{-\frac{1}{2} \sum_{i=1}^{k} \sum_{j=1}^{k} n\left(\frac{\delta_{ij}}{p_i} + \frac{1}{p_{k+1}}\right)(\hat{p}_i - p_i)(\hat{p}_j - p_j)} \tag{18}$$

The inverse of R has elements

$$\begin{aligned} \sigma_{ii} &= p_i(1 - p_i) \\ \sigma_{ij} &= -p_i p_j \qquad i \neq j \qquad i, j = 1, 2, \cdots, k \end{aligned} \tag{19}$$

as may be verified by computing the product $V \cdot R$. The large-sample variances and covariances of the estimators are therefore given by multiplying (19) by $1/n$. These happen to be, in fact, the exact variances and covariances for any sample size.

10.9 Distribution of Order Statistics

Let $\mathbf{x}_1, \cdots, \mathbf{x}_n$ be a random sample from the density $f(x)$, and suppose that we want the joint distribution of $\mathbf{y}_1, \mathbf{y}_2, \cdots, \mathbf{y}_n$, where the $\mathbf{y}_i$ are the $\mathbf{x}_i$ arranged in order of magnitude so that $\mathbf{y}_1 < \mathbf{y}_2 < \cdots < \mathbf{y}_n$. For simplicity in this section we shall discuss the case where $n = 3$, but the methods are completely general; we shall assume that $f(x)$ is the density of a continuous random variable $\mathbf{x}$.

Let $\mathbf{x}_1, \mathbf{x}_2, \mathbf{x}_3$ be a sample of size 3 from $f(x)$, $-\infty < x < \infty$. We shall transform from the x's to the y's as follows:

Let
$$\begin{array}{ll} y_1 = x_1;\ y_2 = x_2;\ y_3 = x_3 & \text{if } x_1 < x_2 < x_3 \\ y_1 = x_1;\ y_2 = x_3;\ y_3 = x_2 & \text{if } x_1 < x_3 < x_2 \\ y_1 = x_2;\ y_2 = x_1;\ y_3 = x_3 & \text{if } x_2 < x_1 < x_3 \\ y_1 = x_2;\ y_2 = x_3;\ y_3 = x_1 & \text{if } x_2 < x_3 < x_1 \\ y_1 = x_3;\ y_2 = x_1;\ y_3 = x_2 & \text{if } x_3 < x_1 < x_2 \\ y_1 = x_3;\ y_2 = x_2;\ y_3 = x_1 & \text{if } x_3 < x_2 < x_1 \end{array} \tag{1}$$

The six regions $x_1 < x_2 < x_3$; $x_1 < x_3 < x_2$; $\cdots$; $x_3 < x_2 < x_1$ are disjoint, and the union of these six regions and certain sets which have probability zero, such as $x_1 = x_2 = x_3$, etc., is the three-dimensional space $-\infty < x_1 < \infty$, $-\infty < x_2 < \infty$, $-\infty < x_3 < \infty$.

We shall find the joint density of $\mathbf{y}_1, \mathbf{y}_2, \mathbf{y}_3$ for each of the six regions above. Now the joint density of the $\mathbf{x}$'s is

$$q(x_1, x_2, x_3) = f(x_1)f(x_2)f(x_3) \qquad \begin{array}{l} -\infty < x_1 < \infty \\ -\infty < x_2 < \infty \\ -\infty < x_3 < \infty \end{array} \tag{2}$$

For the region $x_1 < x_2 < x_3$ the density of the $\mathbf{y}$'s is

$$h(y_1, y_2, y_3) = f(y_1)f(y_2)f(y_3) \qquad y_1 < y_2 < y_3 \tag{3}$$

since the Jacobian is equal to 1. For the region $x_1 < x_3 < x_2$ the density of the $\mathbf{y}$'s is

$$h(y_1, y_2, y_3) = f(y_1)f(y_3)f(y_2) \qquad y_1 < y_2 < y_3 \tag{4}$$

Similarly, for the other regions in (1) we get (the Jacobian is equal to 1 for all the regions)

$$h(y_1, y_2, y_3) = f(y_2)f(y_1)f(y_3) \qquad y_1 < y_2 < y_3 \tag{5}$$
$$h(y_1, y_2, y_3) = f(y_2)f(y_3)f(y_1) \qquad y_1 < y_2 < y_3 \tag{6}$$
$$h(y_1, y_2, y_3) = f(y_3)f(y_1)f(y_2) \qquad y_1 < y_2 < y_3 \tag{7}$$
$$h(y_1, y_2, y_3) = f(y_3)f(y_2)f(y_1) \qquad y_1 < y_2 < y_3 \tag{8}$$

But each portion of the density in (3) to (8) is the same and is over the same region $y_1 < y_2 < y_3$. Hence, by the material earlier in this chapter, the joint density is the sum of these six:

$$h(y_1, y_2, y_3) = 6f(y_1)f(y_2)f(y_3) \qquad -\infty < y_1 < y_2 < y_3 < \infty$$

or

$$h(y_1, y_2, y_3) = 3!f(y_1)f(y_2)f(y_3) \qquad -\infty < y_1 < y_2 < y_3 < \infty \tag{9}$$

To extend this to a sample of size n, we note that the only modification is that there are $n!$ regions of the kind $x_1 < x_2 < \cdots < x_n$ obtained by permuting the x_i. This gives the following theorem.

Theorem 10.9. *Let* $\mathbf{x}_1, \mathbf{x}_2, \cdots, \mathbf{x}_n$ *be a random sample from the density* $f(x)$, $-\infty < x < \infty$. *The joint density of the order statistics* $\mathbf{y}_1, \mathbf{y}_2, \cdots, \mathbf{y}_n$ *is*

$$h(y_1, y_2, \cdots, y_n) = n!f(y_1) \cdots f(y_n) \qquad -\infty < y_1 < y_2 < \cdots < y_n < \infty$$

From this joint distribution we may derive many interesting and useful densities. For instance, the density of the largest variate $\mathbf{y}_n$ may be found, or the smallest variate $\mathbf{y}_1$ or the tth from the largest variate $\mathbf{y}_{n-t}$, etc. We shall illustrate the use of this distribution by finding the density of the range $\mathbf{y}_n - \mathbf{y}_1 = \mathbf{R}$. We shall first find the joint density of the largest and smallest variates, $\mathbf{y}_n$ and $\mathbf{y}_1$. This is

$$p(y_1, y_n) = \int_{y_1}^{y_n} \cdots \int_{y_1}^{y_4} \int_{y_1}^{y_3} h(y_1, \cdots, y_n)\, dy_2\, dy_3 \cdots dy_{n-1} \qquad -\infty < y_1 < y_n < \infty$$

or

$$p(y_1, y_n) = n!f(y_1)f(y_n) \int_{y_1}^{y_n} \cdots \int_{y_1}^{y_4} \int_{y_1}^{y_3} f(y_2)f(y_3) \cdots f(y_{n-1})\, dy_2\, dy_3 \cdots dy_{n-1}$$

We shall perform this integration term by term. First

$$\int_{y_1}^{y_3} f(y_2)\, dy_2 = F(y_3) - F(y_1)$$

where $F(y)$ is $\int_{-\infty}^{y} f(t)\, dt$, and consequently $F'(y) = f(y)$ at points where the derivative exists. Next

$$\int_{y_1}^{y_4} [F(y_3) - F(y_1)]f(y_3)\, dy_3 = \frac{[F(y_4) - F(y_1)]^2}{2}$$

Next

$$\frac{1}{2} \int_{y_1}^{y_5} [F(y_4) - F(y_1)]^2 f(y_4)\, dy_4 = \frac{1}{3!} [F(y_5) - F(y_1)]^3$$

Continuing in this fashion, we get

$$p(y_1, y_n) = n(n-1)[F(y_n) - F(y_1)]^{n-2} f(y_1)f(y_n) \qquad -\infty < y_1 < y_n < \infty$$

To find the distribution of the range $\mathbf{R} = \mathbf{y}_n - \mathbf{y}_1$ we make the transformation

$$\mathbf{R} = \mathbf{y}_n - \mathbf{y}_1$$
$$\mathbf{S} = \mathbf{y}_1$$

and get for the density of **R**, **S** (the absolute value of the Jacobian is unity)

$$k(R, S) = n(n-1)[F(R+S) - F(S)]^{n-2}f(S)f(R+S)$$

The density of **R** can be found by integrating $k(R, S)$ with respect to S.

Example 10.6. Let $f(x) = 1$, $0 < x < 1$, and let $\mathbf{x}_1, \cdots, \mathbf{x}_6$ be a random sample of size 6 from this rectangular density.

$$F(x) = \int_0^x dt = x$$

and so

$$F(R+S) = R+S \qquad F(S) = S$$

The joint density of **R** and **S** is

$$k(R, S) = 6 \cdot 5(R+S-S)^4 = 30R^4 \qquad \begin{matrix} 0 < S < 1-R \\ 0 < R < 1 \end{matrix}$$

The density of **R** is

$$g(R) = 30 \int_0^{1-R} R^4\, dS = 30R^4(1-R) \qquad 0 < R < 1$$

10.10 Studentized Range

Let $\mathbf{x}_1, \cdots, \mathbf{x}_n$ be a random sample of size n from a normal density with mean 0 and variance 1. Let $\mathbf{v}^2$ be a chi-square variable with m degrees of freedom, and let the **x**'s and $\mathbf{v}^2$ be independent. The random variable

$$\mathbf{q} = \frac{\mathbf{y}_n - \mathbf{y}_1}{\mathbf{v}/\sqrt{m}}$$

is called the *Studentized range* and is important in certain applied problems which will be discussed in following chapters (**y**'s are the order statistics of the **x**'s). Let $N(x)$ be the cumulative distribution of the normal density with mean 0 and variance 1, and let $\phi(x)$ be the density function of the same distribution. Then, by Sec. 10.9, the distribution of the range of the **x**'s is

$$g(R) = n(n-1) \int_{-\infty}^{\infty} [N(R+S) - N(S)]^{n-2}\phi(R+S)\phi(S)\, dS \quad (1)$$

where $R = y_n - y_1$.

The joint distribution of $\mathbf{R}$ and $\mathbf{v}^2$, where $\mathbf{v}^2$ is a chi-square variate with m degrees of freedom, is

$$h(R, v^2) = g(R) \cdot p(v^2) \qquad 0 < R < \infty, 0 < v^2 < \infty$$

Make the change of variables from $\mathbf{R}$, $\mathbf{v}^2$ to $\mathbf{q}$, $\mathbf{u}$ by

$$\frac{\mathbf{R}}{\mathbf{v}/\sqrt{m}} = \mathbf{q} \qquad \frac{\mathbf{v}^2}{m} = \mathbf{u} \tag{2}$$

The Jacobian is $m\sqrt{u}$, and we get for the joint density of $\mathbf{q}$ and $\mathbf{u}$

$$k(q, u) = g(q\sqrt{u}) \cdot p(um) \cdot m\sqrt{u} \qquad 0 < q < \infty, 0 < u < \infty \tag{3}$$

The density of q is obtained by integrating $k(q, u)$ with respect to u.

$$f(q) = \int_0^\infty g(\sqrt{u}\, q) \cdot p(um) \cdot m\sqrt{u}\, du \qquad 0 < q < \infty \tag{4}$$

For values of n greater than 2, this function is quite complex, but the integral

$$\int_{q_\alpha}^\infty f(q)\, dq = \alpha$$

has been tabulated for $\alpha = .01, .05$, and $.10$. Tables VI to VIII give q_α for various values of n and m. The foregoing can be summed up by the following theorem.

Theorem 10.10. *Let* $\mathbf{x}_1, \mathbf{x}_2, \ldots, \mathbf{x}_n$ *be a random sample of size n from a normal density with mean* 0 *and variance* 1. Let $\mathbf{v}^2$ *be an independent chi-square variate with m degrees of freedom.* Then

$$\mathbf{q} = \frac{\mathbf{y}_n - \mathbf{y}_1}{\mathbf{v}/\sqrt{m}}$$

is distributed as the Studentized range with n and m degrees of freedom, where $\mathbf{y}_n - \mathbf{y}_1$ *is the range of the* $\mathbf{x}_i$. *The density is given by* (4).

10.11 Problems

1. Apply the method of equation (10.1.4) to Example 10.3.

2. If $\mathbf{x}$ is distributed by $f(x) = 2x$, $0 < x < 1$, find the distribution of $\mathbf{u} = (3\mathbf{x} - 1)^2$.

3. If $\mathbf{x}$ is distributed by $f(x) = 1$, $0 < x < 1$, find the distribution of $\bar{\mathbf{x}}$ for samples $\mathbf{x}_1, \mathbf{x}_2$ of size 2. Observe that the range of $\mathbf{x}_2$ for fixed $\bar{\mathbf{x}}$ is $0 < x_2 < 2\bar{x}$ when $\bar{x} < \frac{1}{2}$, and $2\bar{x} - 1 < x_2 < 1$ when $\bar{x} > \frac{1}{2}$.

4. If $\mathbf{x}$ is normally distributed with mean μ and variance σ^2, show by transforming the variate that $\mathbf{u} = [(\mathbf{x} - \mu)/\sigma]^2$ has the chi-square distribution with one degree of freedom.

5. Obtain the distribution of the mean of a sample of size n from a normal population with mean -2 and variance 4 by using the moment generating function.

6. If $\chi_1^2, \chi_2^2, \chi_3^2, \cdots, \chi_k^2$ are independently distributed chi-square variables with $n_1, n_2, \cdots, n_k$ degrees of freedom, respectively, show by means of the moment generating function that $\mathbf{u} = \Sigma\chi_i^2$ has the chi-square distribution with $n = \Sigma n_i$ degrees of freedom.

7. Using an argument similar to that given for the derivation of the chi-square distribution and the fact that $|(1 - 2t)r_{ij}| = (1 - 2t)^k|r_{ij}|$, show that the quadratic form of a k-variate normal distribution has the chi-square distribution with k degrees of freedom.

8. Find the mean and variance of a chi-square variate with k degrees of freedom.

9. Use the integral of the F distribution over the whole range to obtain an identity in the parameters m and n, and then use the identity to obtain the mean and variance of $\mathbf{F}$.

10. Find the .95 probability level of F for two and four degrees of freedom by direct integration of the distribution function.

11. Show that the transformation

$$w = \frac{mF/n}{1 + (mF/n)}$$

changes the F distribution to the beta distribution.

12. Show, by transforming the variate in the t distribution, that $\mathbf{u} = \mathbf{t}^2$ has the F distribution.

13. If $\mathbf{x}_1, \mathbf{x}_2, \cdots, \mathbf{x}_n$ is a random sample from a normal population with mean μ, show that

$$\mathbf{u} = \frac{\bar{\mathbf{x}} - \mu}{\sqrt{\dfrac{\Sigma(\mathbf{x}_i - \bar{\mathbf{x}})^2}{n(n-1)}}}$$

has the t distribution with $n - 1$ degrees of freedom.

14. If $\mathbf{x}_1$ and $\mathbf{x}_2$ is a random sample of two from a population with $f(x) = e^{-x}$, $x > 0$, show that $\mathbf{u} = \mathbf{x}_1 + \mathbf{x}_2$ and $\mathbf{v} = \mathbf{x}_1/\mathbf{x}_2$ are independently distributed.

15. If $\mathbf{x}, \mathbf{y}, \mathbf{z}$ have the joint density

$$f(x, y, z) = \frac{6}{(1 + x + y + z)^4} \qquad z > 0, y > 0, x > 0$$

find the distribution of $\mathbf{u} = \mathbf{x} + \mathbf{y} + \mathbf{z}$.

16. If $\mathbf{x}_1$ and $\mathbf{x}_2$ is a random sample of two from a population with the uniform distribution over the unit interval, find the distribution of $\mathbf{u} = \mathbf{x}_1\mathbf{x}_2$.

17. If $\mathbf{x}$ and $\mathbf{y}$ have the bivariate normal distribution, show that

$$\mathbf{u} = \frac{\mathbf{x} - \mu_x}{\sigma_x} + \frac{\mathbf{y} - \mu_y}{\sigma_y}$$

and

$$\mathbf{v} = \frac{\mathbf{x} - \mu_x}{\sigma_x} - \frac{\mathbf{y} - \mu_y}{\sigma_y}$$

are independently normally distributed with zero means and variances $2(1 + \rho)$ and $2(1 - \rho)$.

18. If $\mathbf{x}$ and $\mathbf{y}$ are independently and normally distributed with zero means and unit variances, show that $\mathbf{u} = \mathbf{x}^2 + \mathbf{y}^2$ and $\mathbf{v} = \mathbf{x}/\mathbf{y}$ are independently distributed. What are the individual distributions of $\mathbf{u}$ and $\mathbf{v}$?

19. Show that Student's distribution approaches the normal form when the number of degrees of freedom becomes infinite.

20. If $\mathbf{x}_1, \mathbf{x}_2, \cdots, \mathbf{x}_n$ is a random sample from a normal population, find the joint distribution of

$$\mathbf{u} = \sum_1^k \mathbf{x}_i \qquad \text{and} \qquad \mathbf{v} = \sum_r^n \mathbf{x}_i \qquad 0 < r < k < n$$

21. If $\mathbf{x}$ and $\mathbf{y}$ are independently distributed chi-square variables with m and n degrees of freedom, respectively, show that $\mathbf{u} = \mathbf{x} + \mathbf{y}$ and $\mathbf{v} = \mathbf{x}/\mathbf{y}$ are 'ndependently distributed.

22. Consider random samples of size n from a bivariate normal distribution. Show that

$$\frac{(\hat{\mathbf{u}}_x + \hat{\mathbf{u}}_y - \mu_x - \mu_y)\sqrt{n-1}}{\sqrt{\hat{\mathbf{d}}_x^2 + \hat{\mathbf{d}}_y^2 - 2\hat{\mathbf{\rho}}\hat{\mathbf{d}}_x\hat{\mathbf{d}}_y}}$$

has Student's distribution with $n - 1$ degrees of freedom.

23. If $\mathbf{x}$ and $\mathbf{y}$ are horizontal and vertical components of the deviations of a shot from the center of a target, and if $\mathbf{x}$ and $\mathbf{y}$ have a bivariate normal distribution with zero means, $\rho = 0.1$, and standard deviations of 10 inches, find the equation of an ellipse which will contain a shot with probability .95. (Use the result of Prob. 7.)

24. Find the mean and variance of $(1/n)\Sigma(\mathbf{x}_i - \bar{\mathbf{x}})^2$ for samples of size n from a normal population, and show that they approach the large-sample mean and variance, σ^2 and $2\sigma^4/n$, as n increases.

25. If $\mathbf{x}_1, \mathbf{x}_2, \cdots, \mathbf{x}_k$ are independently and normally distributed with means μ_i and variance σ_i^2, show that

$$\mathbf{u} = \sum_{i=1}^k a_i \mathbf{x}_i$$

where the a_i are constants, is normally distributed with mean $\Sigma a_i \mu_i$ and variance $\Sigma a_i^2 \sigma_i^2$. Then deduce the distribution of the sample mean from a normal population by putting $a_i = 1/k$.

26. Obtain a result similar to that of Prob. 25 when the $\mathbf{x}_i$ have the bivariate normal distribution.

27. Find the large-sample distribution for the estimator of the parameter β in the gamma distribution.

28. Find the large-sample distribution for the estimator of the parameter of the Poisson distribution.

29. If $(\mathbf{x}_{1a}, \mathbf{x}_{2a}, \cdots, \mathbf{x}_{ka})$, $a = 1, 2, \cdots, n$, is a sample of size n from the multinomial population with density

$$\prod_1^k p_i^{x_i} \qquad x_i = 0, 1; \sum x_i = 1; \sum p_i = 1$$

find the distribution of the variates $\mathbf{n}_i = \sum_a \mathbf{x}_{ia}$, and find their variances and covariances.

***30.** Verify that (σ_{ij}) defined in equation (10.8.19) is the inverse of (r_{ij}) given by equation (10.8.17).

***31.** Evaluate the determinant of (σ_{ij}) in Prob. 30.

32. If $\mathbf{x}_1, \mathbf{x}_2, \cdots, \mathbf{x}_n$ are independently and normally distributed with the same mean but different variances $\sigma_1^2, \sigma_2^2, \cdots, \sigma_n^2$, show that $\mathbf{u} = \dfrac{\Sigma \mathbf{x}_i/\sigma_i^2}{\Sigma 1/\sigma_i^2}$ and $\mathbf{v} = \Sigma(\mathbf{x}_i - \mathbf{u})^2/\sigma_i^2$ are independently distributed. Show also that $\mathbf{u}$ is normal, while $\mathbf{v}$ has the chi-square distribution with $n - 1$ degrees of freedom.

33. Let $\mathbf{s}^2$ denote $\Sigma(\mathbf{x}_i - \bar{\mathbf{x}})^2/(n - 1)$, the mean square for samples of size n. For three samples from normal populations (with variances σ_1^2, σ_2^2, and σ_3^2), the sample sizes being n_1, n_2, and n_3, find the joint density of

$$\mathbf{u} = \frac{\mathbf{s}_1^2}{\mathbf{s}_3^2} \qquad \text{and} \qquad \mathbf{v} = \frac{\mathbf{s}_2^2}{\mathbf{s}_3^2}$$

where the $\mathbf{s}_1^2$, $\mathbf{s}_2^2$, and $\mathbf{s}_3^2$ are the sample mean squares.

34. Let a sample of size n_1 from a normal population (with variance σ_1^2) have mean square $\mathbf{s}_1^2$, and let a second sample of size n_2 from a second normal population (with mean μ_2 and variance σ_2^2) have mean $\bar{\mathbf{x}}$ and mean square $\mathbf{s}_2^2$. Find the joint density of

$$\mathbf{u} = \frac{\sqrt{n_2}\,(\bar{\mathbf{x}} - \mu_2)}{\mathbf{s}_2} \qquad \text{and} \qquad \mathbf{v} = \frac{\mathbf{s}_1^2}{\mathbf{s}_2^2}$$

* This problem depends on Sec. 10.8.

35. For a random sample of size 2 from a normal density with mean 0 and variance 1, find the distribution of the range.

36. Let $\mathbf{x}_1$, $\mathbf{x}_2$, $\mathbf{x}_3$ be a random sample of size 3 from the density

$$f(x) = e^{-x} \qquad x > 0$$

(*a*) Find the density of the smallest order statistic $\mathbf{y}_1$.

(*b*) Find the expected value of $\mathbf{y}_1$.

37. In Theorem 10.10 find the expected value of $\mathbf{q}$ for $n = 2$.

38. What is the probability that the larger of two random observations from any continuous distribution will exceed the median?

39. If $\mathbf{x}_1$ and $\mathbf{x}_2$ is a sample of two from a population with density $f(x) = e^{-x}$, $x > 0$, and if the smaller of these values is denoted by $\mathbf{y}_1$ and the larger by $\mathbf{y}_2$, what is the joint density of $\mathbf{y}_1$ and $\mathbf{y}_1 + \mathbf{y}_2$?

40. Generalize the result of Prob. 38 to samples of size n, letting $\mathbf{y}_1$ be the smallest and $\mathbf{y}_n$ the largest of the n observations.

41. What is the marginal density of the smallest observation for samples of size n for the density in Prob. 36?

42. Considering random samples of size n from a population with density $f(x)$, what is the expected value of the area under $f(x)$ to the left of the smallest sample observation?

10.12 Bibliography

1. Anderson, R. L., and T. A. Bancroft: "Statistical Theory in Research," McGraw-Hill Book Company, Inc., New York, 1952.
2. Brunk, H.: "An Introduction to Mathematical Statistics," Ginn & Co., Boston, 1960.
3. Graybill, F. A.: "An Introduction to Linear Statistical Models," Vol. I, McGraw-Hill Book Company, Inc., New York, 1961.
4. Hoel, P. G.: "Introduction to Mathematical Statistics," John Wiley & Sons, Inc., New York, 1956.
5. Hogg, R., and A. Craig: "Introduction to Mathematical Statistics," The Macmillan Company, New York, 1959.
6. Kendall, M. G.: "The Advanced Theory of Statistics," Vols. I, II, Charles Griffin & Co., Ltd., London, 1946.
7. Parzen, E.: "Modern Probability Theory and Its Applications," John Wiley & Sons, Inc., New York, 1960.

11

Interval Estimation

11.1 Confidence Intervals

A point estimate of a parameter is not very meaningful without some measure of the possible error in the estimate. An estimate $\hat{\theta}$ of a parameter θ should be accompanied by some interval about $\hat{\theta}$, possibly of the form $\hat{\theta} - d$ to $\hat{\theta} + d$, together with some measure of assurance that the true parameter θ lies within the interval. Estimates are often given in such form. Thus an electronic charge may be estimated to be $(4.770 \pm .005)10^{-10}$ electrostatic unit with the idea that the first factor is very unlikely to be outside the range 4.765 to 4.775. A cost accountant for a publishing company, in trying to allow for all factors which enter into the cost of producing a certain book (actual production costs, proportion of plant overhead, proportion of executive salaries, etc.), may estimate the cost to be 83 ± 4.5 cents per volume with the implication that the correct cost very probably lies between 78.5 and 87.5 cents per volume. The Bureau of Labor Statistics may estimate the number of unemployed to be $2.4 \pm .3$ millions at a given time, feeling rather sure that the actual number is between 2.1 and 2.7 millions.

In order to give precision to these ideas, we shall consider a particular example. Suppose that a sample (1.2, 3.4, .6, 5.6) of four observations is drawn from a normal population with unknown mean μ and known standard deviation 3. The maximum-likelihood estimate of μ is the mean of the sample observations:

$$\bar{x} = 2.7 \tag{1}$$

We wish to determine upper and lower limits which are rather certain to contain the true parameter value between them.

In general, for samples of size 4 from the given distribution, the quantity

$$y = \frac{\bar{x} - \mu}{3/2} \tag{2}$$

will be normally distributed with zero mean and unit variance. $\bar{x}$ is the sample mean, and $3/2$ is $\sigma/\sqrt{n}$. Thus the quantity y has a density

$$f(y) = \frac{1}{\sqrt{2\pi}} e^{-\frac{1}{2}y^2} \tag{3}$$

which is independent of the true value of the unknown parameter, and we can compute the probability that y will be between any two arbitrarily chosen numbers. Thus, for example,

$$P(-1.96 < \mathrm{y} < 1.96) = \int_{-1.96}^{1.96} f(y)\, dy = .95 \tag{4}$$

In this relation the inequality $-1.96 < \mathrm{y}$, or

$$-1.96 < \frac{\bar{\mathrm{x}} - \mu}{3/2} \tag{5}$$

is equivalent to the inequality

$$\mu < \bar{\mathrm{x}} + 3/2(1.96) = \bar{\mathrm{x}} + 2.94$$

and the inequality

$$\mathrm{y} < 1.96$$

is equivalent to

$$\mu > \bar{\mathrm{x}} - 2.94$$

We may therefore rewrite (4) in the form

$$P(\bar{\mathrm{x}} - 2.94 < \mu < \bar{\mathrm{x}} + 2.94) = .95 \tag{6}$$

and, substituting 2.7 for $\bar{\mathrm{x}}$,

$$P(-.24 < \mu < 5.64) = .95 \tag{7}$$

Thus two limits have been obtained $(-.24, 5.64)$, which we may say are 95 per cent certain to contain the true parameter value between them.

The meaning of (6) and (7) needs to be examined carefully. The probability that the *random interval*, $\bar{\mathrm{x}} - 2.94$ to $\bar{\mathrm{x}} + 2.94$, covers the true mean μ is .95. That is, if samples of four were repeatedly drawn from the population, and if the random interval $\bar{\mathrm{x}} - 2.94$ to $\bar{\mathrm{x}} + 2.94$ were computed for each sample, then 95 per cent of those intervals would be expected to contain the true mean μ. We therefore have considerable confidence that the interval $-.24$ to 5.64 covers the true mean. The measure of our confidence is .95 because, *before* the sample was drawn, .95 was the probability that the interval that we were going to construct would cover the true mean.

The interval $-.24$ to 5.64 is called a *confidence interval;* more specifically, it is called a 95 per cent confidence interval; the probability, in this case .95, is called the confidence coefficient. We can obtain intervals with any desired degree of confidence less than 1. Thus, since

$$P(-2.58 < \mathrm{y} < 2.58) = .99 \tag{8}$$

a 99 per cent confidence interval for the true mean is obtained by converting the inequalities as before and substituting $\bar{x} = 2.7$ to get

$$P(-1.17 < \mu < 6.57) = .99 \tag{9}$$

It is to be observed that there are, in fact, many possible intervals with the same probability. Thus, for example, since

$$P(-1.68 < y < 2.70) = .95 \tag{10}$$

another 95 per cent confidence interval for μ is given by

$$P(-1.35 < \mu < 5.22) = .95 \tag{11}$$

This interval is inferior to the one obtained before because its length 6.57 is greater than the length 5.88 of the interval in (7); it gives less precise information about the location of μ. Any numbers a and b such that ordinates at those points include 95 per cent of the area under $f(y)$ will

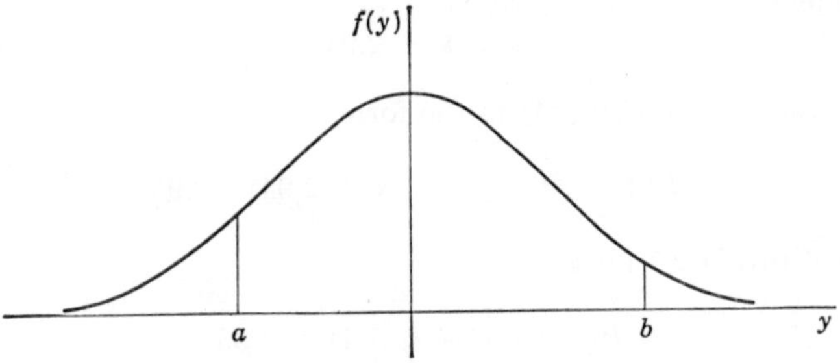

FIG. 11.1

determine a 95 per cent confidence interval. Ordinarily one would want the confidence interval to be as short as possible, and it is made so by making a and b as close together as possible, because the relation $P(a < y < b) = .95$ gives rise to a confidence interval of length $(\sigma/\sqrt{n})(b - a)$. The distance $b - a$ will be minimized for a fixed area when $f(a) = f(b)$, as is evident on referring to Fig. 11.1. If the point b is moved a short distance to the left, the point a will need to be moved a lesser distance to the left in order to keep the area the same; this operation decreases the length of the interval and will continue to do so as long as $f(b) < f(a)$. Since $f(y)$ is symmetric about $y = 0$ in the present example, the minimum value of $b - a$ for a fixed area occurs when $b = -a$. Thus (7) gives the shortest 95 per cent confidence interval, and (9) gives the shortest 99 per cent confidence interval for μ.

In most problems it is not possible to construct confidence intervals which are shortest for a given confidence coefficient. In these cases we may wish to find a confidence interval which has the shortest expected length or is such that the probability is minimized that the confidence interval covers a value μ^*, where $\mu^* \neq \mu$. We shall not discuss these concepts in this book.

The general method illustrated here is as follows: One finds, if possible, a function of the sample observations and the parameter to be estimated (the quantity y above) which has a distribution independent of the parameter and any other parameters. Then any probability statement of the form $P(a < \mathrm{y} < b) = \gamma$, where y is the function, will give rise to a probability statement about the parameter. This technique is applicable in many important problems, but in many others it is not, because it is impossible to find functions of the desired form which are distributed independently of any parameters. These latter problems can be dealt with by a more general technique to be described in Sec. 11.5.

The idea of interval estimation can be extended to include simultaneous estimation of several parameters. Thus the two parameters of the normal distribution may be estimated by some plane region R in the so-called parameter space, the space of all possible combinations of values of μ and σ^2. A 95 per cent confidence region is a region constructible from the sample such that, if samples were repeatedly drawn and a region constructed for each sample, 95 per cent of those regions, on the average, would include the true parameter point (μ_0, σ_0^2) (see Fig. 11.2).

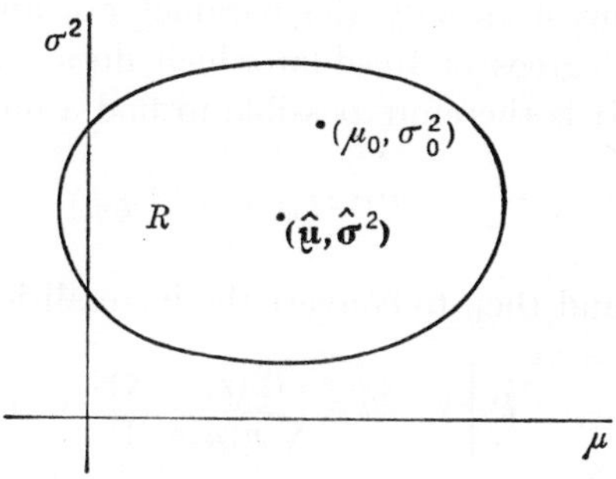

FIG. 11.2

Confidence intervals and regions provide good illustrations of uncertain inferences. In (7) the inference is made that the interval $-.24$ to 5.64 covers the true parameter value, but that statement is not made categorically. A measure, .05, of the uncertainty of the inference is an essential part of the statement.

11.2 Confidence Intervals for the Mean of a Normal Distribution

The method used in the preceding section cannot ordinarily be used to estimate the mean of a normal population, because the variance σ^2 is not ordinarily known. y takes the form (for samples of size n)

$$\mathrm{y} = \frac{\bar{\mathrm{x}} - \mu}{\sigma/\sqrt{n}} \tag{1}$$

and on converting the inequalities in, say,

$$P(-1.96 < \mathrm{y} < 1.96) = .95 \tag{2}$$

one finds

$$P\left(\bar{\mathbf{x}} - 1.96\frac{\sigma}{\sqrt{n}} < \mu < \bar{\mathbf{x}} + 1.96\frac{\sigma}{\sqrt{n}}\right) = .95 \qquad (3)$$

For a given sample, $\bar{\mathbf{x}}$ and n are known, but σ is not, so that limits for μ cannot be computed. Of course, an estimate $\hat{\boldsymbol{\sigma}}$ could be substituted for σ, but then the probability statement would no longer be exact and might be wrong for small samples.

The way around this difficulty was shown by W. S. Gossett (who wrote under the pseudonym of "Student") in a classic paper which introduced the t distribution. He is regarded as the founder of the modern theory of exact statistical inference. The quantity

$$\mathbf{t} = \frac{\bar{\mathbf{x}} - \mu}{\sqrt{\Sigma(\mathbf{x}_i - \bar{\mathbf{x}})^2/n(n-1)}} \qquad (4)$$

involves only the parameter μ and has the t distribution with $n - 1$ degrees of freedom which does not involve any unknown parameters. It is therefore possible to find a number, say $t_{.05}$, such that

$$P(-t_{.05} < \mathbf{t} < t_{.05}) = \int_{-t_{.05}}^{t_{.05}} f(t; n-1)\,dt = .90 \qquad (5)$$

and then to convert the inequalities to obtain

$$P\left[\bar{\mathbf{x}} - t_{.05}\sqrt{\frac{\Sigma(\mathbf{x}_i - \bar{\mathbf{x}})^2}{n(n-1)}} < \mu < \bar{\mathbf{x}} + t_{.05}\sqrt{\frac{\Sigma(\mathbf{x}_i - \bar{\mathbf{x}})^2}{n(n-1)}}\right] = .90 \qquad (6)$$

in which the limits can be computed for a given sample to obtain a 90 per cent confidence interval.

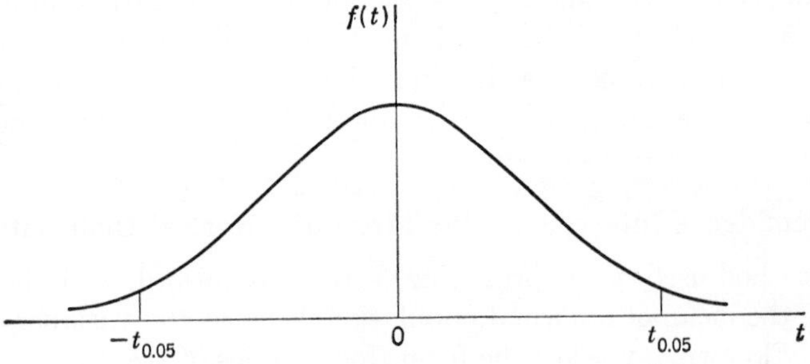

FIG. 11.3

The number $t_{.05}$ is called the 5 per cent level of $\mathbf{t}$ and locates points which cut off 5 per cent of the area under $f(t)$ on the upper tail. Other confidence intervals can be obtained by using other levels of $\mathbf{t}$. Thus a 98 per cent confidence interval may be found by using the number $t_{.01}$, which cuts off area .01 on the upper tail of the t distribution (see Fig. 11.3).

In this example the width of the confidence interval is

$$\mathbf{w} = \bar{\mathbf{x}} + t_{.05}\sqrt{\frac{\Sigma(\mathbf{x}_i - \bar{\mathbf{x}})^2}{n(n-1)}} - \bar{\mathbf{x}} + t_{.05}\sqrt{\frac{\Sigma(\mathbf{x}_i - \bar{\mathbf{x}})^2}{n(n-1)}}$$
$$= 2t_{.05}\sqrt{\frac{\Sigma(\mathbf{x}_i - \bar{\mathbf{x}})^2}{n(n-1)}}$$

The width is a random variable since it is a function of the random variables $\mathbf{x}_i$. It is also a function of the sample size n on which the confidence interval is based. If the confidence interval is very wide, it may be useless even though the probability is high that it covers the unknown parameter. Thus the sample size n needs to be large enough so that the probability is high that the width is small enough to be useful.

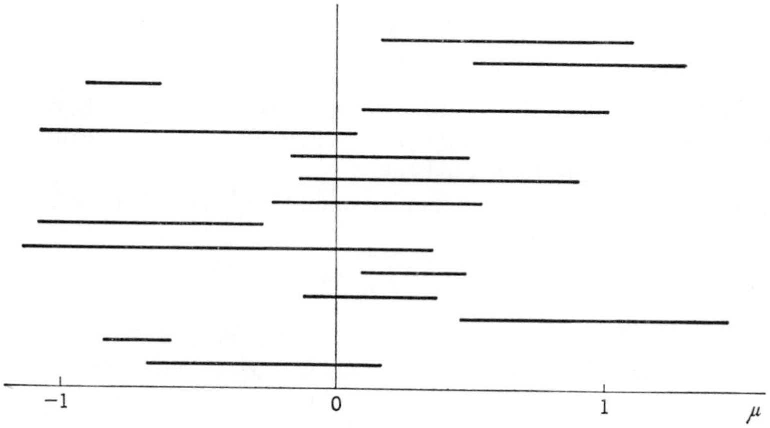

FIG. 11.4

The theory of how large the sample should be is beyond the scope of this book, but the reader can refer to articles cited in the bibliography.

Figure 11.4 shows the result of computing 50 per cent confidence intervals for 15 samples of size 4 actually drawn from a normal population with zero mean and unit variance. The intervals are shown as horizontal lines above the μ axis, and, as expected, about half of them cover the true mean 0. Similarly, if 95 per cent confidence intervals were used, about 95 per cent of them would be expected to cover the true mean. If one repeatedly uses 95 per cent confidence intervals to estimate parameters and states each time that the interval contains the true parameter value, he can expect to be wrong in 5 per cent of those statements.

11.3 Confidence Intervals for the Variance of a Normal Distribution

For a random sample of size n from a normal population, the quantity

$$\mathbf{u} = \frac{\Sigma(\mathbf{x}_i - \bar{\mathbf{x}})^2}{\sigma^2} \tag{1}$$

where $\bar{\mathbf{x}}$ is the sample mean, has the chi-square distribution with $n - 1$ degrees of freedom. Hence a confidence interval with confidence coefficient γ may be set up by finding two numbers, say a and b, such that

$$P(a < \mathbf{u} < b) = \int_a^b f(\chi^2)\, d\chi^2 = \gamma \tag{2}$$

On converting the inequalities, we obtain

$$P\left[\frac{\Sigma(\mathbf{x}_i - \bar{\mathbf{x}})^2}{b} < \sigma^2 < \frac{\Sigma(\mathbf{x}_i - \bar{\mathbf{x}})^2}{a}\right] = \gamma \tag{3}$$

which will determine a confidence interval for σ^2.

Since the length of the confidence interval is

$$\left(\frac{1}{a} - \frac{1}{b}\right) \sum (\mathbf{x}_i - \bar{\mathbf{x}})^2 \tag{4}$$

the shortest confidence interval for a given sample would be obtained by choosing a so as to minimize $[(1/a) - (1/b)]$ for the chosen value of γ. The required computation is tedious.

The ordinary chi-square tables give numbers χ_ϵ^2 such that

$$P(\mathbf{u} > \chi_\epsilon^2) = \int_{\chi_{\epsilon^2}}^{\infty} f(\chi^2)\, d\chi^2 = \epsilon \tag{5}$$

for selected values of ϵ. In setting up, say, a 95 per cent confidence interval, one merely chooses $a = \chi_{.975}^2$ and $b = \chi_{.025}^2$, that is, selects a and

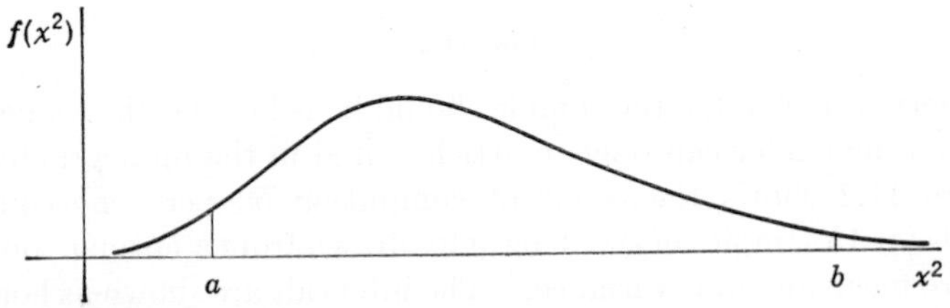

FIG. 11.5

b so that area .025 is cut off from each tail of the distribution. This very nearly minimizes the length of the confidence interval unless the number of degrees of freedom is quite small (see Fig. 11.5).

11.4 Confidence Region for Mean and Variance of a Normal Distribution

In constructing a region for the joint estimation of the mean μ_0 and variance σ_0^2 of a normal distribution, one might at first sight be inclined to use the individual estimates given by the t and the χ^2 distributions.

That is, for example, one might construct a .9025 (= .95²) region as in Fig. 11.6 by using the two relations:

$$P\left[\bar{\mathbf{x}} - t_{.025}\sqrt{\frac{\Sigma(\mathbf{x}_i - \bar{\mathbf{x}})^2}{n(n-1)}} < \mu_0 < \bar{\mathbf{x}} + t_{.025}\sqrt{\frac{\Sigma(\mathbf{x}_i - \bar{\mathbf{x}})^2}{n(n-1)}}\right] = .95 \quad (1)$$

$$P\left[\frac{\Sigma(\mathbf{x}_i - \bar{\mathbf{x}})^2}{\chi^2_{.025}} < \sigma_0^2 < \frac{\Sigma(\mathbf{x}_i - \bar{\mathbf{x}})^2}{\chi^2_{.975}}\right] = .95 \quad (2)$$

assuming that the probability of both occurrences is the product of the separate probabilities. This is incorrect because **t** and **u** are not independently distributed. The joint probability that the two intervals cover the true parameter values is not equal to the product of the separate

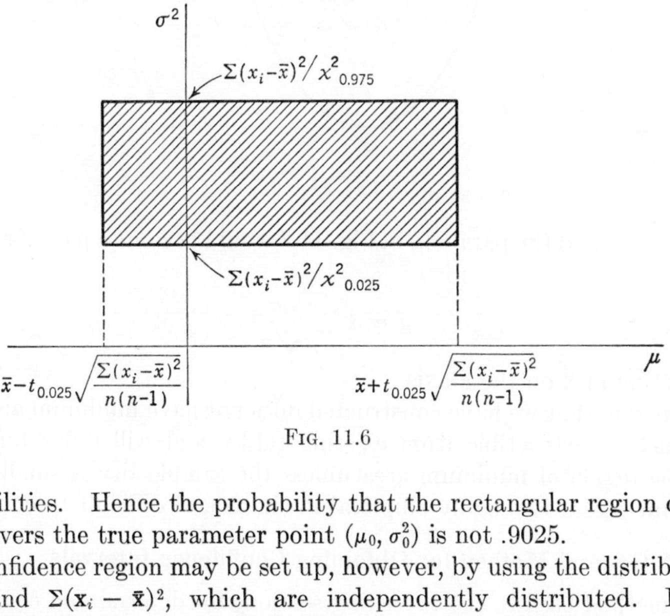

FIG. 11.6

probabilities. Hence the probability that the rectangular region of Fig. 11.6 covers the true parameter point (μ_0, σ_0^2) is not .9025.

A confidence region may be set up, however, by using the distributions of $\bar{\mathbf{x}}$ and $\Sigma(\mathbf{x}_i - \bar{\mathbf{x}})^2$, which are independently distributed. If, for example, a 95 per cent confidence region is desired, we may find numbers a, a', and b' such that

$$P\left(-a < \frac{\bar{\mathbf{x}} - \mu_0}{\sigma_0/\sqrt{n}} < a\right) = \sqrt{.95} \cong .975 \quad (3)$$

$$P\left[a' < \frac{\Sigma(\mathbf{x}_i - \bar{\mathbf{x}})^2}{\sigma_0^2} < b'\right] = \sqrt{.95} \quad (4)$$

The joint probability

$$P\left[-a < \frac{\bar{\mathbf{x}} - \mu_0}{\sigma_0/\sqrt{n}} < a,\ a' < \frac{\Sigma(\mathbf{x}_i - \bar{\mathbf{x}})^2}{\sigma_0^2} < b'\right] = .95 \quad (5)$$

because of the independence of the variables. The four inequalities in (5) determine a region in the parameter space which is easily found by plotting its boundaries. One merely replaces the inequality signs by equality signs and plots each of the four resulting equations as functions of μ and σ^2 in the parameter space. A region such as the shaded area in Fig. 11.7 will result. A confidence region for (μ_0, σ_0) would be obtained in exactly the same way; the equations would be plotted as functions of σ

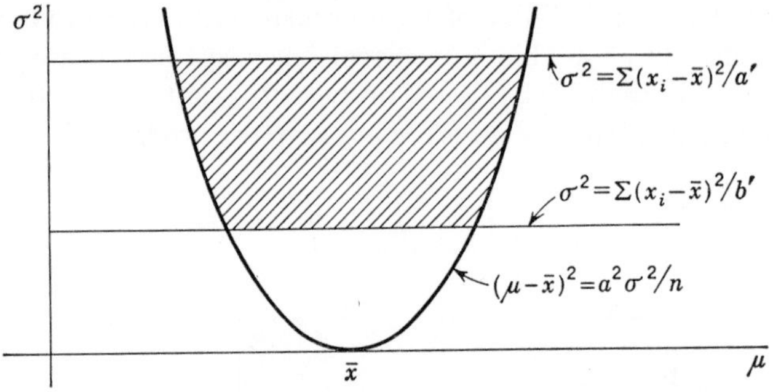

FIG. 11.7

instead of σ^2, and the parabola in Fig. 11.7 would become a pair of straight lines

$$\mu = \bar{\mathbf{x}} \pm \frac{a\sigma}{\sqrt{n}}$$

intersecting at $\bar{\mathbf{x}}$ on the μ axis.

The region that we have constructed does not have minimum area, but it is easily constructible from existing tables and will differ but little from the region of minimum area unless the sample size is small. The minimum region is roughly elliptical in shape and difficult to construct.

11.5 A General Method for Obtaining Confidence Intervals

The method used in the preceding sections for determining confidence intervals and regions required that functions of the sample and parameters be found which were distributed independently of the parameters. It is possible to set up confidence intervals, however, whether or not such functions exist.

Given a population with density $f(x; \theta)$ and an estimator $\hat{\theta}(\mathbf{x}_1, \mathbf{x}_2, \cdots, \mathbf{x}_n)$ for samples of size n (one might ordinarily use the maximum-likelihood estimator), we may determine the density, say $g(\hat{\theta}; \theta)$, of the estimator. We shall suppose, for definiteness, that a 95 per cent confidence interval is desired. If any arbitrary number, say θ', is substituted for θ in $g(\hat{\theta}; \theta)$, the distribution of $\hat{\boldsymbol{\theta}}$ will be completely specified and it will be possible to make probability statements about $\hat{\boldsymbol{\theta}}$. In particular, we may find two numbers h_1 and h_2 such that

$$P(\hat{\boldsymbol{\theta}} < h_1) = \int_{-\infty}^{h_1} g(\hat{\theta}; \theta')\, d\hat{\theta} = .025 \tag{1}$$

$$P(\hat{\boldsymbol{\theta}} > h_2) = \int_{h_2}^{\infty} g(\hat{\theta}; \theta')\, d\hat{\theta} = .025 \tag{2}$$

The numbers h_1 and h_2 will depend, of course, on the number substituted for θ in $g(\hat{\theta}; \theta)$. In fact, we may write h_1 and h_2 as functions of θ: $h_1(\theta)$ and $h_2(\theta)$. The values of these functions for any value of θ are determined by equations (1) and (2). Obviously

$$P[h_1(\theta) < \hat{\boldsymbol{\theta}} < h_2(\theta)] = \int_{h_1(\theta)}^{h_2(\theta)} g(\hat{\theta}; \theta)\, d\hat{\theta} = .95 \tag{3}$$

$h_1(\theta)$ and $h_2(\theta)$ may be plotted against θ as in Fig. 11.8. A vertical line through any chosen value θ' of θ will intersect the two curves in points

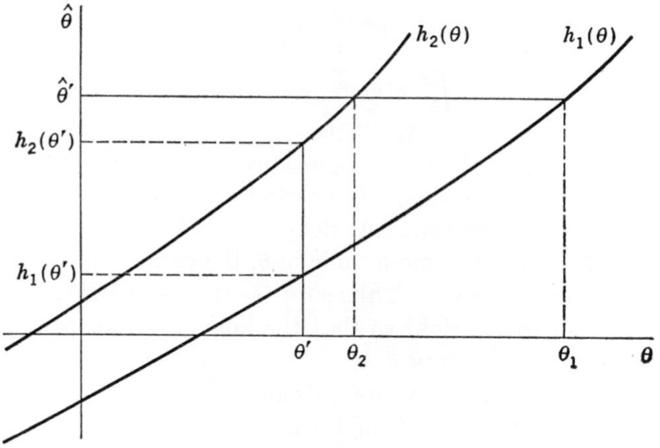

FIG. 11.8

which, projected on the $\hat{\boldsymbol{\theta}}$ axis, will give limits between which $\hat{\boldsymbol{\theta}}$ will fall with probability .95.

Having constructed the two curves $\hat{\theta} = h_1(\theta)$ and $\hat{\theta} = h_2(\theta)$, we may construct a confidence interval for θ as follows: Draw a sample of size n and compute the value of the estimator, say $\hat{\theta}'$. A horizontal line through the point $\hat{\theta}'$ on the $\hat{\theta}$ axis (Fig. 11.8) will intersect the two curves at points which may be projected on the θ axis and labeled θ_1 and θ_2, as in the figure. These two numbers define the confidence interval, for it is easily shown that

$$P(\boldsymbol{\theta}_2 < \theta < \boldsymbol{\theta}_1) = .95 \tag{4}$$

Suppose that we were, in fact, sampling from a population that had θ' as the value of θ. The probability that the estimate $\hat{\boldsymbol{\theta}}$ will fall between

$h_1(\theta')$ and $h_2(\theta')$ is .95. If the estimate does fall between these limits, then the horizontal line will cut the vertical line through θ' at some point between the curves, and the corresponding interval (θ_2, θ_1) will cover θ'. If the estimate does not fall between $h_1(\theta')$ and $h_2(\theta')$, the horizontal line does not cut the vertical line between the curves, and the corresponding interval (θ_2, θ_1) does not cover θ. It follows, therefore, that the probability is exactly .95 that an interval $(\boldsymbol{\theta}_2, \boldsymbol{\theta}_1)$ constructed by this method will cover θ'. And this statement is true for any population value of θ.

It is sometimes possible to determine the limits $\boldsymbol{\theta}_2$ and $\boldsymbol{\theta}_1$ for a given estimate without actually finding $h_1(\theta)$ and $h_2(\theta)$. Referring to Fig. 11.8, the limits for θ are at points θ_2 and θ_1 such that $h_1(\theta_1) = \hat{\theta}'$ and $h_2(\theta_2) = \hat{\theta}'$. In terms of the definition of h_1 and h_2, we may say that $\boldsymbol{\theta}_1$ is the value of θ for which

$$\int_{-\infty}^{\hat{\theta}'} g(\hat{\theta}; \theta)\, d\hat{\theta} = .025 \tag{5}$$

and $\boldsymbol{\theta}_2$ is the value of θ for which

$$\int_{\hat{\theta}'}^{\infty} g(\hat{\theta}; \theta)\, d\hat{\theta} = .025 \tag{6}$$

If the left-hand sides of these two equations can be given explicit expressions in terms of θ and if the equations can be solved for θ uniquely, then those roots are the 95 per cent confidence limits for θ.

If $h_1(\theta)$ and $h_2(\theta)$ are not monotonic in θ, the confidence interval may, in fact, be a set of intervals. Thus suppose that the curves of Fig. 11.8 bent down farther to the right so that the horizontal line at $\hat{\theta}'$ cut them again, for example, at points θ_3 and θ_4. Then the confidence interval would actually consist of two intervals $(\boldsymbol{\theta}_2, \boldsymbol{\theta}_1)$ and $(\boldsymbol{\theta}_3, \boldsymbol{\theta}_4)$. The statement about θ would then be of the form

$$P(\boldsymbol{\theta}_2 < \theta < \boldsymbol{\theta}_1, \text{ or } \boldsymbol{\theta}_3 < \theta < \boldsymbol{\theta}_4) = .95 \tag{7}$$

However, in most situations encountered in practice there will be a single interval, or it will be possible to select a single interval on the basis of other evidence concerning the experiment which produced the sample observations.

The method described here for obtaining confidence intervals may be extended to the case of several parameters, but a geometric representation becomes impossible even for two parameters. Suppose that a distribution depends on two parameters θ_1 and θ_2; we may find a plane region R in the $\hat{\theta}_1\hat{\theta}_2$ plane such that

$$P(\hat{\boldsymbol{\theta}}_1, \hat{\boldsymbol{\theta}}_2 \text{ in } R) = \iint_R g(\hat{\theta}_1, \hat{\theta}_2; \theta_1, \theta_2)\, d\hat{\theta}_1\, d\hat{\theta}_2 = .95 \tag{8}$$

By considering all possible pairs of values of θ_1 and θ_2, we can generate a four-dimensional region in the θ_1, θ_2, $\hat{\theta}_1$, $\hat{\theta}_2$ space which is analogous to the two-dimensional region between the curves in Fig. 11.8. Now suppose that a sample is drawn and the estimates $\hat{\theta}_1'$ and $\hat{\theta}_2'$ calculated. The intersection of the two hyperplanes $\hat{\boldsymbol{\theta}}_1 = \hat{\theta}_1'$ and $\hat{\boldsymbol{\theta}}_2 = \hat{\theta}_2'$ with the four-dimensional region will determine a two-dimensional region, which, when projected on the $\theta_1\theta_2$ plane, will be a 95 per cent confidence region for (θ_1, θ_2).

The argument may be extended to cover the case of k parameters. The method will determine a confidence region for all the parameters of a distribution. If one wishes to estimate some but not all of a set of parameters, the method cannot be used in general, although it may be modified to handle the problem in special circumstances. There is as yet no general solution of the problem of setting up confidence regions for a part of a set of k parameters in a distribution function except in the case of large samples.

Example 11.1. As a simple illustration, we may consider the estimation of α in

$$f(x; \alpha) = \frac{2}{\alpha^2}(\alpha - x) \qquad 0 < x < \alpha \tag{9}$$

for samples of size 1. If $\mathbf{x}$ is the observation, the maximum-likelihood estimator is found to be $\hat{\boldsymbol{\alpha}} = 2\mathbf{x}$ by solving

$$\frac{\partial}{\partial \alpha}\left[\frac{2}{\alpha^2}(\alpha - \mathbf{x})\right] = 0$$

for α. The distribution of the estimator is

$$g(\hat{\alpha}; \alpha) = \frac{1}{2\alpha^2}(2\alpha - \hat{\alpha}) \qquad 0 < \hat{\alpha} < 2\alpha \tag{10}$$

so that 95 per cent confidence intervals are obtained by determining $h_1(\alpha)$ and $h_2(\alpha)$ so that

$$\int_0^{h_1(\alpha)} g(\hat{\alpha}; \alpha)\, d\hat{\alpha} = .025 \tag{11}$$

$$\int_{h_2(\alpha)}^{2\alpha} g(\hat{\alpha}; \alpha)\, d\hat{\alpha} = .025 \tag{12}$$

The integrations are easily performed in this case and give, on solving for h_1 and h_2,

$$h_1(\alpha) = 2(1 - \sqrt{.975})\alpha \tag{13}$$

$$h_2(\alpha) = 2(1 - \sqrt{.025})\alpha \tag{14}$$

These plot as straight lines, as in Fig. 11.9. For a given observation, say $\mathbf{x} = 2$, the estimate is $\hat{\boldsymbol{\alpha}}' = 4$, and the 95 per cent confidence interval is given by

$$P\left(\frac{2}{1-\sqrt{.025}} < \alpha < \frac{2}{1-\sqrt{.975}}\right) = .95 \tag{15}$$

Actually, since

$$\mathbf{u} = \frac{2\alpha - \hat{\boldsymbol{\alpha}}}{\alpha}$$

is distributed independently of α, it was not necessary to use the general method in this problem. We could have found a confidence interval

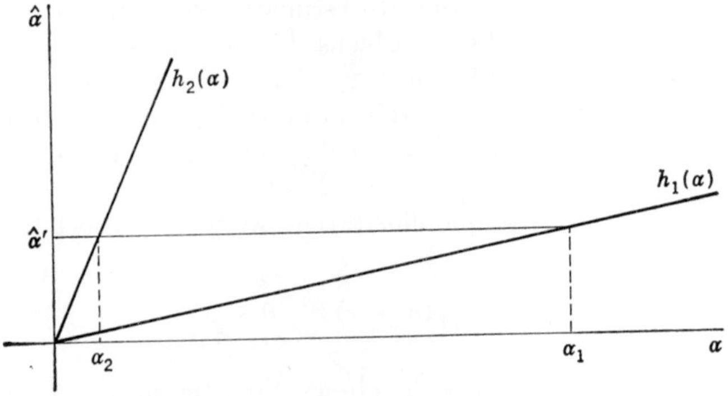

FIG. 11.9

for α by getting .95 limits for $\mathbf{u}$ and then converting the inequalities to get a statement about α.

11.6 Confidence Intervals for the Parameter of a Binomial Distribution

We shall apply the general method described in the preceding section to a problem which requires its use. If a sample, $\mathbf{x}_1, \mathbf{x}_2, \cdots, \mathbf{x}_n$, is drawn from a point binomial with density

$$f(x; p) = p^x(1-p)^{1-x} \qquad x = 0, 1; 0 \le p \le 1 \tag{1}$$

the maximum-likelihood estimator of p is

$$\hat{\mathbf{p}} = \frac{\mathbf{y}}{n} \tag{2}$$

where $\mathbf{y} = \Sigma \mathbf{x}_i$ can have the values $0, 1, 2, \cdots, n$. The density of $\hat{\mathbf{p}}$ is

$$g(\hat{p}; p) = \binom{n}{n\hat{p}} p^{n\hat{p}}(1-p)^{n(1-\hat{p})} \qquad \hat{p} = 0, \frac{1}{n}, \frac{2}{n}, \cdots, 1 \tag{3}$$

and it is not possible to find a function of $\hat{\mathbf{p}}$ and p which is distributed independently of p.

Again we shall suppose for definiteness that a 95 per cent confidence interval is to be constructed. The first step is to determine the functions $h_1(p)$ and $h_2(p)$. For $p = .4$, for example, we would, in accordance with the preceding section, seek a number $h_1(.4)$ such that

$$P[\hat{\mathfrak{p}} < h_1(.4)] = \sum_{y=0}^{nh_1} \binom{n}{y} (.4)^y (.6)^{n-y} = .025 \tag{4}$$

However, in view of the discreteness of the distribution, nh_1 in the sum must be an integer, and it will be impossible to make the sum exactly .025 for every value of p. This need not worry us, though. We do not need a curve $h_1(p)$ defined at every p. The only points of interest are those which correspond to the possible values of $\hat{\mathfrak{p}}$. It is, in fact, possible to use the technique indicated by equations (11.5.5) and (11.5.6), because an explicit expression for the probabilities on the left of these equations is immediately at hand. Assuming that we have an estimate

$$\hat{\mathfrak{p}}' = \frac{k}{n} \tag{5}$$

the 95 per cent confidence upper limit p_1 may be determined by finding the value of p for which

$$\sum_{y=0}^{k} \binom{n}{y} p^y (1-p)^{n-y} = .025 \tag{6}$$

and the lower limit p_2 is the value of p for which

$$\sum_{y=k}^{n} \binom{n}{y} p^y (1-p)^{n-y} = .025 \tag{7}$$

If $k = 0$, the lower limit is taken to be 0, and if $k = n$, the upper limit is taken to be 1.

For small values of n, equations (6) and (7) may be solved by trial and error for the roots p_1 and p_2, but this computation rapidly becomes tedious with increasing n. A simple method of solution is provided by Pearson's tables of the incomplete beta function. The cumulative form of the beta distribution is

$$F(x; \alpha, \beta) = \frac{(\alpha + \beta + 1)!}{\alpha!\beta!} \int_0^x t^\alpha (1-t)^\beta \, dt \tag{8}$$

and repeated integration by parts gives

$$F(x; \alpha, \beta) = -\sum_{i=0}^{\alpha} \binom{\alpha + \beta + 1}{i} x^i (1-x)^{\alpha+\beta+1-i} + 1 \tag{9}$$

It follows that partial binomial sums are given by the table of $F(x; \alpha, \beta)$. We may write equation (6) as

$$\sum_{y=0}^{k} \binom{n}{y} p^y(1-p)^{n-y} = 1 - F(p; k, n-k-1) = .025 \qquad (10)$$

and find at once in the table the value of p which corresponds to $F = .975$ for the given values of k and $n - k - 1$. Similarly, since

$$\sum_{k}^{n} \binom{n}{y} p^y(1-p)^{n-y} = 1 - \sum_{0}^{k-1} \binom{n}{y} p^y(1-p)^{n-y}$$

we may find the lower confidence limit by putting (7) in the form

$$\sum_{k}^{n} \binom{n}{y} p^y(1-p)^{n-y} = F(p; k-1, n-k) = .025 \qquad (11)$$

For values of n beyond the range of the table, the normal approximation to the binomial distribution may be used to obtain confidence intervals for p, as is shown in the following section, or the "Tables of the Binomial Probability Distribution" (National Bureau of Standards, Applied Mathematics Series 6, Washington, D.C., 1950) can be used.

11.7 Confidence Intervals for Large Samples

We have seen in Chap. 10 that, for large samples, the maximum-likelihood estimator $\hat{\boldsymbol{\theta}}$ for a parameter θ in a density $f(x; \theta)$ is approximately normally distributed about θ under rather general conditions. When these conditions are satisfied, it is possible to obtain approximate confidence intervals quite easily. The large-sample variance of the estimator is, say,

$$\sigma^2(\theta) = \frac{-1}{nE[\partial^2 \log f(\mathbf{x}; \theta)/\partial\theta^2]} \qquad (1)$$

where $\sigma^2(\theta)$ indicates that it is a function of θ since it ordinarily will depend on θ. For large samples, therefore, a confidence interval with probability γ may be determined by converting the inequalities in

$$P\left[-d_\gamma < \frac{\hat{\boldsymbol{\theta}} - \theta}{\sigma(\theta)} < d_\gamma\right] \cong 2\gamma \qquad (2)$$

where d_γ is chosen so that

$$\int_{-d_\gamma}^{d_\gamma} \frac{1}{\sqrt{2\pi}} e^{-\frac{1}{2}t^2}\, dt = 2\gamma$$

Example 11.2. As an example, we may consider the binomial distribution with parameter p; the variance of $\hat{\mathfrak{p}}$ is

$$\sigma^2(p) = \frac{p(1-p)}{n} \tag{3}$$

An approximate 2γ confidence interval, for example, is obtained by converting the inequalities in

$$P\left[-d_\gamma < \frac{\hat{\mathfrak{p}} - p}{\sqrt{p(1-p)/n}} < d_\gamma\right] \cong 2\gamma \tag{4}$$

to get

$$P\left[\frac{2n\hat{\mathfrak{p}} + d_\gamma^2 - d_\gamma\sqrt{4n\hat{\mathfrak{p}} + d_\gamma^2 - 4n\hat{\mathfrak{p}}^2}}{2(n + d_\gamma^2)} < p < \frac{2n\hat{\mathfrak{p}} + d_\gamma^2 + d_\gamma\sqrt{4n\hat{\mathfrak{p}} + d_\gamma^2 - 4n\hat{\mathfrak{p}}^2}}{2(n + d_\gamma^2)}\right] \cong 2\gamma \tag{5}$$

These expressions for the limits may be simplified since, in deriving the large-sample distribution, certain terms containing the factor $1/\sqrt{n}$ are neglected; i.e., the asymptotic normal distribution is correct only to within error terms of size $k/\sqrt{n}$. We may therefore neglect terms of this order in the limits in (5) without appreciably affecting the accuracy of the approximation. This means simply that we may omit all the d_γ^2 in (5), because they always occur added to a term with factor n and will be negligible, relative to n when n is large, to within the degree of approximation that we are assuming. Thus (5) may be rewritten as

$$P\left[\hat{\mathfrak{p}} - d_\gamma\sqrt{\frac{\hat{\mathfrak{p}}(1-\hat{\mathfrak{p}})}{n}} < p < \hat{\mathfrak{p}} + d_\gamma\sqrt{\frac{\hat{\mathfrak{p}}(1-\hat{\mathfrak{p}})}{n}}\right] \cong 2\gamma \tag{6}$$

In particular,

$$P\left[\hat{\mathfrak{p}} - 1.96\sqrt{\frac{\hat{\mathfrak{p}}(1-\hat{\mathfrak{p}})}{n}} < p < \hat{\mathfrak{p}} + 1.96\sqrt{\frac{\hat{\mathfrak{p}}(1-\hat{\mathfrak{p}})}{n}}\right] \cong .95$$

gives an approximate 95 per cent confidence interval for p for large samples.

We may observe that (6) is just the expression that would have been obtained had $\hat{\mathfrak{p}}$ been substituted for p in $\sigma^2(p)$. This substitution would imply that

$$\frac{\hat{\mathfrak{p}} - p}{\sqrt{\hat{\mathfrak{p}}(1-\hat{\mathfrak{p}})/n}}$$

is approximately normally distributed with zero mean and unit variance. It is, in fact, true in general that, in the asymptotic normal distribution of a maximum-likelihood estimator $\hat{\theta}$, the variance $\sigma^2(\hat{\theta})$ may be replaced by its estimator $\sigma^2(\hat{\theta})$ without appreciably affecting the accuracy of the approximation. We shall not prove this fact but shall use it because it greatly simplifies the conversion of inequalities in a probability statement to get confidence intervals.

For large samples, therefore, an approximate confidence interval with confidence 2γ is given by

$$P[\hat{\theta} - d_\gamma \sigma(\hat{\theta}) < \theta < \hat{\theta} + d_\gamma \sigma(\hat{\theta})] \cong 2\gamma \tag{7}$$

when $\hat{\theta}$ is asymptotically normally distributed, and $\sigma(\hat{\theta})$ in this expression is the maximum-likelihood estimate of the standard deviation of $\hat{\theta}$.

*11.8 Confidence Regions for Large Samples

When a distribution involves several parameters $(\theta_1, \theta_2, \cdots, \theta_k)$, we have seen in Chap. 10 that under rather general conditions the large-sample maximum-likelihood estimates, $(\hat{\theta}_1, \hat{\theta}_2, \cdots, \hat{\theta}_k)$, are approximately normally distributed with means $(\theta_1, \theta_2, \cdots, \theta_k)$ and coefficients of the quadratic form given by

$$r_{ij} = -nE\left[\frac{\partial^2 \log f(\mathbf{x}; \theta_1, \theta_2, \cdots, \theta_k)}{\partial\theta_i\, \partial\theta_j}\right] \tag{1}$$

The coefficients will, in general, be functions of the θ's as we have indicated.

Now we have seen that the quadratic form of a k-variate normal distribution has the chi-square distribution with k degrees of freedom. We may conclude, therefore, that the quantity

$$\mathbf{u} = \sum_{i=1}^{k} \sum_{j=1}^{k} r_{ij}(\hat{\theta}_i - \theta_i)(\hat{\theta}_j - \theta_j) \tag{2}$$

is approximately distributed as the chi-square distribution with k degrees of freedom for large samples. Here again, the accuracy of the approximation is not seriously impaired by substituting the estimates of the θ's for the θ's in r_{ij}. The quantity

$$\mathbf{v} = \Sigma\Sigma\, \hat{\mathbf{r}}_{ij}(\hat{\theta}_i - \theta_i)(\hat{\theta}_j - \theta_j) \tag{3}$$

is also approximately distributed by the chi-square law with k degrees of freedom. The variate $\mathbf{v}$ enables us to set up a very simple confidence region for the θ_i. If $\chi^2_{1-\gamma}$ is the $1 - \gamma$ point of the chi-square distribution, then

$$P(\mathbf{v} < \chi^2_{1-\gamma}) = \gamma \tag{4}$$

* This section depends on Sec. 10.8 and may be omitted if Sec. 10.8 was omitted.

determines a confidence region in the parameter space. The boundary of the region is given by the equation

$$\Sigma\Sigma\, \hat{\mathbf{r}}_{ij}(\hat{\boldsymbol{\theta}}_i - \theta_i)(\hat{\boldsymbol{\theta}}_j - \theta_j) = \chi^2_{1-\gamma} \tag{5}$$

which is the equation of an ellipsoid in the $(\theta_1, \theta_2, \cdots, \theta_k)$ space with its center at $(\hat{\boldsymbol{\theta}}_1, \hat{\boldsymbol{\theta}}_2, \cdots, \hat{\boldsymbol{\theta}}_k)$.

If one is interested in estimating only a part of a set of k parameters, for example, the set $(\theta_1, \theta_2, \cdots, \theta_r)$, where $r < k$, we first find the marginal distribution of the maximum-likelihood estimators for this set. If we let (a, b) be indices which have the range $1, 2, \cdots, r$, then the elements $\bar{r}_{ij}$ of the matrix of the quadratic form of the large-sample normal distribution of $\hat{\boldsymbol{\theta}}_1, \hat{\boldsymbol{\theta}}_2, \cdots, \hat{\boldsymbol{\theta}}_r$ are given by

$$V_{11}^{-1} = (\bar{r}_{ij})$$

where the matrix V_{11} is obtained by striking out the last $k - r$ rows and columns in V. The $\bar{r}_{ij}$ will, in general, be functions of all k of the original parameters $\theta_1, \theta_2, \cdots, \theta_k$. If we substitute the $\hat{\boldsymbol{\theta}}_i$ for the θ_i in $\bar{r}_{ij}$, we shall obtain the maximum-likelihood estimators $\hat{\bar{\mathbf{r}}}_{ij}$ of the $\bar{r}_{ij}$. The quadratic form

$$\mathbf{w} = \sum_a \sum_b \hat{\bar{\mathbf{r}}}_{ab}(\hat{\boldsymbol{\theta}}_a - \theta_a)(\hat{\boldsymbol{\theta}}_b - \theta_b)$$

is approximately distributed as chi-square with r degrees of freedom and will serve to determine an ellipsoidal confidence region in the $\theta_1, \theta_2, \cdots, \theta_r$ space for those parameters.

As an example of the estimation of more than one parameter, we may consider the large-sample estimation of the mean and variance of a normal population. We have seen in Sec. 10.8 that $\bar{\mathbf{x}}$ and $\hat{\boldsymbol{\sigma}}^2$ are approximately normally distributed with means μ and σ^2 and with the matrix of the quadratic form

$$R = (r_{ij}) = \begin{pmatrix} \dfrac{n}{\sigma^2} & 0 \\ 0 & \dfrac{n}{2\sigma^4} \end{pmatrix} \tag{6}$$

If we substitute $\hat{\boldsymbol{\sigma}}^2$ for σ^2 in (6), then the quadratic form becomes

$$\mathbf{v} = \frac{n}{\hat{\boldsymbol{\sigma}}^2}(\bar{\mathbf{x}} - \mu)^2 + \frac{n}{2\hat{\boldsymbol{\sigma}}^4}(\hat{\boldsymbol{\sigma}}^2 - \sigma^2)^2 \tag{7}$$

which is approximately distributed as chi-square with two degrees of freedom for large samples. In particular, let us suppose that we have an actual sample of 100 observations (3.4, 5.1, · · · , 2.2) with

$$\bar{x} = \tfrac{1}{100}\Sigma x_i = 4$$
$$\hat{\sigma}^2 = \tfrac{1}{100}\Sigma(x_i - \bar{x})^2 = 5$$

Since the .05 level of chi-square with two degrees of freedom is 5.99, a 95 per cent confidence region for μ and σ^2 is determined by

$$P[20(4 - \mu)^2 + 2(5 - \sigma^2)^2 < 5.99] = .95 \tag{8}$$

The values of μ and σ^2 which satisfy the inequality in (8) are the points within the ellipse

$$20(4 - \mu)^2 + 2(5 - \sigma^2)^2 = 5.99$$

which is plotted in Fig. 11.10. This is the 95 per cent confidence region for the true parameter point, say (μ_0, σ_0^2). Before the sample was

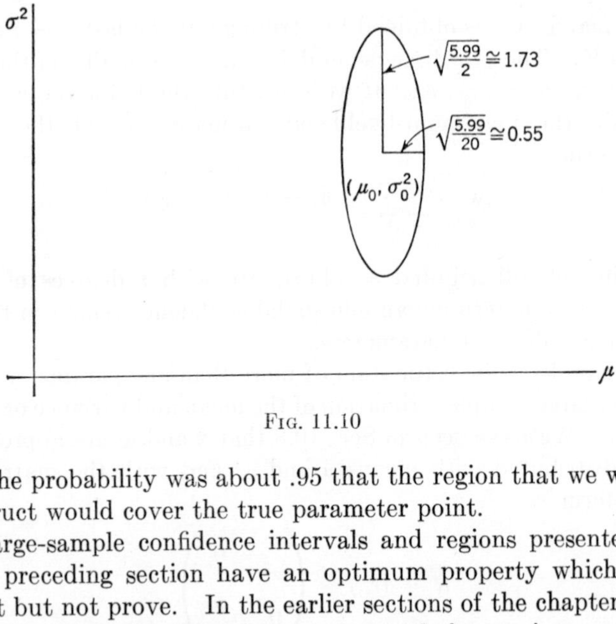

FIG. 11.10

drawn, the probability was about .95 that the region that we were going to construct would cover the true parameter point.

The large-sample confidence intervals and regions presented in this and the preceding section have an optimum property which we shall point out but not prove. In the earlier sections of the chapter, we were concerned with finding the shortest interval for a given probability. Thus the shortest 95 per cent interval for the mean of a normal population when σ is known is given by

$$P\left(\bar{x} - \frac{1.96\sigma}{\sqrt{n}} < \mu < \bar{x} + \frac{1.96\sigma}{\sqrt{n}}\right) = .95$$

and the length of the interval is $2 \times 1.96\sigma/\sqrt{n}$, where n is the sample size. Now let us suppose that, instead of using $\bar{x} = (1/n)\Sigma x_i$ to construct the confidence interval, we used only one of the observations, say the first. The estimator is simply

$$\tilde{\mathbf{u}} = \mathbf{x}_1$$

and the confidence interval is given by

$$P(\tilde{\mathbf{u}} - 1.96\sigma < \mu < \tilde{\mathbf{u}} + 1.96\sigma) = .95$$

which has length $2 \times 1.96\sigma$. This interval is $\sqrt{n}$ times as long as the one obtained by using the sample mean as the estimator.

It is now evident that the length of a confidence interval for a parameter depends strongly on what function of the sample observations is chosen as an estimator. The optimum property of the large-sample intervals and regions based on maximum-likelihood estimators is this:

Large-sample confidence intervals and regions based on maximum-likelihood estimators will be smaller, on an average, than intervals and regions determined by any other estimators of the parameters.

11.9 Multiple Confidence Intervals

In the previous sections we have indicated that the frequency-probability interpretation of confidence intervals is: Upon repeated sampling, 100 $(1 - \alpha)$ per cent of the confidence intervals constructed will contain the unknown parameter θ, where $1 - \alpha$ is the confidence coefficient. To illustrate this more precisely, suppose that a random sample of size k is drawn from each of three normal populations with means μ_1, μ_2, and μ_3, respectively, and common variance σ^2. Denote these by

Population 1: $n(x; \mu_1, \sigma^2)$	Population 2: $n(y; \mu_2, \sigma^2)$	Population 3: $n(z; \mu_3, \sigma^2)$
$\mathbf{x}_1, \mathbf{x}_2, \cdots, \mathbf{x}_k$	$\mathbf{y}_1, \mathbf{y}_2, \cdots, \mathbf{y}_k$	$\mathbf{z}_1, \mathbf{z}_2, \cdots, \mathbf{z}_k$

(1)

We shall set a 95 per cent confidence interval on $\mu_1 - \mu_2$, on $\mu_2 - \mu_3$, and on $\mu_1 - \mu_3$. To set a confidence interval on $\mu_1 - \mu_2$, we use the facts that $\bar{\mathbf{x}} - \mu_1$ is normal with mean 0 and variance σ^2/k; $\bar{\mathbf{y}} - \mu_2$ is normal with mean 0 and variance σ^2/k; $\bar{\mathbf{y}} - \mu_2$ and $\bar{\mathbf{x}} - \mu_1$ are independent. Hence $\mathbf{w} = (\bar{\mathbf{x}} - \mu_1) - (\bar{\mathbf{y}} - \mu_2) = (\bar{\mathbf{x}} - \bar{\mathbf{y}}) - (\mu_1 - \mu_2)$ is normal with mean 0 and variance $2\sigma^2/k$, and so $\dfrac{\mathbf{w}}{\sqrt{2\sigma^2/k}}$ is normal with mean 0 and variance 1. If we let

$$\mathbf{s}_1^2 = \frac{1}{k-1} \sum (\mathbf{x}_i - \bar{\mathbf{x}})^2 \qquad \mathbf{s}_2^2 = \frac{1}{k-1} \sum (\mathbf{y}_i - \bar{\mathbf{y}})^2$$

$$\mathbf{s}_3^2 = \frac{1}{k-1} \sum (\mathbf{z}_i - \bar{\mathbf{z}})^2$$

then

$$\frac{3(k-1)\mathbf{s}^2}{\sigma^2} = \frac{(k-1)\mathbf{s}_1^2 + (k-1)\mathbf{s}_2^2 + (k-1)\mathbf{s}_3^2}{\sigma^2} \tag{2}$$

is distributed as chi-square with $3k - 3$ degrees of freedom and $\mathbf{s}^2$ is independent of $\mathbf{w}$. Hence

$$\mathbf{t} = \frac{\mathbf{w}(\sqrt{k} \cdot \sigma)}{\sqrt{2}\,\mathbf{s}\sigma} = \frac{\mathbf{w}\sqrt{k}}{\mathbf{s}\sqrt{2}}$$

is distributed as Student's t with $3(k - 1)$ degrees of freedom. A 95 per cent confidence interval on $\mu_1 - \mu_2$ is

$$P\left[(\bar{\mathbf{x}} - \bar{\mathbf{y}}) - t_{.025}\sqrt{\frac{2\mathbf{s}^2}{k}} < \mu_1 - \mu_2 < (\bar{\mathbf{x}} - \bar{\mathbf{y}}) + t_{.025}\sqrt{\frac{2\mathbf{s}^2}{k}}\right] = .95 \tag{3}$$

By a similar procedure a 95 per cent confidence interval on $\mu_1 - \mu_3$ is

$$P\left[(\bar{\mathbf{x}} - \bar{\mathbf{z}}) - t_{.025}\sqrt{\frac{2\mathbf{s}^2}{k}} < \mu_1 - \mu_3 < (\bar{\mathbf{x}} - \bar{\mathbf{z}}) + t_{.025}\sqrt{\frac{2\mathbf{s}^2}{k}}\right] = .95 \tag{4}$$

and for a 95 per cent confidence interval on $\mu_2 - \mu_3$

$$P\left[(\bar{\mathbf{y}} - \bar{\mathbf{z}}) - t_{.025}\sqrt{\frac{2\mathbf{s}^2}{k}} < \mu_2 - \mu_3 < (\bar{\mathbf{y}} - \bar{\mathbf{z}}) + t_{.025}\sqrt{\frac{2\mathbf{s}^2}{k}}\right] = .95 \tag{5}$$

If repeated sets of observations (1) are taken and (3) is calculated for each set of $3k$ observations, then, in the long run, 95 per cent of the confidence intervals will cover $\mu_1 - \mu_2$.

If the confidence interval (4) is calculated for each set of the $3k$ observations, then, in the long run, 95 per cent of these intervals will cover $\mu_1 - \mu_3$. Similarly, if the confidence interval (5) is calculated for each set, then, in the long run, 95 per cent of the intervals contain $\mu_2 - \mu_3$. We want to compute confidence intervals on $\mu_1 - \mu_2$, $\mu_1 - \mu_3$, and $\mu_2 - \mu_3$ such that the probability is, say, 95 per cent that all three confidence intervals are simultaneously true. If the three intervals in (3) to (5) were independent, then, in the long run, for $(.95)^3$ of the sets, (3) would cover $\mu_1 - \mu_2$, (4) would cover $\mu_1 - \mu_3$, *and* (5) would cover $\mu_2 - \mu_3$. However, since (3), (4), and (5) are not independent, this probability is not $(.95)^3$. To solve this problem, we shall define the *experimentwise confidence coefficient.* A set of observations such as (1) will be called an *experiment;* there can be t populations instead of three. For each experiment, confidence intervals are put on the $t(t - 1)$ differences $\mu_i - \mu_j$. If in 95 per cent of the experiments each of the $t(t - 1)$ confidence intervals covers its respective difference $(\mu_i - \mu_j)$, we shall say that the *experimentwise confidence coefficient* is .95.

We shall state the following theorem but shall not give the proof.

Theorem 11.1. *Let* $\mathbf{v}_1, \mathbf{v}_2, \cdots, \mathbf{v}_n$ *be a random sample of size n from a normal population with mean* 0 *and variance* σ^2. *Let* **R** *be the range of these random variables; that is,* $\mathbf{R} = \max \mathbf{v}_i - \min \mathbf{v}_i$. *Let* $\nu \mathbf{s}^2/\sigma^2$ *be independent of the* $\mathbf{v}_i$ *and be distributed as a chi-square variable with* ν *degrees of freedom. The random variable*

$$\mathbf{q} = \frac{\mathbf{R}}{\mathbf{s}}$$

is distributed as the Studentized range with n degrees of freedom in the numerator and ν *degrees of freedom in the denominator.*

The frequency function of $\mathbf{q}$ is quite complicated and will not be given here, but the quantity q_α given by $P(\mathbf{q} < q_\alpha) = 1 - \alpha$ can be obtained from Tables VI to VIII for various values of n, ν, and $\alpha = .01, .05$, and .10.

To illustrate how this theorem can be used, we shall find a set of confidence intervals with an experimentwise confidence coefficient of .95. Consider the random variables (we shall discuss the special case of three)

$$\frac{3(k-1)\mathbf{s}^2}{\sigma^2}, \mathbf{u}_1, \mathbf{u}_2, \mathbf{u}_3$$

where $\mathbf{s}^2$ is given by (2), and $\mathbf{u}_1, \mathbf{u}_2, \mathbf{u}_3$ are the order statistics of the three random variables $\mathbf{v}_1, \mathbf{v}_2, \mathbf{v}_3$, where

$$\mathbf{v}_1 = (\bar{\mathbf{x}} - \mu_1)\sqrt{k} \qquad \mathbf{v}_2 = (\bar{\mathbf{y}} - \mu_2)\sqrt{k} \qquad \mathbf{v}_3 = (\bar{\mathbf{z}} - \mu_3)\sqrt{k}$$

Since $\mathbf{v}_i$ are independent normal variables with means 0 and variances σ^2, and since $3(k-1)\mathbf{s}^2/\sigma^2$ is an independent chi-square variable with $\nu = 3(k-1)$ d.f., Theorem 11.1 can be used to show that $\mathbf{q}$ is distributed as the Studentized range with $n = 3$ d.f. in the numerator and $\nu = 3(k-1)$ d.f. in the denominator, where

$$\mathbf{q} = \frac{\mathbf{R}}{\mathbf{s}} = \frac{\mathbf{u}_3 - \mathbf{u}_1}{\mathbf{s}} = \frac{\max \mathbf{v}_i - \min \mathbf{v}_i}{\mathbf{s}}$$

Also

$$1 - \alpha = P(\mathbf{q} < q_\alpha) = P\left(\frac{\mathbf{u}_3 - \mathbf{u}_1}{\mathbf{s}} < q_\alpha\right) = P\left(\frac{\max \mathbf{v}_i - \min \mathbf{v}_i}{\mathbf{s}} < q_\alpha\right)$$
$$= P(\max \mathbf{v}_i - \min \mathbf{v}_i < \mathbf{s}q_\alpha) \tag{6}$$

But if $\max \mathbf{v}_i - \min \mathbf{v}_i < \mathbf{s}q_\alpha$, this implies the following three inequalities:

$$|(\bar{\mathbf{x}} - \mu_1) - (\bar{\mathbf{y}} - \mu_2)| < \frac{\mathbf{s}q_\alpha}{\sqrt{k}}$$

$$|(\bar{\mathbf{x}} - \mu_1) - (\bar{\mathbf{z}} - \mu_3)| < \frac{\mathbf{s}q_\alpha}{\sqrt{k}}$$

and

$$|(\bar{\mathbf{y}} - \mu_2) - (\bar{\mathbf{z}} - \mu_3)| < \frac{\mathbf{s}q_\alpha}{\sqrt{k}}$$

and these imply

$$\begin{aligned}
-\frac{\mathbf{s}q_\alpha}{\sqrt{k}} &< (\bar{\mathbf{x}} - \bar{\mathbf{y}}) - (\mu_1 - \mu_2) < \frac{\mathbf{s}q_\alpha}{\sqrt{k}} \\
-\frac{\mathbf{s}q_\alpha}{\sqrt{k}} &< (\bar{\mathbf{x}} - \bar{\mathbf{z}}) - (\mu_1 - \mu_3) < \frac{\mathbf{s}q_\alpha}{\sqrt{k}} \\
-\frac{\mathbf{s}q_\alpha}{\sqrt{k}} &< (\bar{\mathbf{y}} - \bar{\mathbf{z}}) - (\mu_2 - \mu_3) < \frac{\mathbf{s}q_\alpha}{\sqrt{k}}
\end{aligned} \tag{7}$$

If we use (7) with (6) the probability that all the six statements in (8) are true is $1 - \alpha$.

$$\begin{aligned}
(\bar{\mathbf{x}} - \bar{\mathbf{y}}) - \frac{\mathbf{s}q_\alpha}{\sqrt{k}} &< \mu_1 - \mu_2 < (\bar{\mathbf{x}} - \bar{\mathbf{y}}) + \frac{\mathbf{s}q_\alpha}{\sqrt{k}} \\
(\bar{\mathbf{y}} - \bar{\mathbf{x}}) - \frac{\mathbf{s}q_\alpha}{\sqrt{k}} &< \mu_2 - \mu_1 < (\bar{\mathbf{y}} - \bar{\mathbf{x}}) + \frac{\mathbf{s}q_\alpha}{\sqrt{k}} \\
(\bar{\mathbf{x}} - \bar{\mathbf{z}}) - \frac{\mathbf{s}q_\alpha}{\sqrt{k}} &< \mu_1 - \mu_3 < (\bar{\mathbf{x}} - \bar{\mathbf{z}}) + \frac{\mathbf{s}q_\alpha}{\sqrt{k}} \\
(\bar{\mathbf{z}} - \bar{\mathbf{x}}) - \frac{\mathbf{s}q_\alpha}{\sqrt{k}} &< \mu_3 - \mu_1 < (\bar{\mathbf{z}} - \bar{\mathbf{x}}) + \frac{\mathbf{s}q_\alpha}{\sqrt{k}} \\
(\bar{\mathbf{y}} - \bar{\mathbf{z}}) - \frac{\mathbf{s}q_\alpha}{\sqrt{k}} &< \mu_2 - \mu_3 < (\bar{\mathbf{y}} - \bar{\mathbf{z}}) + \frac{\mathbf{s}q_\alpha}{\sqrt{k}} \\
(\bar{\mathbf{z}} - \bar{\mathbf{y}}) - \frac{\mathbf{s}q_\alpha}{\sqrt{k}} &< \mu_3 - \mu_2 < (\bar{\mathbf{z}} - \bar{\mathbf{y}}) + \frac{\mathbf{s}q_\alpha}{\sqrt{k}}
\end{aligned} \tag{8}$$

If there are more than three populations, the same formulas hold except that the degrees of freedom for q_α are changed and there are $t(t - 1)$ confidence intervals.

Example 11.3. Suppose that an experimenter tests three varieties of wheat by growing each of the varieties on six plots of land. The following data are recorded in bushels per acre

$$[k = 6, n = 3, \nu = 3(k - 1) = 15]$$
$$\bar{\mathbf{x}} = 28.2 \qquad \bar{\mathbf{y}} = 26.1 \qquad \bar{\mathbf{z}} = 30.8 \qquad \mathbf{s}^2 = 3.84$$

To obtain confidence intervals on $\mu_i - \mu_j$ with an experimentwise confidence coefficient of .95, we compute

$$\mathbf{s}q_{.05}/\sqrt{k} = (3.67\sqrt{0.6}) = 2.9$$

$q_{.05}$ is the upper .05 percentage point for the Studentized range in Table VII for 3 and 15 d.f. The confidence intervals with an experimentwise confidence coefficient .95 are

$$\begin{aligned} -.8 &< \mu_1 - \mu_2 < 5.0 \\ -5.5 &< \mu_1 - \mu_3 < .3 \\ -7.6 &< \mu_2 - \mu_3 < -1.8 \\ -5.0 &< \mu_2 - \mu_1 < .8 \\ -.3 &< \mu_3 - \mu_1 < 5.5 \\ 1.8 &< \mu_3 - \mu_2 < 7.6 \end{aligned}$$

For confidence intervals with a fixed experimentwise confidence coefficient for other situations, the reader is referred to papers by Duncan, Scheffé, and Tukey.

11.10 Problems

1. Find a 90 per cent confidence interval for the mean of a normal distribution with $\sigma = 3$, given the sample $(3.3, -.3, -.6, -.9)$. What would be the confidence interval if σ were unknown?

2. The breaking strengths in pounds of five specimens of manila rope of diameter $3/16$ inch were found to be 660, 460, 540, 580, 550. Estimate the mean breaking strength by a 95 per cent confidence interval, assuming normality. Estimate the point at which only 5 per cent of such specimens would be expected to break.

3. Referring to Prob. 2, estimate σ^2 by a 90 per cent confidence interval; also σ.

4. Referring to Prob. 2, plot an 81 per cent confidence region for the joint estimation of μ and σ^2; for μ and σ.

5. Five samples were drawn from populations assumed to be normal and assumed to have the same variance. The values of $(n - 1)\mathbf{s}^2 = \Sigma(\mathbf{x}_i - \bar{\mathbf{x}})^2$ and n, the sample size, were

$\mathbf{s}^2$:	40	30	20	42	50
n:	6	4	3	7	8

Find 98 per cent confidence limits for the common variance.

6. The largest observation $\mathbf{x}'$ of a sample of n from a rectangular density $f(x) = 1/\theta$ $(0 < x < \theta)$ has the density

$$f(x') = \frac{n(x')^{n-1}}{\theta^n} \qquad 0 < x' < \theta$$

Show that $\mathbf{u} = \mathbf{x}'/\theta$ is distributed independently of θ. Using $\mathbf{u}$, find the shortest confidence interval for θ for a confidence coefficient γ.

7. Compute a 95 per cent confidence interval for θ in Prob. 6, given the sample (2.9, 1.8, 4.6, 1.9).

8. To test two promising new lines of hybrid corn under normal farming conditions, a seed company selected eight farms at random in Iowa and planted both lines in experimental plots on each farm. The yields (converted to bushels per acre) for the eight locations were:

Line A:	86	87	56	93	84	93	75	79
Line B:	80	79	58	91	77	82	74	66

Assuming that the two yields are jointly normally distributed, estimate the difference between the mean yields by a 95 per cent confidence interval. (Refer to Prob. 22 of Chap. 10.)

9. Using the density

$$f(x) = \frac{4x^3}{\theta^4} \qquad 0 < x < \theta$$

for the largest of four observations from a rectangular population, set up a general system of 95 per cent confidence intervals for θ by finding $h_1(\theta)$ and $h_2(\theta)$ and plotting these in the $\hat{\theta}\theta$ plane. Find the interval for the sample given in Prob. 7. Why does it differ from the interval found in that problem?

10. Referring to Prob. 9, plot $h_1(\theta)$ and $h_2(\theta)$ for samples of size 8. Then show in general that the lengths of the intervals decrease as the sample size n increases.

11. The sample (2.3, 1.2, .9, 3.2) was drawn from a population distributed by $f(x) = \alpha e^{-\alpha x}$, $x > 0$. Find a 90 per cent confidence interval for α.

12. Referring to Prob. 11, find 90 per cent confidence intervals for the mean and for the variance of the distribution. What is the probability that both these intervals cover the true mean and true variance, respectively?

13. One head and two tails resulted when a coin was tossed three times. Find a 90 per cent confidence interval for the probability of a head.

14. Suppose that 175 heads and 225 tails resulted from 400 tosses of a coin. Find a 90 per cent confidence interval for the probability of a head. Find a 99 per cent confidence interval. Does this appear to be a true coin?

15. A sample of 2000 voters were asked their attitude toward a certain political proposal. It was found that 1200 favored the proposal; 600 opposed it; and 200 were undecided. Assuming that this was a random sample from a trinomial population, construct a 95 per cent confidence region for p_1 and p_2, the proportions of individuals for and against the proposal. (Use the results of Sec. 10.8.)

16. Plot a 95 per cent confidence region like that of Fig. 11.7 for the example used in Sec. 11.8 and compare it with the region of Fig. 11.10.

17. Integrate by parts [integrating $(1 - t)^s$ and differentiating t^r] to show that

$$\int_0^x t^r(1 - t)^s\, dt = -\frac{1}{s + 1}\, x^r(1 - x)^{s+1} + \frac{r}{s + 1}\int_0^x t^{r-1}(1 - t)^{s+1}\, dt$$

18. Apply the above result repeatedly to obtain a cumulative form for the beta distribution, $F(x; \alpha, \beta)$.

19. Show that

$$F(x; \alpha, \beta) = \sum_{i=\alpha+1}^{\alpha+\beta+1} \binom{\alpha + \beta + 1}{i} x^i(1 - x)^{\alpha+\beta+1+i}$$

by using the result of Prob. 18. This is the form that would have arisen had the integration by parts been done the other way—differentiating $(1 - t)^s$ and integrating t^r.

20. Given a sample of size 100 from a normal population with $\hat{\mu} = 3$, $\hat{\sigma}^2 = .25$, what is the maximum-likelihood estimate of the number α for which

$$\int_\alpha^\infty \frac{1}{\sqrt{2\pi}\,\sigma}\, e^{-(1/2\sigma^2)(x-\mu)^2}\, dx = .05$$

21. Find the large-sample distribution of $\hat{\mu}$ and $\hat{\sigma}$ for samples from a normal population. Since it is known that $\hat{\mu}$ and $\hat{\sigma}$ will be approximately normally and independently distributed with means μ and σ, it is only necessary to find their variance.

22. Referring to the above problem, find the large-sample distribution of $\hat{\mu} + k\hat{\sigma}$, where k is a given constant. Use this to obtain an approximate 95 per cent confidence interval for α in Prob. 20.

23. Develop a method for estimating the ratio of the variances of two normal populations by a confidence interval.

24. Develop a method for estimating the parameter of the Poisson distribution by a confidence interval.

25. Work through the details of the derivation of equation (11.2.6).

26. What is the probability that the length of a t confidence interval will be less than σ for samples of size 20?

27. Compare the average length of a 95 per cent confidence interval for the mean of a normal population based on the t distribution with the length that the interval would have were the variance known.

28. Show that the length and the variance of the length of the t confidence interval approach 0 with increasing sample size.

29. How large a sample must be drawn from a normal population to make the probability .95 that a 90 per cent confidence interval (based on t) for the mean will have a length less than $\sigma/5$?

30. Show that the length of the confidence interval for σ (of a normal population) approaches 0 with increasing sample size.

31. Consider a *truncated* normal population with density

$$f(x) = \frac{1}{\sqrt{2\pi}\,\sigma\alpha} e^{-\frac{1}{2}(x-\mu)^2/\sigma^2} \qquad x < a$$
$$= 0 \qquad x \geq a$$

where

$$\alpha = \int_{-\infty}^{a} \frac{1}{\sqrt{2\pi}\,\sigma} e^{-\frac{1}{2}(x-\mu)^2/\sigma^2}\,dx$$

Show that $(\partial/\partial\mu) \log f(\mathbf{x})$ and $(\partial/\partial\sigma) \log f(\mathbf{x})$ have zero expectations.

32. Referring to Prob. 31, let $\hat{\mu}$ and $\hat{\sigma}$ be maximum-likelihood estimators of μ and σ. Show that the matrix of coefficients of the quadratic form for the large-sample distribution of $\hat{\mu}$ and $\hat{\sigma}$ is

$$(r_{ij}) = \begin{pmatrix} \dfrac{n(1 - tb - b^2)}{\sigma^2} & \dfrac{-nb(1 + tb + t^2)}{\sigma^2} \\ \dfrac{-nb(1 + tb + t^2)}{\sigma^2} & \dfrac{n(2 - tb - t^2b^2 - t^3b)}{\sigma} \end{pmatrix}$$

where $b = \sigma f(a)$ and where $t = (a - \mu)/\sigma$.

33. Assume that the following data are normal with means μ_1, μ_2, μ_3, respectively, and variance σ^2.

	1	60.3	61.2	60.5	60.2	59.7
Population	2	62.2	62.8	61.8	60.9	59.3
	3	60.2	61.8	62.3	61.7	61.8

Set a confidence interval with a 95 per cent experimentwise confidence coefficient on the differences $\mu_i - \mu_j$.

11.11 Bibliography

1. Anderson, R. L., and T. A. Bancroft: "Statistical Theory in Research," McGraw-Hill Book Company, Inc., New York, 1952.
2. Cramér, H.: "Mathematical Methods of Statistics," Princeton University Press, Princeton, N.J., 1946.
3. Duncan, D. B.: "Multiple range and multiple *F*-tests," *Biometrics*, Vol. 11(1955), pp. 1–42.
4. Kendall, M. G.: "The Advanced Theory of Statistics," Vols. I, II, Charles Griffin & Co., Ltd., London, 1946.
5. Scheffé, H.: "A method for judging all contrasts in the analysis of variance," *Biometrika*, Vol. 40(1953), pp. 87–104.
6. Snedecor, G. W.: "Statistical Methods," 5th ed., Iowa State College Press, Ames, Iowa, 1956.
7. Tukey, J. W.: "The Problem of Multiple Comparisons," dittoed MS, Princeton University, 1953.

12

Tests of Hypotheses

12.1 Introduction

There are two major areas of statistical inference: the estimation of parameters and the testing of hypotheses. We shall study the second of these two areas in this chapter. Our aim will be to develop general methods for testing hypotheses and to apply those methods to some common problems. The methods will be of further use in later chapters.

In experimental research, the object is sometimes merely to estimate parameters. Thus one may wish to estimate the yield of a new hybrid line of corn. But more often the ultimate purpose will involve some use of the estimate. One may wish, for example, to compare the yield of the new line with that of a standard line and perhaps recommend that the new line replace the standard line if it appears superior. This is a common situation in research. One may wish to determine whether a new method of sealing light bulbs will increase the life of the bulbs, whether a new germicide is more effective in treating a certain infection than a standard germicide, whether one method of preserving foods is better than another in so far as retention of vitamins is concerned, and so on.

Using the light-bulb example as an illustration, let us suppose that the average life of bulbs made under a standard manufacturing procedure is 1400 hours. It is desired to test a new procedure for manufacturing the bulbs. The statistical model here is this: We are dealing with two populations of light bulbs: those made by the standard process and those made by the proposed process. We know (from numerous past investigations) that the mean of the first population is about 1400. The question is whether the mean of the second population is greater than or less than 1400. Traditionally, to answer this question, we set up the hypothesis that one mean is greater than the other mean. On the basis of a sample from the populations, we shall either accept or reject the hypothesis. (Naturally we hope that the new process is better and that the hypothesis will be rejected.)

To test the hypothesis, a number of bulbs are made by the new process and their lives measured. Suppose that the mean of this sample of observations is 1550 hours. The indication is that the new process is better, but suppose that the estimate of the standard deviation of the mean $\hat{\sigma}/\sqrt{n}$ is 125 (n being the sample size). Then a 95 per cent confidence interval for the mean of the second population (assuming normality) is roughly 1300 to 1800 hours. The sample mean 1550 could very easily have come from a population with mean 1400. We have no strong grounds for rejecting the hypothesis. If, on the other hand, $\hat{\sigma}/\sqrt{n}$ were 25, then we could very confidently reject the hypothesis and pronounce the proposed manufacturing process to be superior.

The testing of hypotheses is seen to be closely related to the problem of estimation. It will be instructive, however, to develop the theory of testing independently of the theory of estimation, at least in the beginning.

The procedure of testing hypotheses can be put into the framework of the general decision problem as follows: There are two possible terminal actions, a_1 and a_2. The appropriate action to take depends on the value of the unknown parameter (sometimes called the *state of nature*) θ which is an element of the parameter space Ω. The set Ω can be decomposed into two sets ω_1 and ω_2 so that action a_1 is preferred if θ is in ω_1 and a_2 is preferred if θ is in ω_2. The loss associated with action a and the state of nature θ is given by $l(a; \theta)$, where $l(a; \theta) \geq 0$ and

$$\begin{aligned} l(a_1; \theta) &= 0 \qquad \text{if } \theta \text{ is in } \omega_1 \\ l(a_2; \theta) &= 0 \qquad \text{if } \theta \text{ is in } \omega_2 \end{aligned} \tag{1}$$

Let $\mathbf{s} = (\mathbf{x}_1, \mathbf{x}_2, \cdots, \mathbf{x}_n)$ be a random sample from $f(x; \theta)$, and let S be the n-dimensional sample space. A strategy (decision function) is a function d which assigns an action of A to each possible sample, where $A = \{a: a = a_1 \text{ or } a_2\}$. The action which is taken is

$$\mathbf{a} = d(\mathbf{x}_1, \mathbf{x}_2, \cdots, \mathbf{x}_n)$$

In this problem where there are only two actions, each strategy (decision function) d can be represented by a partition of the n-dimensional sample space into two disjoint sets S_1 and S_2, where $S_2 = \bar{S}_1 = S - S_1$, such that action a_1 is taken if the sample point $\mathbf{s}$ falls in S_1 and action a_2 is taken if $\mathbf{s}$ falls in S_2. The risk (expected loss) corresponding to strategy d is given by

$$
\begin{aligned}
R(d;\theta) &= \iint \cdots \int_S l[d(x_1, x_2, \cdots, x_n); \theta] f(x_1;\theta) \cdots \\
&\qquad\qquad\qquad\qquad f(x_n;\theta)\, dx_1 \cdots dx_n \\
&= \iint \cdots \int_{S_1} l[d(x_1, x_2, \cdots, x_n); \theta] f(x_1;\theta) \cdots f(x_n;\theta) \times \\
&\quad dx_1 \cdots dx_n + \iint \cdots \int_{S_2} l[d(x_1, x_2, \cdots, x_n); \theta] f(x_1;\theta) \\
&\qquad\qquad\qquad\qquad \cdots f(x_n;\theta)\, dx_1 \cdots dx_n \\
&= \iint \cdots \int_{S_1} l(a_1;\theta) f(x_1;\theta) \cdots f(x_n;\theta)\, dx_1 \cdots dx_n \\
&\quad + \iint \cdots \int_{S_2} l(a_2;\theta) f(x_1;\theta) \cdots f(x_n;\theta)\, dx_1 \cdots dx_n \\
&= l(a_1;\theta) \iint \cdots \int_{S_1} f(x_1;\theta) \cdots f(x_n;\theta)\, dx_1 \cdots dx_n \\
&\quad + l(a_2;\theta) \iint \cdots \int_{S_2} f(x_1;\theta) \cdots f(x_n;\theta)\, dx_1 \cdots dx_n \\
&= l(a_1;\theta) P(\mathbf{s} \in S_1|\theta) + l(a_2;\theta) P(\mathbf{s} \in S_2|\theta) \qquad (2)
\end{aligned}
$$

where $P(\mathbf{s} \in S_1|\theta)$ denotes the probability that the sample point $\mathbf{s}$ falls in S_1 when θ is the parameter value (state of nature) and similarly for $P(\mathbf{s} \in S_2|\theta)$.

Since action a_1 is taken if $\mathbf{s}$ falls in S_1 and action a_2 is taken if $\mathbf{s}$ falls in S_2, the probabilities in the above equation are the probabilities of taking actions a_1 and a_2, respectively, when θ is the state of nature. They are called the *action probabilities.*

Definition 12.1. *Let S be an n-dimensional sample space, let S_1 and S_2 be a partition of the sample space such that if a sample point*

$$\mathbf{s} = (\mathbf{x}_1, \cdots, \mathbf{x}_n)$$

falls in S_1 action a_1 is taken and if $\mathbf{s}$ *falls in S_2 action a_2 is taken. The following probabilities are then called action probabilities:*

$$P(\mathbf{s} \in S_1|\theta) \qquad P(\mathbf{s} \in S_2|\theta)$$

where $P(\mathbf{s} \in S_i|\theta)$ is the probability that $\mathbf{s}$ *falls in S_i* (the probability that action a_i is taken) *when the true state of nature is θ.*

If we evaluate the risk in equation (2) when θ belongs to ω_1, which we write as $R(d; \theta \in \omega_1)$, we obtain

$$
\begin{aligned}
R(d;\theta \in \omega_1) = l(a_1;\theta \in \omega_1) P(\mathbf{s} \in S_1|\theta \in \omega_1) \\
+ l(a_2;\theta \in \omega_1) P(\mathbf{s} \in S_2|\theta \in \omega_1)
\end{aligned}
\qquad (3)
$$

By using equation (1), this becomes

$$R(d;\theta \in \omega_1) = l(a_2;\theta \in \omega_1) P(\mathbf{s} \in S_2|\theta \in \omega_1) \qquad (4)$$

By a similar procedure, we can evaluate the risk when θ is in ω_2 and obtain

$$R(d;\theta \in \omega_2) = l(a_1;\theta \in \omega_2) P(\mathbf{s} \in S_1|\theta \in \omega_2) \qquad (5)$$

That is, since one of the two losses $l(a_1; \theta)$ and $l(a_2; \theta)$ is equal to 0, we can also write the risk in equation (2) as

$$R(d; \theta) = l(\theta)\mathcal{E}(d; \theta) \tag{6}$$

where

$$l(\theta) = \begin{cases} l(a_1; \theta) & \text{if } \theta \text{ is in } \omega_2 \\ l(a_2; \theta) & \text{if } \theta \text{ is in } \omega_1 \end{cases} \tag{7}$$

that is, $l(\theta)$ is the loss associated with the wrong action when θ is the state of nature and $\mathcal{E}(d; \theta)$ is as defined below.

Definition 12.2. *Error Probabilities. The error probability, denoted by* $\mathcal{E}(d; \theta)$ *in equation* (6), *is the probability of taking the wrong action. That is, it is the probability of taking action a_1 if θ is in ω_2 or taking action a_2 if θ is in ω_1.*

If $\theta \in \omega_1$, this can be written as

$$\mathcal{E}_1(d; \theta) = P[(\mathbf{x}_1, \mathbf{x}_2, \cdots, \mathbf{x}_n) \in S_2 | \theta \in \omega_1] = P(\mathbf{s} \in S_2 | \theta \in \omega_1)$$

which is the probability of taking action a_2 when θ is in ω_1; and if $\theta \in \omega_2$ this can be written as

$$\mathcal{E}_2(d; \theta) = P[(\mathbf{x}_1, \mathbf{x}_2, \cdots, \mathbf{x}_n) \in S_1 | \theta \in \omega_2] = P(\mathbf{s} \in S_1 | \theta \in \omega_2)$$

which is the probability of taking action a_1 when θ is in ω_2. We shall now define *test of hypothesis.*

Definition 12.3. *The sets ω_1 and ω_2 in the above decision-function formulation of the problem are associated with the hypothesis or statement H_1: "θ is in ω_1" and the alternative hypothesis H_2: "θ is in ω_2," respectively. The action a_1 is called accepting the hypothesis (accepting H_1), and the action a_2 is called rejecting the hypothesis (rejecting H_1). The decision function d, which, when applied to the data, leads to accepting or rejecting a hypothesis, is called a test of the hypothesis.*

The objective is to find the test (the decision function d) that minimizes the risk for every value of θ in Ω. However, *this is not generally possible,* but the fact is that one decision function may give minimum risk for certain values of θ and another decision function may give minimum risk for other values of θ, etc. Therefore, since θ is unknown, there may be no clear-cut method of determining which decision function gives minimum risk in a particular problem.

Another difficulty in using equations (4) and (5) is that in many (in fact, most) of the applied problems where an experimenter wants to use tests of hypotheses the loss function is not known at all or else it is not known accurately enough to warrant its use. If the loss function is not known, it seems that a decision function that in some sense minimizes the error probabilities will be a reasonable procedure. The traditional procedure is to select a probability α, which is usually in the neighborhood of .01, .05, .10, .20, and find the class of decision functions (i.e., find the sets S_2) such that

$$P(\mathbf{s} \in S_2 | \theta \in \omega_1) \leq \alpha \tag{8}$$

is satisfied. Then from the class of tests that satisfies (8), the one test such that

$$P(\mathbf{s} \in S_1 | \theta \in \omega_2) \tag{9}$$

is a minimum is termed the "best" test. In this formulation the quantity $P(\mathbf{s} \in S_2 | \theta \in \omega_1)$ in (8) is called the probability of rejecting a true hypothesis (rejecting the hypothesis H_1 when it is in fact true) or sometimes is referred to as the probability of a Type I error, and (8) is written $P(\text{I}) \leq \alpha$. The quantity $P(\mathbf{s} \in S_1 | \theta \in \omega_2)$ in (9) is called the probability of accepting a false hypothesis (accepting H_1 when it is in fact false) or sometimes is referred to as the probability of a Type II error and written $P(\text{II})$. Notice that $\mathcal{E}_1(d; \theta) = P(\text{I})$ and $\mathcal{E}_2(d; \theta) = P(\text{II})$. The region S_2 is called the *rejection region* or the *critical region*, and S_1 is called the *acceptance region*. If the statement in (8) is true we say: The size of the test is equal to α. Instead of the quantity $P(\mathbf{s} \in S_1 | \theta \in \omega_2)$ in (9), it is sometimes more convenient to use $P(\mathbf{s} \in S_2 | \theta \in \omega_2)$, where, of course,

$$1 - P(\mathbf{s} \in S_1 | \theta \in \omega_2) = P(\mathbf{s} \in S_2 | \theta \in \omega_2) \tag{10}$$

which is the probability of rejecting the hypothesis H_1 when it is in fact false. The quantity $P(\mathbf{s} \in S_2 | \theta)$ is called the power of the test and is denoted by $\beta(\theta)$, and it is a function of θ. Notice that $\beta(\theta) = P(\text{I})$ when $\theta \in \omega_1$. Also $\beta(\theta) = 1 - P(\text{II})$ when $\theta \in \omega_2$.

It may appear at first sight that *this* formulation of the hypothesis-testing problem ignores the loss function. In reality it does not *completely* ignore the loss function, since to arrive at a reasonable value for α requires an experimenter to weigh the consequences of making a Type I and a Type II error. The above formulation of the problem is the one that has received the most attention from mathematical statisticians and is used quite extensively by experimenters.

Next we shall give an example to illustrate the above ideas; then we shall study in detail the simplest case, that where ω_1 and ω_2 each contain only a single point.

Example 12.1. Let the random variable $\mathbf{x}$ have a normal distribution with mean μ and variance 1, where μ can be equal to -1 or 0 only. Suppose that we desire to test the hypothesis H_1: $\mu = -1$ with the alternative hypothesis H_2: $\mu = 0$. Thus the parameter space Ω is $\Omega = \{\mu: \mu = -1, 0\}$; the action space contains two points, a_1 and a_2, where a_1 is the statement "accept H_1 that $\mu = -1$," and a_2 is the statement "accept H_2 that $\mu = 0$," or "reject H_1 that $\mu = -1$." Also $\omega_1 = \{\mu: \mu = -1\}$; $\omega_2 = \{\mu: \mu = 0\}$. Suppose that we choose a loss function for this problem to be

$$\begin{aligned} l(a_1; \mu \in \omega_1) &= 0 \\ l(a_1; \mu \in \omega_2) &= 1 \\ l(a_2; \mu \in \omega_2) &= 0 \\ l(a_2; \mu \in \omega_1) &= 4 \end{aligned}$$

and suppose that a random sample of size 1 is used. Then the sample space S is one-dimensional and is defined by $S = \{x: -\infty < x < \infty\}$. Suppose that we partition S into S_1 and S_2 so that

$$S_1 = \{x: -\infty < x < -1\}$$

$S_2 = \{x: -1 \leq x < \infty\}$, that is, take action a_1 (accept H_1 that $\mu = -1$) if $\mathbf{x} < -1$ and take action a_2 (accept H_2 that $\mu = 0$) if $\mathbf{x} \geq -1$. The decision function d is defined by

$$\begin{aligned} &\text{Value of } d \text{ is } a_1 \qquad \text{if } x < -1 \\ &\text{Value of } d \text{ is } a_2 \qquad \text{if } x \geq -1 \end{aligned}$$

The risk for this decision function is, by (2),

$$\begin{aligned} R(d; \mu \in \omega_1) &= 4 \cdot P(\mathbf{x} \geq -1 | \mu = -1) = 4(.50) = 2 \\ R(d; \mu \in \omega_2) &= 1 \cdot P(\mathbf{x} < -1 | \mu = 0) \quad = 1(.16) = .16 \end{aligned}$$

The action probabilities for this problem are in the following table.

		State of Nature	
		ω_1	ω_2
		$\mu = -1$	$\mu = 0$
Action	a_1	.50	.16
	a_2	.50	.84

The error probabilities can be obtained from this table; they are

$$\mathcal{E}(d; \mu) \begin{cases} P(\text{II}) = P(\text{action } a_1 | \mu \in \omega_2) = P(\mathbf{x} < -1 | \mu = 0) = .16 \\ \\ P(\text{I}) = P(\text{action } a_2 | \mu \in \omega_1) = P(\mathbf{x} \geq -1 | \mu = -1) = .50 \end{cases} \tag{11}$$

Two things should be noted: The action probabilities can be obtained from the error probabilities and vice versa, and these probabilities are, in general, a function of the parameter if there is more than one point in ω_1 or ω_2.

If the loss function is not known, we could formulate the problem by examining the Type I and Type II errors. These can be obtained from $\mathcal{E}(d; \mu)$. When we speak of *the hypothesis* we shall mean H_1, where in this example H_1: $\mu = -1$ and the *alternative hypothesis* is H_2: $\mu = 0$. Thus the quantity $P(\mathrm{I})$, which is the probability of *rejecting* the *hypothesis* when it is *true*, is

$$P(\text{rejecting } H_1|H_1 \text{ is true}) = P(\text{taking action } a_2|H_1 \text{ is true}) = P(\mathbf{x} \in S_2|H_1) = P(\mathrm{I})$$

Also $P(\mathrm{II})$, which is the probability of *accepting* the *hypothesis* when it is *false*, is

$$P(\text{accepting } H_1|H_1 \text{ is false}) = P(\text{accepting } H_1|H_2 \text{ is true}) = P(\text{taking action } a_1|H_2 \text{ is true}) = P(\mathbf{x} \in S_1|H_2) = P(\mathrm{II})$$

Using the same rejection region as above, we get, from (11), $P(\mathrm{II}) = .16$. In this example the size of the test is $\alpha = .50$. If we wanted α to be some other value, we must change the critical region S_2. Notice that when we use the expressions "probability of rejecting *the hypothesis* when it is true" and "probability of accepting *the hypothesis* when it is false" *the hypothesis* refers to H_1, and the experimenter can let H_1 be either $\mu = -1$ or $\mu = 0$, with the remaining one being the alternative hypothesis. However, once the experimenter has decided upon H_1, this is *the hypothesis* that is used throughout the discussion.

12.2 Test of a Simple Hypothesis against a Simple Alternative

A hypothesis $H: \theta \in \omega$ is called simple if ω consists of a single point. Thus, if ω_1 consists of the point θ_1 and if ω_2 is the point θ_2, our problem is called one of testing a simple hypothesis against a simple alternative.

Here, the risk function for a strategy d takes on two values,

$$R(d; \theta_1) = l(\theta_1)P(\mathrm{I}) \quad \text{and} \quad R(d; \theta_2) = l(\theta_2)P(\mathrm{II})$$

hence for each decision function d, the risk $R(d; \theta)$ can be represented by a point on a graph whose coordinates are $R(d; \theta_1)$ and $R(d; \theta_2)$. Similarly $\mathcal{E}(d; \theta)$ can be represented on a simply related graph whose coordinates are the error probabilities $P(\mathrm{I})$ and $P(\mathrm{II})$. The latter graph does not involve the loss function and is useful in those applications where the loss function is not precisely known and $P(\mathrm{I})$ and $P(\mathrm{II})$ can be used as explained in the previous section.

We illustrate with a simplified problem.

Example 12.2. It is desired to bet on the toss of a coin whose probability p of falling heads is known to be either $p_1 = .6$ or $p_2 = .3$. The bettor decides to test the hypothesis H_1: $p = p_1 = .6$ with the alternative hypothesis H_2: $p = p_2 = .3$. The two actions are a_1: accept H_1 (reject H_2) and a_2: accept H_2(reject H_1). The loss function that we shall consider is specified by $l(a_1; p_1) = l(a_2; p_2) = 0$, $l(a_2; p_1) = l(p_1) = 1$, and $l(a_1; p_2) = l(p_2) = 2$. The prospective bettor is allowed one observation on the toss of the coin, that is, $\mathbf{x} = 1$ if the coin falls heads and $\mathbf{x} = 0$ if it falls tails. Since the sample space contains only two points, 0 and 1, there are only four possible decision functions; they are d_1, d_2, d_3, d_4, where

$$\begin{array}{lll} d_1: & d_1(1) = a_1 & d_1(0) = a_1 \\ d_2: & d_2(1) = a_1 & d_2(0) = a_2 \\ d_3: & d_3(1) = a_2 & d_3(0) = a_1 \\ d_4: & d_4(1) = a_2 & d_4(0) = a_2 \end{array}$$

where, for example, $d_4(0) = a_2$ means: Decision function d_4 indicates that action a_2 is taken when $\mathbf{x} = 0$, i.e., when the coin falls tails.

The corresponding risks and error probabilities are given in the following table and the graphs in Figs. 12.1 and 12.2.

Error probabilities			Risk		
	$P(\mathrm{I})$	$P(\mathrm{II})$		$R(d;\,p_1)$	$R(d;\,p_2)$
d_1	0	1	d_1	0	2
d_2	.4	.3	d_2	.4	.6
d_3	.6	.7	d_3	.6	1.4
d_4	1	0	d_4	1	0

To illustrate how to calculate the error probabilities we shall compute $\mathcal{E}_1(d_2;\,p_1)$. Now $\mathcal{E}_1(d_2;\,p_1) = P$ (taking the wrong action when using d_2 and p_1) $= P$(taking action a_2 when using d_2 and p_1) $= P(\mathbf{x} = 0|p_1) = .4$. The remaining error probabilities are calculated similarly. To illustrate the method of calculating the risks, we shall compute $R(d_3;\,p_2)$. Now

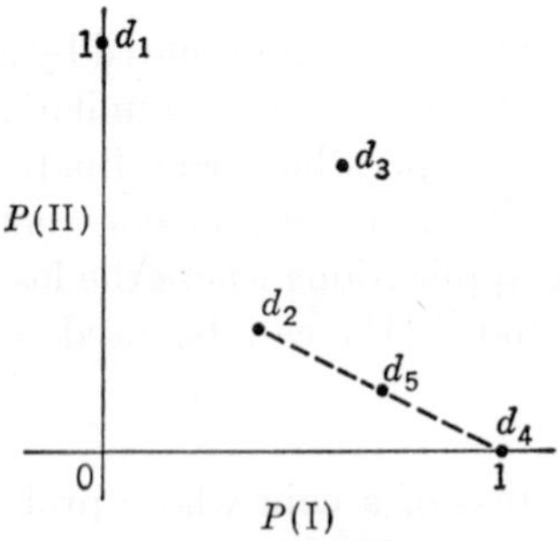

FIG. 12.1

$$R(d_3;\,p_2) = \mathcal{E}_2(d_3;\,p_2)l(p_2) = (.7)(2) = 1.4$$

A more detailed look at $R(d_3;\,p_2)$ yields

$$\begin{aligned} R(d_3;\,p_2) &= l(a_1;\,p_2)\,P(\text{action } a_1|p_2) \\ &\quad + l(a_2;\,p_2)\,P(\text{action } a_2|p_2) \\ &= 2P(\mathbf{x} = 0|p_2) + 0 \cdot P(\mathbf{x} = 1|p_2) \\ &= (2)(.7) = 1.4 \end{aligned}$$

as before. The reader can verify the remaining risks in the table. By looking at the risks for the four decision functions we see that even in this simple example it is not, in general, clear when one strategy is to be preferred over another. Strategy d_2 appears to be a good one to choose, but we see that, if p_1 is the true state of nature, d_1 is better (smaller risk) than d_2; if p_2 is the true state of nature, then d_4 is better than d_2. Since the state of nature is not known, it is not possible to select a strategy that has minimum risk for every state of nature. There is one thing, however, that is apparent: Strategy d_2 has smaller risk than d_3 regardless of what the state of nature is, and hence we would discard d_3 as a possible strategy and we say that strategy d_2 *dominates* (is better than) strategy d_3. If we plot the risks for different strategies on a graph as in Fig. 12.2, where for d_1 we plot the point (0, 2), for d_2 the point (.4, .6), etc., we see that if one strategy (say d_i) dominates another (say d_j) then d_i must be below and to the left of d_j. If it is below, it has smaller risk for the state of nature p_2; if it is to the left, it has smaller risk for the state of nature p_1. Thus from Fig. 12.2 we see that d_2 dominates d_3, but that d_1, d_2, and d_4 do not dominate each other.

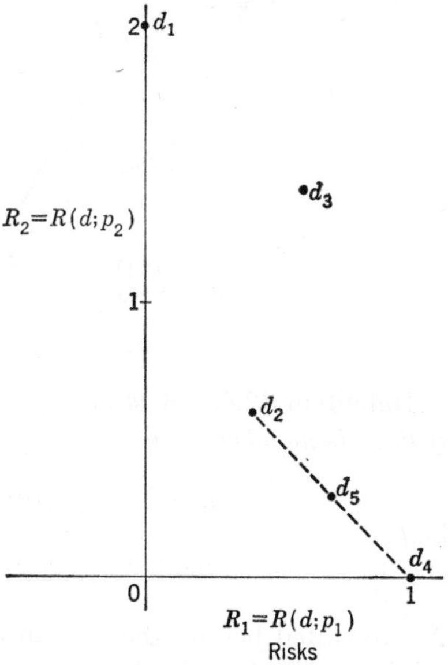

FIG. 12.2

Suppose that the prospective bettor cannot decide between d_2 and d_4 and elects instead to toss a "fair" coin to choose between them. Then if H_1: $p = p_1$ is correct, he will have a risk of .4 with probability $\frac{1}{2}$ and a risk of 1 with probability $\frac{1}{2}$. This yields an expected risk of .7; similarly, if H_2: $p = p_2$ is correct, his risk will be .3. Thus by permitting himself to randomize in his choice of decision function, he has a new strategy d_5, called a *randomized strategy*, represented by the risks .7 and .3. Clearly this point is halfway between the risk points corresponding to d_2 and d_4 on the graph. By selecting between d_2 and d_4 with other probabilities than $\frac{1}{2}$, $\frac{1}{2}$, one can find a randomized strategy corresponding to any point on the line segment connecting these two risk points.

A set of points is called *convex* if, given any two points of the set, the line segment connecting these is in the set. The set T of all risk points $[R(d; p_1), R(d; p_2)]$ obtained by considering all strategies including randomized strategies is convex. The same is true for the set U of error points $[P(\text{I}), P(\text{II})]$. In fact, T and U are the smallest convex sets containing the points corresponding to the original *nonrandomized* or *pure* strategies. These sets are represented in Figs. 12.3 and 12.4.

A glance at Fig. 12.4 suffices to show that d_3 is an undesirable test. In fact, the only reasonable tests are those corresponding to points on the line segments connecting d_1 to d_2, and d_2 to d_4. All other strategies can be improved upon. We shall now introduce the notion of an *admissible strategy* (*admissible decision function*).

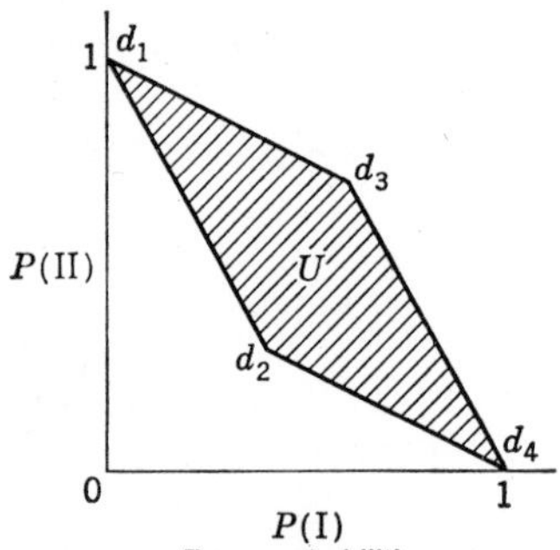

FIG. 12.3

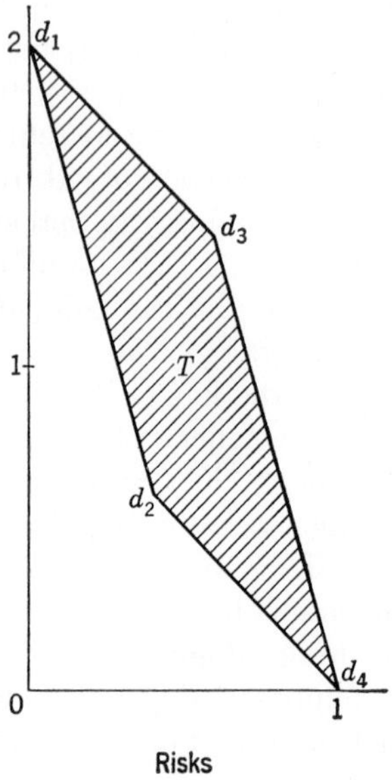

FIG. 12.4

Definition 12.4. *A strategy (decision function, or test) d is admissible if there is no other strategy d^* such that*

$$R(d^*; \theta) \leq R(d; \theta) \qquad \textit{for all } \theta \textit{ in } \Omega$$

and

$$R(d^*; \theta) < R(d; \theta) \qquad \textit{for some } \theta \textit{ in } \Omega$$

As we stated before, there is, in general, no decision function that gives minimum risk for all values of θ in Ω; hence it seems that the most reasonable thing to do is to find the class of admissible decision functions and select a decision function from this class.

To help in finding the class of admissible strategies, we shall prove that *every admissible strategy is a Bayes strategy* and that *every Bayes strategy is a likelihood-ratio test.* Hence every *admissible strategy is a likelihood-ratio test.* Therefore, if we can find the class of likelihood-ratio tests, these will include all the admissible strategies, and the class of likelihood-ratio tests is often quite easy to obtain. These ideas will be the context of the remainder of this section. It should be recalled that we are discussing a *simple* hypothesis and a *simple* alternative.

We shall now define a Bayes strategy (see Chap. 8).

Definition 12.5. *Bayes Strategy. A strategy d is a Bayes strategy corresponding to a priori probabilities h_1 and $h_2 = 1 - h_1$ ($h_i \geq 0$) if it minimizes $B(d)$, where*

$$B(d) = E[R(d; \boldsymbol{\theta})] = h_1R(d; \theta_1) + h_2R(d; \theta_2)$$

We shall sketch the proof of the following theorem.

Theorem 12.1. *For testing a simple hypothesis against a simple alternative every admissible strategy is a Bayes strategy.*

Proof. First, referring to Fig. 12.5, we note that the Bayes strategy corresponding to h_1 and h_2 can be represented geometrically by drawing

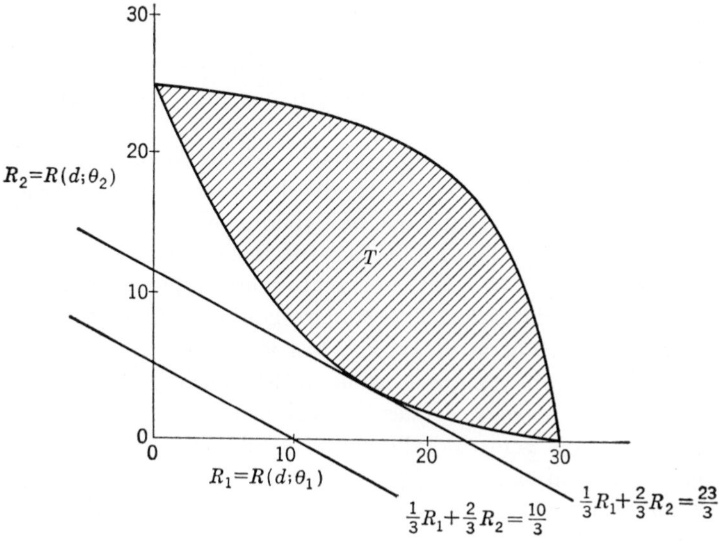

Fig. 12.5

the line $h_1R_1 + h_2R_2 = c$ and moving it parallel to itself by changing c until it touches T. The point or points where it just touches T correspond to the Bayes strategies. As h_1 changes from 0 to 1, the slope of the line changes from 0 to $-\infty$. It is a property of convex sets that, given any point on the boundary, there is a line through that point which *supports* the set. Thus for any admissible strategy, i.e., any point of the lower boundary of T, there is a corresponding line of support through that point. Since this line can be drawn so as not to have positive slope, it can be expressed in the form $h_1R_1 + h_2R_2 = c$, where h_1 and h_2 are possible a priori probabilities (that is, $0 \leq h_i \leq 1$). Thus the admissible strategy is a Bayes strategy.

While Theorem 12.1 applies to more general problems, the special case of testing a simple hypothesis versus a simple alternative yields a particularly interesting result; i.e., every Bayes strategy is a *likelihood-ratio test*. We shall now define likelihood-ratio test.

Definition 12.6. *Likelihood-ratio Test. A test based on a random sample* $\mathbf{x}_1, \mathbf{x}_2, \cdots, \mathbf{x}_n$ *from the density* $f(x; \theta)$ *for testing* $H_1: \theta = \theta_1$ *against* $H_2: \theta = \theta_2$ *is a likelihood-ratio test if there is a number k such that the test calls for*

$$\begin{array}{lll} \text{Accepting } H_1 & (\text{action } a_1) & \text{if } \lambda > k \\ \text{Rejecting } H_1 & (\text{action } a_2) & \text{if } \lambda < k \end{array}$$

and

$$\begin{array}{ll} \text{Either action} & \text{if } \lambda = k \end{array}$$

where λ *is the likelihood-ratio given by*

$$\lambda = t(\mathbf{x}_1, \cdots, \mathbf{x}_n) = \frac{f(\mathbf{x}_1; \theta_1)f(\mathbf{x}_2; \theta_1) \cdots f(\mathbf{x}_n; \theta_1)}{f(\mathbf{x}_1; \theta_2)f(\mathbf{x}_2; \theta_2) \cdots f(\mathbf{x}_n; \theta_2)} \tag{1}$$

We shall discuss this definition briefly. Since θ_1 and θ_2 are known numbers, the inequality $\lambda > k$ for fixed k defines a set S_1. Another way of stating this is: For a fixed value of k there is a set of $\mathbf{x}$'s that satisfies the inequality $\lambda > k$. This set of $\mathbf{x}$'s is the acceptance region S_1, and the set of $\mathbf{x}$'s defined by $\lambda < k$ is the critical region (rejection region) S_2 for that particular value of k. The reader should recall that we use the terms decision function, strategy, and test interchangeably. They each mean a function from the observations to the action space. The likelihood-ratio test, if it exists, defines the regions S_1 and S_2, and the test is: Take action a_1 if $\mathbf{s}$ is in S_1; take action a_2 if $\mathbf{s}$ is in S_2, where $\mathbf{s}$ is the n-dimensional point $(\mathbf{x}_1, \cdots, \mathbf{x}_n)$.

Example 12.3. Let $\mathbf{x}$ be a sample of size 1 from a normal distribution with mean μ and variance 1. We shall test the hypothesis $H_1: \mu = -1$ with the alternative hypothesis $H_2: \mu = 0$. The likelihood-ratio is, by (1),

$$\lambda = \frac{f(\mathbf{x}: -1)}{f(\mathbf{x}: 0)} = \frac{e^{-\frac{1}{2}(\mathbf{x}+1)^2}}{e^{-\frac{1}{2}\mathbf{x}^2}} = e^{-\frac{1}{2}(\mathbf{x}^2+2\mathbf{x}+1-\mathbf{x}^2)} = e^{-\frac{1}{2}(2\mathbf{x}+1)}$$

To illustrate, we shall select $k = e^{\frac{1}{2}}$; then $\lambda > k$ becomes $e^{-\frac{1}{2}(2\mathbf{x}+1)} > e^{\frac{1}{2}}$ or $e^{-\mathbf{x}} \cdot e^{-\frac{1}{2}} > e^{\frac{1}{2}}$ or $e^{-\mathbf{x}} > e$. There is a set (call it S_1) on the x axis that satisfies $e^{-\mathbf{x}} > e$, and this is the set $S_1 = \{x: -\infty < x < -1\}$, since taking the logarithm to the base e of $e^{-\mathbf{x}} > e$ yields $-\mathbf{x} > 1$ or $\mathbf{x} < -1$; this is the set where action a_1 (H_1 is accepted) is taken.

Theorem 12.2. *For testing the simple hypothesis* $H_1: \theta = \theta_1$ *versus the simple alternative* $H_2: \theta = \theta_2$, *every Bayes strategy is a likelihood-ratio test.*

Before giving a formal proof of this theorem, let us discuss and illustrate it. It may be interpreted to indicate that the likelihood-ratio λ

is a measure of how much the evidence supports H_1. Thus, reasonable procedures consist of accepting H_1 when λ is sufficiently large. Note that what constitutes "sufficiently large" may depend on such factors as the losses due to error and the degree of prior belief, if any, in the hypotheses.

In Example 12.2, where there is only one observation,

$$\lambda = \frac{p_1}{p_2} = 2 \qquad \text{if } \mathbf{x} = 1$$

and

$$\lambda = \frac{1 - p_1}{1 - p_2} = \frac{4}{7} \qquad \text{if } \mathbf{x} = 0$$

Example 12.4. For another example of the likelihood-ratio test let us select a random sample of size n to test the hypothesis that the mean is 0 against the alternative that μ, the mean, is 2 in a normal density with $\sigma^2 = 1$. This can be described as a test of

$$H_1: \mu = \mu_1 = 2 \qquad \text{against the alternative} \qquad H_2: \mu = \mu_2 = 0$$

with

$$f(x_i; 2) = \frac{1}{\sqrt{2\pi}} e^{-(x_i-2)^2/2} \qquad i = 1, 2, \cdots, n$$

and

$$f(x_i; 0) = \frac{1}{\sqrt{2\pi}} e^{-x_i^2/2} \qquad i = 1, 2, \cdots, n$$

and

$$\lambda = \frac{\prod_{i=1}^{n} f(\mathbf{x}_i; \mu_1)}{\prod_{i=1}^{n} f(\mathbf{x}_i; \mu_2)} = \exp(2n\bar{\mathbf{x}} - 2n)$$

The likelihood-ratio test consists of accepting H_1 if

$$\lambda = \exp(2n\bar{\mathbf{x}} - 2n) > k$$

Taking logarithms and simplifying gives us

$$2n\bar{\mathbf{x}} > \log k + 2n$$

or

$$\bar{\mathbf{x}} > \frac{1}{2n} \log k + 1$$

If we set $(1/2n) \log k + 1 = c$, then we accept H_1 if $\bar{\mathbf{x}} > c$ and reject H_1 if $\bar{\mathbf{x}} < c$.

Since the likelihood-ratio test can be expressed in terms of $\bar{\mathbf{x}}$, the error probabilities, $P(\mathrm{I})$ and $P(\mathrm{II})$, may be represented by the shaded areas in Fig. 12.6. The curves in this figure are the densities of $\bar{\mathbf{x}}$ under the two hypotheses H_1 and H_2. Note that, as c increases, $P(\mathrm{II})$ decreases but $P(\mathrm{I})$ increases. For each c we obtain a point on the lower boundary of the set U of error points for the problem (similar to Fig. 12.3). This lower boundary is sometimes called the *error curve.*

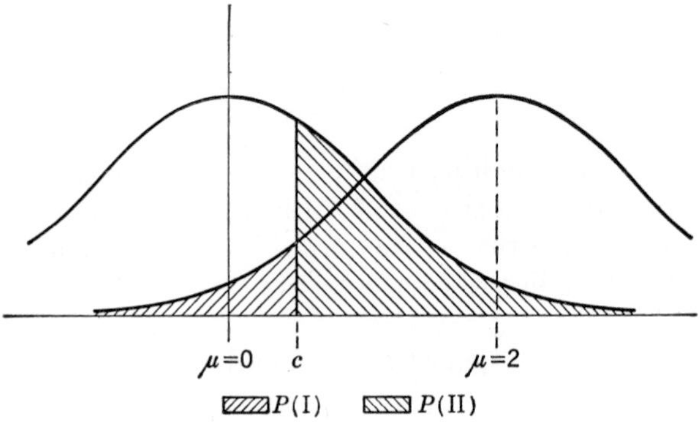

FIG. 12.6

It is particularly simple to find a point on this curve for a given value of $P(\mathrm{I})$, say .05, when $n = 4$. Then we note that when $\mu = \mu_1 = 2$

$$P(\mathrm{I}) = P(\bar{\mathbf{x}} < c|\mu = 2) = .05$$

if

$$c = \mu_1 - \frac{1.645}{\sqrt{4}} = 2 - .8225 = 1.1775$$

Then

$$P(\mathrm{II}) = P(\bar{\mathbf{x}} > 1.1775|\mu = 0) = .009$$

Another problem which is of interest is that of finding a sample size n such that $P(\mathrm{I})$ and $P(\mathrm{II})$ take on prescribed values, say .02 and .01, respectively. Then, for $P(\mathrm{I}) = .02$, it is required that

$$c = \mu_1 - \frac{2.054}{\sqrt{n}} = 2 - \frac{2.054}{\sqrt{n}}$$

For $P(\mathrm{II}) = .01$, it is required that

$$c = \mu_2 + \frac{2.323}{\sqrt{n}} = \frac{2.323}{\sqrt{n}}$$

It follows that

$$2 - \frac{2.054}{\sqrt{n}} = \frac{2.323}{\sqrt{n}}$$

$$2 = \frac{4.377}{\sqrt{n}}$$

and

$$n = \left(\frac{4.377}{2}\right)^2 = 4.8$$

Furthermore

$$c = \frac{2.323}{\sqrt{n}} = 1.06$$

Thus a sample of size $n = 5$ would suffice to yield error probabilities slightly less than .02 and .01, respectively. Here the test procedure would consist of accepting $H_1\colon \mu = 2$ if $\bar{\mathbf{x}} > c$, where c is approximately 1.06.

It remains to prove that the Bayes strategies are likelihood-ratio tests. To do so, we note that

$$P(\mathrm{I}) = \int\int_{\bar{S}_1} \cdots \int f(x_1; \theta_1) \cdots f(x_n; \theta_1)\, dx_1 \cdots dx_n$$

$$= 1 - \int\int_{S_1} \cdots \int f(x_1; \theta_1) \cdots f(x_n; \theta_1)\, dx_1 \cdots dx_n$$

$$P(\mathrm{II}) = \int\int_{S_1} \cdots \int f(x_1; \theta_2) \cdots f(x_n; \theta_2)\, dx_1 \cdots dx_n$$

$$\begin{aligned} B(d) &= h_1R(d; \theta_1) + h_2R(d; \theta_2) \\ &= h_1l(\theta_1)P(\mathrm{I}) + h_2l(\theta_2)P(\mathrm{II}) \\ &= h_1l(\theta_1) + \int\int_{S_1} \cdots \int \left[-h_1l(\theta_1) \prod_{i=1}^{n} f(x_i; \theta_1) + h_2l(\theta_2) \prod_{i=1}^{n} f(x_i; \theta_2) \right] dx_1 \cdots dx_n \end{aligned}$$

The minimization of $B(d)$ consists of selecting the set S_1 to minimize the above integral. Clearly this can be done by putting into S_1 all those points $(x_1, x_2, \cdots, x_n)$ for which the integrand is negative and leaving out all those points for which the integrand is positive. Hence the Bayes strategy involves taking action a_1 if

$$0 > -h_1l(\theta_1) \prod_{i=1}^{n} f(\mathbf{x}_i; \theta_1) + h_2l(\theta_2) \prod_{i=1}^{n} f(\mathbf{x}_i; \theta_2)$$

or if

$$\lambda = \frac{\prod_{i=1}^{n} f(\mathbf{x}_i;\, \theta_1)}{\prod_{i=1}^{n} f(\mathbf{x}_i;\, \theta_2)} > \frac{h_2 l(\theta_2)}{h_1 l(\theta_1)} = k \qquad \text{(say)}$$

Similarly, we must take action a_2 if $\lambda < k$, and either action or a randomized selection between them may be taken if $\lambda = k$.

This concludes our discussion of the case of testing a simple hypothesis versus a simple alternative. This case is not very useful in applied statistics, but it has served the purpose of introducing us to the theory of testing hypotheses. We have illustrated the fact that a major difficulty in testing hypotheses is in selecting a "best" test, i.e., a test that gives minimum risk for all (both) values of the parameter. To circumvent this difficulty somewhat, we defined an admissible test and proved that the likelihood-ratio test is a method for obtaining the class that contains all the admissible tests. If this class is obtained, an experimenter can select a test from this class by using additional criteria.

Another difficulty in testing hypotheses is the fact that in most problems an experimenter does not know the loss function with a high degree of accuracy. This difficulty is circumvented somewhat if a very rough approximation of the relative importance of errors of Type I and Type II is known. This is the traditional method that has been used by experimenters in the past, and it will be developed for other problems later in this chapter.

12.3 Composite Hypotheses

In practice, most testing problems involve *composite hypotheses*. These are hypotheses of the form $H_1\colon \theta \in \omega_1$, with the alternative $H_2\colon \theta \in \omega_2$, where either ω_1 and/or ω_2 has more than one element. For example, let us reexamine the light-bulb illustration of Sec. 12.1 from the decision-theory point of view. Two actions are contemplated. One action consists of deciding that the new bulbs represent a substantial improvement over the old and of adopting the new manufacturing process (a_1). The other action, a_2, consists of sticking to the old process. For definiteness let us suppose that the lifetime of bulbs made with the new process has an exponential distribution with unknown mean $\mu > 0$; that is,

$$\begin{aligned} f(x;\, \mu) &= \frac{1}{\mu} e^{-x/\mu} && \text{for } x > 0 \\ &= 0 && \text{for } x \le 0 \end{aligned}$$

The manufacturer, balancing expected profit and the cost of modifying his plant, decides on a value of μ above which it would be profitable to introduce the new procedure and below which it would not be profitable. Suppose that this value of μ is $\mu = 1450$. The manufacturer may, in fact, compute the loss $l(a_1; \mu)$ and $l(a_2; \mu)$ and represent it as in Fig. 12.7. He may be interested in testing the hypothesis $H_1: \mu > 1450$ versus the alternative $H_2: \mu \leq 1450$. For any given test procedure d, one may compute the probability of accepting H_1 for each value of μ. In Fig. 12.8 we present a graph giving this probability (approximately) for four tests based on samples of size 400.

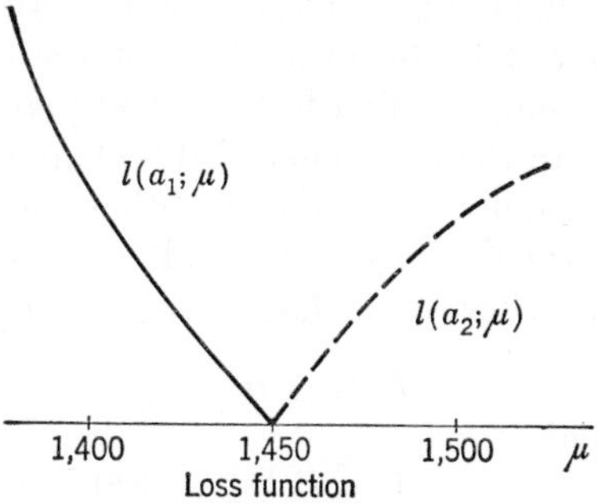

FIG. 12.7

d_1: accept H_1 if $\bar{x} > 1400$
d_2: accept H_1 if $\bar{x} > 1425$
d_3: accept H_1 if $\bar{x} > 1450$
d_4: accept H_1 if $\bar{x} > 1475$

To evaluate these probabilities, we apply the central-limit theorem and the fact that the exponential distribution has mean μ and standard deviation μ. Thus $\bar{x}$ is approximately normally distributed with mean μ and standard deviation $\mu/20$.

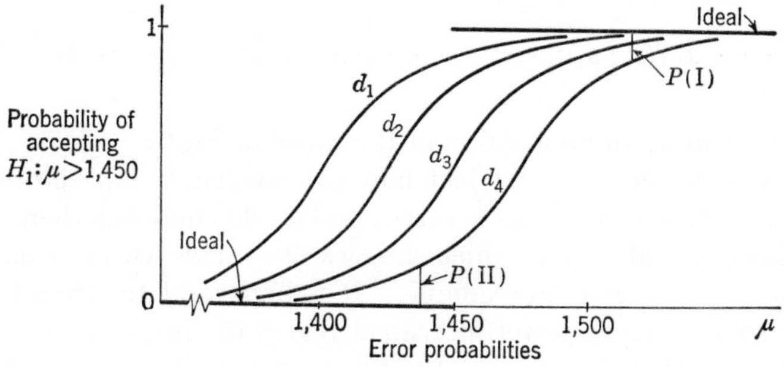

FIG. 12.8

These curves are contrasted with the *ideal* probability of accepting H_1, that is, the function which is 0 for $\mu \leq 1450$ and 1 for $\mu > 1450$. The ideal cannot be attained with a finite sample. The deviations from the ideal represent the error probabilities. Notice that by shifting strategies one may reduce the error probability on one side of 1450 but only at the cost of increasing it on the other side of 1450. In testing composite hypotheses the situation is much more complex than when the hypotheses are simple. In fact, in the composite case the admissible tests are difficult or impossible to obtain. In this case we shall, in general, restrict ourselves to an analysis of the error probabilities $P(\text{I})$ and $P(\text{II})$ and attempt to find tests that will control them in some fashion.

In the remainder of this chapter we shall be interested in the following formulation of the hypothesis-testing problem: To test the hypothesis $H_1: \theta \in \omega_1$ against the alternative hypothesis $H_2: \theta \in \omega_2$, we shall search for a test such that for a selected α $(0 < \alpha < 1)$

$$
\begin{aligned}
&P(\text{I}) \leq \alpha && \text{for all } \theta \in \omega_1 \\
\text{and} \qquad & && \qquad (1)\\
&1 - P(\text{II}) = \beta(\theta) \text{ is a maximum} && \text{for all } \theta \in \omega_2
\end{aligned}
$$

In other words, we look for tests that have maximum power for a fixed size α. The first solution of this problem was given by Neyman and Pearson for a simple hypothesis versus a simple alternative. It is often referred to as the Neyman-Pearson fundamental lemma. It will be stated below but the proof will be omitted.

Theorem 12.3. *The critical region R_k of size α which maximizes the power of the test of the hypothesis $H_1: \theta = \theta_1$ against the alternative $H_2: \theta = \theta_2$, where $\mathbf{x}_1, \cdots, \mathbf{x}_n$ is a random sample of size n, from $f(\mathbf{x}; \theta)$, is obtained by finding the region R_k, if it exists, which satisfies*

$$\lambda = \frac{f(\mathbf{x}_1; \theta_1)f(\mathbf{x}_2; \theta_1) \cdots f(\mathbf{x}_n; \theta_1)}{f(\mathbf{x}_1; \theta_2)f(\mathbf{x}_2; \theta_2) \cdots f(\mathbf{x}_n; \theta_2)} < k \tag{2}$$

for a fixed number k and such that

$$\int\int_{R_k} \cdots \int f(x_1; \theta_1)f(x_2; \theta_1) \cdots f(x_n; \theta_1)\, dx_1\, dx_2 \cdots dx_n = \alpha \tag{3}$$

This is, of course, an application of the likelihood ratio.

It may be obscure at first just how (3) involves k, but the region in which (2) is true changes as k varies, and as this happens there may be one region (one value of k) which satisfies (3). This will be brought out in detail when we give an example. It is important to stress that this theorem gives a most powerful critical region of size α for testing *only* that θ is a *single* point against the alternative that θ is a *single* point. The theorem does *not* necessarily give a method for finding a most powerful critical region of size α when either ω_1 or ω_2 contains more than one point. We shall see later that it can *sometimes* be used in these situations, which are clearly the most useful cases. That is, an experimenter may want to test that the mean yield of the difference of two varieties of wheat is zero against the alternative that it is positive. Or a manufacturer may want to test the hypothesis $H_1: \mu \leq 0$ against the alternative $H_2: \mu > 0$, where μ is the difference in the mean potency of two drugs. In these cases ω_1 or ω_2 or both ω_1 and ω_2 contain more than one point. There are actually four distinct cases: (1) ω_1 contains one point and ω_2 contains one point; (2) ω_1 contains one point and ω_2 contains more than one point; (3) ω_1 contains more than one point and ω_2 contains one point; (4) both ω_1 and ω_2 contain more than one point. The Neyman-Pearson lemma in general applies to case 1 only but we shall see that it is sometimes useful in other cases as well.

Example 12.5. For a simple example of how the Neyman-Pearson lemma can be used, let us test the hypothesis that the mean is 0 against the alternative hypothesis that the mean is 2 in a normal density with $\sigma^2 = 1$ (see Example 12.4). This can be written

$$H_1: \mu = 0 \qquad H_2: \mu = 2$$

$$f(x_i: 0) = \frac{1}{\sqrt{2\pi}} e^{-\frac{1}{2}x_i^2} \qquad i = 1, 2, \cdots, n$$

and

$$f(x_i; 2) = \frac{1}{\sqrt{2\pi}} e^{-\frac{1}{2}(x_i-2)^2} \qquad i = 1, 2, \cdots, n$$

and

$$\lambda = \frac{\prod_{i=1}^{n} f(\mathbf{x}_i; \mu_1)}{\prod_{i=1}^{n} f(\mathbf{x}_i; \mu_2)} = \exp\left[+\tfrac{1}{2}(-4n\bar{\mathbf{x}} + 4n)\right]$$

By (2), we need to find the region in the n-dimensional space such that

$$\exp\left[+\tfrac{1}{2}(-4n\bar{\mathbf{x}} + 4n)\right] < k$$

Taking logarithms and simplifying gives us

$$-2n\bar{\mathbf{x}} < \log k - 2n$$

or

$$\bar{\mathbf{x}} > -\frac{1}{2n}\log k + 1$$

If we set $-(1/2n)\log k + 1 = c$, then the rejection region R_k is such that $\bar{\mathbf{x}} > c$. Of course c is unknown because k is unknown. However, we do know the *form* of the rejection region. The distribution of $\bar{\mathbf{x}}$, when H_1 is true, is normal with mean 0; hence by (3) we get for $\alpha = .05$, say,

$$\frac{\sqrt{n}}{\sqrt{2\pi}} \int_c^\infty \exp\left(-\frac{n\bar{x}^2}{2}\right) d\bar{x} = .05 \tag{4}$$

If we let $y = \sqrt{n}\,\bar{x}$, then (4) becomes

$$\frac{1}{\sqrt{2\pi}} \int_{c\sqrt{n}}^{\infty} e^{-y^2/2}\,dy = .05$$

and, by Table II, $\sqrt{n}\,c = 1.645$ and $c = 1.645/\sqrt{n}$. In this problem we do not need to know the value of k since the critical region depends on c. We have shown that the critical region of size .05, with maximum power of the test $H_1\colon \mu = 0$ against the alternative $H_2\colon \mu = 2$, is $\bar{\mathbf{x}} > 1.645/\sqrt{n}$. Consequently H_1 is to be rejected if $\bar{\mathbf{x}} > 1.645/\sqrt{n}$.

Even though the Neyman-Pearson fundamental lemma applies specifically to problems involving a simple hypothesis against a simple alternative, we shall show that it can *sometimes* be used to advantage in composite hypotheses.

12.4 Tests of $\theta \le \theta_1$ versus $\theta > \theta_1$ for Densities with a Single Parameter θ

There are many densities in applied statistics which have a single unknown parameter such as binomial, Poisson, normal with mean known, normal with variance known, exponential, etc. Many times an experimenter may want to test the hypothesis $H_1\colon \theta \le \theta_1$ with the alternative hypothesis $H_2\colon \theta > \theta_1$, where θ_1 is known and $f(x; \theta)$ is the density.

Example 12.6. Let us consider for an example a normal density with variance 1 and unknown mean μ. Suppose that we want to test the hypothesis $H_1\colon \mu = \mu_1$ against the alternative hypothesis $H_2\colon \mu > \mu_1$, where μ_1 is known. Let us select any number μ_2, where $\mu_2 > \mu_1$, and form a new hypothesis $H_1^*\colon \mu = \mu_1$ against the alternative $H_2^*\colon \mu = \mu_2$, where μ_2 is any value so long as $\mu_2 > \mu_1$. The likelihood-ratio for a random sample of size n reduces to

$$\lambda = \exp - \tfrac{1}{2}[2n\bar{\mathbf{x}}(\mu_2 - \mu_1) + n(\mu_1^2 - \mu_2^2)]$$

By Theorem 12.3, the critical region is the set of $\mathbf{x}$'s such that $\lambda < k$. After some simplifying, we obtain

$$-n\bar{\mathbf{x}}(\mu_2 - \mu_1) < \log k + \frac{n}{2}(\mu_1^2 - \mu_2^2)$$

Since $\mu_2 - \mu_1 > 0$, we can divide by $-n(\mu_2 - \mu_1)$ and obtain

$$\bar{\mathbf{x}} > -\frac{\log k}{n(\mu_2 - \mu_1)} + \tfrac{1}{2}(\mu_1 + \mu_2)$$

If we set

$$-\frac{\log k}{n(\mu_2 - \mu_1)} + \tfrac{1}{2}(\mu_1 + \mu_2) = c$$

then the critical region is of the form $\bar{\mathbf{x}} > c$ *regardless* of the value of μ_2 (just so long as $\mu_2 > \mu_1$). The particular value that c assumes depends on the value of α and in no way depends on the value that μ_2 assumes if $\mu_2 > \mu_1$, and if H_1 is rejected if $\bar{\mathbf{x}} > c$ this is a test of $H_1: \mu = \mu_1$ against the alternative $H_2: \mu > \mu_1$. We evaluate c by

$$P(\mathrm{I}) = .05 = \frac{\sqrt{n}}{\sqrt{2\pi}} \int_c^\infty \exp\left[-\frac{n}{2}(\bar{x} - \mu_1)^2\right] d\bar{x}$$

which gives $c = 1.645/\sqrt{n} + \mu_1$. This is called a *uniformly most powerful test* (UMP test) of size α of the hypothesis H_1 against H_2. We shall now define UMP.

Definition 12.7. *A test of the hypothesis $H_1: \theta \in \omega_1$ against the alternative $H_2: \theta \in \omega_2$ is called a UMP test of size α if the critical region R of the test is such that*

$$\begin{aligned} &P(\mathrm{I}) \le \alpha && \text{for all } \theta \text{ in } \omega_1 \\ &\beta(\theta) = 1 - P(\mathrm{II}) \text{ is a maximum} && \text{for each } \theta \text{ in } \omega_2 \end{aligned} \tag{1}$$

In the formulation of tests of hypotheses as given in (12.3.1) a UMP test is the "best" test.

Next we shall give a theorem that is often useful in determining a UMP test of $H_1: \theta \le \theta_1$ against the alternative hypothesis $H_2: \theta > \theta_1$.

Theorem 12.4. *Let $\mathbf{x} = (\mathbf{x}_1, \cdots, \mathbf{x}_n)$ be a random sample from a density with a single parameter θ in an interval Ω. Let $f(x; \theta)$ be the joint density of the random variables. Suppose that we can write $f(x; \theta)$ as*

$$f(x; \theta) = s(\theta) U(x) e^{v(x)t(\theta)} \tag{2}$$

where $t(\theta)$ is a strictly increasing function of θ in Ω. If there exists a constant c such that $P[v(\mathbf{x}) > c|\theta_1] = \alpha$ for a given α between 0 and 1, then a UMP critical region of size α for testing $H_1: \theta \le \theta_1$ against $H_2: \theta > \theta_1$ is R, where $R = \{x: v(x) > c\}$. If $t(\theta)$ is a strictly decreasing function of θ in Ω and if there exists a constant c such that $P[v(\mathbf{x}) < c|\theta_1] = \alpha$ for a given α between 0 and 1 then R is a UMP critical region of size α for testing H_1 above against H_2, where $R = \{x: v(x) < c\}$.

Example 12.7. Let us test $H_1: \theta \le 1$ against $H_2: \theta > 1$ for a sample $\mathbf{x}$ of size one in the density $\theta e^{-\theta x}, \theta > 0$. The density of $\mathbf{x}$ can be written as (2) by setting $s(\theta) = \theta$, $U(x) = 1$, $v(x) = x$, $t(\theta) = -\theta$ so that $t(\theta)$ is a strictly decreasing function of θ. We want a test of size $\alpha = .05$, and so we set

$$P[v(\mathbf{x}) < c|\theta = 1] = P[v(\mathbf{x}) < c|1] = .05$$

and obtain

$$.05 = P(\mathbf{x} < c|1) = \int_0^c e^{-x}\, dx = -e^{-c} + 1$$

or $e^{-c} = .95$, which gives $c = -\log_e .95$. Thus a UMP test of H_1 against H_2 is: Reject H_1 if $\mathbf{x} < -\log_e .95$.

This theorem can also be used to obtain a UMP test of the hypothesis $H_1\colon \theta = \theta_1$ against the alternative $H_2\colon \theta > \theta_1$. To test the hypothesis $H_1\colon \theta \geq \theta_1$ against the alternative hypothesis $H_2\colon \theta < \theta_1$ the theorem can be used to obtain a UMP test by reversing all the inequalities in the theorem. Also the theorem can be used to test $H_1\colon \theta = \theta_1$ against the alternative $H_2\colon \theta < \theta_1$ by reversing the inequalities in the theorem. Many of the densities with a single parameter θ that are important in applied statistics can be written as (2) and the theorem applies.

12.5 Test of Hypothesis $H_1\colon \theta_1 \leq \theta \leq \theta_2$ with the Alternative Hypothesis $H_2\colon \theta > \theta_2,\ \theta < \theta_1$

A test that has been quite extensively applied in various fields of science is $H_1\colon \theta = \theta_0$ against $H_1\colon \theta \neq \theta_0$. For example, let θ be the mean difference of yield between two varieties of wheat. It is oftimes suggested that it is desirable to test the hypothesis $H_1\colon \theta = 0$ against $H_2\colon \theta \neq 0$, that is, to test if the two varieties are different in their mean yields. However, in this situation, and many others where θ can vary continuously in some interval, it is inconceivable that θ is exactly equal to 0 (that the varieties are identical in their mean yields). Yet this is what the test is stating: Are the two mean yields identical (to one-ten-billionth of a bushel, etc.)? In many cases it seems more realistic for an experimenter to select an interval about θ_0, say $\theta_1 \leq \theta_0 \leq \theta_2$, and test $H_1\colon \theta_1 \leq \theta \leq \theta_2$ against the alternative $H_2\colon \theta < \theta_1;\ \theta > \theta_2$. For example, it may be feasible to set $\theta_1 = -\frac{1}{2}$ and $\theta_2 = \frac{1}{2}$ in the above illustration and test if the difference of the mean yields of the two varieties is between $-\frac{1}{2}$ bushel and $+\frac{1}{2}$ bushel, against the alternative that it is not in this interval. A test that is UMP for the above hypothesis may be difficult or impossible to devise, but if $f(x; \theta)$ is a density with a single parameter, then the maximum-likelihood estimator $\hat{\boldsymbol{\theta}}$ may sometimes be used to construct a test and the power of this test compared with the ideal power function for a test of size α. A test of the following form may be used for some densities:

$$\begin{array}{ll} \text{Reject } H_1 \textit{ if } \hat{\boldsymbol{\theta}} \text{ is } \textit{not} \text{ in the interval} & c_1 \leq \hat{\boldsymbol{\theta}} \leq c_2 \\ \text{Accept } H_1 \text{ if } \hat{\boldsymbol{\theta}} \textit{ is} \text{ in the interval} & c_1 \leq \hat{\boldsymbol{\theta}} \leq c_2 \end{array} \tag{1}$$

where c_1 and c_2 are chosen so that the test has size α. Often c_1 and c_2 can be chosen so that

$$\int_{c_1}^{c_2} g(\hat{\theta}; \theta_1)\, d\hat{\theta} = \int_{c_1}^{c_2} g(\hat{\theta}; \theta_2)\, d\hat{\theta} = 1 - \alpha$$

where $g(\hat{\theta}; \theta)$ is the density of $\hat{\boldsymbol{\theta}}$ when θ is the parameter. The power of this test is

$$\beta(\theta) = 1 - \int_{c_1}^{c_2} g(\hat{\theta}; \theta)\, d\hat{\theta} \qquad \text{for } \theta \text{ in } \Omega = \{\theta: b_0 < \theta < b_1\} \tag{2}$$

This can be compared with the ideal power function which is given by

$$\begin{aligned} \beta(\theta) &= 1 \qquad & b_0 < \theta < \theta_1 \\ \beta(\theta) &= \alpha \qquad & \theta_1 \le \theta \le \theta_2 \\ \beta(\theta) &= 1 \qquad & b_1 > \theta > \theta_2 \end{aligned}$$

If the power (2) of the test (1) does not deviate farther from the *ideal* than the experimenter can tolerate, the test may be useful even though it may not be a UMP test.

There are many hypotheses-testing problems for which a UMP test does not exist, and the one discussed in this section is one such problem. In these cases it may be possible to restrict the class of tests and find a UMP test in the restricted class. One such class that has some merit is the class of unbiased tests.

Definition 12.8. *Unbiased Tests. A test of the hypothesis H_1: $\theta \in \omega_1$ against the alternative hypothesis H_2: $\theta \in \omega_2$ is an unbiased test of size α if*

$$P(\mathrm{I}) \le \alpha \qquad \textit{for all } \theta \textit{ in } \omega_1$$

and

$$\beta(\theta) \ge \alpha \qquad \textit{for all } \theta \textit{ in } \omega_2$$

Consequently in an unbiased test the probability of rejecting the hypothesis H_1 when it is false is at least as large as the probability of rejecting the hypothesis H_1 when it is true. In many respects this seems to be a reasonable restriction to place on a test. If within this restricted class a test exists that is UMP, then we have a UMP unbiased (UMPU) test.

12.6 Generalized Likelihood-ratio Test

In many cases the preceding theory will not apply, and no UMP nor UMPU test exists. In these cases it may be possible to restrict the class of tests further than to unbiased tests and search for UMP tests in the restricted class. Another approach is to use a general method of constructing a test that has desirable large-sample properties. Such a test is the generalized likelihood-ratio test which we shall now define.

For the remainder of this chapter we shall consider a general family of distributions $f(x; \theta_1, \theta_2, \cdots, \theta_k)$, and the hypothesis to be tested will be called a null hypothesis denoted by H_0, and will state that the parameters belong to some subspace ω of the parameter space Ω.

The alternative hypothesis will be denoted by H_a but will not be stated when it is quite clear from the context what it is. Let $\mathbf{x}_1, \mathbf{x}_2, \cdots, \mathbf{x}_n$

be a sample of size n from a population with density $f(x; \theta_1, \theta_2, \cdots, \theta_k)$, where Ω, the parameter space, is the totality of all the points that $(\theta_1, \theta_2, \cdots, \theta_k)$ can assume. On the basis of this sample, suppose that it is desired to test the hypothesis: H_0: $(\theta_1, \theta_2, \cdots, \theta_k)$ is a point in ω. The alternative hypothesis is: H_a: $(\theta_1, \theta_2, \cdots, \theta_k)$ is a point in $\bar{\omega}$, where $\bar{\omega}$ is $\Omega - \omega$.

The likelihood of the sample is

$$L = \prod_{i=1}^{n} f(\mathbf{x}_i; \theta_1, \theta_2, \cdots, \theta_k) \tag{1}$$

The likelihood as a function of the parameters will ordinarily have a maximum as the parameters are allowed to vary over the entire parameter space Ω; we shall denote this maximum value by $L(\hat{\theta}_1, \hat{\theta}_2, \cdots, \hat{\theta}_k)$, or, more briefly, by $L(\hat{\Omega})$. In the subspace ω, L will also ordinarily have a maximum value which we shall denote by $L(\hat{\omega})$.

Definition 12.9. *The generalized likelihood-ratio is the quotient*

$$\lambda = \frac{L(\hat{\omega})}{L(\hat{\Omega})}$$

where $L(\hat{\omega})$ is the maximum of the likelihood function in the region ω with respect to the parameters, and $L(\hat{\Omega})$ is the maximum of the likelihood function in the region Ω with respect to the parameters.

We shall refer to this simply as the likelihood-ratio if there is no chance of confusing it with the likelihood-ratio of Definition 12.6. This quantity is necessarily a nonnegative number; L is nonnegative because it is a ratio of density functions, and $L(\hat{\omega})$ will be smaller than or at most equal to $L(\hat{\Omega})$ because there is less freedom for maximizing L in ω than in Ω. The ratio λ is a function of the sample observations only; it does not involve any parameters. λ varies from 0 to 1.

Example 12.8. Let $f(x; \mu)$ be a normal density with variance one and unknown mean μ, and let the random sample consist of n observations $\mathbf{x}_1, \mathbf{x}_2, \cdots, \mathbf{x}_n$. We shall test the null hypothesis

$$H_0: \mu = 3 \quad \text{against the alternative} \quad H_a: \mu \neq 3$$

The point $\mu = 3$ is ω while the whole μ axis is Ω. The likelihood is

$$L = \left(\frac{1}{\sqrt{2\pi}}\right)^n e^{-\frac{1}{2}\Sigma(\mathbf{x}_i - \mu)^2}$$

which may be written

$$L = \left(\frac{1}{\sqrt{2\pi}}\right)^n \exp\left[-\frac{1}{2}\sum (\mathbf{x}_i - \bar{\mathbf{x}})^2 - \frac{n}{2}(\bar{\mathbf{x}} - \mu)^2\right]$$

The maximum value of this quantity in Ω is, of course, given by putting $\mu = \bar{x}$ to obtain

$$L(\hat{\Omega}) = \left(\frac{1}{\sqrt{2\pi}}\right)^n \exp\left[-\frac{1}{2}\sum (x_i - \bar{x})^2\right]$$

Since in this example ω is a point (the null hypothesis is simple), there is no opportunity to vary μ, and the largest value of L in ω is simply its only value:

$$L(\hat{\omega}) = \left(\frac{1}{\sqrt{2\pi}}\right)^{n/2} \exp\left[-\frac{1}{2}\sum (x_i - 3)^2\right]$$

$$= \left(\frac{1}{\sqrt{2\pi}}\right)^n \exp\left[-\frac{1}{2}\sum (x_i - \bar{x})^2 - \frac{n}{2}(\bar{x} - 3)^2\right]$$

The likelihood-ratio is then

$$\lambda = \exp\left[-\frac{n}{2}(\bar{x} - 3)^2\right]$$

If $\bar{x}$ happens to be quite near 3, then the sample is reasonably consistent with H_0, and λ will be near 1. If $\bar{x}$ is much greater than or less than 3, the sample will not be consistent with H_0 and λ will be near 0.

Clearly the proper critical region for testing H_0 is an interval

$$0 < \lambda < A$$

where A is some number (less than 1) chosen to give the desired control of the Type I error.

If we take the probability of a Type I error to be .05, we must determine A such that

$$\int_0^A g(\lambda|H_0)\, d\lambda = .05$$

where $g(\lambda|H_0)$ is the density of λ when H_0 is true, i.e., when $\mu = 3$ in this problem. Thus $\bar{x}$ is normal with mean 3 and variance $1/n$, and $(\bar{x} - 3)^2 n$ is distributed as a chi-square with one degree of freedom. Consequently $-2 \log \lambda$ is a chi-square variate with one degree of freedom. Let $y = -2 \log \lambda$; then

$$.05 = \int_0^A g(\lambda|H_0)\, d\lambda = \int_{-2\log A}^{\infty} h(y)\, dy = \int_{3.84}^{\infty} h(y)\, dy$$

since $h(y)$ is a chi-square density with one d.f. Thus the critical region is $(\bar{x} - 3)^2 n > 3.84$, or the region defined by the inequalities

$$\bar{x} > 3 + \frac{1.96}{\sqrt{n}}$$

$$\bar{x} < 3 - \frac{1.96}{\sqrt{n}}$$

This example illustrates the general situation. If the maximum-likelihood estimates fall in or near ω, the sample will be considered consistent with H_0 and the ratio λ will be near 1. If the estimate is distant from ω, then the sample will not be in accord with H_0 and λ will ordinarily be small. This can be summed up as follows:

Theorem 12.5. *The critical region for testing a simple hypothesis H_0 by a likelihood-ratio test is $0 < \lambda < A$, where A is determined by*

$$\int_0^A g(\lambda | H_0)\, d\lambda = \alpha$$

where α is the Type I error probability.

If the distribution of λ is not tabulated but the distribution of some function of λ is known, then it can be utilized.

Theorem 12.6. *Let λ be a likelihood-ratio for testing a simple hypothesis H_0, and let $\mathbf{y} = u(\lambda)$ be a monotonic increasing (decreasing) function of λ; then the test based on $\mathbf{y}$ is equivalent to the likelihood-ratio test. The critical region for the test based on $\mathbf{y}$ is $u(0) < \mathbf{y} < u(A)[u(A) < \mathbf{y} < u(0)]$.*

Proof. The critical region is $0 < \lambda < A$, where A is determined by

$$\alpha = \int_0^A g(\lambda | H_0)\, d\lambda$$

If $\mathbf{y} = u(\lambda)$ is a monotonic increasing function of λ, then we get

$$\alpha = \int_0^A g(\lambda | H_0)\, d\lambda = \int_{u(0)}^{u(A)} h(y | H_0)\, dy$$

where $h(y|H_0)$ is the density of $\mathbf{y}$ when H_0 is true. Thus the critical region is $u(0) < \mathbf{y} < u(A)$. The inequalities are reversed when $u(\lambda)$ is a monotonic decreasing function of λ. This theorem is illustrated in Example 12.8, where $\mathbf{y} = -2 \log \lambda = (\bar{\mathbf{x}} - 3)^2 n$ is a monotonic decreasing function of λ, and so we can use $(\bar{\mathbf{x}} - 3)^2 n$ as a test function.

In order to prescribe the critical region for λ, it is necessary to know the distribution of λ when H_0 is true. If H_0 is simple hypothesis [ω is a point $(\theta_1^0, \theta_2^0, \cdots, \theta_k^0)$, for example], then there will be a unique distribution determined for λ. But if H_0 is a composite, there may or may not be a unique distribution for λ. It is quite possible that the distribution of λ may be different for different parameter points in ω. If this is the case, then A is chosen such that the integral in Theorem 12.5 is $\leq \alpha$ for all values of the parameters in ω.

As is often the case a satisfactory solution of the problem of testing hypotheses exists when one is dealing with large samples. The solution is based on a theorem which we shall not be able to prove because of the advanced character of its proof.

Theorem 12.7. *Let* $\mathbf{x}_1, \mathbf{x}_2, \cdots, \mathbf{x}_n$ *be a random sample of size n from a density* $f(x; \theta_1, \theta_2, \cdots, \theta_k)$ *that satisfies quite general regularity conditions, and suppose* Ω *is k-dimensional. Suppose that it is desired to test the hypothesis*

$$H_0: \theta_1 = \theta_1^0; \theta_2 = \theta_2^0; \cdots ; \theta_t = \theta_t^0 \qquad t < k$$

where $\theta_1^0, \theta_2^0, \cdots, \theta_t^0$ *are known numbers. When* H_0 *is true,* $-2 \log \lambda$ *is approximately distributed as chi-square with t degrees of freedom when n is large.*

Since $-2 \log \lambda$ increases as λ decreases and approaches infinity as λ approaches 0, the critical region for $-2 \log \lambda$ is the right-hand tail of the chi-square distribution. Therefore if we are dealing with a large sample and wish to test a null hypothesis with probability .05 for a Type I error, for example, it is only necessary to compute $-2 \log \lambda$ and compare it with the .05 level of chi square; if $-2 \log \lambda$ exceeds the chi-square level, H_0 would be rejected; otherwise H_0 would be accepted.

12.7 Tests on the Mean of a Normal Population

The foregoing ideas are well illustrated by a very common practical problem—that of testing whether the mean of a normal population has a specified value. We shall suppose that we have a sample of n observations, $\mathbf{x}_1, \mathbf{x}_2, \cdots, \mathbf{x}_n$, from a normal population with mean μ and variance σ^2. We wish to test the null hypothesis:

$$H_0: \mu = \mu_0 \qquad 0 < \sigma^2 < \infty \qquad H_a: \mu \neq \mu_0 \qquad 0 < \sigma^2 < \infty$$

where μ_0 is a given number. The parameter space Ω is the half plane $\Omega = \{\mu, \sigma^2: -\infty < \mu < \infty; 0 < \sigma^2 < \infty\}$. The subspace ω characterized by the null hypothesis is the vertical line $\mu = \mu_0$; i.e.,

$$\omega = \{\mu, \sigma^2: \mu = \mu_0; 0 < \sigma^2 < \infty\}$$

where μ_0 is a given number.

We shall test H_0 by means of the likelihood-ratio. The likelihood is

$$L = \left(\frac{1}{\sqrt{2\pi}\,\sigma}\right)^n e^{-\frac{1}{2}\Sigma[(\mathbf{x}_i-\mu)/\sigma]^2} \tag{1}$$

We have already seen that the values of μ and σ^2 which maximize L in Ω are

$$\hat{\boldsymbol{\mu}} = \frac{1}{n}\sum \mathbf{x}_i = \bar{\mathbf{x}}$$

$$\hat{\boldsymbol{\sigma}}^2 = \frac{1}{n}\sum (\mathbf{x}_i - \bar{\mathbf{x}})^2 \tag{2}$$

Substituting these values in L, we have

$$L(\hat{\Omega}) = \left[\frac{1}{(2\pi/n)\Sigma(\mathbf{x}_i - \bar{\mathbf{x}})^2}\right]^{n/2} e^{-(n/2)} \tag{3}$$

To maximize L in ω, we put $\mu = \mu_0$, and the only remaining parameter is σ^2; the value of σ^2 which then maximizes L is readily found to be

$$\hat{\sigma}^2 = \frac{1}{n} \sum (\mathbf{x}_i - \mu_0)^2$$

which gives

$$L(\hat{\omega}) = \left[\frac{1}{(2\pi/n)\Sigma(\mathbf{x}_i - \mu_0)^2}\right]^{n/2} e^{-(n/2)} \tag{4}$$

The ratio of (4) to (3) is the likelihood-ratio:

$$\lambda = \left[\frac{\Sigma(\mathbf{x}_i - \bar{\mathbf{x}})^2}{\Sigma(\mathbf{x}_i - \mu_0)^2}\right]^{n/2} \tag{5}$$

Our next step is to obtain the distribution of λ under H_0 and use that distribution to determine a number A so that the critical region $0 < \lambda < A$ will give the desired probability, .10, for example, of rejecting H_0 when it is true.

It happens that the distribution of λ is easily obtained in this case. The sum of squares in the denominator of (5) may be put in the form

$$\Sigma(\mathbf{x}_i - \mu_0)^2 = \Sigma(\mathbf{x}_i - \bar{\mathbf{x}})^2 + n(\bar{\mathbf{x}} - \mu_0)^2$$

so that λ may be written

$$\lambda = \left\{\frac{1}{1 + [n(\bar{\mathbf{x}} - \mu_0)^2/\Sigma(\mathbf{x}_i - \bar{\mathbf{x}})^2]}\right\}^{n/2} \tag{6}$$

We recall that the quantity in the denominator in the braces is

$$1 + \frac{\mathbf{t}^2}{n - 1}$$

where $\mathbf{t}$ has the t distribution with $n - 1$ degrees of freedom when H_0 is true. To obtain the distribution of λ, we need merely to transform the t distribution by the substitution

$$\lambda = \left\{\frac{1}{1 + [\mathbf{t}^2/(n - 1)]}\right\}^{n/2} \tag{7}$$

It is not actually necessary to obtain the distributon of λ, because it is a monotonic function of $\mathbf{t}^2$ and the test can be done just as well with $\mathbf{t}^2$ as a criterion as with λ. Since $\mathbf{t}^2 = 0$ when $\lambda = 1$ and $\mathbf{t}^2$ becomes infinite when λ approaches 0, a critical region of the form $0 < \lambda < A$ is equivalent to a critical region $\mathbf{t}^2 > B$, where B may be determined from A by equation (7). The critical values of $\mathbf{t}$ are therefore the extreme values, either positive or negative, and a .10 critical region for $\mathbf{t}$ is the pair of intervals

$$\mathbf{t} < -t_{.05} \qquad \text{and} \qquad \mathbf{t} > t_{.05}$$

where $t_{.05}$ is the number for which

$$\int_{t_{.05}}^{\infty} f(t; n-1)\, dt = .05 \tag{8}$$

$f(t; n-1)$ representing the t distribution with $n-1$ degrees of freedom. The test of H_0 may therefore be performed as follows: We compute the quantity

$$\frac{\sqrt{n(n-1)}\,(\bar{\mathbf{x}} - \mu_0)}{\sqrt{\Sigma(\mathbf{x}_i - \bar{\mathbf{x}})^2}} \tag{9}$$

If it lies between $-t_{.05}$ and $t_{.05}$, H_0 is accepted; otherwise H_0 is rejected.

It is worth while to observe the connection between this test and the confidence-interval estimate of the mean. Supposing the mean of the population is μ', a 90 per cent confidence interval for μ' is just the set of values μ for which

$$-t_{.05} < \frac{\sqrt{n(n-1)}\,(\bar{\mathbf{x}} - \mu)}{\sqrt{\Sigma(\mathbf{x}_i - \bar{\mathbf{x}})^2}} < t_{.05} \tag{10}$$

Hence the test of H_0 is equivalent to the following test: Construct a confidence interval for the population mean. If μ_0 lies in the confidence interval, accept H_0; if μ_0 does not lie in the confidence interval, reject H_0.

The power of the test for a two-tailed critical region is

$$\beta(\mu, \sigma^2) = 1 - \int_{-t_{.05}}^{t_{.05}} f(t; \mu, \sigma^2)\, dt$$

where $f(t; \mu, \sigma^2)$ is the density of $(\bar{\mathbf{x}} - \mu_0)\sqrt{n-1}/\hat{\boldsymbol{\sigma}}$ when the mean of $\bar{\mathbf{x}}$ is equal to μ. This density is termed the noncentral t distribution and has been tabulated for various parameter combinations.

12.8 The Difference between Means of Two Normal Populations

In many situations it is necessary to compare two means when neither is known; in the preceding section we assumed that one was known. If, for example, one wished to compare two proposed new processes for manufacturing light bulbs, he would have to base the comparison on estimates of both process means. In comparing the yield of a new line of hybrid corn with that of a standard line, one would also have to use estimates of both mean yields because it is impossible to state the mean yield of the standard line for the given weather conditions under which the new line will be grown. It is necessary to compare the two lines by planting them in the same season and on the same soil type and thereby obtain estimates of the mean yields for both lines under similar conditions. Of course the comparison is thus specialized; a complete comparison of the two lines would require tests over a period of years on a variety of soil types.

The general problem is this: We have two normal populations—one with variate $\mathbf{x}_1$ which has mean μ_1 and variance σ_1^2, and one with variate $\mathbf{x}_2$ which has mean μ_2 and variance σ_2^2. On the basis of two samples, one from each population, we wish to test the null hypothesis:

$$H_0: \mu_1 = \mu_2 \qquad \sigma_2^2 > 0, \sigma_1^2 > 0 \qquad H_a: \mu_1 \neq \mu_2 \qquad \sigma_1^2 > 0, \sigma_2^2 > 0$$

The parameter space Ω here is four-dimensional; a joint distribution of $\mathbf{x}_1$ and $\mathbf{x}_2$ is specified when values are assigned to the four quantities $(\mu_1, \mu_2, \sigma_1^2, \sigma_2^2)$. The subspace ω is three-dimensional because values for only three quantities $(\mu, \sigma_1^2, \sigma_2^2)$ need be specified in order to specify completely the joint distribution under the hypothesis that $\mu_1 = \mu_2 = \mu$, say.

We shall suppose that there are m observations $(\mathbf{x}_{11}, \mathbf{x}_{12}, \cdots, \mathbf{x}_{1m})$ in the sample from the first population and n observations $(\mathbf{x}_{21}, \mathbf{x}_{22}, \cdots, \mathbf{x}_{2n})$ from the second. The likelihood is

$$L = \left(\frac{1}{2\pi\sigma_1^2}\right)^{\frac{m}{2}} e^{-\frac{1}{2}\sum_1^m\left(\frac{\mathbf{x}_{1i}-\mu_1}{\sigma_1}\right)^2} \left(\frac{1}{2\pi\sigma_2^2}\right)^{\frac{n}{2}} e^{-\frac{1}{2}\sum_1^n\left(\frac{\mathbf{x}_{2j}-\mu_2}{\sigma_2}\right)^2} \tag{1}$$

and its maximum in Ω is readily seen to be

$$L(\hat{\Omega}) = \left[\frac{m}{2\pi \sum_1^m (\mathbf{x}_{1i} - \bar{\mathbf{x}}_1)^2}\right]^{m/2} \left[\frac{n}{2\pi \sum_1^n (\mathbf{x}_{2j} - \bar{\mathbf{x}}_2)^2}\right]^{n/2} e^{-(m/2)}e^{-(n/2)} \tag{2}$$

If we put μ_1 and μ_2 equal to μ, say, and try to maximize L with respect to μ, σ_1^2, and σ_2^2, it will be found that the estimate of μ is given as the root of a cubic equation and will be a very complex function of the observations. The resulting likelihood-ratio λ will therefore be a complicated function, and to find its distribution is a tedious task indeed and involves the ratio of the two variances. This makes it impossible to determine a critical region $0 < \lambda < A$ for a given probability of a Type I error, because the ratio of the population variances is ordinarily unknown. A number of special devices can be employed in an attempt to circumvent this difficulty, but we shall not pursue the problem further here. Of course, for large samples the following criterion may be used. The root of the cubic can be computed in any given instance by numerical methods, and λ can then be calculated. The quantity $-2 \log \lambda$ will have approximately the chi-square distribution with one degree of freedom.

When it can be assumed that the two populations have the same variance, the problem becomes relatively simple. The parameter space Ω is then three-dimensional with coordinates (μ_1, μ_2, σ^2), while ω, for the null hypothesis $\mu_1 = \mu_2$, is two-dimensional with coordinates (σ^2, μ). In Ω we find

$$\hat{\mathbf{u}}_1 = \bar{\mathbf{x}}_1 \qquad \hat{\mathbf{u}}_2 = \bar{\mathbf{x}}_2$$

$$\hat{\mathbf{d}}^2 = \frac{1}{m+n}\left[\sum_1^m (\mathbf{x}_{1i} - \bar{\mathbf{x}}_1)^2 + \sum_1^n (\mathbf{x}_{2j} - \bar{\mathbf{x}}_2)^2\right]$$

so that

$$L(\hat{\Omega}) = \left\{\frac{m+n}{2\pi[\Sigma(\mathbf{x}_{1i} - \bar{\mathbf{x}}_1)^2 + \Sigma(\mathbf{x}_{2j} - \bar{\mathbf{x}}_2)^2]}\right\}^{(m+n)/2} e^{-[(m+n)/2]} \tag{3}$$

In ω

$$\hat{\mathbf{u}} = \frac{1}{m+n}\left(\sum_1^m \mathbf{x}_{1i} + \sum_1^n \mathbf{x}_{2j}\right) = \frac{m\bar{\mathbf{x}}_1 + n\bar{\mathbf{x}}_2}{m+n}$$

$$\hat{\mathbf{d}}^2 = \frac{1}{m+n}\left[\sum (\mathbf{x}_{1i} - \hat{\mathbf{u}})^2 + \sum (\mathbf{x}_{2j} - \hat{\mathbf{u}})^2\right]$$

$$= \frac{1}{m+n}\left[\sum (\mathbf{x}_{1i} - \bar{\mathbf{x}}_1)^2 + \sum (\mathbf{x}_{2j} - \bar{\mathbf{x}}_2)^2 + \frac{mn}{m+n}(\bar{\mathbf{x}}_1 - \bar{\mathbf{x}}_2)^2\right]$$

which gives

$$L(\hat{\omega}) = \left\{\frac{m+n}{2\pi\left[\sum (\mathbf{x}_{1i} - \bar{\mathbf{x}}_1)^2 + \sum (\mathbf{x}_{2j} - \bar{\mathbf{x}}_2)^2 + \frac{mn}{m+n}(\bar{\mathbf{x}}_1 - \bar{\mathbf{x}}_2)^2\right]}\right\}^{(m+n)/2} e^{-[(m+n)/2]} \tag{4}$$

and finally

$$\lambda = \left[\frac{1}{1 + \dfrac{\frac{mn}{m+n}(\bar{\mathbf{x}}_1 - \bar{\mathbf{x}}_2)^2}{\Sigma(\mathbf{x}_{1i} - \bar{\mathbf{x}}_1)^2 + \Sigma(\mathbf{x}_{2j} - \bar{\mathbf{x}}_2)^2}}\right]^{(m+n)/2} \tag{5}$$

This last expression is very similar to the corresponding one obtained in the preceding section, and it turns out that this test can also be performed in terms of a quantity which has the t distribution. We know that $\bar{\mathbf{x}}_1$ and $\bar{\mathbf{x}}_2$ are independently normally distributed with means μ_1 and μ_2 and with variances σ^2/m and σ^2/n. Referring to Prob. 25 of Chap. 10, it is readily seen that $\mathbf{u} = \bar{\mathbf{x}}_1 - \bar{\mathbf{x}}_2$ is normally distributed with mean $\mu_1 - \mu_2$ and variance $\sigma^2[(1/m) + (1/n)]$. Under the null hypothesis the mean of $\mathbf{u}$ will be 0. The quantities $\Sigma(\mathbf{x}_{1i} - \bar{\mathbf{x}}_1)^2/\sigma^2$ and $\Sigma(\mathbf{x}_{2j} - \bar{\mathbf{x}}_2)^2/\sigma^2$ are independently distributed as chi square with $m - 1$ and $n - 1$ degrees of freedom, respectively; hence their sum, say $\mathbf{v}$, has the chi-square distribution with $m + n - 2$ degrees of freedom. Since under the null hypothesis

$$\mathbf{z} = \frac{\bar{\mathbf{x}}_1 - \bar{\mathbf{x}}_2}{\sigma\sqrt{(1/m) + (1/n)}}$$

is normally distributed with zero mean and unit variance, the quantity

$$\mathbf{t} = \frac{\mathbf{z}}{\sqrt{\mathbf{v}/(m + n - 2)}} = \frac{\sqrt{mn/(m + n)}\,(\bar{\mathbf{x}}_1 - \bar{\mathbf{x}}_2)}{\sqrt{[\Sigma(\mathbf{x}_{1i} - \bar{\mathbf{x}}_1)^2 + \Sigma(\mathbf{x}_{2j} - \bar{\mathbf{x}}_2)^2]/(m + n - 2)}} \tag{6}$$

has the t distribution with $m + n - 2$ degrees of freedom. The likelihood-ratio is

$$\lambda = \left\{\frac{1}{1 + [\mathbf{t}^2/(m + n - 2)]}\right\}^{(m+n)/2} \tag{7}$$

and its distribution is determined by the t distribution. The test would, of course, be done in terms of $\mathbf{t}$ rather than λ. A 5 per cent critical region for $\mathbf{t}$ is $\mathbf{t}^2 > (t_{.025})^2$. If we wanted to test $H_0\colon \mu_1 = \mu_2$ with the alternative $H_a\colon \mu_1 < \mu_2$, and with $\alpha = .05$ (for example, if the first population referred to the yield of a variety of corn in common use, while the second referred to the yield of a proposed substitute), the critical region would be $\mathbf{t} < -t_{.05}$.

We may observe here that it is possible to determine a confidence interval for the difference $\mu_1 - \mu_2$ of the population means by using the t distribution. The quantity

$$\mathbf{y} = \frac{\bar{\mathbf{x}}_1 - \bar{\mathbf{x}}_2 - (\mu_1 - \mu_2)}{\sigma\sqrt{(1/m) + (1/n)}}$$

is normally distributed with zero mean and unit variance so that

$$\mathbf{t} = \frac{\mathbf{y}}{\sqrt{\mathbf{v}/(m + n - 2)}}$$

has the t distribution with $m + n - 2$ degrees of freedom. Since $\mathbf{t}$ does not involve σ^2 but only the parameter $\theta = \mu_1 - \mu_2$, a confidence interval for θ can be obtained. Upper and lower limits, for a 90 per cent confidence interval, for example, would be obtained by solving the equations

$$\mathbf{t} = \pm t_{.05}$$

for θ.

12.9 Tests on the Variance of a Normal Distribution

To test the null hypothesis that the variance of a normal population has a specified value σ_0^2 on the basis of a sample of size n, that is, $H_0: \sigma^2 = \sigma_0^2$ with the alternative $H_a: \sigma^2 \neq \sigma_0^2$, we first maximize

$$L = \left(\frac{1}{2\pi\sigma^2}\right)^{n/2} e^{-\frac{1}{2}\Sigma[(\mathbf{x}_i - \mu)/\sigma]^2} \tag{1}$$

in Ω, which is a two dimensional space, and in ω, which is the line $\sigma^2 = \sigma_0^2$. The ratio of these maxima is readily found to be

$$\lambda = \left(\frac{\mathbf{u}}{n}\right)^{n/2} e^{-\frac{1}{2}(\mathbf{u}-n)} \tag{2}$$

where

$$\mathbf{u} = \sum_1^n \frac{(\mathbf{x}_i - \bar{\mathbf{x}})^2}{\sigma_0^2} \tag{3}$$

Since $\mathbf{u}$ is known to have the chi-square distribution with $n - 1$ degrees of freedom, the distribution of λ could be found by transforming the

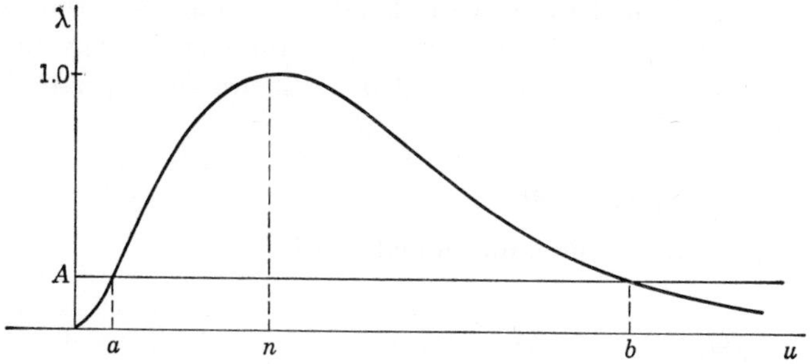

FIG. 12.9

chi-square distribution by (2). The test may, however, be done using $\mathbf{u}$ as a criterion. On plotting equation (2) (Fig. 12.9), it is seen that a critical region for λ of the form $0 < \lambda < A$ corresponds to the pair of intervals $0 < \mathbf{u} < a$ and $b < \mathbf{u} < \infty$ for $\mathbf{u}$, where a and b are such that the ordinates of (2) are equal. Here again if H_a is $\sigma^2 < \sigma_0^2$ or H_a is $\sigma^2 > \sigma_0^2$, the one-tailed tests, $\mathbf{u} < \chi^2_{.95}$ or $\mathbf{u} > \chi^2_{.05}$, would be used.

Equality of Two Variances. Given samples from each of two normal populations with means and variances (μ_1, σ_1^2) and (μ_2, σ_2^2), we may test

$$H_0: \sigma_1^2 = \sigma_2^2 \qquad H_a: \sigma_1^2 \neq \sigma_2^2 \tag{4}$$

The likelihood-ratio is found to be

$$\lambda = \frac{\left\{\dfrac{m+n}{2\pi[\Sigma(\mathbf{x}_{1i}-\bar{\mathbf{x}}_1)^2 + \Sigma(\mathbf{x}_{2j}-\bar{\mathbf{x}}_2)^2]}\right\}^{(m+n)/2}}{\left[\dfrac{m}{2\pi\Sigma(\mathbf{x}_{1i}-\bar{\mathbf{x}}_1)^2}\right]^{m/2}\left[\dfrac{n}{2\pi\Sigma(\mathbf{x}_{2j}-\bar{\mathbf{x}}_2)^2}\right]^{n/2}} \tag{5}$$

where the notation is the same as that of the preceding section. This criterion may be put in the form

$$\lambda = \frac{(m+n)^{(m+n)/2}}{m^{m/2}n^{n/2}} \frac{\left(\dfrac{m-1}{n-1}\mathbf{F}\right)^{m/2}}{\left(1+\dfrac{m-1}{n-1}\mathbf{F}\right)^{(m+n)/2}} \tag{6}$$

where $\mathbf{F}$ is the variance ratio:

$$\mathbf{F} = \frac{(n-1)\Sigma(\mathbf{x}_{1i}-\bar{\mathbf{x}}_1)^2}{(m-1)\Sigma(\mathbf{x}_{2j}-\bar{\mathbf{x}}_2)^2} \tag{7}$$

which has the F distribution with $m-1$ and $n-1$ degrees of freedom when H_0 is true. On plotting λ as a function of $\mathbf{F}$, it is apparent that the critical region $0 < \lambda < A$ corresponds to a two-tailed test on $\mathbf{F}$. It is customary to make the two tails have equal areas (although this is not quite the best test) because the tabulations of F make this region easy to determine. Again one-tailed tests are appropriate if H_a is $\sigma_1^2 < \sigma_2^2$ or $H_a\colon \sigma_2^2 < \sigma_1^2$.

12.10 The Goodness-of-fit Test

If a population has the multinomial density

$$f(x_i; p_i) = \prod_{i=1}^{k} p_i^{x_i} \qquad x_i = 0, 1; \Sigma x_i = 1; \Sigma p_i = 1 \tag{1}$$

as would be the case in sampling with replacement from a population of individuals who could be classified into k classes, a common problem is that of testing whether the probabilities have specified numerical values. Thus the result of casting a die may be classified into one of six classes. On the basis of a sample of observations, we may wish to test whether the die is true, i.e., whether

$$p_i = \tfrac{1}{6} \qquad i = 1, 2, \cdots, 6$$

Let us suppose that n observations are drawn from a population with distribution (1) and that the number of observations that fall in the

ith class is $\mathbf{n}_i(\Sigma \mathbf{n}_i = n)$. The likelihood of the sample is

$$L = \prod_1^k p_i^{\mathbf{n}_i} \tag{2}$$

and we shall test the null hypothesis

$$H_0 \colon p_i = p_{0i}$$

where the p_{0i} are given numbers. The parameter space Ω has $k - 1$ dimensions (given $k - 1$ of the p_i, the remaining one is determined by $\Sigma p_i = 1$), while ω is a point. It is readily found that L is maximized in Ω when

$$\hat{\mathbf{p}}_i = \frac{\mathbf{n}_i}{n} \tag{3}$$

Hence

$$L(\hat{\Omega}) = \frac{1}{n^n} \prod_1^k \mathbf{n}_i^{\mathbf{n}_i} \tag{4}$$

In ω the maximum value of L is its only value

$$L(\hat{\omega}) = \prod_1^k p_{0i}^{\mathbf{n}_i} \tag{5}$$

The likelihood-ratio is

$$\lambda = n^n \prod_1^k \left(\frac{p_{0i}}{\mathbf{n}_i} \right)^{\mathbf{n}_i} \tag{6}$$

and the critical region is $0 < \lambda < A$, where A is chosen to give the desired probability of a Type I error. For small n, the distribution of λ may be tabulated directly in order to determine A; for large values of n, we may use the fact that $-2 \log \lambda$ has approximately the chi-square distribution with $k - 1$ degrees of freedom. The chi-square approximation is surprisingly good even if n is small, provided that $k > 2$.

Another test commonly used for testing H_0 was proposed (by Karl Pearson) before the general theory of testing hypotheses was developed. This test criterion is

$$\mathbf{u} = \sum \frac{(\mathbf{n}_i - np_{0i})^2}{np_{0i}} \tag{7}$$

which in large samples has approximately the chi-square distribution with $k - 1$ degrees of freedom when H_0 is true. The argument for using (7) as a criterion is briefly this: The approximate large-sample distribution of the $\hat{\mathbf{p}}_i = \mathbf{n}_i/n$ $(i = 1, 2, \cdots, k-1)$ is normal and is in fact

$$f(\hat{p}_1, \hat{p}_2, \cdots, \hat{p}_{k-1}) = \left(\frac{n}{2\pi}\right)^{\frac{k-1}{2}} \sqrt{\frac{1}{\prod_1^k p_i}}\, e^{-\frac{1}{2}\Sigma\Sigma n\left(\frac{\delta_{ij}}{p_i}+\frac{1}{p_k}\right)(\hat{p}_i - p_i)(\hat{p}_j - p_j)} \tag{8}$$

as follows from equation (10.8.18) on replacing k by $k - 1$. We have seen in Chap. 10 that the quadratic form of a multivariate normal distribution in $k - 1$ variates has the chi-square distribution with $k - 1$ degrees of freedom; hence

$$\mathbf{v} = \sum_1^{k-1} \sum_1^{k-1} n\left(\frac{\delta_{ij}}{p_i} + \frac{1}{p_k}\right)(\hat{\mathbf{p}}_i - p_i)(\hat{\mathbf{p}}_j - p_j) \tag{9}$$

has approximately that distribution for large samples. On summing (9) with respect to j and remembering that

$$p_k = 1 - \sum_1^{k-1} p_i$$

we find

$$\mathbf{v} = \sum_{i=1}^{k} \frac{n(\hat{\mathbf{p}}_i - p_i)^2}{p_i} \tag{10}$$

or

$$\mathbf{v} = \sum_1^k \frac{(\mathbf{n}_i - np_i)^2}{np_i} \tag{11}$$

which is the same as (7) if the true values of the p_i are p_{0i}. But let us suppose that the true p_i are p_{1i}, at least some of which are different from p_{0i}; then

$$\mathbf{v} = \sum \frac{(\mathbf{n}_i - np_{1i})^2}{np_{1i}} \tag{12}$$

has approximately the chi-square distribution with expected value $k - 1$. The quantity

$$\mathbf{u} = \sum \frac{(\mathbf{n}_i - np_{0i})^2}{np_{0i}} \tag{13}$$

is easily shown to have an expected value

$$E(\mathbf{u}) = \sum \frac{1}{np_{0i}} [np_{1i}(1 - p_{1i}) + n^2(p_{1i} - p_{0i})^2] \tag{14}$$

which is certainly larger than $k - 1$ for sufficiently large n and, in fact, is larger than $k - 1$ for any n, because if $E(\mathbf{u})$ is minimized with respect to the p_{0i}, it is found that the minimum occurs when $p_{0i} = p_{1i}$ and is therefore $k - 1$. The argument for using $\mathbf{u}$ as a test criterion is now evident. If the true p_i are p_{0i}, $\mathbf{u}$ will have the chi-square distribution approximately, while if the true p_i are not p_{0i}, $\mathbf{u}$ will be distributed with a larger mean value, and that mean value becomes infinite as n becomes infinite. Hence it is reasonable to test H_0 by using $\mathbf{u}$ as a criterion and the right-hand tail of the distribution as the critical region.

We have discussed Pearson's chi-square criterion because of its historical interest and because it is still commonly used to test H_0. It is, in fact, equivalent to the likelihood-ratio test in large samples. Perhaps the easiest way to show this is to write λ in the form

$$\boldsymbol{\lambda} = K \frac{n!}{\Pi \mathbf{n}_i!} \prod p_{0i}^{\mathbf{n}_i}$$

where

$$K = \frac{n^n}{\Pi \mathbf{n}_i^{\mathbf{n}_i}} \frac{\Pi \mathbf{n}_j!}{n!}$$

If the variates of (8) are changed from $\hat{\mathbf{p}}_i$ to $\mathbf{n}_i$, the function will be unchanged except for the change in $n^{(k-1)/2}$ since $n\, d\hat{p}_i = dn_i$. It follows from Sec. 10.8 that $\lambda n^{k-1}/K$ approaches (8). By using Stirling's formula (in Chap. 2) for the factorials in K, it can be shown that K/n^{k-1} just cancels the coefficient of the exponential in (8) to within terms of order $1/\sqrt{n}$; hence $-2 \log \lambda$ is asymptotically equivalent to $\mathbf{u}$.

12.11 Tests of Independence in Contingency Tables

A contingency table is a multiple classification. Thus in a public-opinion survey the individuals interviewed may be classified according to their attitude on a political proposal and according to sex, to obtain a table of the form:

	Favor	Oppose	Undecided
Men	1154	475	243
Women	1083	442	362

This is a 2×3 contingency table. The individuals are classified by two criteria, one having two categories and the other three categories. The six distinct classifications are called *cells*. A three-way contingency table would have been obtained had the individuals been further classified according to a third criterion, say according to annual income group. If there were five income groups set up (such as: under \$1000, \$1000 to \$3000, $\cdots$), the contingency table would be called a $2 \times 3 \times 5$ table and would have 30 cells into which a person might be put. It is often quite convenient to think of the cells as cubes in a block two units wide, three units long, and five units deep. If the individuals were still further classified into eight geographical locations, one would have a four-way ($2 \times 3 \times 5 \times 8$) contingency table with 240 cells in a four-dimensional block with edges 2, 3, 5, and 8 units long. The contingency table provides a technique for investigating suspected relationships. Thus one may suspect that men and women will react differently to a certain political proposal, in which case he would construct such a table as the one above and test the null hypothesis that their attitudes were independent of their sex. To consider another example, a geneticist may suspect that susceptibility to a certain disease is heritable. He would classify a sample of individuals according to (1) whether or not they ever had the disease, (2) whether or not their fathers had the disease, (3) whether or not their mothers had the disease. In the resulting $2 \times 2 \times 2$ contingency table he would test the null hypothesis that classification 1 was independent of 2 and 3. Again a medical research worker might suspect a certain environmental condition favored a given disease and classify individuals according to (1) whether or not they ever had the disease, (2) whether or not they were subject to the condition. An industrial engineer would use a contingency table to discover whether or not two kinds of defects in a manufactured product were due to the same underlying cause or to different causes. It is apparent that the technique can be a very useful tool in any field of research.

Two-way Contingency Tables. We shall suppose that n individuals or items are classified according to two criteria A and B, that there are r classifications $A_1, A_2, \cdots, A_r$ in A and s classifications $B_1, B_2, \cdots, B_s$ in B, and that the number of individuals belonging to A_i and B_j is $\mathbf{n}_{ij}$. We have then an $r \times s$ contingency table with cell frequencies $\mathbf{n}_{ij}$ and $\Sigma \mathbf{n}_{ij} = n$.

	B_1	B_2	B_3	$\cdots$	B_s
A_1	$\mathbf{n}_{11}$	$\mathbf{n}_{12}$	$\mathbf{n}_{13}$	$\cdots$	$\mathbf{n}_{1s}$
A_2	$\mathbf{n}_{21}$	$\mathbf{n}_{22}$	$\mathbf{n}_{23}$	$\cdots$	$\mathbf{n}_{2s}$
A_3	$\mathbf{n}_{31}$	$\mathbf{n}_{32}$	$\mathbf{n}_{33}$	$\cdots$	$\mathbf{n}_{3s}$
$\vdots$					
A_r	$\mathbf{n}_{r1}$	$\mathbf{n}_{r2}$	$\mathbf{n}_{r3}$	$\cdots$	$\mathbf{n}_{rs}$

(1)

As a further notation we shall denote the row totals by $\mathbf{n}_{i.}$ and the column totals by $\mathbf{n}_{.j}$,

$$\mathbf{n}_{i.} = \sum_j \mathbf{n}_{ij} \qquad \mathbf{n}_{.j} = \sum_i \mathbf{n}_{ij}$$

Of course

$$\sum_i \mathbf{n}_{i.} = \sum_j \mathbf{n}_{.j} = n$$

We shall now set up a probability model for the problem with which we wish to deal. The n individuals will be regarded as a sample of size n from a multinomial population with probabilities p_{ij} ($i = 1, 2, \cdots, r; j = 1, 2, \cdots, s$). The probability distribution for a single observation is (Sec. 10.8)

$$f(x_{11}, x_{12}, \cdots, x_{rs}) = \prod_{ij} p_{ij}^{x_{ij}} \qquad x_{ij} = 0, 1; \sum_{i,j} x_{ij} = 1 \tag{2}$$

We wish to test the null hypothesis that the A and B classifications are independent, i.e., that the probability that an individual falls in B_j is not affected by the A class to which the individual happens to belong. Using the symbolism of Chap. 2, we would write

$$P(B_j|A_i) = P(B_j) \qquad P(A_i|B_j) = P(A_i)$$

or

$$P(A_i, B_j) = P(A_i)P(B_j)$$

If we denote the marginal probabilities $P(A_i)$ by p_i ($i = 1, 2, \cdots, r$) and the marginal probabilities $P(B_j)$ by q_j, the null hypothesis is simply

$$H_0: p_{ij} = p_i q_j \qquad \Sigma p_i = 1, \Sigma q_j = 1 \tag{3}$$

When the null hypothesis is not true, there is said to be *interaction* between the two criteria of classification.

The complete parameter space Ω for the distribution (1) has $rs - 1$ dimensions (having specified all but one of the p_{ij}, the remaining one is fixed by $\sum_{ij} p_{ij} = 1$), while under H_0 we have a parameter space ω with $r - 1 + s - 1$ dimensions. The likelihood for a sample of size n is

$$L = \prod_{ij} p_{ij}^{\mathbf{n}_{ij}} \tag{4}$$

and its maximum in Ω occurs when

$$\hat{\mathbf{p}}_{ij} = \frac{\mathbf{n}_{ij}}{n} \tag{5}$$

In ω,

$$L = \prod_{ij} (p_i q_j)^{\mathbf{n}_{ij}} = \left(\prod_i p_i^{\mathbf{n}_{i.}}\right)\left(\prod_j q_j^{\mathbf{n}_{.j}}\right) \tag{6}$$

and its maximum occurs at

$$\hat{\mathbf{p}}_i = \frac{\mathbf{n}_{i.}}{n} \qquad \hat{\mathbf{q}}_j = \frac{\mathbf{n}_{.j}}{n} \tag{7}$$

The likelihood-ratio is therefore

$$\boldsymbol{\lambda} = \frac{\left(\prod_i \mathbf{n}_{i.}^{\mathbf{n}_{i.}}\right)\left(\prod_j \mathbf{n}_{.j}^{\mathbf{n}_{.j}}\right)}{n^n \prod_{i,j} \mathbf{n}_{ij}^{\mathbf{n}_{ij}}} \tag{8}$$

The distribution of $\boldsymbol{\lambda}$ under the null hypothesis is not unique because the hypothesis is composite and the exact distribution of $\boldsymbol{\lambda}$ does involve the unknown parameters p_i and q_j. For large samples we do have a test, however, because $-2 \log \boldsymbol{\lambda}$ is, in that case, approximately distributed as a chi square with

$$rs - 1 - (r + s - 2) = (r - 1)(s - 1)$$

degrees of freedom, and on the basis of this distribution a unique critical region for $\boldsymbol{\lambda}$ may be determined.

In casting about for a test which may be used when the sample is not large, we may inquire how it is that a test criterion comes to have a unique distribution for large samples when the distribution actually depends on unknown parameters which may have any values in certain ranges. The answer is that the parameters are not really unknown; they can be estimated, and their estimates approach their true values as the sample size increases. In the limit as n becomes infinite the parameters are known exactly, and it is at that point that the distribution of $\boldsymbol{\lambda}$ actually becomes unique. It is unique because a particular point in ω is selected as the true parameter point, so that the $\mathbf{n}_{ij}$ are given a unique distribution, and the distribution of $\boldsymbol{\lambda}$ is then determined by this distribution.

It would appear reasonable to employ a similar procedure to set up a test for small samples, i.e., to define a distribution for $\boldsymbol{\lambda}$ by using the estimates for the unknown parameters. In the present problem, since the estimates of the p_i and q_j are given by (7), we might just substitute those values in the distribution function of the $\mathbf{n}_{ij}$ and use that distribution to obtain a distribution for $\boldsymbol{\lambda}$. However we should still be in trouble; the critical region would depend on the marginal totals $\mathbf{n}_{i.}$

and $\mathbf{n}_{.j}$; hence the probability of a Type I error would vary from sample to sample for any fixed critical region $0 < \lambda < A$.

There is a way out of this difficulty which is well worth investigation because of its own interest and because the problem is important in applied statistics. Let us denote the joint density of all the $\mathbf{n}_{ij}$ briefly by $f(n_{ij})$, the marginal density of all the $\mathbf{n}_{i.}$ and $\mathbf{n}_{.j}$ by $g(n_{i.}, n_{.j})$, and the conditional density of the $\mathbf{n}_{ij}$, given the marginal totals, by

$$f(n_{ij}|n_{i.}, n_{.j}) = \frac{f(n_{ij})}{g(n_{i.}, n_{.j})}$$

Under the null hypothesis, this conditional distribution happens to be independent of the unknown parameters (as we shall show presently); the estimators $\mathbf{n}_{i.}/n$ and $\mathbf{n}_{.j}/n$ form a sufficient set of statistics for the p_i and q_j. This fact will enable us to construct a test.

The joint density of the $\mathbf{n}_{ij}$ is simply the multinomial

$$f(n_{11}, n_{12}, \cdots, n_{rs}) = \frac{n!}{\prod\limits_{ij} n_{ij}!} \prod_{ij} p_{ij}^{n_{ij}} \tag{9}$$

in Ω, and in ω (we are interested in the distribution of λ under H_0) this becomes

$$f(n_{11}, n_{12}, \cdots, n_{rs}) = \frac{n!}{\prod\limits_{ij} n_{ij}!} \left(\prod_i p_i^{n_{i.}}\right)\left(\prod_j q_j^{n_{.j}}\right) \tag{10}$$

To obtain the desired conditional distribution, we must first find the distribution of the $\mathbf{n}_{i.}$ and $\mathbf{n}_{.j}$, and this is accomplished by summing (10) over all sets of n_{ij} such that

$$\sum_i n_{ij} = n_{.j} \qquad \sum_j n_{ij} = n_{i.} \tag{11}$$

For fixed marginal totals, only the factor $1/\Pi n_{ij}!$ in (10) is involved in the sum, so that we have in effect to sum that factor over all n_{ij} subject to (11). The desired sum is given by comparing the coefficients of $\prod\limits_i x_i^{n_{i.}}$ in the expression

$$(x_1 + \cdots + x_r)^{n_{.1}}(x_1 + \cdots + x_r)^{n_{.2}} \cdots (x_1 + \cdots + x_r)^{n_{.s}} = (x_1 + \cdots + x_r)^n \tag{12}$$

On the right the coefficient of $\Pi x_i^{n_{i.}}$ is simply

$$\frac{n!}{\prod\limits_i n_{i.}!} \tag{13}$$

On the left there are terms with coefficients of the form

$$\frac{n_{.1}!}{\prod_i n_{i1}!}\,\frac{n_{.2}!}{\prod_i n_{i2}!}\,\cdots\,\frac{n_{.s}!}{\prod_i n_{is}!} = \frac{\prod_j n_{.j}!}{\prod_{ij} n_{ij}!} \tag{14}$$

where n_{ij} is the exponent of x_i in the jth multinomial. In this expression the n_{ij} satisfy conditions (11); the first condition is satisfied in view of the multinomial theorem, while the second is satisfied because we require the exponent of x_i in these terms to be $n_{i.}$. The sum of all such coefficients (14) must equal (13); hence we may write

$$\sum \frac{1}{\Pi n_{ij}!} = \frac{n!}{\prod_i n_{i.}! \prod_j n_{.j}!} \tag{15}$$

This is precisely the sum that we require, because there is obviously one and only one coefficient of the form of (14) on the left of (12) for every possible contingency table (1) with given marginal totals. The distribution of the $\mathbf{n}_{i.}$ and $\mathbf{n}_{.j}$ is, therefore,

$$g(n_{i.}, n_{.j}) = \frac{(n!)^2}{(\Pi n_{i.}!)(\Pi n_{.j}!)} \left(\prod p_i^{n_{i.}}\right)\left(\prod q_j^{n_{.j}}\right) \tag{16}$$

which shows incidentally that the $\mathbf{n}_{i.}$ are distributed independently of the $\mathbf{n}_{.j}$; this is unexpected because $\mathbf{n}_{1.}$ and $\mathbf{n}_{.1}$, for example, have the variate $\mathbf{n}_{11}$ in common.

The conditional distribution of the $\mathbf{n}_{ij}$, given the marginal totals, is obtained by dividing (10) by (16) to obtain

$$f(n_{11}, n_{12}, \cdots, n_{rs} | n_{1.}, n_{2.}, \cdots, n_{.s}) = \frac{(\Pi n_{i.}!)(\Pi n_{.j}!)}{n!\Pi n_{ij}!} \tag{17}$$

which, happily, does not involve the unknown parameters and shows that the estimators are sufficient.

To see how a test may be constructed, let us consider the general situation in which a criterion $\boldsymbol{\lambda}$ for some test has a distribution $u(\lambda; \theta)$ which involves an unknown parameter θ. If θ has a sufficient statistic $\hat{\boldsymbol{\theta}}$, then the joint density of $\boldsymbol{\lambda}$ and $\hat{\boldsymbol{\theta}}$ may be written

$$v(\lambda, \hat{\theta}; \theta) = v_1(\lambda|\hat{\theta})v_2(\hat{\theta}; \theta) \tag{18}$$

and the conditional density of $\boldsymbol{\lambda}$, given $\hat{\boldsymbol{\theta}}$, will not involve θ. Using the conditional distribution, we may find a number $A(\hat{\theta})$ for every $\hat{\theta}$ such that

$$\int_0^{A(\hat{\theta})} v_1(\lambda|\hat{\theta})\, d\lambda = .05$$

for example. In the $\lambda\hat{\theta}$ plane the curve $\lambda = A(\hat{\theta})$ together with the line $\lambda = 0$ will determine a region R. See Fig. 12.10. The probability that a sample will give rise to a pair of values $(\lambda, \hat{\theta})$ which correspond to a point in R is exactly .05 because

$$\begin{aligned} P[(\boldsymbol{\lambda}, \hat{\boldsymbol{\theta}}) \text{ in } R] &= \int_{-\infty}^{\infty} \int_0^{A(\hat{\theta})} v(\lambda, \hat{\theta}; \theta)\, d\lambda\, d\hat{\theta} \\ &= \int_{-\infty}^{\infty} \left[\int_0^{A(\hat{\theta})} v_1(\lambda|\hat{\theta})\, d\lambda\right] v_2(\hat{\theta}; \theta)\, d\hat{\theta} \\ &= \int_{-\infty}^{\infty} .05 v_2(\hat{\theta}; \theta)\, d\hat{\theta} \\ &= .05 \end{aligned} \tag{19}$$

Hence we may test the hypothesis by using $\hat{\boldsymbol{\theta}}$ in conjunction with $\boldsymbol{\lambda}$. The critical region is a plane region instead of an interval $0 < \boldsymbol{\lambda} < A$;

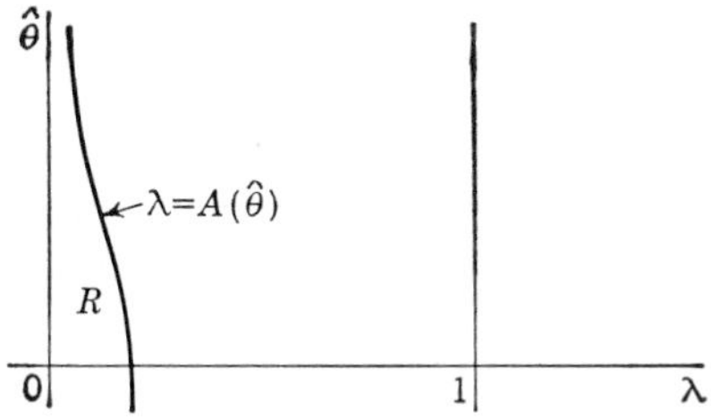

FIG. 12.10

it is such a region that, whatever the unknown value of θ may be, the Type I error has a specified probability. The test in any given situation actually amounts to a conditional test; we observe $\hat{\boldsymbol{\theta}}$ and test $\boldsymbol{\lambda}$ by an interval $0 < \boldsymbol{\lambda} < A(\hat{\boldsymbol{\theta}})$ using the conditional distribution of $\boldsymbol{\lambda}$, given $\hat{\boldsymbol{\theta}}$. It is to be observed that this device cannot be employed unless θ has a sufficient statistic.

The above technique is obviously applicable when θ is a set of parameters rather than a single parameter and has a set of sufficient statistics. In particular, the technique may be employed to test the criterion (8) for the null hypothesis of a two-way contingency table. One merely uses the conditional distribution (17) and determines an interval $0 < \boldsymbol{\lambda} < A(\mathbf{n}_{i.}; \mathbf{n}_{.j})$ which has the desired probability of a Type I error for the observed marginal totals.

In applications of this test one is confronted with a very tedious computation in determining the distribution of $\boldsymbol{\lambda}$ unless r, s, and the marginal totals are quite small. It can be shown, however, that the large-sample approximation may be used without appreciable error except when both r and s equal 2. In the latter instance, other simplifying approximations have been developed (see, for example, Fisher and Yates, "Tables for Statisticians and Biometricians," Oliver & Boyd, Ltd.,

Edinburgh and London, 1938), but we shall not explore the problem that far.

If the distribution (17) is replaced by its multivariate normal approximation, it can be shown that the criterion

$$\mathbf{u} = \sum_{i,j} \frac{[\mathbf{n}_{ij} - (\mathbf{n}_{i.}\mathbf{n}_{.j}/n)]^2}{\mathbf{n}_{i.}\mathbf{n}_{.j}/n} \tag{20}$$

has approximately the chi-square distribution with $(r - 1)(s - 1)$ degrees of freedom and is a reasonable criterion for testing H_0 of (3). This is the criterion first proposed (by Karl Pearson) for testing the hypothesis, and it differs from $-2 \log \lambda$ by terms of order $1/\sqrt{n}$. The two criteria are therefore essentially equivalent unless n is small. The argument that $\mathbf{u}$ is a reasonable criterion is entirely analogous to that used to justify (12.10.7).

Three-way Contingency Tables. If the elements of a population can be classified according to three criteria A, B, C with classifications A_i $(i = 1, 2, \cdots, s_1)$, B_j $(j = 1, 2, \cdots, s_2)$, and C_k $(k = 1, 2, \cdots, s_3)$, a sample of n individuals may be classified in a three-way $s_1 \times s_2 \times s_3$ contingency table. We shall let p_{ijk} represent the probabilities associated with the individual cells, $\mathbf{n}_{ijk}$ be the numbers of sample elements in the individual cells, and, as before, marginal totals will be indicated by replacing the summed index by a dot; thus

$$\mathbf{n}_{i.k} = \sum_{j=1}^{s_2} \mathbf{n}_{ijk} \qquad \mathbf{n}_{..k} = \sum_{i=1}^{s_1} \sum_{j=1}^{s_2} \mathbf{n}_{ijk} \tag{21}$$

There are four hypotheses that may be tested in connection with this table. We may test whether all three criteria are mutually independent, in which case the null hypothesis is

$$p_{ijk} = p_i q_j r_k \tag{22}$$

or we may test whether any one of the three criteria is independent of the other two. Thus to test whether the B classification was independent of A and C, we would set up the null hypothesis

$$p_{ijk} = p_{ik} q_j \tag{23}$$

The procedure for testing these hypotheses is entirely analogous to that for the two-way tables. The likelihood of the sample is

$$L = \prod_{ijk} p_{ijk}^{\mathbf{n}_{ijk}} \qquad \sum_{ijk} p_{ijk} = 1 \qquad \sum_{ijk} \mathbf{n}_{ijk} = n \tag{24}$$

In Ω the maximum of L occurs when

$$\hat{\mathbf{p}}_{ijk} = \frac{\mathbf{n}_{ijk}}{n} \tag{25}$$

so that

$$L(\hat{\Omega}) = \frac{1}{n^n} \prod_{ijk} \mathbf{n}_{ijk}^{\mathbf{n}_{ijk}} \tag{26}$$

To test (23), for example, we would make the substitution (23) in (24) and maximize L with respect to the $p_{ik}q_j$ to find

$$\hat{\mathbf{p}}_{ik} = \frac{\mathbf{n}_{i.k}}{n} \qquad \hat{\mathbf{q}}_j = \frac{\mathbf{n}_{.j.}}{n} \tag{27}$$

and

$$L(\hat{\omega}) = \frac{1}{n^{2n}} \left(\prod_{ik} \mathbf{n}_{i.k}^{\mathbf{n}_{i.k}}\right) \left(\prod_{j} \mathbf{n}_{.j.}^{\mathbf{n}_{.j.}}\right) \tag{28}$$

The likelihood-ratio λ is given by the quotient of (28) and (26), and in large samples $-2 \log \lambda$ has the chi-square distribution with

$$s_1s_2s_3 - 1 - [(s_1s_3 - 1) + s_2 - 1] = (s_1s_3 - 1)(s_2 - 1)$$

degrees of freedom. Again the large-sample distribution is quite adequate for many purposes.

12.12 Problems

1. The random variable $\mathbf{x}$ is distributed normally with mean μ and variance 1. It is desired to test H_1: $\mu = 6$ with the alternative hypothesis H_2: $\mu = 7$. Formulate this problem as a two-action decision problem and define the action space.

2. In Prob. 1, define the parameter space.

3. A random sample of size 3 is taken from the density in Prob. 1. Define a decision function for this problem.

4. In Prob. 3, can $|\bar{\mathbf{x}}|$ be a loss function for the problem? Give reasons. Can $(\bar{\mathbf{x}} - \mu)$ be a loss function? Give reasons.

5. In Prob. 1, d is a decision function, where d is as follows ($\bar{\mathbf{x}}$ is based on a random sample of size 4):

Take action a_1, that is, accept H_1, if $\bar{\mathbf{x}} < 7$
Take action a_2, that is, accept H_2, if $\bar{\mathbf{x}} \geq 7$

Find $P(\text{I})$, $P(\text{II})$.

6. Give the action probabilities for Prob. 5.

7. Give the error probabilities for Prob. 5.

8. A loss function for Prob. 1 is (action a_1 is the statement "accept H_1," and action a_2 is the statement "accept H_2"):

$$l(a_1; \mu = 6) = 0 \qquad l(a_2; \mu = 6) = 2$$
$$l(a_1; \mu = 7) = 1 \qquad l(a_2; \mu = 7) = 0$$

Find and plot the risk for the following decision functions ($\mathbf{x}$ is a single observation):

Decision function	Take action a_1 if	Take action a_2 if
d_1	$\mathbf{x} < 6.0$	$\mathbf{x} \geq 6.0$
d_2	$\mathbf{x} < 6.5$	$\mathbf{x} \geq 6.5$
d_3	$\mathbf{x} < 7.0$	$\mathbf{x} \geq 7.0$
d_4	$\mathbf{x} < 7.5$	$\mathbf{x} \geq 7.5$
d_5	$\mathbf{x} > 6.5$	$\mathbf{x} \leq 6.5$

9. Are any of the five strategies, d_i, in Prob. 8 dominated by any of the other strategies? If so, which ones?

10. Find and plot the risk in Prob. 8 for the decision function

$$d_c: \quad \text{take action } a_1 \quad \text{if } \mathbf{x} < c$$
$$\qquad \text{take action } a_2 \quad \text{if } \mathbf{x} \geq c$$

as a function of c for $-\infty < c < \infty$.

11. A manufacturer of television sets has a certain inspection system for each set. If it passes inspection it is labeled as the first-class brand and sold at a higher price than the second-class brand, which are those sets that do not pass inspection. Let the action space A be

$$A = \{a : a = a_1 \text{ or } a_2\}$$

where we define a_1: sell as brand 1; a_2: sell as brand 2. The year's production of television sets falls into two distinct classes which we shall label θ_1: superior grade; θ_2: inferior grade. After considering manufacturing and other types of costs, the following loss function is considered adequate for this problem:

$$l(a_1; \theta_1) = 0 \qquad l(a_2; \theta_1) = 3$$
$$l(a_1; \theta_2) = 5 \qquad l(a_2; \theta_2) = 0$$

The inspection system consists of an engineer who examines each set and classifies it as excellent, good, or fair. The probabilities of each classification are

State of nature	Probability of classifying a set as		
	1 (excellent)	2 (good)	3 (fair)
θ_1	$\frac{1}{2}$	$\frac{1}{3}$	$\frac{1}{6}$
θ_2	$\frac{1}{9}$	$\frac{1}{2}$	$\frac{7}{18}$

List the eight available pure strategies for this problem.

12. In Prob. 11, calculate the risk for each pure strategy for each state of nature. Plot these risks.

13. In Prob. 11, let strategy 1 and 2 be, respectively,

	Classification		
	1 (excellent)	2 (good)	3 (fair)
d_1	a_1	a_2	a_2
d_2	a_1	a_1	a_2

If we choose d_1 with probability $\frac{1}{2}$ and d_2 with probability $\frac{1}{2}$, find the risk for the resulting randomized strategy d_g.

14. In Prob. 13, calculate the risk for the randomized strategy d_p, where d_1 is chosen with probability p and d_2 with probability $1 - p$, where $0 \leq p \leq 1$. Plot this risk as a function of p.

15. Let $\mathbf{x}$ be distributed normally with mean μ and variance 1. Suppose that we want to test the hypothesis H_1 against the alternative H_2, where

$$H_1: \mu < 0 \qquad H_2: \mu \geq 0$$

The loss function for this problem is

$$\begin{aligned} l(a_1; \mu) &= 0 && \text{if } \mu < 0 \\ l(a_1; \mu) &= \mu^2 && \text{if } \mu \geq 0 \\ l(a_2; \mu) &= \mu^2 && \text{if } \mu < 0 \\ l(a_2; \mu) &= 0 && \text{if } \mu \geq 0 \end{aligned}$$

where action a_i is the statement "accept hypothesis H_i." Find the risk for each of the two decision functions d_1, d_2, where

d_1: take action a_2 if $\mathbf{x} \geq 2$; take action a_1 if $\mathbf{x} < 2$
d_2: take action a_2 if $\mathbf{x} \geq 3$; take action a_1 if $\mathbf{x} < 3$

16. In Prob. 15, plot the risk for the two decision functions as a function of μ.

17. Given the sample $(-.2, -.9, -.6, .1)$ from a normal population with unit variance, test whether the population mean is less than 0 at the .05 level of significance (i.e., with probability .05 of a Type I error). That is, test H_0: $\mu \leq 0$ at the .05 level relative to H_a: $\mu > 0$.

18. Given the sample $(-4.4, 4.0, 2.0, -4.8)$ from a normal population with variance 4 and the sample $(6.0, 1.0, 3.2, -.4)$ from a normal population with variance 5, test at the .05 level that the means differ by no more than one unit. (Use the method in Sec. 12.5.) Plot the power function for this test. Plot the ideal power function.

19. A metallurgist made four determinations of the melting point of manganese: 1269, 1271, 1263, 1265 degrees centigrade. Test the hypothesis that the mean μ of this population is within five units of the published value of 1260 at the .05 level. (Assume normality and $\sigma^2 = 5$.)

20. Plot the power function for a test of the null hypothesis H_0: $-1 < \mu < 1$ for a normal distribution with known variance, using sample sizes 1, 4, 16, 64. (Use the standard deviation σ as the unit of measurement on the μ axis, and .05 probability of Type I error. Use Sec. 12.5.) Plot the ideal power function.

21. Let $\mathbf{x}_1, \mathbf{x}_2, \cdots, \mathbf{x}_n$ be a random sample of size n from a normal density with known variance. What is the best critical region R for testing the null hypothesis that the mean is 6 against the alternative that the mean is 4?

22. Use Theorem 12.4 for testing H_0: $\sigma^2 < 10$ against H_a: $\sigma^2 \geq 10$ for a sample of size n from a normal population with a mean of 0.

23. In testing between two values, μ_0 and μ_1, for the mean of a normal population, show that the probabilities for both types of error can be made arbitrarily small by taking a sufficiently large sample.

24. A cigarette manufacturer sent each of two laboratories presumably identical samples of tobacco. Each made five determinations of the nicotine content in milligrams as follows: (*a*) 24, 27, 26, 21, 24 and (*b*) 27, 28, 23, 31, 26. Were the two laboratories measuring the same thing? (Assume normality and a common variance.)

25. The metallurgist of Prob. 19, after assessing the magnitude of the various errors that might accrue in his experimental technique, decided that his measurements should have a standard deviation of two degrees or less. Are the data consistent with this supposition at the .05 level? (That is, test H_0: $\sigma \leq 2$.)

26. Test the hypothesis that the two samples of Prob. 18 came from populations with the same variance at the .05 level.

27. The power function for a test that the means of two normal populations are equal depends on the values of the two means, μ_1 and μ_2, and is therefore a surface. But the value of the function depends only on the difference $\theta = \mu_1 - \mu_2$, so that it can be adequately represented by a curve, say $\beta(\theta)$. Plot $\beta(\theta)$ when samples of four are drawn from one population with variance 2, and samples of two are drawn from another population with variance 3 for tests at the .01 level.

28. Given the samples (1.8, 2.9, 1.4, 1.1), (5.0, 8.6, 9.2) from normal populations, test whether the variances are equal at the .05 level.

29. Given a sample of size 100 with $\bar{\mathbf{x}} = 2.7$ and $\Sigma(\mathbf{x}_i - \bar{\mathbf{x}})^2 = 225$, test the null hypothesis:

$$H_0: \mu = 3 \qquad \text{and} \qquad \sigma^2 = 2.5$$

at the .01 level, assuming that the population is normal.

30. Using the sample of Prob. 29, test the hypothesis that $\mu = \sigma^2$ at the .01 level.

31. Using the sample of Prob. 29, test at the .01 level whether the 95 per cent point α of the population distribution is 3 relative to alternatives $\alpha < 3$. The 95 per cent point is the number α such that $\int_{-\infty}^{\alpha} f(x)\,dx = .95$, where $f(x)$ is the population density; it is, of course, $\mu + 1.645\sigma$ in the present instance where the distribution is assumed to be normal.

32. A sample of size n is drawn from each of k normal populations with the same variance. Derive the likelihood-ratio criterion for testing the hypothesis that the means are all 0. Show that the criterion is a function of a ratio which has the F distribution.

33. Derive the likelihood-ratio criterion for testing whether the correlation of a bivariate normal distribution is 0.

34. If $\mathbf{x}_1, \mathbf{x}_2, \cdots, \mathbf{x}_n$ are observations from normal populations with known variances $\sigma_1^2, \sigma_2^2, \cdots, \sigma_n^2$, how would one test whether their means were all equal?

35. A newspaper in a certain city observed that driving conditions were much improved in the city because the number of fatal automobile accidents in the past year was 9, whereas the average number per year over the past several years was 15. Is it possible that conditions were more hazardous than before? Assume that the number of accidents in a given year has a Poisson distribution.

36. Six 1-foot specimens of insulated wire were tested at high voltage for weak spots in the insulation. The numbers of such weak spots were found to be 2, 0, 1, 1, 3, 2. The manufacturer's quality standard states that there are less than 120 such defects per 100 feet. Is the batch from which these specimens were taken worse than the standard at the .05 level of significance? (Use the Poisson distribution.)

37. A psychiatrist newly employed by a medical clinic remarked at a staff meeting that about 40 per cent of all chronic headaches were of the psychosomatic variety. His disbelieving colleagues mixed some pills of plain flour and water, giving them to all such patients on the clinic's rolls with the story that they were a new headache remedy and asking for comments. When the comments were all in, they could be fairly accurately classified as follows: (1) better than aspirin, 8; (2) about the same as aspirin, 3; (3) slower than aspirin, 1; (4) worthless, 29. While the doctors were somewhat surprised by these results, they nevertheless accused the psychiatrist of exaggeration. Did they have good grounds?

38. A die was cast 300 times with the following results:

Occurrence	1	2	3	4	5	6
Frequency	43	49	56	45	66	41

Are the data consistent at the .05 level with the hypothesis that the die is true?

39. Of 64 offspring of a certain cross between guinea pigs, 34 were red, 10 were black, 20 were white. According to the genetic model, these numbers should be in the ratio 9:3:4. Are the data consistent with the model at the .05 level?

40. A prominent baseball player's batting average dropped from .313 in one year to .280 in the following year. He was at bat 374 times during the first year and 268 times during the second. Is the hypothesis tenable at the .05 level that his hitting ability was the same during the two years?

41. Find the mean and variance of $\mathbf{n}_{ij}$ in the conditional distribution (12.11.17).

42. Show that the expected value of $\mathbf{u}$ defined by (12.11.20) is $[n(r-1)(s-1)]/(n-1)$ under the conditional distribution (12.11.17).

43. Using the data of Prob. 40, assume that one has a sample of 374 from one binomial population and 268 from another. Derive the λ criterion for testing whether the probability of a hit is the same for the two populations. How does this test compare with the ordinary test for a 2×2 contingency table?

44. The progeny of a certain mating were classified by a physical attribute into three groups, the numbers being 10, 53, 46. According to a genetic model the frequencies should be in the ratios $p^2:2p(1-p):(1-p)^2$. Are the data consistent with the model at the .05 level?

45. A thousand individuals were classified according to sex and according to whether or not they were color-blind as follows:

	Male	Female
Normal	442	514
Color-blind	38	6

According to the genetic model these numbers should have relative frequencies given by

$$\begin{array}{cc} \dfrac{p}{2} & \dfrac{p^2}{2} + pq \\[2ex] \dfrac{q}{2} & \dfrac{q^2}{2} \end{array}$$

where $q = 1 - p$ is the proportion of defective genes in the population. Are the data consistent with the model?

46. Treating the table of Prob. 45 as a 2×2 contingency table, test the hypothesis that color blindness is independent of sex.

47. Gilby classified 1725 school children according to intelligence and apparent family economic level. A condensed classification follows:

	Dull	Intelligent	Very capable
Very well clothed.......	81	322	233
Well clothed...........	141	457	153
Poorly clothed.........	127	163	48

Test for independence at the .01 level.

48. A serum supposed to have some effect in preventing colds was tested on 500 individuals, and their records for 1 year were compared with the records of 500 untreated individuals as follows:

	No colds	One cold	More than one cold
Treated.............	252	145	103
Untreated...........	224	136	140

Test at the .05 level whether the two trinomial populations may be regarded as the same.

49. Derive the general λ criterion for testing for independence in an $r \times s$ table when one set of marginal totals (the row totals, for example) are fixed in advance as in Prob. 48. Each row is regarded as a sample from an s-fold multinomial population with probabilities p_{ij} such that $\sum_j p_{ij} = 1$ for all i. The hypothesis of independence becomes: $p_{1j} = p_{2j} = p_{3j} = \cdots = p_{rj}$ for all j. How many degrees of freedom does $-2 \log \lambda$ have?

50. According to the genetic model the proportion of individuals having the four blood types should be given by:

$$\begin{aligned} \text{O}&: q^2 \\ \text{A}&: p^2 + 2pq \\ \text{B}&: r^2 + 2qr \\ \text{AB}&: 2pr \end{aligned}$$

where $p + q + r = 1$. Given the sample: O, 374; A, 436; B, 132; AB, 58; how would you test the correctness of the model?

51. Given cell frequencies $\mathbf{n}_{ijk}$ $(i = 1, 2, \cdots, r; j = 1, 2, \cdots, s; k = 1, 2, \cdots, t)$ in a three-way classification, derive the criterion for testing whether all three criteria of classification are independent. How many degrees of freedom does $-2 \log \lambda$ have?

52. Galton investigated 78 families, classifying children according to whether or not they were light-eyed, whether or not they had a light-eyed parent, whether or not they had a light-eyed grandparent. The following $2 \times 2 \times 2$ table resulted:

		Grandparent			
		Light		Not	
		Parent			
		Light	Not	Light	Not
Child	Light	1928	552	596	508
	Not	303	395	225	501

Test for complete independence at the .01 level. Test whether the child classification is independent of the other two classifications at the .01 level.

53. Derive the λ criterion for testing whether the i classification is independent of the jk classification in a three-way contingency table when the marginal totals $\mathbf{n}_{i..}$ are fixed in advance. The probabilities satisfy the relations $\sum_{jk} p_{ijk} = 1$ for all i, and the null hypothesis is

$$p_{1jk} = p_{2jk} = \cdots = p_{rjk} \qquad \text{or simply} \qquad p_{ijk} = p_{jk}$$

How many degrees of freedom does $-2 \log \lambda$ have?

54. Derive the test for complete independence in the situation described in Prob. 53. The null hypothesis is $p_{ijk} = p_j q_k$. How many degrees of freedom does $-2 \log \lambda$ have? How does this test compare with that for the case in which the $n_{i..}$ are not fixed in advance?

55. Compute the exact distribution of λ for a 2×2 contingency table with marginal totals $n_{1.} = 4$; $n_{2.} = 7$; $n_{.1} = 6$; $n_{.2} = 5$. What is the exact probability that $-2 \log \lambda$ exceeds 3.84, the .05 level of chi square for one degree of freedom?

12.13 Bibliography

1. Blackwell, D., and M. A. Girschick: "Theory of Games and Statistical Decisions," John Wiley & Sons, Inc., New York, 1954.
2. Chernoff, H., and L. E. Moses: "Elementary Decision Theory," John Wiley & Sons, Inc., New York, 1959.
3. Fisher, R. A.: "On the mathematical foundations of theoretical statistics," *Philosophical Transactions of the Royal Society, London,* Series A, Vol. 222(1922), pp. 309–368.
4. Fraser, D.A.S.: "Nonparametric Methods in Statistics," John Wiley & Sons, Inc., New York, 1957.
5. Kendall, M. G.: "The Advanced Theory of Statistics," Vol. 2, Charles Griffin & Co., Ltd., London, 1946.
6. Lehmann, E. L.: "On families of admissible tests," *Annals of Mathematical Statistics,* Vol. 18(1947), pp. 97–104.
7. Lehmann, E. L.: "Some principles of the theory of hypothesis testing," *Annals of Mathematical Statistics,* Vol. 21(1950), pp. 1–26.
8. Lehmann, E. L.: "A general concept of unbiasedness," *Annals of Mathematical Statistics,* Vol. 22(1951), pp. 587–597.
9. Lehmann, E. L.: "Ordered families of distributions," *Annals of Mathematical Statistics,* Vol. 26(1955), pp. 399–419.
10. Lehmann, E. L.: "Testing Statistical Hypotheses," John Wiley & Sons, Inc., New York, 1959.
11. Neyman, J., and E. S. Pearson: "On the use and interpretation of certain test criteria for purposes of statistical inference," *Biometrika,* Vol. 20A(1928), pp. 175–240, 263–294.
12. Neyman, J., and E. S. Pearson: "On the problem of the most efficient tests of statistical hypotheses," *Philosophical Transactions of the Royal Society of London,* Series A, Vol. 231(1933), pp. 289–337.
13. Stein, C. M.: "A property of some tests of composite hypotheses," *Annals of Mathematical Statistics,* Vol. 22(1951), pp. 475–476.
14. Student (W. S. Gosset): "On the probable error of a mean," *Biometrika,* Vol. 6(1908), pp. 1–25.
15. Wald, Abraham: "Contributions to the theory of statistical estimation and testing hypotheses," *Annals of Mathematical Statistics,* Vol. 10(1939), pp. 299–326.
16. Wald, Abraham: "Statistical Decision Functions," John Wiley & Sons, Inc., New York, 1950.
17. Weiss, L.: "Statistical Decision Theory," McGraw-Hill Book Company, Inc., New York, 1961.

13

Regression and Linear Hypotheses

13.1 Introduction

In this chapter we shall study linear models of which the following two examples are special cases.

Example 13.1. The distance s that a particle travels in time t is given by the formula $s = \alpha + \beta t$, where β is the average velocity and α is the position (initial) at time $t = 0$. If α and β are unknown, then s can be observed for two distinct values of t and the resulting two equations solved for α and β. For example, suppose that s is observed to be 2 when $t = 1$, and s is 11 when $t = 4$. This gives $2 = \alpha + \beta$; $11 = \alpha + 4\beta$, and the solution is $\alpha = -1$; $\beta = 3$, and so $s = -1 + 3t$. Suppose that for some reason the distance cannot be observed accurately but there is a measurement error which is of a random nature. Therefore s cannot be observed, but suppose that we can observe $\mathbf{y}$, where $\mathbf{y} = s + \mathbf{e}$ and $\mathbf{e}$ is a random error whose mean is 0. Substituting for s gives us

$$\mathbf{y} = \alpha + \beta t + \mathbf{e} \tag{1}$$

where $\mathbf{y}$ is an observable random variable, t is an observable mathematical variable (not random), $\mathbf{e}$ is an unobservable random variable, and α and β are unknown parameters. We cannot solve for α and β by observing two sets of values of $\mathbf{y}$ and t as we did s and t above since there is no functional relationship between $\mathbf{y}$ and t. The objective in this model is to find α and β and hence evaluate $s = \alpha + \beta t$ for various values of t. Since s is subject to errors and cannot be observed, we cannot know α and β, but by observing various sets of $\mathbf{y}$ and t values, statistical methods can be used to obtain estimates of α, β, and s. This type of model is a *functional relationship* model with a measurement error.

Example 13.2. For another example, consider the relationship between the height h and weight w of individuals in a certain city. Certainly there is no functional relationship between w and h, but there does seem to be some kind of relation. We shall consider them as random variables and shall postulate that $(\mathbf{w}, \mathbf{h})$ has a bivariate normal distribution. Then the expected value of **h** for a given value of **w** is given by

$$E(\mathbf{h}|w) = \alpha + \beta w \tag{2}$$

where α and β are functions of the parameters in a bivariate normal density. Although there is no functional relationship between **h** and **w**, if they are jointly normal there is a linear functional relationship between the weights and the average value of the heights. Thus we can write: **h** and **w** are jointly normal and

$$E(\mathbf{h}|w) = \alpha + \beta w$$

or we can write

$$\mathbf{h}_w = \alpha + \beta w + \mathbf{e}$$

This is a regression model, and although it came from a somewhat different problem than the functional relationship in Example 13.1, they both are special cases of a linear statistical model which will be discussed in this chapter.

13.2 Simple Linear Models

The two examples in the previous section gave rise to models which are included in a general class of linear models, and even though the real-world situations which they represent are distinct, from a statistical point of view they are similar. In this section we shall discuss a class of models which are called *simple linear models.*

Definition 13.1. *Let* $\mathbf{y}_1, \mathbf{y}_2, \cdots, \mathbf{y}_n$ *be uncorrelated, observable random variables such that* $\mathbf{y}_i = \alpha + \beta x_i + \mathbf{e}_i$, *where* α *and* β *are unknown parameters,* x_i *are observable mathematical (nonrandom) variables, and* $\mathbf{e}_i$ *are uncorrelated, unobservable random variables with mean* 0 *and variance* σ^2, *where* σ^2 *is not a function of* α, β, *or* x_i. *These specifications define a simple linear model.*

For the simple linear model we shall discuss two cases:

Case A: The random variables are normally distributed.

Case B: The random variables are *not* normally distributed.

For both cases we shall be interested in point estimation, and for Case A we shall examine point and interval estimation and hypotheses testing.

Case A: Point Estimation. This situation is represented in Fig. 13.1; for any given value of x, the random variable $\mathbf{y}$ is normally distributed with mean $\alpha + \beta x$ and variance σ^2. Let $(\mathbf{y}_i, x_i)$, $i = 1, 2, \cdots, n$, be a sample of $\mathbf{y}$'s together with the corresponding values of x. Some of the x_i may be equal, as would be the case if more than one $\mathbf{y}$ value were drawn from any specific distribution. It is convenient to label the x's differently even when some of them are the same. It is necessary that there be at least two different values of x, however. Obviously one cannot expect to estimate α and β from a sample drawn from a single member of the family of distributions. The method of maximum likelihood will

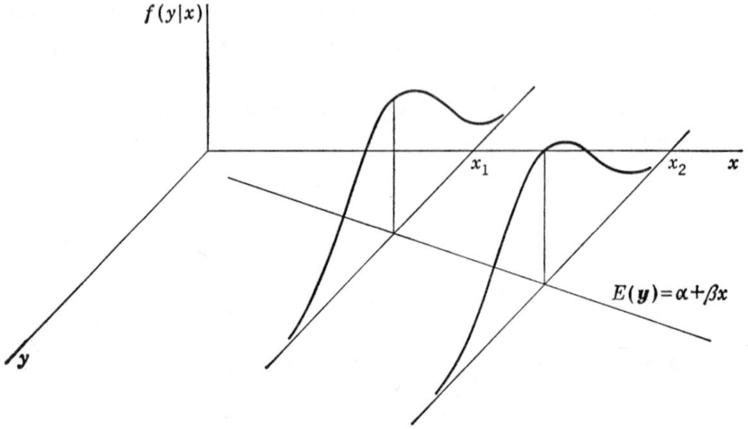

FIG. 13.1

be employed to estimate the parameters. The likelihood is

$$L = f(\mathbf{e}_1, \cdots, \mathbf{e}_n) = \left(\frac{1}{\sqrt{2\pi}\,\sigma}\right)^n \exp\left(-\frac{1}{2\sigma^2}\sum \mathbf{e}_i^2\right) \tag{1}$$

$$= \left(\frac{1}{\sqrt{2\pi}\,\sigma}\right)^n \exp\left\{\left(-\frac{1}{2\sigma^2}\right)\sum [\mathbf{y}_i - (\alpha + \beta x_i)]^2\right\} \tag{2}$$

and its logarithm is

$$\log L = -\frac{n}{2}\log 2\pi - \frac{n}{2}\log \sigma^2 - \frac{1}{2\sigma^2}\sum_i [\mathbf{y}_i - (\alpha + \beta x_i)]^2 \tag{3}$$

On putting the derivatives of this expression with respect to α, β, σ^2 equal to 0, we obtain

$$n\hat{\boldsymbol{\sigma}}^2 = \Sigma(\mathbf{y}_i - \hat{\boldsymbol{\alpha}} - \hat{\boldsymbol{\beta}}x_i)^2 \tag{4}$$

$$\Sigma(\mathbf{y}_i - \hat{\boldsymbol{\alpha}} - \hat{\boldsymbol{\beta}}x_i) = 0 \tag{5}$$

$$\Sigma x_i(\mathbf{y}_i - \hat{\boldsymbol{\alpha}} - \hat{\boldsymbol{\beta}}x_i) = 0 \tag{6}$$

which must be solved for the unknown parameters. The last two equations are called the *normal equations* which determine the coefficients $\hat{\boldsymbol{\alpha}}$, $\hat{\boldsymbol{\beta}}$. They are linear in $\hat{\boldsymbol{\alpha}}$ and $\hat{\boldsymbol{\beta}}$ and therefore readily solved. We shall let

$$\bar{x} = \frac{1}{n}\sum x_i \qquad \bar{\mathbf{y}} = \frac{1}{n}\sum \mathbf{y}_i \tag{7}$$

The solutions of (5) to (7) may then be written

$$\hat{\beta} = \frac{\Sigma(x_i - \bar{x})(y_i - \bar{y})}{\Sigma(x_i - \bar{x})^2} \tag{8}$$

$$\hat{\alpha} = \bar{y} - \hat{\beta}\bar{x} \tag{9}$$

$$\hat{\sigma}^2 = \frac{1}{n}\sum (y_i - \hat{\alpha} - \hat{\beta}x_i)^2 \tag{10}$$

which are the required point estimators of the unknown parameters. We notice that the solution could not be carried through if all the x_i were equal because the denominator of (8) would vanish.

Distribution of the Estimators. Since $\hat{\alpha}$ and $\hat{\beta}$ are linear functions of the y_i (which are normally distributed), it follows that $\hat{\alpha}$ and $\hat{\beta}$ must themselves have a bivariate normal distribution. One could specify that distribution by simply finding the means, variances, and covariance of the $\hat{\alpha}$ and $\hat{\beta}$. We shall, however, find the distribution another way. The main objective is to show that $\hat{\alpha}$ and $\hat{\beta}$ are distributed independently of $\hat{\sigma}^2$, and in doing this their distribution will fall out incidentally.

We shall evaluate the joint moment generating function:

$$m(s_1, s_2, s_3) = E\left[\exp\left(s_1\frac{\hat{\alpha} - \alpha}{\sigma} + s_2\frac{\hat{\beta} - \beta}{\sigma} + s_3\frac{n\hat{\sigma}^2}{\sigma^2}\right)\right] \tag{11}$$

$$= \int_{-\infty}^{\infty} \cdots \int_{-\infty}^{\infty} \left(\frac{1}{2\pi\sigma^2}\right)^{n/2} \exp\left[s_1\frac{\hat{\alpha} - \alpha}{\sigma} + s_2\frac{\hat{\beta} - \beta}{\sigma} + s_3\frac{n\hat{\sigma}^2}{\sigma^2} - \frac{1}{2\sigma^2}\sum (y_i - \alpha - \beta x_i)^2\right]\prod dy_i \tag{12}$$

for the three variates $(\hat{\alpha} - \alpha)/\sigma$, $(\hat{\beta} - \beta)/\sigma$, and $n\hat{\sigma}^2/\sigma^2$. The first step in evaluating the integral is to transform the variates y_i to

$$z_i = \frac{1}{\sigma}(y_i - \alpha - \beta x_i) \tag{13}$$

This removes the factor $1/\sigma^n$ from the integrand and changes the exponent in the integrand of (12) to

$$\sum_{i=1}^{n} c_i z_i - (\tfrac{1}{2})\sum_{i,j=1}^{n} r_{ij} z_i z_j \tag{14}$$

where

$$c_i = \frac{s_1[(\Sigma x_i^2/n) - \bar{x}x_i] + s_2(x_i - \bar{x})}{\Sigma(x_i - \bar{x})^2} = a_i s_1 + b_i s_2 \tag{15}$$

and

$$r_{ij} = \delta_{ij}(1 - 2s_3) + 2s_3[na_ia_j + n\bar{x}(a_ib_j + a_jb_i) + b_ib_j\Sigma x_i^2] \tag{16}$$

where a_i and b_i are defined by (15) and δ_{ij} is 1 or 0, according as i is or is not equal to j. We have then to evaluate an integral of the form

$$\int_{-\infty}^{\infty} \cdots \int_{-\infty}^{\infty} \left(\frac{1}{2\pi}\right)^{n/2} \exp\left[\sum c_i z_i - (\tfrac{1}{2})\sum\sum r_{ij} z_i z_j\right] \prod dz_i \tag{17}$$

which, apart from a factor $\sqrt{|(r_{ij})|}$, is just the integral in equation (9.3.20) with the μ_i's put equal to 0. The value of that integral is given in Theorem 9.13, and it follows that

$$m(s_1, s_2, s_3) = \frac{\exp\left[(\tfrac{1}{2})\Sigma\Sigma\sigma_{ij}c_ic_j\right]}{\sqrt{|(r_{ij})|}} \tag{18}$$

The algebraic reduction of (18) may be accomplished as follows: Since

$$a_i + \bar{x}b_i = \frac{1}{n}$$

equation (16) may be written

$$r_{ij} = \delta_{ij}(1 - 2s_3) + 2s_3\left[b_ib_j \sum (x_i - \bar{x})^2 + \frac{1}{n}\right] \tag{19}$$

or

$$r_{ij} = \delta_{ij}(1 - 2s_3) + 2s_3\left(d_id_j + \frac{1}{n}\right) \tag{20}$$

where

$$d_i = \frac{x_i - \bar{x}}{\sqrt{\Sigma(x_i - \bar{x})^2}} \tag{21}$$

so that $\Sigma d_i = 0$ and $\Sigma d_i^2 = 1$. It is not difficult to verify that

$$|(r_{ij})| = (1 - 2s_3)^{n-2} \tag{22}$$

and that the elements of the inverse of the matrix (r_{ij}) are

$$\sigma_{ij} = \frac{\delta_{ij}}{1 - 2s_3} - \frac{2s_3}{1 - 2s_3}\left(d_id_j + \frac{1}{n}\right) \tag{23}$$

These last two relations enable one to put (18) in the form

$$m(s_1, s_2, s_3) = \frac{\exp\left[(\tfrac{1}{2})\Sigma(x_i - \bar{x})^2\right]\left[s_1^2(1/n)\Sigma x_i^2 - 2\bar{x}s_1s_2 + s_2^2\right]}{(1 - 2s_3)^{(n-2)/2}} \tag{24}$$

The form of the moment generating function (24) enables one to draw several important conclusions. Remembering that s_1 is associated with $(\hat{\alpha} - \alpha)/\sigma$, s_2 with $(\hat{\beta} - \beta)/\sigma$, s_3 with $n\hat{\sigma}^2/\sigma^2$, we observe the following:

1. The pair of variates $\hat{\alpha}$ and $\hat{\beta}$ are distributed independently of $\hat{\sigma}^2$ because $m(s_1, s_2, s_3)$ factors into a function of s_3 alone and a function

of s_1 and s_2 alone (see Sec. 10.4). We shall let

$$m(s_1, s_2, s_3) = m_1(s_1, s_2)m_2(s_3) \tag{25}$$

2. The functional form of $m_1(s_1, s_2)$ is that of the moment generating function for a bivariate normal distribution (Theorem 9.1); hence $\hat{\alpha}$ and $\hat{\beta}$ are jointly normally distributed with means α and β, respectively, and variances and covariances

$$\sigma_{11} = \sigma_{\hat{\alpha}}^2 = \frac{\sigma^2 \Sigma x_i^2}{n\Sigma(x_i - \bar{x})^2} \tag{26}$$

$$\sigma_{22} = \sigma_{\hat{\beta}}^2 = \frac{\sigma^2}{\Sigma(x_i - \bar{x})^2} \tag{27}$$

$$\sigma_{12} = \operatorname{cov}(\hat{\alpha}, \hat{\beta}) = -\frac{\sigma^2 \bar{x}}{\Sigma(x_i - \bar{x})^2} \tag{28}$$

The inverse of the matrix of these variances and covariances is

$$\begin{pmatrix} \dfrac{n}{\sigma^2} & \dfrac{n\bar{x}}{\sigma^2} \\ \dfrac{n\bar{x}}{\sigma^2} & \dfrac{\Sigma x_i^2}{\sigma^2} \end{pmatrix} \tag{29}$$

which are the coefficients of the quadratic form in the distribution of $(\hat{\alpha} - \alpha)$ and $(\hat{\beta} - \beta)$.

3. $\hat{\alpha}$ and $\hat{\beta}$ will be independently distributed if the x_i are chosen so that $\bar{x} = 0$.

4. The quadratic form of the joint distribution of $\hat{\alpha}$ and $\hat{\beta}$,

$$Q = \frac{1}{\sigma^2}[n(\hat{\alpha} - \alpha)^2 + 2n\bar{x}(\hat{\alpha} - \alpha)(\hat{\beta} - \beta) + \Sigma x_i^2(\hat{\beta} - \beta)^2] \tag{30}$$

has the chi-square distribution with two degrees of freedom.

5. $m_2(s_3)$ is the moment generating function for a chi-square distribution with $n - 2$ degrees of freedom; hence $n\hat{\sigma}^2/\sigma^2$ has that distribution (Sec. 10.3).

6. By factoring the exponent in (2) and using the Neyman criterion for sufficiency, it follows that $\hat{\alpha}$, $\hat{\beta}$, $\hat{\sigma}^2$ are sufficient statistics for α, β, σ^2. It can also be shown that they are complete.

Theorem 13.1. *For Case A of the linear model in Definition* 13.1 *the estimators* $\hat{\alpha}$, $\hat{\beta}$, $[n/(n-2)]\hat{\sigma}^2$ *defined in* (8) *to* (10) *are* (1) *minimum-variance unbiased;* (2) *consistent;* (3) *asymptotically efficient;* (4) *sufficient, complete;* (5) $n\hat{\sigma}^2/\sigma^2$ *is distributed as chi square with* $n - 2$ *d.f.;* (6) $\hat{\alpha}$, $\hat{\beta}$ *are distributed as the bivariate normal with covariance matrix whose elements are given by* (26) *to* (28)*; and,* (7) $\hat{\alpha}$, $\hat{\beta}$ *are independent of* $\hat{\sigma}^2$.

Confidence Regions and Tests of Hypotheses. In these models the main interest is usually in the coefficients α and β. Of course there is no trouble in estimating σ^2 or in testing hypotheses about σ^2, because the chi-square distribution above provides confidence intervals and tests directly.

To obtain a confidence interval for α, we need only to observe that the marginal distribution of $\hat{\boldsymbol{\alpha}}$ is normal with mean α and variance given by (26); hence

$$\mathbf{u} = \frac{\hat{\boldsymbol{\alpha}} - \alpha}{\sigma} \sqrt{\frac{n\Sigma(x_i - \bar{x})^2}{\Sigma x_i^2}}$$

has a normal distribution with zero mean and unit variance. Since $\mathbf{u}$ and $n\hat{\boldsymbol{\sigma}}^2/\sigma^2$ are independently distributed, it follows from Sec. 10.6 that

$$\begin{aligned} \mathbf{t} &= \frac{\sigma\mathbf{u}}{\sqrt{n}\hat{\boldsymbol{\sigma}}/\sqrt{n-2}} \\ &= (\hat{\boldsymbol{\alpha}} - \alpha)\sqrt{\frac{n(n-2)\Sigma(x_i - \bar{x})^2}{\Sigma x_i^2 \Sigma(\mathbf{y}_i - \hat{\boldsymbol{\alpha}} - \hat{\boldsymbol{\beta}}x_i)^2}} \end{aligned} \qquad (31)$$

has the t distribution with $n - 2$ degrees of freedom. Since α is the only unknown quantity in this expression, the inequalities in

$$P(-t_{\epsilon/2} < \mathbf{t} < t_{\epsilon/2}) = 1 - \epsilon$$

may be converted to obtain a confidence interval with probability $1 - \epsilon$ for α. The quantity $\mathbf{t}$ also provides a test criterion for testing hypotheses about α in just the same way that it does for the mean of a normal distribution. Thus to test whether the line $E(\mathbf{y}) = \alpha + \beta x$ passes through the origin in the yx plane, we should simply put $\alpha = 0$ in (31) and observe whether $|\mathbf{t}| < t_{\epsilon/2}$ if the level of significance is to be ϵ. One-tailed tests may also be made.

Confidence intervals for β and tests on β may be made in a quite similar way. It is readily seen that

$$\mathbf{t} = (\hat{\boldsymbol{\beta}} - \beta)\sqrt{\frac{(n-2)\Sigma(x_i - \bar{x})^2}{\Sigma(\mathbf{y}_i - \hat{\boldsymbol{\alpha}} - \hat{\boldsymbol{\beta}}x_i)^2}} \qquad (32)$$

also has the t distribution with $n - 2$ degrees of freedom and involves only the unknown parameter β. To test, for example, whether the means of the family of normal distributions under consideration were independent of the observable parameter, one would put $\beta = 0$ in (32) and observe whether $|\mathbf{t}| < t_{\epsilon/2}$, where ϵ is the chosen significance level.

For simultaneous estimation of α and β, we may use the fact that

$$\mathbf{F} = \frac{\mathbf{Q}}{n\hat{\boldsymbol{\sigma}}^2/\sigma^2} \cdot \frac{n-2}{2} \tag{33}$$

where $\mathbf{Q}$ is defined by (30), has the F distribution with 2 and $n - 2$ degrees of freedom (Sec. 10.5), and involves only the unknown parameters α and β. The inequality in

$$P(\mathbf{F} < F_\epsilon) = 1 - \epsilon$$

is readily seen to define an elliptical confidence region in the $\alpha\beta$ plane for α and β. To test whether α and β had certain specified values α_0 and β_0, one would put $\alpha = \alpha_0$ and $\beta = \beta_0$ in (33) and observe whether or not the resulting value of $\mathbf{F}$ exceeded F_ϵ.

All these tests on α and β could have been obtained by the likelihood-ratio method.

It is worth observing that the accuracy of the estimation of α and β depends on the choice of the x_i. Thus the variance of $\hat{\boldsymbol{\alpha}}$ will be as small as possible when x_i are chosen so that $\bar{x} = 0$. For, since

$$\Sigma(x_i - \bar{x})^2 = \Sigma x_i^2 - n\bar{x}^2$$

the least possible value for $\sigma_{\hat{\boldsymbol{\alpha}}}^2$ [equation (26)] is σ^2/n and occurs when $\bar{x} = 0$. Evidently the confidence interval for α will be shortest, on an average, for given n when $\bar{x} = 0$. The variance of $\hat{\boldsymbol{\beta}}$ [equation (27)] can evidently be made small by choosing widely separated values for the x_i. In fact, if x_1 is the smallest practicable value of x and x_2 is the largest, then β will be best estimated when half of the values of y are chosen at each of those two values of x if n is even. It often happens in practice, however, that there is some doubt about the linearity of the model and it is desired to test for linearity. In this case it is necessary to have observations for more than two values of x.

13.3 Prediction

Let us suppose that $E(\mathbf{y}) = y_x = \alpha + \beta x$ has been estimated by $\hat{\mathbf{y}}_x = \hat{\boldsymbol{\alpha}} + \hat{\boldsymbol{\beta}}x$ on the basis of a sample of n observations. We now wish to predict the value of $\mathbf{y}$ for some specified value of x, say x_0. Thus if $\mathbf{y}$ is a son's adult height and x is the father's height, a sample of observations will provide estimates $\hat{\boldsymbol{\alpha}}$ and $\hat{\boldsymbol{\beta}}$ for a linear function. A prospective father of height x_0 may wish to predict his son's height. The predicted height is, of course, $\hat{\mathbf{y}}_0 = \hat{\boldsymbol{\alpha}} + \hat{\boldsymbol{\beta}}x_0$. Or to consider a different problem: Let $\mathbf{y}$ be the demand for some commodity, and let x be the wholesale price of the item two months earlier or the wholesale price of some ingredient or part of the item two months earlier. It is desired to predict the demand two months hence. From past records one may collect a set of pairs of observations (x_i, $\mathbf{y}_i$), where $\mathbf{y}_i$ is the demand at a given time and x_i is the wholesale price two months previous to that time, and estimate coefficients α and β in a linear model. If x_0 is the present wholesale price, then the predicted demand two months hence is $\hat{\mathbf{y}}_0 = \hat{\boldsymbol{\alpha}} + \hat{\boldsymbol{\beta}}x_0$.

The worth of a prediction depends on the magnitude of its possible error, and we shall take account of that error by obtaining a *prediction interval* which is analogous to a confidence interval. The variate $\mathbf{y}_0$ is a random variable with a normal distribution having mean $\alpha + \beta x_0$ and variance σ^2. The predicted value $\hat{\mathbf{y}}_0 = \hat{\boldsymbol{\alpha}} + \hat{\boldsymbol{\beta}}x_0$ has two sources of error: In the first place, $\hat{\boldsymbol{\alpha}} + \hat{\boldsymbol{\beta}}x_0$ is merely an estimate of the mean of $\mathbf{y}_0$, and the actual value of $\mathbf{y}_0$ may, of course, deviate from its mean; in the second place, the estimated mean is subject to the random-sampling errors inherent in $\hat{\boldsymbol{\alpha}}$ and $\hat{\boldsymbol{\beta}}$. If α, β, and σ were exactly known, then a 95 per cent prediction interval for $\mathbf{y}_0$ would be simply

$$\alpha + \beta x_0 - 1.96\sigma \text{ to } \alpha + \beta x_0 + 1.96\sigma$$

since the probability that $\mathbf{y}_0$ will fall within 1.96σ of its mean is .95 for a normal distribution. Since all these parameters except x_0 are unknown, we must attempt to set up an interval in terms of their estimates.

The variate

$$\mathbf{u} = \mathbf{y}_0 - \hat{\boldsymbol{\alpha}} - \hat{\boldsymbol{\beta}}x_0 \tag{1}$$

is necessarily normally distributed since it is a linear function of the normal variates $\mathbf{y}_0$, $\hat{\boldsymbol{\alpha}}$, $\hat{\boldsymbol{\beta}}$. The distribution of $\mathbf{u}$ is therefore known when its mean and variance are given. Since

$$E(\mathbf{y}_0) = \alpha + \beta x_0 \qquad E(\hat{\boldsymbol{\alpha}}) = \alpha \qquad E(\hat{\boldsymbol{\beta}}) = \beta$$

we have

$$E(\mathbf{u}) = 0$$

The variance of $\mathbf{u}$ is therefore

$$\begin{aligned} \sigma_u^2 &= E(\mathbf{u}^2) \\ &= E(\mathbf{y}_0 - \hat{\boldsymbol{\alpha}} - \hat{\boldsymbol{\beta}}x_0)^2 \\ &= \sigma_{y_0}^2 + \sigma_{\hat{\alpha}}^2 + x_0^2\sigma_{\hat{\beta}}^2 + 2x_0E[(\hat{\boldsymbol{\alpha}} - \alpha)(\hat{\boldsymbol{\beta}} - \beta)] \end{aligned} \tag{2}$$

remembering that $\mathbf{y}_0$ is independent of $\hat{\boldsymbol{\alpha}}$ and $\hat{\boldsymbol{\beta}}$. $\sigma_{y_0}^2$ is simply σ^2, the variance of the normal distribution, and the other terms in (2) are given by (13.2.26) to (13.2.28), so that

$$\begin{aligned} \sigma_u^2 &= \sigma^2 \left[1 + \frac{(1/n)\Sigma x_i^2 + x_0^2 - 2x_0\bar{x}}{\Sigma(x_i - \bar{x})^2} \right] \\ &= \sigma^2 \left[1 + \frac{1}{n} + \frac{(x_0 - \bar{x})^2}{\Sigma(x_i - \bar{x})^2} \right] \\ &= \sigma^2 \left[\frac{n+1}{n} + \frac{(x_0 - \bar{x})^2}{\Sigma(x_i - \bar{x})^2} \right] \end{aligned} \tag{3}$$

A 95 per cent prediction interval for $\mathbf{u}$ is just $-1.96\sigma_u$ to $1.96\sigma_u$, but this still involves one unknown parameter σ which appears in σ_u. We can eliminate σ by using the t distribution. The variate $\mathbf{u}/\sigma_u$ is normally distributed with zero mean and unit variance and is distributed independently of $n\hat{\sigma}^2/\sigma^2$; hence

$$\mathbf{t} = \frac{\mathbf{u}/\sigma_u}{\sqrt{n\hat{\sigma}^2/(n-2)\sigma^2}} \tag{4}$$

has the t distribution with $n - 2$ degrees of freedom and involves no unknown parameters. The inequalities in

$$P(-t_{\epsilon/2} < \mathbf{t} < t_{\epsilon/2}) = 1 - \epsilon$$

may be converted to determine a $100(1 - \epsilon)$ per cent prediction interval for $\mathbf{y}_0$. The interval is given by

$$P(\hat{\alpha} + \hat{\beta}x_0 - \mathbf{A} < \mathbf{y}_0 < \hat{\alpha} + \hat{\beta}x_0 + \mathbf{A}) = 1 - \epsilon \tag{5}$$

where

$$\mathbf{A} = t_{\epsilon/2}\hat{\sigma}\sqrt{\frac{n}{n-2}\left[\frac{n+1}{n} + \frac{(x_0 - \bar{x})^2}{\Sigma(x_i - \bar{x})^2}\right]} \tag{6}$$

Several properties of the prediction interval should be observed:

1. The length of the interval is greater than $2t_{\epsilon/2}\sigma$, on an average, regardless of how large a sample was used to estimate α and β. This is entirely reasonable because we are predicting a single observation $\mathbf{y}_0$ which is normally distributed with standard deviation σ.

2. The average length of the prediction interval increases as x_0 moves away from $\bar{x}$. If it is possible, the values x_i chosen for obtaining observations to estimate the parameters should be selected so as to have a mean value near x_0.

3. The relation (5) holds only for a single prediction based on the estimates $\hat{\alpha}$, $\hat{\beta}$, $\hat{\sigma}$. The relation has meaning only if α, β, σ are reestimated each time a prediction on $\mathbf{y}_0$ is made. The probability statement takes account of sampling variation in the estimates as well as in $\mathbf{y}_0$, and if the original estimates are used repeatedly (not allowed to vary), the statement may not be accurate.

It is easy to generalize the above technique to take account of the prediction of the mean of a sample of size m observed for $x = x_0$. Let $\mathbf{y}'_1, \mathbf{y}'_2, \cdots, \mathbf{y}'_m$ be a sample of m observations at x_0 with mean $\bar{\mathbf{y}}'$. The mean of

$$\mathbf{v} = \bar{\mathbf{y}}' - \hat{\alpha} - \hat{\beta}x_0$$

is 0, and its variance σ^2 is the same as (3) except that $(n + 1)/n$ is replaced by $1/m + 1/n$. The variate

$$\mathrm{t} = \frac{\mathrm{v}/\sigma_{\mathrm{v}}}{\sqrt{n\hat{\boldsymbol{\delta}}^2/(n-2)\sigma^2}}$$

has the t distribution with $n - 2$ degrees of freedom and involves no unknown parameters; hence it may be employed to construct a prediction interval for $\bar{\mathrm{y}}'$.

13.4 Discrimination

The discrimination problem is an estimation problem and is in a sense the reverse of the prediction problem. In prediction one wishes to predict y, knowing x_0, on the basis of estimates of α, β, σ. In discrimination one wishes to estimate x_0, having observed y. The general class of biological assay problems are of this character. Thus, for example, the concentration of a certain vitamin may be measured by observing the gain in weight of a week-old chick when its diet is augmented by daily doses of the vitamin for several days. A manufacturer of the vitamin might determine the strength of a new batch as follows: Let y be the gain in weight, and let x be the concentration. Using material of known concentration, he would feed several chicks with different concentrations x_i $(i = 1, 2, \cdots, n)$ and observe their gains in weight y_i. At the same time other chicks would receive their vitamins from the batch with unknown concentration x_0, and their gains in weight, say y'_j $(j = 1, 2, \cdots, m)$, would be observed. On the basis of these data, it is desired to estimate the parameter x_0.

The general problem of classification is a discrimination problem. Anthropologists, for example, make measurements y on skulls of known age x and then estimate the age x_0 of a skull of unknown age with measurements y′. Taxonomists use the technique to discriminate between varieties of plants with quite similar appearance.

Using the notation of the first paragraph and the model of Sec. 13.2, the likelihood of the observations $\mathrm{y}_1, \mathrm{y}_2, \cdots, \mathrm{y}_n$ and $\mathrm{y}'_1, \mathrm{y}'_2, \cdots, \mathrm{y}'_m$ is

$$L = \left(\frac{1}{\sqrt{2\pi}\,\sigma}\right)^{m+n} \exp\left[-\frac{1}{2\sigma^2}\sum_1^n (\mathrm{y}_i - \alpha - \beta x_i)^2 - \frac{1}{2\sigma^2}\sum_1^m (\mathrm{y}'_j - \alpha - \beta x_0)^2\right] \quad (1)$$

and on differentiating the logarithm of this expression with respect to σ^2, α, β, x_0 in turn, one can readily determine the maximum-likelihood estimates of these parameters; they are

$$\hat{\beta} = \frac{\Sigma(y_i - \bar{y})(x_i - \bar{x})}{\Sigma(x_i - \bar{x})^2} \tag{2}$$

$$\hat{\alpha} = \bar{y} - \hat{\beta}\bar{x} \tag{3}$$

$$\hat{\sigma}^2 = \frac{1}{m+n}\left[\sum (y_i - \hat{\alpha} - \hat{\beta}x_i)^2 + \sum (y_j' - \bar{y}')^2\right] \tag{4}$$

$$\hat{x}_0 = \frac{\bar{y}' - \hat{\alpha}}{\hat{\beta}} \tag{5}$$

where

$$\bar{x} = \frac{1}{n}\sum x_i \qquad \bar{y} = \frac{1}{n}\sum y_i \qquad \bar{y}' = \frac{1}{m}\sum y_j'$$

Equations (2) and (3) are the same as (13.2.8) and (13.2.9); equation (5) gives the desired point estimate of x_0.

A confidence interval for x_0 is also easily set up. The quantity

$$v = \bar{y}' - \hat{\alpha} - \hat{\beta}x_0 \tag{6}$$

is normally distributed since it is a linear function of normal variates; its mean is 0, and its variance is

$$\sigma_v^2 = \sigma^2\left[\frac{1}{m} + \frac{1}{n} + \frac{(x_0 - \bar{x})^2}{\Sigma(x_i - \bar{x})^2}\right] \tag{7}$$

just as was found in Sec. 13.3. The two sums in (4) both have chi-square distributions when they are divided by σ^2, the first with $n - 2$ and the second with $m - 1$ degrees of freedom. The two chi-squares are independent since they are functions of independent samples; hence their sum has the chi-square distribution with $m + n - 3$ degrees of freedom. Furthermore the two chi-squares are obviously independent of v. It follows then that

$$t = \frac{v/\sigma_v}{\sqrt{(m+n)\hat{\sigma}^2/(m+n-3)\sigma^2}} \tag{8}$$

has the t distribution and will provide a confidence interval for x_0 since that is the only unknown parameter which appears in (8).

We have considered a very much simplified discrimination problem, but it is one which occurs frequently in practice. The more general problem has to do with the case in which each observation consists of several components $(y_1, y_2, \cdots, y_k)$ which have a multivariate normal distribution with means $\alpha_1 + \beta_1 x$, $\alpha_2 + \beta_2 x$, $\cdots$, $\alpha_k + \beta_k x$. Given estimates of the α's and β's on the basis of a sample of observations $(y_{1i}, y_{2i}, \cdots, y_{ki})$, one wishes to estimate x_0 for an observation $(y_{10}, y_{20}, \cdots, y_{k0})$. We shall have to omit this problem because it is very cumbersome to handle by elementary methods.

13.5 Point Estimation Case B

Let the model be

$$\mathbf{y} = \alpha + \beta x + \mathbf{e}$$

where $\mathbf{y}$ is an observable random variable with $E(\mathbf{y}) = \alpha + \beta x$, where x is a known mathematical variable (nonrandom) and α and β are unknown parameters. n values of x are chosen, and for each x_i a $\mathbf{y}_i$ value is selected from a density whose mean is $\alpha + \beta x_i$ and whose variance is σ^2. The following assumptions will be made:

The random variables $\mathbf{y}_1, \mathbf{y}_2, \cdots, \mathbf{y}_n$ are uncorrelated variates with mean $E(\mathbf{y}_i) = \alpha + \beta x_i$ and variance σ^2 which is independent of x_i, α, β. This implies that $\mathbf{e}_i$ are uncorrelated random variables with $E(\mathbf{e}_i) = 0$ and var $(\mathbf{e}_i) = \sigma^2$, which can be written

$$\begin{aligned} E(\mathbf{y}_i) &= \alpha + \beta x_i \\ \text{cov}\ (\mathbf{y}_i,\mathbf{y}_j) &= 0 \qquad \text{if } j \neq i \\ \text{var}\ (\mathbf{y}_i) &= \sigma^2 \end{aligned} \tag{1}$$

Since the density of the random variables $\mathbf{y}_i$ (also the $\mathbf{e}_i$) is not specified, maximum-likelihood estimators of α and β cannot be obtained. In situations such as these the *least-squares* method of estimation can be utilized.

Definition 13.2. *Let* $(\mathbf{y}_i, x_i)$, $i = 1, 2, \cdots, n$, *be* n *points which satisfy the simple linear model* $\mathbf{y}_i = \alpha + \beta x_i + \mathbf{e}_i$. *The least-squares estimators of* α *and* β *are the values of* α *and* β *that minimize the sum of squares of errors* $\sum_{i=1}^{n} \mathbf{e}_i^2$.

Substituting for $\mathbf{e}_i$, we obtain

$$L(\alpha, \beta) = \sum \mathbf{e}_i^2 = \sum_{i=1}^{n} (\mathbf{y}_i - \alpha - \beta x_i)^2$$

Clearly, the values of α and β which minimize this are the same values that maximize L in equation (13.2.2). Therefore the least-squares estimators are

$$\begin{aligned} \hat{\boldsymbol{\alpha}} &= \bar{\mathbf{y}} - \hat{\boldsymbol{\beta}}\bar{x} \\ \hat{\boldsymbol{\beta}} &= \frac{\Sigma(\mathbf{y}_i - \bar{\mathbf{y}})(x_i - \bar{x})}{\Sigma(x_i - \bar{x})^2} \end{aligned} \tag{2}$$

The least-squares method gives no estimator of σ^2, but an estimator for σ^2 *based* on the least-squares estimators of α and β is

$$\hat{\boldsymbol{\sigma}}^2 = \frac{1}{n-2} \sum (\mathbf{y}_i - \hat{\boldsymbol{\alpha}} - \hat{\boldsymbol{\beta}} x_i)^2 \tag{3}$$

When the $\mathbf{y}_i$ are assumed to be normally distributed, the maximum-likelihood estimator of σ^2 is $[(n-2)/n]\hat{\boldsymbol{\sigma}}^2$, but this estimator is biased. When the $\mathbf{y}_i$ are normal variables, the properties of the maximum-likelihood estimators adjusted for bias of α, β, and σ^2 are listed in Theorem 13.1.

The first property stated is that the estimators are minimum-variance unbiased. That is to say, in the class of *all* unbiased estimators of α, β, σ^2, the estimators $\hat{\boldsymbol{\alpha}}$, $\hat{\boldsymbol{\beta}}$, $\hat{\boldsymbol{\sigma}}^2$ in (3) have minimum variance. No such property is enjoyed by the least-squares estimators (2) and (3), but we define a similar property as follows:

Definition 13.3. *Consider only the class of estimators of α and β which are linear functions of the random variables $\mathbf{y}_i$. In this class consider only the subclass of estimators which are unbiased. If, in this restricted class, estimators of α* and *β exist which have smaller variance than any other estimators of α and β, these will be called "best linear unbiased estimators" (best refers to minimum variance).*

We shall prove an important theorem for the simple linear model when assumptions (1) hold. This theorem is often referred to as the Gauss-Markoff theorem.

Theorem 13.2. *Let the model $\mathbf{y}_i = \alpha + \beta x_i + \mathbf{e}_i$ be such that the x_i are known mathematical variables and $\mathbf{y}_i$ are observable random variables. Also suppose that the unobservable random variables $\mathbf{e}_i$ are uncorrelated with mean 0 and variance σ^2. Then the least-squares estimators (2) for α and β are best linear unbiased estimators.*

Proof. We shall demonstrate the proof for α; the proof for β is similar. Since we are restricting the class of estimators to be linear, we have $\hat{\boldsymbol{\alpha}} = \Sigma a_p \mathbf{y}_p$. We must determine the constants a_p such that

(*a*) $E(\hat{\boldsymbol{\alpha}}) = \alpha$, that is, unbiased.
(*b*) Variance ($\hat{\boldsymbol{\alpha}}$) is a minimum of all estimators satisfying (*a*).

For (*a*) we must have

$$\alpha = E(\hat{\boldsymbol{\alpha}}) = \Sigma a_p(E\mathbf{y}_p) = \Sigma a_p(\alpha + \beta x_p)$$

This gives the two equations which must be satisfied:

$$\begin{aligned} \Sigma a_p &= 1 \\ \Sigma a_p x_p &= 0 \end{aligned} \tag{4}$$

Now

$$\begin{aligned} \text{var}\,(\hat{\boldsymbol{\alpha}}) &= E(\hat{\boldsymbol{\alpha}} - \alpha)^2 = E(\Sigma a_p \mathbf{y}_p - \alpha)^2 = E[\Sigma a_p(\alpha + \beta x_p + \mathbf{e}_p) - \alpha]^2 \\ &= E(\alpha \Sigma a_p + \beta \Sigma a_p x_p + \Sigma a_p \mathbf{e}_p - \alpha)^2 \end{aligned}$$

By the restriction (4) this becomes

$$\text{var}\,(\hat{\boldsymbol{\alpha}}) = E\left(\sum_p a_p \mathbf{e}_p\right)^2 = E\left(\sum_p a_p^2 \mathbf{e}_p^2 + \sum_{p}\sum_{\substack{q \\ p \neq q}} a_p a_q \mathbf{e}_p \mathbf{e}_q\right)$$

The quantity $E(\mathbf{e}_p\mathbf{e}_q)$ is 0 if $p \neq q$ since, by assumption, the $\mathbf{e}_i$ are uncorrelated and have means 0. Hence

$$\text{var}(\hat{\alpha}) = \sigma^2 \Sigma a_p^2$$

Since σ^2 is a constant, to minimize var $(\hat{\alpha})$ we need to minimize Σa_p^2. Thus constants a_p must be found which minimize Σa_p^2 subject to restrictions (4). Using the theory of Lagrange multipliers, we must minimize

$$L = \Sigma a_p^2 - \lambda_1(\Sigma a_p - 1) - \lambda_2(\Sigma a_p x_p)$$

Taking derivatives, one finds

$$\begin{aligned} \frac{\partial L}{\partial a_t} &= 2a_t - \lambda_1 - \lambda_2 x_t = 0 \qquad t = 1, 2, \cdots, n \\ \frac{\partial L}{\partial \lambda_1} &= -\sum a_p + 1 \qquad = 0 \\ \frac{\partial L}{\partial \lambda_2} &= -\sum a_p x_p \qquad = 0 \end{aligned} \tag{5}$$

If we sum over the first n equations, we get (using $\Sigma a_t = 1$)

$$2 = n\lambda_1 + \lambda_2 \Sigma x_i \tag{6}$$

If we multiply the pth equation in (5) by x_p and add, we get

$$2\Sigma x_p a_p = \lambda_1 \Sigma x_p + \lambda_2 \Sigma x_p^2$$

or, since $\Sigma a_p x_p = 0$, this becomes

$$\lambda_1 = -\lambda_2 \frac{\Sigma x_i^2}{\Sigma x_i} \tag{7}$$

If we substitute this into (6), we get

$$\lambda_2 = \frac{-2\Sigma x_i/n}{\Sigma x_i^2 - n\bar{x}^2} = \frac{-2\bar{x}}{\Sigma(x_i - \bar{x})^2}$$

and

$$\lambda_1 = \frac{2\Sigma x_i^2/n}{\Sigma(x_i - \bar{x})^2}$$

Substituting λ_1 and λ_2 into the tth equation in (5) and solving for a_t give

$$a_t = \frac{\Sigma x_i^2/n - \bar{x}x_t}{\Sigma(x_i - \bar{x})^2}$$

The best linear unbiased estimator of α is therefore

$$\hat{\alpha} = \Sigma a_t \mathbf{y}_t = \frac{\bar{\mathbf{y}}\Sigma x_i^2 - \bar{x}\Sigma \mathbf{y}_t x_t}{\Sigma(x_i - \bar{x})^2} = \bar{\mathbf{y}} - \hat{\boldsymbol{\beta}}\bar{x}$$

which is the one given by least squares and so the proof is complete. A similar proof holds for β.

*13.6 The General Linear Model

In this section we shall discuss what is sometimes called "multiple regression." We shall derive the distributions of pertinent statistics needed for estimation and for testing hypotheses of certain parameters in general linear models.

Consider the density function of a random variable $\mathbf{y}$, $f(y; x_1, x_2, \cdots, x_p; \beta_1, \cdots, \beta_p)$, which depends on p known quantities $x_1, \cdots, x_p$ and on p unknown parameters, β_i. This density function will be denoted by $f(y; x; \beta)$, $f(y; \beta)$, or $f(y)$. We shall assume throughout the discussion that $E(\mathbf{y}) = \sum_{i=1}^{p} \beta_i x_i$ and that the variance of $\mathbf{y}$ equals σ^2, where σ^2 does not depend on the β_i nor on the x_i. The point

$$\mathbf{P}_j' = (\mathbf{y}_j, x_{j1}, x_{j2}, \cdots, x_{jp})$$

in $(p + 1)$-dimensional space will represent an observation from this distribution. That is to say, when an observation $\mathbf{y}$ is taken from this distribution, the corresponding x_i values must be specified. Throughout this section the x_i will be considered known constants, not random variables.

If in $f(y; x; \beta)$ we make the transformation $\mathbf{e} = \mathbf{y} - \Sigma\beta_i x_i$, then $\mathbf{e}$ is a random variable such that $E(\mathbf{e}) = 0$ and $E(\mathbf{e}^2) = \sigma^2$. This can be written

$$\mathbf{y} = \sum_{i=1}^{p} \beta_i x_i + \mathbf{e} \tag{1}$$

This is an extension of the simple linear model in the previous sections.

To estimate the β_i, a random sample of size n will be taken from the distribution $f(y; x; \beta)$. The sample will be denoted by $\mathbf{P}_1', \mathbf{P}_2', \cdots, \mathbf{P}_n'$, and the relationship between the system of observations can be written as

$$\mathbf{y}_j = \sum_{i=1}^{p} \beta_i x_{ji} + \mathbf{e}_j \qquad j = 1, 2, \cdots, n \tag{2}$$

or in vector form as

$$\mathbf{Y} = X\beta + \mathbf{e} \tag{3}$$

* In this section matrices are used quite extensively. If the reader is not prepared in matrix theory, this section should be omitted.

where

$$\mathbf{Y} = \begin{pmatrix} \mathbf{y}_1 \\ \mathbf{y}_2 \\ \cdot \\ \cdot \\ \cdot \\ \mathbf{y}_n \end{pmatrix} \qquad X = \begin{pmatrix} x_{11} & x_{12} & \cdots & x_{1p} \\ x_{21} & x_{22} & \cdots & x_{2p} \\ \cdot & \cdot & & \cdot \\ \cdot & \cdot & & \cdot \\ \cdot & \cdot & & \cdot \\ x_{n1} & x_{n2} & \cdots & x_{np} \end{pmatrix}$$

$$\beta = \begin{pmatrix} \beta_1 \\ \beta_2 \\ \cdot \\ \cdot \\ \cdot \\ \beta_p \end{pmatrix} \qquad \mathbf{e} = \begin{pmatrix} \mathbf{e}_1 \\ \mathbf{e}_2 \\ \cdot \\ \cdot \\ \cdot \\ \mathbf{e}_n \end{pmatrix} \tag{4}$$

Examining $\mathbf{Y} = X\beta + \mathbf{e}$ in more detail, we see that we must first select (either at random or by design) a set of x's, say $x_{11}, x_{12}, \cdots, x_{1p}$, and then randomly select an observation $\mathbf{y}_1$, from the distribution $f(y; x_1 = x_{11}, x_2 = x_{12}, \cdots, x_p = x_{1p})$. Then another set of x's is selected, that is, $x_{21}, x_{22}, \cdots, x_{2p}$, and an observation $\mathbf{y}_2$ is selected at random from the distribution $f(y; x_1 = x_{21}, x_2 = x_{22}, \cdots, x_p = x_{2p})$. This process is repeated until n values of $\mathbf{y}$ are drawn. No stipulation has yet been put on the x_{ij}. They need not all be distinct. However, some restriction will be put on the matrix of the x_{ij} in special instances. Therefore, whenever the model $\mathbf{Y} = X\beta + \mathbf{e}$ appears, it will be assumed that it was constructed by the sampling process defined above. On the basis of the observed matrix X and observed random vector $\mathbf{Y}$, estimators for the β_i and for σ^2 will be derived.

The preceding will be formulated in the following definition:

Definition 13.4. *The model* $\mathbf{Y} = X\beta + \mathbf{e}$ [*where the quantities given in* (4) *are such that* $\mathbf{Y}$ *is a random observed vector,* $\mathbf{e}$ *is a random vector,* X *is an* $n \times p$ *matrix of known fixed quantities, and* β *is a* $p \times 1$ *vector of unknown parameters*] *will be called the general linear model.*

If the rank of X is p then the model will be called full rank. Two cases will be examined concerning the distribution of the vector $\mathbf{e}$. They are:

Case A: $\mathbf{e}$ is distributed as the p-variate normal with mean $\mathbf{0}$ and covariance $\sigma^2 I$.

Case B: $\mathbf{e}$ is a random vector such that $E(\mathbf{e}) = \mathbf{0}$ and

$$\textbf{cov}\ (\mathbf{e}) = E(\mathbf{e}\mathbf{e}') = \sigma^2 I$$

where σ^2 is unknown [**cov** ($\mathbf{e}$) denotes the covariance matrix of $\mathbf{e}$].

Case A is equivalent to saying that each $\mathbf{e}_i$ is normally distributed with mean equal to 0 and with variance equal to σ^2 and that the $\mathbf{e}_i$ are jointly independent. Case B is equivalent to saying that the expected value of each $\mathbf{e}_i$ is 0, the $\mathbf{e}_i$ are uncorrelated, and each $\mathbf{e}_i$ has a common unknown variance σ^2. Case A will be referred to as the normal-theory case.

Point Estimation. The point estimates of the parameters in the general linear model will be considered separately for the two cases.

Case A: The Estimates of β and σ^2 under Normal Theory. Since we are considering the case where the vector of errors, $\mathbf{e}$, is normally distributed, the maximum-likelihood method will be used to estimate $\beta_1, \beta_2, \cdots, \beta_p$ and σ^2. The likelihood equation is

$$f(\mathbf{e}; \beta, \sigma^2) = \frac{1}{(2\pi)^{n/2}\sigma^n} e^{-\mathbf{e}'\mathbf{e}/2\sigma^2} = \frac{1}{(2\pi\sigma^2)^{n/2}} e^{-[(\mathbf{Y}-X\beta)'(\mathbf{Y}-X\beta)/2\sigma^2]} \tag{5}$$

Using logarithms, we get

$$\log f(\mathbf{e}; \beta, \sigma^2) = -\frac{n}{2}\log(2\pi) - \frac{n}{2}\log\sigma^2 - \frac{1}{2\sigma^2}(\mathbf{Y} - X\beta)'(\mathbf{Y} - X\beta)$$

The maximum-likelihood estimates of β and σ^2 are the solutions of the equations

$$\begin{aligned} \frac{\partial \log f(\mathbf{e}; \beta, \sigma^2)}{\partial \beta_1} &= 0 \\ \frac{\partial \log f(\mathbf{e}; \beta, \sigma^2)}{\partial \beta_2} &= 0 \\ \cdots\cdots\cdots & \\ \frac{\partial \log f(\mathbf{e}; \beta, \sigma^2)}{\partial \beta_p} &= 0 \\ \frac{\partial \log f(\mathbf{e}; \beta, \sigma^2)}{\partial \sigma^2} &= 0 \end{aligned} \tag{6}$$

To find the derivatives of $(\mathbf{Y} - X\beta)'(\mathbf{Y} - X\beta)$ with respect to each β_i we can multiply and obtain

$$(\mathbf{Y} - X\beta)'(\mathbf{Y} - X\beta) = \mathbf{Y}'\mathbf{Y} - 2\mathbf{Y}'X\beta + \beta'X'X\beta$$

since $\beta'X'\mathbf{Y}$ is a scalar and hence equals $\mathbf{Y}'X\beta$. We can write this as

$$\begin{aligned} (\mathbf{Y} - X\beta)'(\mathbf{Y} - X\beta) &= \mathbf{Y}'\mathbf{Y} + 2A\beta + \beta'S\beta \\ &= \mathbf{Y}'\mathbf{Y} + 2\sum_{i=1}^{p} a_i\beta_i + \sum_{\substack{i=1\\ i\neq j}}^{p}\sum_{j=1}^{p} \beta_i\beta_j s_{ij} + \sum_{i=1}^{p} \beta_i^2 s_{ii} \end{aligned}$$

where a_i is the ith element of A which is equal to $-\mathbf{Y}'X$, and s_{ij} is the

ijth element of $X'X$. If we take the derivative with respect to β_t, we get

$$\frac{\partial[(\mathbf{Y} - X\beta)'(\mathbf{Y} - X\beta)]}{\partial\beta_t} = 2a_t + \sum_{\substack{i=1\\ i\neq t}}^{p} \beta_i s_{it} + \sum_{\substack{j=1\\ j\neq t}}^{p} \beta_j s_{tj} + 2\beta_t s_{tt}$$

$$= 2a_t + 2\sum_{i=1}^{p} \beta_i s_{it}$$

If this is done for each t for $t = 1, 2, \cdots, p$, and the result set equal to 0, we get

$$\frac{\partial[(\mathbf{Y} - X\beta)'(\mathbf{Y} - \beta X)]}{\partial\beta_1} = 2a_1 + 2\sum_i \beta_i s_{i1} = 0$$

$$\frac{\partial[(\mathbf{Y} - X\beta)'(\mathbf{Y} - X\beta)]}{\partial\beta_2} = 2a_2 + 2\sum_i \beta_i s_{i2} = 0$$

$$\cdots\cdots\cdots\cdots\cdots\cdots\cdots\cdots$$

$$\frac{\partial[(\mathbf{Y} - X\beta)'(\mathbf{Y} - X\beta)]}{\partial\beta_p} = 2a_p + 2\sum_i \beta_i s_{ip} = 0$$

which gives

$$2A' + 2S\beta = \mathbf{0}$$

or

$$-2X'\mathbf{Y} + 2X'X\beta = \mathbf{0}$$

If $\hat{\boldsymbol{\beta}}$ and $\tilde{\boldsymbol{\sigma}}^2$ denote the solutions of the resulting equations, we get

$$X'X\hat{\boldsymbol{\beta}} = X'\mathbf{Y}$$

and

$$\tilde{\boldsymbol{\sigma}}^2 = \frac{1}{n}(\mathbf{Y} - X\hat{\boldsymbol{\beta}})'(\mathbf{Y} - X\hat{\boldsymbol{\beta}})$$

The matrix equation $X'X\hat{\boldsymbol{\beta}} = X'\mathbf{Y}$ is called the normal equation and will play an extremely important role in our theory. Since X is of rank p, $X'X$ is of rank p and hence has an inverse. Therefore, we get

$$\hat{\boldsymbol{\beta}} = \begin{pmatrix} \hat{\boldsymbol{\beta}}_1 \\ \hat{\boldsymbol{\beta}}_2 \\ \cdot \\ \cdot \\ \cdot \\ \hat{\boldsymbol{\beta}}_p \end{pmatrix} = S^{-1}X'\mathbf{Y}$$

where $S = X'X$. Since $\hat{\boldsymbol{\beta}}$ and $\tilde{\boldsymbol{\sigma}}^2$ are maximum-likelihood estimators, they are consistent and asymptotically efficient, but we must examine them to see if they are unbiased or sufficient. To examine $\hat{\boldsymbol{\beta}}$ for unbiasedness, we proceed as follows:

$$E(\hat{\boldsymbol{\beta}}) = E(S^{-1}X'\mathbf{Y}) = S^{-1}X'E(\mathbf{Y}) = S^{-1}X'E(X\beta + \mathbf{e}) = S^{-1}X'X\beta = \beta$$

Thus $\hat{\boldsymbol{\beta}}$ is an unbiased estimate of β. We shall omit the proof, but it can be shown that

$$\tilde{\boldsymbol{\sigma}}^2 \frac{n}{n-p} = \hat{\boldsymbol{\sigma}}^2 = \frac{(\mathbf{Y} - X\hat{\boldsymbol{\beta}})'(\mathbf{Y} - X\hat{\boldsymbol{\beta}})}{n-p}$$

is an unbiased estimator of σ^2.

Next we shall examine the sufficiency property. The joint frequency of the $\mathbf{e}_i$ can be written as

$$f(e) = \frac{1}{(2\pi\sigma^2)^{n/2}} \exp\left[-\frac{1}{2\sigma^2}(Y - X\beta)'(Y - X\beta)\right]$$

The identity in β

$$(\mathbf{Y} - X\beta)'(\mathbf{Y} - X\beta) = (\mathbf{Y} - X\hat{\boldsymbol{\beta}})'(\mathbf{Y} - X\hat{\boldsymbol{\beta}}) + (\beta - \hat{\boldsymbol{\beta}})'S(\beta - \hat{\boldsymbol{\beta}})$$

can be readily established. Using this identity, the joint density is

$$f(e) = \frac{1}{(2\pi\sigma^2)^{n/2}} \exp\left[-\frac{(Y - X\beta)'(Y - X\beta)}{2\sigma^2}\right]$$
$$= \frac{1}{(2\pi\sigma^2)^{n/2}} \exp\left[-\frac{(n-p)\hat{\sigma}^2 + (\beta - \hat{\beta})'S(\beta - \hat{\beta})}{2\sigma^2}\right]$$

and by using the definition of sufficiency in Chap. 8, it is clear that $\hat{\boldsymbol{\sigma}}^2, \hat{\boldsymbol{\beta}}_1, \hat{\boldsymbol{\beta}}_2, \cdots, \hat{\boldsymbol{\beta}}_p$ form a set of estimators which are jointly sufficient for $\sigma^2, \beta_1, \beta_2, \cdots, \beta_p$. We shall not give the proof but it can be shown that the estimators $\hat{\boldsymbol{\sigma}}^2, \hat{\boldsymbol{\beta}}_1, \hat{\boldsymbol{\beta}}_2, \cdots, \hat{\boldsymbol{\beta}}_p$ are complete.

Since $\hat{\boldsymbol{\beta}}$ is equal to the product of a constant matrix $S^{-1}X'$ and a vector $\mathbf{Y}$ which is normally distributed, Prob. 9.21 can be used to show that $\hat{\boldsymbol{\beta}}$ has the p-variate normal distribution. We have already shown that the mean of $\hat{\boldsymbol{\beta}}$ is β. The covariance matrix of $\hat{\boldsymbol{\beta}}$ is

$$\text{cov}(\hat{\boldsymbol{\beta}}) = E(\hat{\boldsymbol{\beta}} - \beta)(\hat{\boldsymbol{\beta}} - \beta)' = E(S^{-1}X'\mathbf{Y} - \beta)(S^{-1}X'\mathbf{Y} - \beta)'$$

If we substitute $X\beta + \mathbf{e}$ for $\mathbf{Y}$, we get

$$\text{cov}(\hat{\boldsymbol{\beta}}) = E[S^{-1}X'(X\beta + \mathbf{e}) - \beta][S^{-1}X'(X\beta + \mathbf{e}) - \beta]'$$
$$= E(S^{-1}X'\mathbf{e})(S^{-1}X'\mathbf{e})'$$
$$= E(S^{-1}X'\mathbf{e}\mathbf{e}'XS^{-1}) = S^{-1}X'E(\mathbf{e}\mathbf{e}')XS^{-1} = \sigma^2 S^{-1}X'XS^{-1} = \sigma^2 S^{-1}$$

Thus $\hat{\boldsymbol{\beta}}$ is distributed as the p-variate normal with mean β and covariance matrix $\sigma^2 S^{-1}$. The proof will be omitted but it can be shown that

$$(n - p)\frac{\hat{\sigma}^2}{\sigma^2} = \frac{(\mathbf{Y} - X\hat{\boldsymbol{\beta}})'(\mathbf{Y} - X\hat{\boldsymbol{\beta}})}{\sigma^2}$$

is distributed as chi square with $n - p$ degrees of freedom.

The foregoing can be summed up in the following theorem:

Theorem 13.3. *If* $\mathbf{Y} = X\beta + \mathbf{e}$ *is a general linear model of full rank and if* $\mathbf{e}$ *is distributed as the p-variate normal with mean* $\mathbf{0}$ *and covariance matrix* $\sigma^2 I$, then

$$\hat{\boldsymbol{\beta}} = S^{-1}X'\mathbf{Y} \qquad \hat{\sigma}^2 = \frac{\mathbf{Y}'(I - XS^{-1}X')\mathbf{Y}}{n - p}$$

satisfy the following:

1. Consistent.
2. Asymptotically efficient.
3. Minimum-variance unbiased.
4. Sufficient, complete.
5. $\hat{\boldsymbol{\beta}}$ is distributed as p-variate normal with mean β and covariance matrix $\sigma^2 S^{-1}$.
6. $(n - p)\hat{\sigma}^2/\sigma^2$ is distributed as chi square with $n - p$ degrees of freedom.
7. $\hat{\boldsymbol{\beta}}$ and $\hat{\sigma}^2$ are independent.

The Estimation of β and σ^2, Case B: The Gauss-Markoff Theorem. As in Sec. 13.5, the method of least squares can be used to estimate β when the density function of $\mathbf{Y}$ is not known. That is to say, we shall find the value of β, say $\hat{\boldsymbol{\beta}}$, such that the sum of squares $\sum_{i=1}^{n} \mathbf{e}_i^2$ is a minimum. This gives

$$\sum_{i=1}^{n} \mathbf{e}_i^2 = \mathbf{e}'\mathbf{e} = (\mathbf{Y} - X\beta)'(\mathbf{Y} - X\beta)$$

The value of β which minimizes $\mathbf{e}'\mathbf{e}$ is given by the solution of

$$\frac{\partial(\mathbf{e}'\mathbf{e})}{\partial\beta_t} = 0 \qquad t = 1, 2, \cdots, p$$

The solution of these equations gives (see Case A) $2X'\mathbf{Y} - 2X'X\hat{\boldsymbol{\beta}} = \mathbf{0}$. The least-squares estimate of β is, therefore,

$$\hat{\boldsymbol{\beta}} = S^{-1}X'\mathbf{Y}$$

which, of course, is the same as the maximum-likelihood estimate under normal theory. Minimizing the sum of squares, $\mathbf{e}'\mathbf{e}$, does not provide an estimate of σ^2. However, the estimate of σ^2 which is based on the least-squares estimate of β and which is unbiased is given by

$$\hat{\sigma}^2 = \frac{(\mathbf{Y} - X\hat{\boldsymbol{\beta}})'(\mathbf{Y} - X\hat{\boldsymbol{\beta}})}{n - p} = \frac{\mathbf{Y}'(I - XS^{-1}X')\mathbf{Y}}{n - p}$$

The next consideration will be to investigate the *properties* of the least-squares estimators. Since the distribution of the random vector $\mathbf{e}$ is unspecified, in general it will not be possible to examine the "goodness" of the estimator $\hat{\boldsymbol{\beta}}$, relative to all functions. Instead, we shall have to limit ourselves to a subset of all functions; for example, since $\hat{\boldsymbol{\beta}}$ is a linear function of the $\mathbf{y}_i$, we could examine $\hat{\boldsymbol{\beta}}$ to see what properties it possesses relative to all *linear* functions of the $\mathbf{y}_i$. When the vector $\mathbf{e}$ is normally distributed, we proved that $\hat{\boldsymbol{\beta}}_i$ had smaller variance than any other unbiased estimator of β_i regardless of what function of the $\mathbf{y}_i$ that is used as an estimator of β.

For the least-squares estimator we cannot make such a broad statement, but we can compare the "goodness" of $\hat{\boldsymbol{\beta}}_i$ with other estimators which are *linear* functions of the observations $\mathbf{y}_i$. However, if we are interested in a general function $h(\mathbf{y}_1, \mathbf{y}_2, \cdots, \mathbf{y}_n)$ as an estimator for β_i, then under quite general conditions the function $h(\mathbf{y}_1, \mathbf{y}_2, \cdots, \mathbf{y}_n)$ could be expanded into a Taylor series and the linear term used as a first approximation. While there are some good reasons why we *would* want to restrict ourselves to linear functions of the observations $\mathbf{y}_i$ as estimators of β_i, there are many times we would *not*. A theorem which asserts the quality of least-squares estimates in the model $\mathbf{Y} = X\beta + \mathbf{e}$ is the Gauss-Markoff theorem.

Theorem 13.4. *If the general linear model* $\mathbf{Y} = X\beta + \mathbf{e}$ *is such that the two conditions on the random vector* $\mathbf{e}$ *hold*

(*a*) $E(\mathbf{e}) = 0$
(*b*) $E(\mathbf{ee}') = \sigma^2 I$

then the best (minimum-variance) linear (linear functions of the $\mathbf{y}_i$*) unbiased estimate of* β *is given by least squares; that is,* $\hat{\boldsymbol{\beta}} = S^{-1}X'\mathbf{Y}$ *is the best linear unbiased estimate of* β.

The proof of this theorem will be omitted, but it follows the proof of the Gauss-Markoff theorem for the simple linear model.

In the foregoing the discussion has centered around the estimation of the β_i. However, we are often also interested in estimating certain functions of the β_i. Because of the invariance property of maximum-likelihood estimators, it is a straightforward procedure to obtain the maximum-likelihood estimator of any function of the β_i with a single-valued inverse. The situation is not so simple in the case of least-squares estimators. There is one important case, however, when the invariant property holds for least-squares estimators, and this is the case of linear functions of the β_i. This is stated in the following:

Theorem 13.5. *Under the general linear model as given in Theorem* 13.4 *the best linear unbiased estimate of any linear combination of the* β_i *is the same linear combination of the best linear unbiased estimates of the* β_i. *That is to say, the best linear unbiased estimate of* $t'\beta$ *(where* t *is a* $p \times 1$ *vector of constants) is* $t'\hat{\boldsymbol{\beta}}$, *where* $\hat{\boldsymbol{\beta}}$ *is the best linear unbiased estimate of* β, that is, $t'\hat{\boldsymbol{\beta}} = t'S^{-1}X'\mathbf{Y}$.

The proof follows the line of Theorem 13.4 and will be left as an exercise for the reader.

Example 13.3. A simple linear model is given by

$$\mathbf{y}_i = \beta_1 + \beta_2 x_i + \mathbf{e}_i \qquad i = 1, 2, \cdots, n$$

where β_1 and β_2 are unknown scalar constants and the x_i are known scalar constants. Therefore, by referring to equation (4), we find that $(p = 2)$

$$X = \begin{pmatrix} 1 & x_1 \\ 1 & x_2 \\ \cdot & \cdot \\ \cdot & \cdot \\ \cdot & \cdot \\ 1 & x_n \end{pmatrix} \qquad \beta = \begin{pmatrix} \beta_1 \\ \beta_2 \end{pmatrix}$$

It is easy to see that

$$S = X'X = \begin{pmatrix} n & \Sigma x_i \\ \Sigma x_i & \Sigma x_i^2 \end{pmatrix}$$

$$S^{-1} = \frac{1}{n\Sigma(x_i - \bar{x})^2} \begin{pmatrix} \Sigma x_i^2 & -\Sigma x_i \\ -\Sigma x_i & n \end{pmatrix}$$

and

$$X'\mathbf{Y} = \begin{pmatrix} \Sigma \mathbf{y}_i \\ \Sigma x_i \mathbf{y}_i \end{pmatrix}$$

Thus

$$\hat{\boldsymbol{\beta}} = \begin{pmatrix} \hat{\boldsymbol{\beta}}_1 \\ \hat{\boldsymbol{\beta}}_2 \end{pmatrix} = S^{-1}X'\mathbf{Y} = \frac{1}{n\Sigma(x_i - \bar{x})^2} \begin{pmatrix} (\Sigma x_i^2)(\Sigma \mathbf{y}_i) - (\Sigma x_i)(\Sigma x_i \mathbf{y}_i) \\ -(\Sigma x_i)(\Sigma \mathbf{y}_i) + n\Sigma \mathbf{y}_i x_i \end{pmatrix}$$

or

$$\hat{\boldsymbol{\beta}}_2 = \frac{\Sigma(x_i - \bar{x})(\mathbf{y}_i - \bar{\mathbf{y}})}{\Sigma(x_i - \bar{x})^2} \qquad \hat{\boldsymbol{\beta}}_1 = \bar{\mathbf{y}} - \hat{\boldsymbol{\beta}}_2 \bar{x}$$

β_2 is the slope, and β_1 is the value of $E(\mathbf{y})$ when $x = 0$.

Since the cov $(\hat{\boldsymbol{\beta}}) = S^{-1}\sigma^2$, we see that

$$\text{cov}\,(\hat{\boldsymbol{\beta}}_1, \hat{\boldsymbol{\beta}}_2) = -\frac{\sigma^2\Sigma x_i}{n\Sigma(x_i - \bar{x})^2}$$

$$\text{var}\,\hat{\boldsymbol{\beta}}_1 = \frac{\sigma^2\Sigma x_i^2}{n\Sigma(x_i - \bar{x})^2}$$

and

$$\text{var}\,\hat{\boldsymbol{\beta}}_2 = \frac{\sigma^2}{\Sigma(x_i - \bar{x})^2}$$

These results are exactly those given in Sec. 13.2, and they were reproduced here to show how matrices can be used even in that situation.

Interval Estimation of β_i. We shall now turn our attention to the problem of interval estimation of β_i for Case A only.

To set a $1 - \alpha$ confidence interval on β_i, we use the fact that $\hat{\boldsymbol{\beta}}_i$ is distributed $n(\beta_i, c_{ii}\sigma^2)$, where c_{ij} is the ijth element of $C = S^{-1}$. Therefore,

$$\mathbf{y} = \frac{\hat{\boldsymbol{\beta}}_i - \beta_i}{\sigma\sqrt{c_{ii}}}$$

is distributed $n(y; 0, 1)$ and is independent of $(n - p)\hat{\boldsymbol{\sigma}}^2/\sigma^2$ which is distributed as chi-square with $n - p$ degrees of freedom. It follows that

$$\mathbf{u} = \frac{\hat{\boldsymbol{\beta}}_i - \beta_i}{\sigma\sqrt{c_{ii}}}\sqrt{\frac{\sigma^2}{\hat{\boldsymbol{\sigma}}^2}} = \frac{\hat{\boldsymbol{\beta}}_i - \beta_i}{\sqrt{\hat{\boldsymbol{\sigma}}^2 c_{ii}}}$$

is distributed as Student's t with $n - p$ degrees of freedom. Thus

$$\int_{-t_{\alpha/2}}^{t_{\alpha/2}} t(u)\,du = P\left(-t_{\alpha/2} < \frac{\hat{\boldsymbol{\beta}}_i - \beta_i}{\sqrt{\hat{\boldsymbol{\sigma}}^2 c_{ii}}} < t_{\alpha/2}\right) = 1 - \alpha$$

where $t(u)$ is the density of Student's t. After some manipulations we get

$$P(\hat{\boldsymbol{\beta}}_i - t_{\alpha/2}\sqrt{c_{ii}\hat{\boldsymbol{\sigma}}^2} < \beta_i < \hat{\boldsymbol{\beta}}_i + t_{\alpha/2}\sqrt{c_{ii}\hat{\boldsymbol{\sigma}}^2}) = 1 - \alpha \tag{7}$$

and the quantity in parentheses is a $1 - \alpha$ confidence interval on β_i. The width of the interval is $2t_{\alpha/2}\sqrt{c_{ii}\hat{\boldsymbol{\sigma}}^2}$.

Test of the Hypothesis $\beta_1 = \beta_2 = \cdots = \beta_r = 0$ $(r \le p)$ *in the Model* $\mathbf{Y} = X\beta + \mathbf{e}$ *in Definition* 13.4. This is a very useful and very important test; for example, for the case $p = 3$ the model is

$$\mathbf{y} = x_1\beta_1 + x_2\beta_2 + x_3\beta_3 + \boldsymbol{\varepsilon}$$

Now suppose that an experimenter wants to know if he can replace this model with the model

$$\mathbf{y} = x_1\beta_1 + x_2\beta_2 + \boldsymbol{\varepsilon}$$

In other words, he wants to test the hypothesis $\beta_3 = 0$ in the model with no stipulation about the value of β_1 or β_2. We shall state a theorem which will enable us to test any set of the β_i equal to 0 in the general linear model $\mathbf{Y} = X\beta + \mathbf{e}$.

In the model

$$\mathbf{Y} = X\beta + \mathbf{e}$$

we shall partition the matrix X and the vector β so that

$$X = (X_1, X_2) \qquad \beta = \begin{pmatrix} \gamma_1 \\ \gamma_2 \end{pmatrix}$$

where X_1 has dimension $n \times r$ and γ_1 has dimension $r \times 1$. Then the model can be written

$$\mathbf{Y} = X\beta + \mathbf{e} = (X_1, X_2) \begin{pmatrix} \gamma_1 \\ \gamma_2 \end{pmatrix} + \mathbf{e}$$

or

$$\mathbf{Y} = X_1\gamma_1 + X_2\gamma_2 + \mathbf{e}$$

We desire a test of the hypothesis $\gamma_1 = \mathbf{0}$ with no stipulations on γ_2. Since

$$\gamma_1 = \begin{pmatrix} \beta_1 \\ \beta_2 \\ \cdot \\ \cdot \\ \cdot \\ \beta_r \end{pmatrix}$$

this test is equivalent to testing the hypothesis $\beta_1 = \beta_2 = \cdots = \beta_r = 0$ $(r \leq p)$ in the general linear model.

$$\mathbf{y}_j = \sum_{i=1}^{p} x_{ji}\beta_i + \mathbf{e}_j \qquad j = 1, 2, \cdots, n$$

The test of the hypothesis H_0: $\gamma_1 = \mathbf{0}$ and its construction are stated in the following:

Theorem 13.6. *Let the model* $\mathbf{Y} = X\beta + \mathbf{e}$ *given in Definition* 13.1 *be partitioned so that*

$$\mathbf{Y} = X_1\gamma_1 + X_2\gamma_2 + \mathbf{e}$$

where γ_1 *is of dimension* $r \times 1$, *and let* $\mathbf{e}$ *be distributed as the p-variate normal with mean* $\mathbf{0}$ *and covariance matrix* $\sigma^2 I$. *Then to test the hypothesis* H_0: $\gamma_1 = \mathbf{0}$ *by the likelihood-ratio test the procedure is:*

1. *Obtain the normal equations* $X'X\hat{\beta} = X'\mathbf{Y}$, *and from these compute* $\hat{\beta}'X'\mathbf{Y}$.
2. *From the model* $\mathbf{Y} = X_2\gamma_2 + \mathbf{e}$ *(this is called the model restricted by the hypothesis* H_0*) obtain the normal equations* $X_2'X_2\tilde{\gamma}_2 = X_2'\mathbf{Y}$, *and*

from these compute $\tilde{\gamma}_2'X_2'\mathbf{Y}$. *Notice that the reduced normal equations can be obtained from the original normal equations,* $X'X\hat{\beta} = X'\mathbf{Y}$, *by setting* $\hat{\beta}_1 = \hat{\beta}_2 = \cdots = \hat{\beta}_r = 0$ *and using only the last* $p - r$ *equations.*

3. *Compute*

$$\mathbf{u} = \frac{\hat{\beta}'X'\mathbf{Y} - \tilde{\gamma}_2'X_2'\mathbf{Y}}{\mathbf{Y}'\mathbf{Y} - \hat{\beta}'X'\mathbf{Y}} \frac{n-p}{r} \tag{8}$$

and reject H_0 *if* $\mathbf{u} > F_\alpha(r, n-p)$, *where* $F_\alpha(r, n-p)$ *is the upper* 100α *percentage point of the F distribution with* r *and* $n - p$ *degrees of freedom. This gives a Type I error probability* α.

The proof of this theorem is beyond the scope of this book, but a proof can be found in Ref. 3.

The quantities in this theorem are often put into a table as in Table 13.1.

TABLE 13.1. ANALYSIS-OF-VARIANCE TABLE

Source	Degrees of freedom	Sum of squares	Mean square	F
Total	n	$\mathbf{Y}'\mathbf{Y}$		
Reduction due to β	p	$\hat{\beta}'X'\mathbf{Y}$		
Reduction due to γ_2	$p - r$	$\tilde{\gamma}_2'X_2'\mathbf{Y}$		
Reduction due to γ_1 (adjusted for γ_2)	r	$\hat{\beta}'X'\mathbf{Y} - \tilde{\gamma}_2'X_2'\mathbf{Y} = r\mathbf{s}_1^2$	$\mathbf{s}_1^2$	$\frac{\mathbf{s}_1^2}{\mathbf{s}_2^2}$
Error	$n - p$	$\mathbf{Y}'\mathbf{Y} - \hat{\beta}'X'\mathbf{Y} = (n-p)\mathbf{s}_2^2$	$\mathbf{s}_2^2$	

We shall illustrate this theorem by some examples.

Example 13.4. To illustrate the foregoing theory, we shall use an example of a model $\mathbf{y} = \beta_1 + \beta_2 x_2 + \beta_3 x_3 + \mathbf{e}$. In this model the appropriate matrices are

$$X'\mathbf{Y} = \begin{pmatrix} \sum \mathbf{y}_i \\ \sum x_{2i}\mathbf{y}_i \\ \sum x_{3i}\mathbf{y}_i \end{pmatrix} \qquad X = \begin{pmatrix} 1 & x_{21} & x_{31} \\ 1 & x_{22} & x_{32} \\ 1 & x_{23} & x_{33} \\ \cdot & \cdot & \cdot \\ \cdot & \cdot & \cdot \\ 1 & x_{2n} & x_{3n} \end{pmatrix}$$

$$X'X = \begin{pmatrix} n & \sum_i x_{2i} & \sum_i x_{3i} \\ \sum_i x_{2i} & \sum_i x_{2i}^2 & \sum_i x_{2i}x_{3i} \\ \sum_i x_{3i} & \sum_i x_{2i}x_{3i} & \sum_i x_{3i}^2 \end{pmatrix}$$

Notice that $x_{1i} = 1$ for all i. For simplicity we shall use artificial data. Suppose that $\mathbf{Y'Y} = \Sigma \mathbf{y}_i^2 = 6540$ and that

$$S = X'X = \begin{pmatrix} 16 & 8 & 4 \\ 8 & 6 & 2 \\ 4 & 2 & 6 \end{pmatrix} \qquad X'\mathbf{Y} = \begin{pmatrix} 80 \\ 120 \\ 40 \end{pmatrix} \qquad p = 3,\ n = 16 \quad (9)$$

The normal equations $X'X\hat{\boldsymbol{\beta}} = X'\mathbf{Y}$ are

$$\begin{aligned} 16\hat{\beta}_1 + 8\hat{\beta}_2 + 4\hat{\beta}_3 &= 80 \\ 8\hat{\beta}_1 + 6\hat{\beta}_2 + 2\hat{\beta}_3 &= 120 \\ 4\hat{\beta}_1 + 2\hat{\beta}_2 + 6\hat{\beta}_3 &= 40 \end{aligned} \qquad (10)$$

We find that

$$C = S^{-1} = \begin{pmatrix} .20 & -.25 & -.05 \\ -.25 & .50 & 0 \\ -.05 & 0 & .20 \end{pmatrix}$$

and

$$\hat{\boldsymbol{\beta}} = \begin{pmatrix} \hat{\beta}_1 \\ \hat{\beta}_2 \\ \hat{\beta}_3 \end{pmatrix} = S^{-1}X'\mathbf{Y} = \begin{pmatrix} .20 & -.25 & -.05 \\ -.25 & .50 & 0 \\ -.05 & 0 & .20 \end{pmatrix} \begin{pmatrix} 80 \\ 120 \\ 40 \end{pmatrix} = \begin{pmatrix} -16 \\ 40 \\ 4 \end{pmatrix}$$

Thus the estimates are $\hat{\beta}_1 = -16$, $\hat{\beta}_2 = 40$, $\hat{\beta}_3 = 4$, and $\hat{\boldsymbol{\beta}}'X'\mathbf{Y} = 3680$, and

$$\hat{\sigma}^2 = \frac{(\mathbf{Y} - X\hat{\boldsymbol{\beta}})'(\mathbf{Y} - X\hat{\boldsymbol{\beta}})}{n - p} = \frac{\mathbf{Y'Y} - \hat{\boldsymbol{\beta}}'X'\mathbf{Y}}{n - p} = \frac{6540 - 3680}{13} = 220$$

To test the hypothesis $\beta_2 = \beta_3 = 0$, set β_2 and β_3 equal to 0 in the model, and the reduced normal equations are $X_2'X_2\tilde{\boldsymbol{\gamma}}_2 = X_2'\mathbf{Y}$, which by Theorem 13.6 are obtained from (10) by setting $\hat{\beta}_2$ and $\hat{\beta}_3$ equal to 0 and striking out the last two equations (the $\hat{\beta}_2$ and $\hat{\beta}_3$ equations). This gives the reduced normal equations (only one equation in this particular case)

$$16\tilde{\beta}_1 = 80$$

which gives $\tilde{\beta}_1 = 5$ and again we state: The reduced normal equations can always be found by striking the rows and columns from $X'X$ corresponding to the elements in β which are to be tested equal to 0 and by striking the rows from $X'\mathbf{Y}$ corresponding to these same elements. For instance, in this example we are testing the last two elements of β equal to 0, and so we cross the last two rows and columns from $X'X$, which leaves 16; cross the last two elements from $X'\mathbf{Y}$, which leaves 80; and so the reduced normal equation corresponding to $X_2'X_2\tilde{\boldsymbol{\gamma}}_2 = X_2'\mathbf{Y}$ is $n\tilde{\beta}_1 = \Sigma \mathbf{y}_i$. Then compute

$$\tilde{\boldsymbol{\gamma}}_2'X_2'\mathbf{Y} = \tilde{\beta}_1(\Sigma \mathbf{y}_i) = (5)(80) = 400$$

Then

$$\hat{\beta}'X'Y = 3680$$
$$\tilde{\gamma}_2'X_2'Y = \tilde{\beta}_1(\Sigma y_i) = 400$$
$$\hat{\beta}X'Y - \tilde{\gamma}_2'X_2'Y = 3280$$

Error sum of squares $= Y'Y - \hat{\beta}X'Y = 2860.$

The quantity

$$u = \frac{3280/2}{2860/13} = \frac{1640}{220} = 7.5$$

which is greater than $F_{.01}$, and so the hypothesis is rejected at the 1 per cent level. The quantities can be summarized in an analysis-of-variance table (see Table 13.2).

TABLE 13.2. ANALYSIS-OF-VARIANCE TABLE FOR TESTING $\beta_2 = \beta_3 = 0$

Source	Degrees of freedom	Sum of squares	Mean square	F
Total	16	6540		
Reduction due to $(\beta_1, \beta_2, \beta_3)$	3	3680		
Reduction due to (β_1)	1	400		
Reduction due to (β_2, β_3 adjusted for β_1)	2	3280	1640	7.5
Error	13	2860	220	

Example 13.5. We shall illustrate further by testing the hypothesis $\beta_3 = 0$ in Example 13.4. Of course the normal equations $\hat{\beta}'X'Y$ are the same as in Example 13.4; hence $\hat{\beta}'X'Y = 3680$, and the error sum of squares is $Y'Y - \hat{\beta}'X'Y = 2860$. To get the reduced normal equations, cross the row and column corresponding to $\hat{\beta}_3$ (last row and column) from $X'X$ and from $X'Y$. This gives

$$X_2'X_2\tilde{\gamma}_2 = X_2'Y$$

as

$$\begin{pmatrix} 16 & 8 \\ 8 & 6 \end{pmatrix}\begin{pmatrix} \tilde{\beta}_1 \\ \tilde{\beta}_2 \end{pmatrix} = \begin{pmatrix} 80 \\ 120 \end{pmatrix}$$

Thus

$$\tilde{\gamma}_2 = \begin{pmatrix} \tilde{\beta}_1 \\ \tilde{\beta}_2 \end{pmatrix} = \begin{pmatrix} .19 & -.25 \\ -.25 & .50 \end{pmatrix}\begin{pmatrix} 80 \\ 120 \end{pmatrix} = \begin{pmatrix} -14.8 \\ 40.0 \end{pmatrix}$$

and $r = 1$, $n = 16$, $p = 3$; also

$$\tilde{\gamma}_2'X_2'Y = (-14.8)(80) + (120)(40) = 3616$$

The F value is less than 1.

13.7 Problems

1. Assume that the following data satisfy the model

$$\mathbf{y}_i = \beta_1 + \beta_2 x_i + \mathbf{e}_i$$

y	−6.1	−.5	7.2	6.9	−.2	−2.1	−3.9	3.8
x	−2.0	.6	1.4	1.3	.0	−1.6	−1.7	.7

(*a*) Find $X'X$. (*b*) Find $X'\mathbf{Y}$. (*c*) Find $\hat{\beta}' = (\hat{\beta}_1, \hat{\beta}_2)$.

2. In Prob. 1, set a .95 confidence interval on β_2.

3. In the model defined by Definition 13.1, find var $(\hat{\alpha} + \hat{\beta} x_0)$ for a fixed value x_0.

4. For Case A on the errors in the model in Definition 13.1, find the distribution of $(\hat{\alpha} + \hat{\beta} x_0)$ for a fixed value x_0.

5. In Prob. 4, show that $[(\hat{\alpha} + \hat{\beta} x_0) - (\alpha + \beta x_0)]/\sqrt{a\hat{\sigma}^2}$ is distributed as Student's t with $n - 2$ degrees of freedom, where $a\sigma^2$ is var $(\hat{\alpha} + \hat{\beta} x_0)$ in Prob. 4.

6. Use the results of Prob. 5 to set a .95 confidence interval on $(\alpha + \beta)$ for the data in Prob. 1.

7. In Prob. 1, test the hypothesis $H_0 : \beta_2 = 0$ with a Type I error probability of .05.

***8.** By using Theorem 13.3, show that $\mathbf{u} = (\hat{\beta} - \beta)' S (\hat{\beta} - \beta)/\sigma^2$ is distributed as chi square with p degrees of freedom.

***9.** By using Theorem 13.3 and Prob. 8, show that

$$\mathbf{v} = \frac{(\hat{\beta} - \beta)' S (\hat{\beta} - \beta)}{p\hat{\sigma}^2}$$

is distributed as F with p and $n - p$ degrees of freedom.

***10.** Use Prob. 9 and the data in Prob. 1 to find a .95 confidence region on β_1 and β_2. Plot the region.

***11.** Given the data:

y	12.1	11.9	10.2	8.0	7.7	5.3	7.9	7.8	5.5	2.6
x_1	0	1	2	3	4	5	6	7	8	9
x_2	7	4	44	6	4	2	1	1	1	0

fit the model $\mathbf{y} = \beta_0 + \beta_1 x_1 + \beta_2 x_2 + \mathbf{e}$, and find a .95 confidence interval for σ^2.

* The starred problems depend on Sec. 13.6.

***12.** Find a 95 per cent confidence interval for β_1 of Prob. 11.

***13.** Test the null hypothesis that β_2 of Prob. 11 is 0.

***14.** Test the null hypothesis that $\beta_1 + 10\beta_2 = 0$ in Prob. 11.

***15.** Using only the first two rows of the data of Prob. 11, fit the model

$$\mathbf{y} = \beta_0 + \beta_1 x_1 + \beta_2 x_1^2 + \mathbf{e}$$

and test the null hypothesis that $\beta_2 = 0$.

***16.** The fitting of polynomials such as the quadratic of Prob. 15 is much simplified when the values are equally spaced by using *orthogonal polynomials.* Let $x = 0, 1, \cdots, n$. The first three orthogonal polynomials are

$$P_1 = x - \frac{n}{2}$$

$$P_2 = \left(x - \frac{n}{2}\right)^2 - \frac{n(n+2)}{12}$$

$$P_3 = \left(x - \frac{n}{2}\right)^3 - \frac{3n(n+2) - 4}{20}\left(x - \frac{n}{2}\right)$$

Show that

$$\sum_x P_1P_2 = \sum_x P_1P_3 = \sum_x P_2P_3 = 0$$

***17.** Rework Prob. 15, fitting instead the model

$$\mathbf{y} = \beta_0 + \beta_1 P_1 + \beta_2 P_2 + \mathbf{e}$$

where P_1 and P_2 are defined in Prob. 16.

18. If $\mathbf{y}_1$ and $\mathbf{y}_2$ have a bivariate normal distribution, what are the coefficients (in terms of σ_{11}, σ_{22}, and ρ) of the regression function for the conditional distribution of $\mathbf{y}_1$? For the conditional distribution of $\mathbf{y}_2$? If the two regression lines were estimated from the same sample, would they, in general, be different?

19. If $\mathbf{y}_1$, $\mathbf{y}_2$, $\mathbf{y}_3$ have a trivariate normal distribution, what are the coefficients of the regression function for the conditional distribution of $\mathbf{y}_1$, given $\mathbf{y}_2$ and $\mathbf{y}_3$, in terms of the variances and correlations?

20. Let the two-dimensional random variable $(\mathbf{y}, \mathbf{x})$ have a bivariate normal density with correlation ρ equal to 0. Let $(\mathbf{y}_1, \mathbf{x}_1), \cdots, (\mathbf{y}_n, \mathbf{x}_n)$ be a random sample of size n from this density and let

$$\hat{\boldsymbol{\rho}} = \frac{\Sigma(\mathbf{y}_i - \bar{\mathbf{y}})(\mathbf{x}_i - \bar{\mathbf{x}})}{\sqrt{\Sigma(\mathbf{y}_i - \bar{\mathbf{y}})^2\Sigma(\mathbf{x}_i - \bar{\mathbf{x}})^2}}$$

Show that $\hat{\boldsymbol{\rho}}$ has the density

$$f(\hat{\rho}) = \frac{[(n-3)/2]!(1-\hat{\rho}^2)^{(n-4)/2}}{\sqrt{\pi}\,[(n-4)/2]!} \qquad -1 < \hat{\rho} < 1$$

21. Referring to Prob. 20, transform $\hat{\varrho}$ to a new variate

$$\mathbf{t} = \hat{\varrho}\left(\frac{n-2}{1-\hat{\varrho}^2}\right)^{\frac{1}{2}}$$

Show that $\mathbf{t}$ has "Student's" distribution with $n - 2$ degrees of freedom so that the t tables may be used for testing the null hypothesis $\rho = 0$.

22. Assume that the data of Prob. 1 are from a bivariate normal population and test the null hypothesis that $\rho = 0$.

23. When ρ is not zero, the distribution of $\hat{\varrho}$ is not a simple function, but it has been tabulated for n, the sample size, less than 25. Fisher has shown that

$$\mathbf{z} = \frac{1}{2}\log\frac{1+\hat{\varrho}}{1-\hat{\varrho}}$$

is approximately normally distributed with mean

$$\epsilon = \frac{1}{2}\log\frac{1+\rho}{1-\rho}$$

and variance $1/(n-3)$. Using this result, find an approximate 95 per cent confidence interval for ρ of Prob. 22.

24. Go through the details of the proof of Theorem 13.2 for the parameter β.

25. In Prob. 2, find the expected width of the confidence interval.

***26.** For the model and data in Prob. 11, we want to test the hypothesis H_0: $\beta_1 = \beta_2 = 0$. If Theorem 13.6 is used, (*a*) identify γ_1 and X_1 and (*b*) identify γ_2 and X_2.

***27.** In Prob. 26, find the normal equations $X'X\hat{\mathfrak{F}} = X'\mathbf{Y}$, and $\hat{\mathfrak{F}}'X'\mathbf{Y}$.

***28.** In Prob. 26, find the reduced normal equations $X_2'X_2\tilde{\gamma}_2 = X_2'\mathbf{Y}$, and $\tilde{\gamma}_2'X_2'\mathbf{Y}$.

***29.** In Theorem 13.6, show that $\hat{\mathfrak{F}}'X'\mathbf{Y} - \tilde{\gamma}_2'X_2'\mathbf{Y}$ is equal to

$$\mathbf{Y}'[XS^{-1}X' - X_2(X_2'X_2)^{-1}X_2']\mathbf{Y}$$

30. A variate $\mathbf{y}$ is distributed about $\alpha + \beta x$ by the density

$$f(y|x) = 1 \qquad \alpha + \beta x - \tfrac{1}{2} < y < \alpha + \beta x + \tfrac{1}{2}$$

Find the maximum-likelihood estimate of α and β, given the sample of four points (y, x): $(.3, 1)$, $(-.7, 2)$, $(-1.7, 3)$, $(-1.8, 4)$. Compare it with the least-squares line.

31. If x and y have the trinomial distribution

$$f(x, y) = \frac{m!}{x!y!(m-x-y)!}\,p^x q^y (1-p-q)^{m-x-y}$$

find the regression function of y on x.

13.8 Bibliography

1. Anderson, R. L., and T. A. Bancroft: "Statistical Theory in Research," McGraw-Hill Book Company, Inc., New York, 1952.
2. Fisher, R. A.: "The goodness of fit and regression formulae, and the distribution of regression coefficients," *Journal of the Royal Statistical Society*, Vol. 85, Pt. IV (1922); reprinted in "Contributions to Mathematical Statistics," John Wiley & Sons, Inc., New York, 1950.
3. Graybill, F. A.: "An Introduction to Linear Statistical Models," Vol. I, McGraw-Hill Book Company, Inc., New York, 1961.
4. Kempthorne, O.: "Design and Analysis of Experiments," John Wiley & Sons, Inc., New York, 1952.
5. Kolodziejczyk, S.: "On an important class of statistical hypotheses," *Biometrika*, Vol. 27 (1935).
6. Kullback, S.: "Information Theory and Statistics," John Wiley & Sons, Inc., New York, 1959.
7. Mann, H. B.: "Analysis and Design of Experiments," Dover Publications, New York, 1949.
8. Rao, C. R.: "Advanced Statistical Methods in Biometric Research," John Wiley & Sons, Inc., New York, 1952.
9. Wilks, S. S.: "Mathematical Statistics," Princeton University Press, Princeton, N.J., 1943.

14

*Experimental Design Models**

14.1 Introduction

In the previous chapter we discussed the techniques which an experimenter could use if he was primarily interested in finding a formula from which he could predict the value of a factor under study by using the value of a related factor. For instance, he may wish to predict the hardness $\mathbf{y}$ of a metal by knowing the temperature T of the chemical process and the time t of a certain chemical operation. The model would be of the form

$$\mathbf{y} = f(T, t) + \mathbf{e}$$

In this chapter we shall discuss a somewhat different situation in which the interest is not in predicting the value of one factor by using the value of related factors, but the interest is mainly in comparing the *effects* of two or more factors.

Example 14.1. Let us suppose that a factory manager wishes to buy machines to perform a certain operation in a production process. There are three companies which make such machines, and he obtains one on trial from each company with a view to determining which of the three is best suited to his purposes. Suppose also that a machine is operated by one man. The manager intends to have several of his men operate the machines for a few days in order to discover which machine produces the most items per day. In this simple experiment the measurement is the number of items produced, and the factor under study is the type of machine.

Let us suppose that six men are to be used in the experiment, two being assigned at random to each machine, and that each man will work one day on the particular machine to which he is assigned. There will then be two observations for each of the three machines, each observation being the amount produced by the machine in one day. The data might be such as appear in the accompanying table. The question of interest is whether or not the machines are different with respect to the number of items produced.

* In this chapter matrices are used quite extensively.

Machine number		
1	2	3
64	41	65
39	48	57

The model for this experiment can be written

$$\begin{aligned} \mathbf{y}_{11} &= \mu + \tau_1 + \mathbf{e}_{11} \\ \mathbf{y}_{12} &= \mu + \tau_1 + \mathbf{e}_{12} \\ \mathbf{y}_{21} &= \mu + \tau_2 + \mathbf{e}_{21} \\ \mathbf{y}_{22} &= \mu + \tau_2 + \mathbf{e}_{22} \\ \mathbf{y}_{31} &= \mu + \tau_3 + \mathbf{e}_{31} \\ \mathbf{y}_{32} &= \mu + \tau_3 + \mathbf{e}_{32} \end{aligned} \tag{1}$$

where $\mathbf{y}_{ij}$ is the jth observation (by some method of identification) on the ith machine, μ is a general mean, τ_i is the effect of the ith machine, and $\mathbf{e}_{ij}$ are unobservable random errors which account for the uncontrollable variation such as difference between operators, temperature, etc. A realistic model is one such that the restriction $\tau_1 + \tau_2 + \tau_3 = 0$ is imposed. Then the general mean μ is $E[\frac{1}{6}\Sigma \mathbf{y}_{ij}]$. However, for proving the general theorems, we shall not impose this condition. This will be discussed later in more detail. Model (1) can be written in more compact form

$$\mathbf{y}_{ij} = \mu + \tau_i + \mathbf{e}_{ij} \qquad i = 1, 2, 3; j = 1, 2 \tag{2}$$

The system of equations (1) can be written in matrix notation as

$$\begin{pmatrix} \mathbf{y}_{11} \\ \mathbf{y}_{12} \\ \mathbf{y}_{21} \\ \mathbf{y}_{22} \\ \mathbf{y}_{31} \\ \mathbf{y}_{32} \end{pmatrix} = \begin{pmatrix} 1 & 1 & 0 & 0 \\ 1 & 1 & 0 & 0 \\ 1 & 0 & 1 & 0 \\ 1 & 0 & 1 & 0 \\ 1 & 0 & 0 & 1 \\ 1 & 0 & 0 & 1 \end{pmatrix} \begin{pmatrix} \mu \\ \tau_1 \\ \tau_2 \\ \tau_3 \end{pmatrix} + \begin{pmatrix} \mathbf{e}_{11} \\ \mathbf{e}_{12} \\ \mathbf{e}_{21} \\ \mathbf{e}_{22} \\ \mathbf{e}_{31} \\ \mathbf{e}_{32} \end{pmatrix} \tag{3}$$

or as

$$\mathbf{Y} = X\beta + \mathbf{e}$$

where $\mathbf{Y}$ is a 6×1 vector of observations, β is a 4×1 vector of the unknown parameters, $\mathbf{e}$ is a 6×1 vector of unobservable errors, and X is a matrix of 0's and 1's. The reader can multiply the matrix system (3) to verify that it is equivalent to (1). The thing to notice is that this model $\mathbf{Y} = X\beta + \mathbf{e}$ is the same as in the previous chapter except that the entries are 0's and 1's, and we also notice that the X matrix in (3) is a 6×4 matrix but the rank is 3. Hence $X'X$ also has rank 3, and so the inverse does not exist. This presents some difficulty that is not generally present in the theory of general linear models as discussed in Chap. 13.

14.2 Experimental Design Model

Although we shall use (14.1.3) as an example, the general experimental design model is given in the following definition.

Definition 14.1. *Let the random observable $n \times 1$ vector* $\mathbf{Y}$ *be such that*

$$\mathbf{Y} = X\beta + \mathbf{e} \tag{1}$$

where X is a known $n \times p$ matrix of rank r, where $r < p \le n$, and X contains only 0's and 1's. β is a vector of unknown parameters; and $\mathbf{e}$ *is a vector of unobservable random variables. This will be defined as an experimental design model.*

We notice that, since the rank of X is r, the rank of $X'X$ is also r and hence $X'X$ has no inverse. In general, an experimental design model can be written as

$$\mathbf{y}_{ij\cdots m} = \mu_{ij\cdots m} + \mathbf{e}_{ij\cdots m} \tag{1a}$$

where $\mu_{ij\cdots m}$ is a linear combination of the parameters. For instance, in Example 14.1, $\mu_{ij} = \mu + \tau_i$.

We shall make the following assumptions on the $\mathbf{e}_{ij}$:

Case A: $\mathbf{e}_{ij}$ are normal variables which are uncorrelated, with mean 0 and variance σ^2.

Case B: $\mathbf{e}_{ij}$ are uncorrelated random variables (not necessarily normal) with mean 0 and variance σ^2.

Point Estimation. Whether we use Case A and maximum likelihood or Case B and least squares, when the derivatives with respect to the β_i are set equal to 0, the same system of equations is obtained,

$$X'X\hat{\boldsymbol{\beta}} = X'\mathbf{Y} \tag{2}$$

We can also obtain

$$\tilde{\boldsymbol{\sigma}}^2 = \frac{1}{n}(\mathbf{Y} - X\hat{\boldsymbol{\beta}})'(\mathbf{Y} - X\hat{\boldsymbol{\beta}}) \tag{3}$$

In obtaining the normal equations (2) and the equation for $\tilde{\boldsymbol{\sigma}}^2$ in (3) the fact that $X'X$ has no inverse is not encountered. However, if $X'X$ has an inverse, then the normal equations have a unique solution

$$\hat{\boldsymbol{\beta}} = (X'X)^{-1}X'\mathbf{Y}$$

which are the point estimators for the elements of β. The situation is somewhat different for the case that $X'X$ has no inverse; there may be two situations: (1) there is no vector $\hat{\boldsymbol{\beta}}$ which satisfies equation (2) or

(2) there are an infinite number of vectors which satisfy (2). It can be shown that the latter situation holds; i.e., there are an infinite number of vectors $\hat{\boldsymbol{\beta}}$ which satisfy the normal equations (2). This can be proved by using a theorem from matrix algebra which states that, if a square matrix $X'X$ has no inverse and the rank of $X'X$ equals the rank of the matrix $(X'X|X'\mathbf{Y})$, then there are an infinite number of vectors $\hat{\boldsymbol{\beta}}$ which satisfy (2). The matrix $(X'X|X'\mathbf{Y})$ is the matrix $X'X$ with $X'\mathbf{Y}$ put on as an extra column.

This is not a very satisfactory situation; two experimenters with the same model and the same observations get the same normal equations but each gets a different estimate of β_i.

We shall be interested in unbiased estimates of the β_i (elements of β) if they exist, and so we shall be interested to see which solutions $\hat{\boldsymbol{\beta}}$ of the normal equations (2) are unbiased estimators. Any solution of (2) must be a linear function of the **y**'s; hence we can write

$$\hat{\boldsymbol{\beta}} = A\mathbf{Y} \tag{4}$$

where A is a $p \times n$ matrix of constants which may depend on the elements in X. To be unbiased, we must have $E(\hat{\boldsymbol{\beta}}) = \beta$ or

$$\beta = E(\hat{\boldsymbol{\beta}}) = E(A\mathbf{Y}) = E[A(X\beta + \mathbf{e})] = AX\beta + AE(\mathbf{e}) = AX\beta$$

Thus $AX\beta = \beta$ for all values of β_i, which implies that $AX = I$. But I is the $p \times p$ identity matrix, and it has rank p. But the rank of the product of two matrices cannot have rank larger than the rank of either matrix. By Definition 14.1, X is of rank $r < p$; hence the rank of AX must be less than p. Therefore there is no matrix A such that $E(A\mathbf{Y}) = \beta$ and hence no unbiased estimator of β. For instance, in Example 14.1 there are no unbiased estimators of μ, τ_1, τ_2, and τ_3. In most cases of an experimental design model, there is interest in estimating certain linear combinations of the parameters, and so we shall examine these.

Definition 14.2. *Let λ be a $p \times 1$ vector of known constants; then the linear combination of β given by $\lambda'\beta = \sum_{i=1}^{p} \lambda_i\beta_i$ is called an estimable function if there exists a linear combination of the* **y**'*s whose expected value is $\lambda'\beta$.*

In other words, $\lambda'\beta$ is estimable if there exists an $n \times 1$ vector a such that $E(a'\mathbf{Y}) = \lambda'\beta$.

Let the X matrix be partitioned as

$$X = \begin{pmatrix} X_1 \\ X_2 \\ \cdot \\ \cdot \\ \cdot \\ X_n \end{pmatrix}$$

where X_i is a $1 \times p$ vector which is the ith row of X. We are interested in seeing if $X_i\beta$ is estimable for each i. By Definition 14.2, the set $X_1\beta$, $X_2\beta, \cdots, X_n\beta$ is a set of n estimable functions if there exist n vectors $A_1, A_2, \cdots, A_n$ such that $E(A_i\mathbf{Y}) = X_i\beta$, in other words, if there exists an $n \times p$ matrix A such that $E(A\mathbf{Y}) = X\beta$, because if A_i is the ith row of A and if $X_i\beta$ is estimable, then

$$E(A\mathbf{Y}) = E\begin{pmatrix} A_1 \\ A_2 \\ \cdot \\ \cdot \\ \cdot \\ A_n \end{pmatrix} \mathbf{Y} = \begin{pmatrix} E(A_1\mathbf{Y}) \\ E(A_2\mathbf{Y}) \\ \cdot \\ \cdot \\ \cdot \\ E(A_n\mathbf{Y}) \end{pmatrix}$$

$$= \begin{pmatrix} X_1\beta \\ X_2\beta \\ \cdot \\ \cdot \\ \cdot \\ X_n\beta \end{pmatrix} = \begin{pmatrix} X_1 \\ X_2 \\ \cdot \\ \cdot \\ \cdot \\ X_n \end{pmatrix} \beta = X\beta$$

Let $A = I$; then $E(I\mathbf{Y}) = E(\mathbf{Y}) = E(X\beta + \mathbf{e}) = E(X\beta) + E(\mathbf{e}) = X\beta$.

Theorem 14.1. *$X\beta$ represents a set of n estimable functions; i.e. each element in $E(\mathbf{Y})$ is estimable.*

By representing (1) by (1*a*), Theorem 14.1 tells us that $E(\mathbf{y}_{ij\ldots m})$ is estimable. In Example 14.1, $E(\mathbf{y}_{ij})$ is estimable for every i and j, and so $\mu + \tau_1$, $\mu + \tau_2$, and $\mu + \tau_3$ are estimable.

Theorem 14.2. *$(X'X)\beta$ represents a set of p estimable functions.*

Proof. Partition the $p \times n$ matrix X' into p rows, and let X_i^* be the vector which is the ith row; then

$$X' = \begin{pmatrix} X_1^* \\ X_2^* \\ \cdot \\ \cdot \\ \cdot \\ X_p^* \end{pmatrix}$$

Now $E(X'\mathbf{Y}) = X'E(\mathbf{Y}) = X'(X\beta) = X'X\beta$. Consequently

$$E(X'\mathbf{Y}) = E\begin{pmatrix} X_1^* \\ X_2^* \\ \cdot \\ \cdot \\ \cdot \\ X_p^* \end{pmatrix} \mathbf{Y} = \begin{pmatrix} EX_1^*\mathbf{Y} \\ EX_2^*\mathbf{Y} \\ \cdot \\ \cdot \\ \cdot \\ EX_p^*\mathbf{Y} \end{pmatrix} = \begin{pmatrix} X_1^*X\beta \\ X_2^*X\beta \\ \cdot \\ \cdot \\ \cdot \\ X_p^*X\beta \end{pmatrix} = X'X\beta$$

Thus $X_i^* X\beta$ is estimable since $E(X_i^* \mathbf{Y}) = X_i^* X\beta$. But the ith element of $X'X\beta$ is $X_i^* X\beta$; hence $X'X\beta$ is a set of p estimable functions.

Next we shall find the set of "all" estimable functions.

Definition 14.3. *Let $\theta_1, \theta_2, \cdots, \theta_t$ be $p \times 1$ vectors such that $\theta_1'\beta, \theta_2'\beta, \cdots, \theta_t'\beta$ are estimable and such that the rank of the $p \times t$ matrix $(t \le p)$*

$$(\theta_1, \theta_2, \cdots, \theta_t)$$

is equal to t; then $\theta_1'\beta, \cdots, \theta_t'\beta$ are called linearly independent estimable functions.

Since $X'X\beta$ is a set of p estimable functions and since $X'X$ has rank r, there are at least r linearly independent estimable functions in the general linear model (1) where the rank of X is r. Let us assume that there are $k > r$ linearly independent estimable functions given by $\theta_1'\beta, \theta_2'\beta, \cdots, \theta_k'\beta$. We can write this set as

$$L'\beta = \begin{pmatrix} \theta_1' \\ \cdot \\ \cdot \\ \cdot \\ \theta_k' \end{pmatrix} \beta$$

where L' is a $k \times p$ matrix of rank $k > r$. By Definitions 14.2 and 14.3, there must exist a $k \times n$ matrix A such that $E(A\mathbf{Y}) = L'\beta$. However, $E(A\mathbf{Y}) = AX\beta$ and thus $AX = L'$, but AX has rank less than or equal to the rank of X, which is r, which contradicts the statement $k > r$. We have proved the following theorem.

Theorem 14.3. *In the general linear model* (1), *there are exactly r linearly independent estimable functions, where r is the rank of X.*

Since $X'X\beta$ is a set of p estimable functions and the rank of $X'X$ is r, by Theorem 14.3, every estimable function must be a linear combination of the rows of $X'X\beta$. This result is stated in the next theorem.

Theorem 14.4. *Let $\lambda'\beta$ be any estimable function; then there exists a $p \times 1$ vector b such that $b'X'X = \lambda'$ and $b'X'\mathbf{Y}$ is the best (minimum variance) linear unbiased estimator of $\lambda'\beta$ under Case B and the ML estimator of $\lambda'\beta$ under Case A.*

This theorem again stresses the importance of the normal equations, since the least-squares estimator, under Case B, or the maximum-likelihood estimator, under Case A, of any estimable function must come from a solution of the normal equations. Thus under Case B, $\lambda'\beta$ is an estimable function and the best linear unbiased estimator is $b'X'\mathbf{Y}$, where b' is a $1 \times p$ vector such that $b'X'X = \lambda'$. Ordinarily b' does not need to be found, but $b'X'\mathbf{Y}$ can be obtained by taking linear combinations of the left-hand side of the normal equations until the desired $\lambda'\hat{\boldsymbol{\beta}}$ is found;

then the same linear combination of the right-hand side gives the best linear unbiased estimator of $\lambda'\beta$. Under Case A, the same procedure gives the maximum-likelihood estimator of $\lambda'\beta$. Another way to find the maximum-likelihood (or least-squares) estimator of $\lambda'\beta$ is to find *any* solution $\hat{\boldsymbol{\beta}}$ of the normal equations and use $\lambda'\hat{\boldsymbol{\beta}}$ as the estimator. We shall show that any solution $\hat{\boldsymbol{\beta}}$ of the normal equations, $X'X\hat{\boldsymbol{\beta}} = X'\mathbf{Y}$, gives the same value $\lambda'\hat{\boldsymbol{\beta}}$ if $\lambda'\beta$ is estimable. This result can be formally stated as follows:

Theorem 14.5. *Let $\lambda'\beta$ be any estimable function in the model $\mathbf{Y} = X\beta + \mathbf{e}$, and let $\hat{\boldsymbol{\gamma}}$ and $\hat{\boldsymbol{\alpha}}$ be any two $p \times 1$ vectors satisfying the normal equations; that is, $X'X\hat{\boldsymbol{\gamma}} = X'\mathbf{Y}$ and $X'X\hat{\boldsymbol{\alpha}} = X'\mathbf{Y}$. Then $\lambda'\hat{\boldsymbol{\gamma}} = \lambda'\hat{\boldsymbol{\alpha}}$ and $E(\lambda'\hat{\boldsymbol{\gamma}}) = E(\lambda'\hat{\boldsymbol{\alpha}}) = \lambda'\beta$.*

Proof. By the hypothesis of the theorem, $\hat{\boldsymbol{\gamma}}$ and $\hat{\boldsymbol{\alpha}}$ are two $p \times 1$ vectors which satisfy the normal equations; that is

$$X'X\hat{\boldsymbol{\gamma}} = X'\mathbf{Y}$$

and

$$X'X\hat{\boldsymbol{\alpha}} = X'\mathbf{Y}$$

But by the hypothesis of the theorem, $\lambda'\beta$ is estimable, and so, by Theorem 14.4, there is a vector b' such that $b'X'X = \lambda'$. Multiply both equations on the left by b' and we get

$$\begin{aligned} b'X'X\hat{\boldsymbol{\gamma}} &= b'X'\mathbf{Y} \\ b'X'X\hat{\boldsymbol{\alpha}} &= b'X'\mathbf{Y} \\ \lambda'\hat{\boldsymbol{\gamma}} &= b'X'\mathbf{Y} \\ \lambda'\hat{\boldsymbol{\alpha}} &= b'X'\mathbf{Y} \end{aligned}$$

and so

$$\lambda'\hat{\boldsymbol{\gamma}} = \lambda'\hat{\boldsymbol{\alpha}}$$

Now $E(\lambda'\hat{\boldsymbol{\gamma}}) = E(\lambda'\hat{\boldsymbol{\alpha}}) = E(b'X'\mathbf{Y}) = b'X' \cdot E(\mathbf{Y}) = b'X'X\beta = \lambda'\beta$, and the proof is complete.

Theorem 14.6. *If $\lambda_1'\beta, \cdots, \lambda_s'\beta$ is a set of s estimable functions, then any linear combination of these is estimable.*

This theorem is similar to Theorem 13.5, and the proof will be left for the reader.

Example 14.2. Consider the model in Example 14.1. The $X'X$ matrix is, by (14.1.3),

$$X'X = \begin{pmatrix} 1 & 1 & 1 & 1 & 1 & 1 \\ 1 & 1 & 0 & 0 & 0 & 0 \\ 0 & 0 & 1 & 1 & 0 & 0 \\ 0 & 0 & 0 & 0 & 1 & 1 \end{pmatrix} \cdot \begin{pmatrix} 1 & 1 & 0 & 0 \\ 1 & 1 & 0 & 0 \\ 1 & 0 & 1 & 0 \\ 1 & 0 & 1 & 0 \\ 1 & 0 & 0 & 1 \\ 1 & 0 & 0 & 1 \end{pmatrix} = \begin{pmatrix} 6 & 2 & 2 & 2 \\ 2 & 2 & 0 & 0 \\ 2 & 0 & 2 & 0 \\ 2 & 0 & 0 & 2 \end{pmatrix}$$

The $X'\mathbf{Y}$ vector is

$$X'\mathbf{Y} = \begin{pmatrix} 1 & 1 & 1 & 1 & 1 & 1 \\ 1 & 1 & 0 & 0 & 0 & 0 \\ 0 & 0 & 1 & 1 & 0 & 0 \\ 0 & 0 & 0 & 0 & 1 & 1 \end{pmatrix} \begin{pmatrix} \mathbf{y}_{11} \\ \mathbf{y}_{12} \\ \mathbf{y}_{21} \\ \mathbf{y}_{22} \\ \mathbf{y}_{31} \\ \mathbf{y}_{32} \end{pmatrix} = \begin{pmatrix} \mathbf{Y}_{..} \\ \mathbf{Y}_{1.} \\ \mathbf{Y}_{2.} \\ \mathbf{Y}_{3.} \end{pmatrix}$$

where $\mathbf{Y}_{i.} = \sum_j \mathbf{y}_{ij}$; $\mathbf{Y}_{..} = \sum_i \sum_j \mathbf{y}_{ij}$. We shall also use the notation

$$\mathbf{Y}_{.j} = \sum_i \mathbf{y}_{ij} \qquad \bar{\mathbf{y}}_{i.} = \frac{\mathbf{Y}_{i.}}{n} \qquad \bar{\mathbf{y}}_{.j} = \frac{\mathbf{Y}_{.j}}{t}$$

where n is the range of the subscript j and t is the range of the subscript i. The normal equations are

$$\begin{aligned} 6\hat{\boldsymbol{\mu}} + 2\hat{\boldsymbol{\tau}}_1 + 2\hat{\boldsymbol{\tau}}_2 + 2\hat{\boldsymbol{\tau}}_3 &= \mathbf{Y}_{..} \\ 2\hat{\boldsymbol{\mu}} + 2\hat{\boldsymbol{\tau}}_1 \qquad\qquad\qquad &= \mathbf{Y}_{1.} \\ 2\hat{\boldsymbol{\mu}} \qquad + 2\hat{\boldsymbol{\tau}}_2 \qquad\quad &= \mathbf{Y}_{2.} \\ 2\hat{\boldsymbol{\mu}} \qquad\qquad\qquad + 2\hat{\boldsymbol{\tau}}_3 &= \mathbf{Y}_{3.} \end{aligned} \tag{5}$$

Theorem 14.1 tells us that $E(\mathbf{y}_{ij}) = \mu + \tau_i$ is estimable for all i. Thus $\mu + \tau_1$, $\mu + \tau_2$, and $\mu + \tau_3$ are estimable. By Theorem 14.4, we must be able to take linear combinations of the rows of the normal equations (5) and obtain $\hat{\mu} + \hat{\tau}_i$ on the left-hand side, and the estimator is the same linear combination of the right-hand side. We see that if we take ½ times the second equation in (5) we get

$$\hat{\mu} + \hat{\tau}_1 = (\tfrac{1}{2})\mathbf{Y}_{1.} = \bar{\mathbf{y}}_{1.}$$

Similarly for the third equation:

$$\hat{\mu} + \hat{\tau}_2 = (\tfrac{1}{2})\mathbf{Y}_{2.} = \bar{\mathbf{y}}_{2.}$$

and the fourth:

$$\hat{\mu} + \hat{\tau}_3 = (\tfrac{1}{2})\mathbf{Y}_{3.} = \bar{\mathbf{y}}_{3.}$$

Thus the ML (maximum-likelihood) or LS (least-squares) estimator of $\mu + \tau_i$ is $\bar{\mathbf{y}}_{i.}$. It is easy to verify that $E(\bar{\mathbf{y}}_{i.}) = \mu + \tau_i$. There are other unbiased estimators of $\mu + \tau_1$, for example, $E(\mathbf{y}_{11}) = \mu + \tau_1$, but this estimator, $\mathbf{y}_{11}$, does not have all the optimum properties that the estimator $\bar{\mathbf{y}}_{1.}$ has, since $\bar{\mathbf{y}}_{1.}$ comes from the *normal equations*. By Theorem 14.4, if an unbiased estimator exists for a linear combination of the parameters, it must be possible to obtain an unbiased estimator from the *normal equations*, and by Theorem 14.4 this is the *best* unbiased estimator. Thus we may examine the *model* to see what functions are estimable, but we use the *normal equations* to *obtain* the estimator. Since the rank of X in (14.1.3) is 3, by Theorem 14.3, there are exactly three linearly independent estimable functions. The three estimable functions $\mu + \tau_1$, $\mu + \tau_2$, and $\mu + \tau_3$ which can be written

$$\mu + \tau_1 = \lambda_1'\beta = (1 \quad 1 \quad 0 \quad 0)\begin{pmatrix}\mu \\ \tau_1 \\ \tau_2 \\ \tau_3\end{pmatrix}$$

$$\mu + \tau_2 = \lambda_2'\beta = (1 \quad 0 \quad 1 \quad 0)\begin{pmatrix}\mu \\ \tau_1 \\ \tau_2 \\ \tau_3\end{pmatrix}$$

$$\mu + \tau_3 = \lambda_3'\beta = (1 \quad 0 \quad 0 \quad 1)\begin{pmatrix}\mu \\ \tau_1 \\ \tau_2 \\ \tau_3\end{pmatrix}$$

have rank 3; hence the three estimable functions are linearly independent, and therefore *all* estimable functions must be linear combinations of these three. The reader can easily verify that each of the two vectors

$$\hat{\gamma} = \begin{pmatrix}\bar{\mathbf{y}}_{..} \\ \bar{\mathbf{y}}_{1.} - \bar{\mathbf{y}}_{..} \\ \bar{\mathbf{y}}_{2.} - \bar{\mathbf{y}}_{..} \\ \bar{\mathbf{y}}_{3.} - \bar{\mathbf{y}}_{..}\end{pmatrix} \qquad \hat{\alpha} = \begin{pmatrix}\bar{\mathbf{y}}_{2.} \\ \bar{\mathbf{y}}_{1.} - \bar{\mathbf{y}}_{2.} \\ 0 \\ \bar{\mathbf{y}}_{3.} - \bar{\mathbf{y}}_{2.}\end{pmatrix}$$

satisfies the normal equations (5). Now $\lambda_1'\beta = \mu + \tau_1$ is estimable; hence, by Theorem 14.5, $\lambda_1'\hat{\gamma}$ must equal $\lambda_1'\hat{\alpha}$, which must equal $\bar{\mathbf{y}}_{1.}$. The reader can easily verify that this is true. In (14.1.2),

$$E(\mathbf{y}_{11} - \mathbf{y}_{21}) = \tau_1 - \tau_2$$

and so, by Theorem 14.1, $\tau_1 - \tau_2$ is estimable. In (5) subtract $\frac{1}{2}$ times the third equation from $\frac{1}{2}$ times the second equation to obtain

$$\hat{\tau}_1 - \hat{\tau}_2 = (\bar{\mathbf{y}}_{1.} - \bar{\mathbf{y}}_{2.})$$

as the estimator of $\tau_1 - \tau_2$. Take $\frac{1}{2}$ of the second equation plus $\frac{1}{2}$ of the third equation minus the fourth equation and obtain

$$\hat{\tau}_1 + \hat{\tau}_2 - 2\hat{\tau}_3 = \bar{\mathbf{y}}_{1.} + \bar{\mathbf{y}}_{2.} - 2\bar{\mathbf{y}}_{3.}$$

as the estimator of $\tau_1 + \tau_2 - 2\tau_3$. To estimate σ^2, we notice that, by (3), $\tilde{\sigma}^2 = (\mathbf{Y} - X\hat{\beta})'(\mathbf{Y} - X\hat{\beta})/n$, where $\hat{\beta}$ is any solution of the normal equations. Let $\hat{\alpha}$ and $\hat{\gamma}$ be any two solutions of the normal equations; then, by Theorem 14.1, $X\beta$ is a set of estimable functions, and by Theorem

14.5, $X\hat{\gamma} = X\hat{\alpha}$; that is, $X\hat{\beta}$ is the same for any vector $\hat{\beta}$ satisfying the normal equations. Hence $\mathbf{Y} - X\hat{\beta}$ is the same, regardless of which solution of the normal equations is used, and thereby $\hat{\sigma}^2$ is also unchanged. Since the unbiased estimator of σ^2 is $(\mathbf{Y} - X\hat{\beta})'(\mathbf{Y} - X\hat{\beta})/(n - r)$, we shall use this as $\hat{\sigma}^2$.

To test various hypotheses about estimable functions we shall state the following theorem, but the proof will not be given.

Theorem 14.7. *Let $\lambda_1'\beta, \lambda_2'\beta, \cdots, \lambda_k'\beta$ be k linearly independent estimable functions, and suppose that we wish to test the hypothesis H_0 that they are all simultaneously equal to 0 in the model 1 under Case A. From the normal equations*

$$X'X\hat{\beta} = X'\mathbf{Y} \tag{6}$$

find $\hat{\beta}'X'\mathbf{Y}$, where $\hat{\beta}$ is any solution of (6). Substitute

$$\lambda_1'\beta = \lambda_2'\beta = \cdots = \lambda_k'\beta = 0$$

into the model $\mathbf{Y} = X\beta + \mathbf{e}$ and obtain the reduced model denoted by $\mathbf{Y} = Z\gamma + \mathbf{e}$. From the normal equations for this model

$$Z'Z\tilde{\gamma} = Z'\mathbf{Y} \tag{7}$$

find $\tilde{\gamma}'Z'\mathbf{Y}$, where $\tilde{\gamma}$ is any solution of (7). Then when the hypothesis H_0 is true,

$$\mathbf{u} = \frac{(\hat{\beta}'X'\mathbf{Y} - \tilde{\gamma}'Z'\mathbf{Y})/k}{(\mathbf{Y}'\mathbf{Y} - \hat{\beta}'X'\mathbf{Y})/(n - r)} \tag{8}$$

has the F distribution with k and $n - r$ degrees of freedom. H_0 is rejected with a Type I error probability of α when $\mathbf{u} > F_\alpha(k, n - r)$. This is obtained from the likelihood-ratio.

The proof of this theorem follows the line of proof for Theorem 13.6 except that the $X'X$ matrix and $Z'Z$ do not have inverses. We are now in a position to test any hypothesis which can be put into the form of linearly independent estimable functions.

Example 14.3. We shall be interested in testing the hypothesis H_0: $\tau_1 = \tau_2 = \tau_3$ in Example 14.1. To use Theorem 14.7, we must first see if H_0 is equivalent to linearly independent estimable functions being 0. Let $\lambda_1'\beta = \tau_1 - \tau_2$ so that $\lambda_1' = (0, 1, -1, 0)$; let $\lambda_2'\beta = \tau_1 + \tau_2 - 2\tau_3$ so that $\lambda_2' = (0, 1, 1, -2)$. Clearly these are linearly independent estimable functions. It is also clear that $\lambda_1'\beta = \lambda_2'\beta = 0$ if and only if $\tau_1 = \tau_2 = \tau_3$, and so we can use Theorem 14.7 to test H_0. Notice that the hypothesis is *not* that the τ_i are equal to 0, but it is the fact that they are equal to each other. We can write H_0: $\tau_1 = \tau_2 = \tau_3 = \tau^*$, where τ^* is unknown.

The normal equations are given in (5), and a solution is

$$\hat{\boldsymbol{\beta}} = \begin{pmatrix} \hat{\boldsymbol{\mu}} \\ \hat{\boldsymbol{\tau}}_1 \\ \hat{\boldsymbol{\tau}}_2 \\ \hat{\boldsymbol{\tau}}_3 \end{pmatrix} = \begin{pmatrix} \bar{\mathbf{y}}_{..} \\ \bar{\mathbf{y}}_{1.} - \bar{\mathbf{y}}_{..} \\ \bar{\mathbf{y}}_{2.} - \bar{\mathbf{y}}_{..} \\ \bar{\mathbf{y}}_{3.} - \bar{\mathbf{y}}_{..} \end{pmatrix}$$

which gives $\hat{\boldsymbol{\beta}}'X'\mathbf{Y} = (\bar{\mathbf{y}}_{..})(\mathbf{Y}_{..}) + \sum_{i=1}^{3} (\bar{\mathbf{y}}_{i.} - \bar{\mathbf{y}}_{..})\mathbf{Y}_{i.}$.

Set $\tau_1 = \tau^*$, $\tau_2 = \tau^*$, $\tau_3 = \tau^*$, and the reduced model is

$$\mathbf{y}_{ij} = \mu + \tau^* + \mathbf{e}_{ij} = \mu^* + \mathbf{e}_{ij}$$

and there is only one unknown parameter μ^*. The normal equation is found by finding the value of μ^* which minimizes $\sum \mathbf{e}_{ij}^2 = \sum_{ij} (\mathbf{y}_{ij} - \mu^*)^2$. It is clearly

$$6\tilde{\boldsymbol{\mu}}^* = \mathbf{Y}_{..}$$

which is the reduced set of normal equations identified with $Z'Z\tilde{\boldsymbol{\gamma}} = Z'\mathbf{Y}$ in Theorem 14.7. The solution is $\tilde{\boldsymbol{\mu}}^* = \bar{\mathbf{y}}_{..}$ and $\tilde{\boldsymbol{\gamma}}'Z'\mathbf{Y} = \tilde{\boldsymbol{\mu}}^*\mathbf{Y}_{..} = (\bar{\mathbf{y}}_{..})(\mathbf{Y}_{..})$. Thus $\hat{\boldsymbol{\beta}}'X'\mathbf{Y} - \tilde{\boldsymbol{\gamma}}'Z'\mathbf{Y} = \sum_{i=1}^{3} (\bar{\mathbf{y}}_{i.} - \bar{\mathbf{y}}_{..})\mathbf{Y}_{i.}$ which can be written as $\sum_{j=1}^{2} \sum_{i=1}^{3} (\bar{\mathbf{y}}_{i.} - \bar{\mathbf{y}}_{..})^2$ or as $\sum_i \frac{\mathbf{Y}_{i.}^2}{2} - \frac{\mathbf{Y}_{..}^2}{6}$. The error sum of squares is

$$\mathbf{Y}'\mathbf{Y} - \hat{\boldsymbol{\beta}}'X'\mathbf{Y} = \sum_i \sum_j \mathbf{y}_{ij}^2 - \frac{\mathbf{Y}_{..}^2}{6} - \sum_{ij} (\bar{\mathbf{y}}_{i.} - \bar{\mathbf{y}}_{..})^2$$
$$= \sum_i \sum_j (\mathbf{y}_{ij} - \bar{\mathbf{y}}_{..})^2 - \sum_{ij} (\bar{\mathbf{y}}_{i.} - \bar{\mathbf{y}}_{..})^2 = \sum_i \sum_j (\mathbf{y}_{ij} - \bar{\mathbf{y}}_{i.})^2$$

The quantity $\mathbf{u}$ is

$$\mathbf{u} = \frac{\sum_i \sum_j (\bar{\mathbf{y}}_{i.} - \bar{\mathbf{y}}_{..})^2/2}{\sum_i \sum_j (\mathbf{y}_{ij} - \bar{\mathbf{y}}_{i.})^2/3}$$

since $k = 2$ (the number of linearly independent estimable functions in H_0) and $n - r = 6 - 3 = 3$ (r is the rank of X). Also

$$\hat{\boldsymbol{\sigma}}^2 = \frac{\Sigma\Sigma(\mathbf{y}_{ij} - \bar{\mathbf{y}}_{i.})^2}{3}$$

is an unbiased estimate of σ^2 since it is $\hat{\boldsymbol{\sigma}}^2 = [1/(n - r)](\mathbf{Y} - X\hat{\boldsymbol{\beta}})'(\mathbf{Y} - X\hat{\boldsymbol{\beta}})$.

Notice that the identity holds:

$$\sum_{ij} \mathbf{y}_{ij}^2 = \frac{\mathbf{Y}_{..}^2}{6} + \sum_{ij} (\bar{\mathbf{y}}_{i.} - \bar{\mathbf{y}}_{..})^2 + \sum_{ij} (\mathbf{y}_{ij} - \bar{\mathbf{y}}_{i.})^2$$

which we can write as

$$\sum_{ij} y_{ij}^2 = \frac{Y_{..}^2}{6} + \left(\sum_{i=1}^{3} \frac{Y_{i.}^2}{2} - \frac{Y_{..}^2}{6}\right) + \left(\sum_{ij} y_{ij}^2 - \sum_{i=1}^{3} \frac{Y_{i.}^2}{2}\right)$$

the second identity being useful for computing the various quantities. $\frac{Y_{..}^2}{6}$ is called the sum of squares for the mean; $\sum_{ij} (\bar{y}_{i.} - \bar{y}_{..})^2$ is called the sum of squares due to the τ_i (often called treatments); $\sum_{ij} (y_{ij} - \bar{y}_{i.})^2$ is called the sum of squares for error; Σy_{ij}^2 is called the total uncorrected sum of squares.

Interval Estimation. To set a confidence interval on any estimable function, the variance of the function and an independent unbiased estimate of this variance are needed.

Theorem 14.8. *A confidence interval on the estimable function $\lambda'\beta$ with confidence coefficient $1 - \alpha$ is*

$$\lambda'\hat{\beta} - t_{\alpha/2}\sqrt{\widehat{\text{var}}\,(\lambda'\hat{\beta})} < \lambda'\beta < \lambda'\hat{\beta} + t_{\alpha/2}\sqrt{\widehat{\text{var}}\,(\lambda'\hat{\beta})} \qquad (9)$$

where $\widehat{\text{var}}\,(\lambda'\hat{\beta})$ is the unbiased estimate of the variance of $\lambda'\hat{\beta}$.

To find the confidence interval on $\lambda'\beta$, the variance of the quantity $\lambda'\hat{\beta}$ must first be found; this will be a constant times σ^2; let it be denoted by $a\sigma^2$. Then $\widehat{\text{var}}\,(\lambda'\hat{\beta}) = a\hat{\sigma}^2$, where $\hat{\sigma}^2 = (Y - X\hat{\beta})'(Y - X\hat{\beta})/(n - r)$.

Example 14.4. To set a confidence interval on $\tau_1 - \tau_2$ in Example 14.3, $\lambda'\hat{\beta} = \bar{y}_{1.} - \bar{y}_{2.}$. The variance is

$$E[(\bar{y}_{1.} - \bar{y}_{2.}) - (\tau_1 - \tau_2)]^2 = E[(\mu + \tau_1 + \bar{e}_{i.} - \mu - \tau_2 - \bar{e}_{2.}) - (\tau_1 - \tau_2)]^2 = E(\bar{e}_{1.} - \bar{e}_{2.})^2 = \sigma^2$$

where $\bar{e}_{i.} = \frac{1}{2}\sum_{j=1}^{2} e_{ij}$. Then var $(\hat{\tau}_1 - \hat{\tau}_2) = \sigma^2$, and, from Example 14.3, $\hat{\sigma}^2 = \sum_i \sum_j \frac{(y_{ij} - \bar{y}_{i.})^2}{3}$; these values can be used in (9) for the confidence interval.

Since the normal equations play such an extremely important role in experimental design models, we shall give a rule whereby they can be found from the model $y_{ij\ldots m} = \mu_{ij\ldots m} + e_{ij\ldots m}$ without actually constructing the X matrix. To do this, notice that in the model $Y = X\beta + e$ there is an equation in the set of normal equations which corresponds to each parameter in β, since, to obtain the set, the derivative with respect to each parameter was set equal to 0. Also notice that the component β_i appears in the sth element of the $n \times 1$ vector $X\beta$ if and only if the ith column of X has a 1 in the sth row. That is, there are n equations in the model $\mathbf{Y} = X\beta + \mathbf{e}$, and whether the parameter β_i appears in certain equations depends on the 0's and 1's in the ith column of X; if a 1 appears in the sth row of the ith column of X, then β_i appears in the sth equation. To illustrate this, look at equation (14.1.3) and notice that τ_1 occurs only in the first and second equations of the model. This is verified by looking at equation (14.1.1), where the model is written out in detail. Similarly, to find in which equations μ appears, since μ is the first element in β, we look at the first column of the X matrix. This column has a 1 in each row, and so μ appears in every equation in the model, as can be verified by equation (14.1.1).

To find the normal equations $X'X\hat{\beta} = X'\mathbf{Y}$, we shall study the vector $X'\mathbf{Y}$. The ith *column* of X pertains to the ith component of β; hence the ith *row* of X' pertains to the ith element in β. Let X_i be the ith column of X; then $X_i'\mathbf{Y}$ is the ith element in the vector $X'\mathbf{Y}$, and since X_i is composed of 0's and 1's, the quantity $X_i'\mathbf{Y}$ is the sum of the elements in $\mathbf{Y}$, where there is a 1 in X_i. But where there is a 1 in X_i is exactly the equation in the model in which β_i appears. Hence the rule: *The ith element of $X'\mathbf{Y}$ is the sum of the elements in $\mathbf{Y}$ over those equations in which β_i appears in the model $\mathbf{Y} = X\beta + \mathbf{e}$.*

Referring again to Sec. 14.1, since μ appears in *every* equation in equation (14.1.1), the first element in $X'\mathbf{Y}$ is $\mathbf{Y}_{..}$. Also τ_1 appears in only the first two equations (or in only those equations where $\mathbf{y}_{ij}$ has the first subscript equal to 1); hence the second element is $\sum_{j=1}^{2} \mathbf{y}_{1j} = \mathbf{Y}_{1.}$ Similarly, for τ_2 the element is $\mathbf{Y}_{2.}$, etc. Thus $X'\mathbf{Y}$ can be constructed by looking at the model written as equation (14.1.2). Also $E(X'\mathbf{Y}) = X'X\beta$, and so the left-hand side of the normal equations can be found by taking the expected value of $X'\mathbf{Y}$.

In this section we have illustrated the general methods for estimation and testing the parameters in experimental design models. In some of the following sections we shall illustrate the use of the theory by examining certain important special cases.

14.3 One-way Classification Model

Suppose that a company wants to determine if there is any difference in the various methods of making steel cable. Suppose that a sample of n_i pieces of cable made by process i is examined for each of t processes, and the breaking strength of the jth piece of wire made by the ith process is $\mathbf{y}_{ij}$, where

$$\mathbf{y}_{ij} = \mu + \tau_i + \mathbf{e}_{ij} \qquad j = 1, 2, \cdots, n_i; i = 1, 2, \cdots, t \tag{1}$$

where μ is an over-all mean, τ_i is the effect of the ith process, and $\mathbf{e}_{ij}$ is an unobservable random error due to the uncontrollable variations in the manufacturing and measuring process. We shall discuss in detail how to find the normal equations for this model. μ occurs in every equation, and so the element in $X'\mathbf{Y}$ corresponding to μ is $\sum_{ij} \mathbf{y}_{ij} = \mathbf{Y}_{..}$. τ_p occurs in each equation which has the first subscript equal to p; that is, $\sum_j \mathbf{y}_{pj} = \mathbf{Y}_{p.}$. Thus

$$X'\mathbf{Y} = \begin{pmatrix} \mathbf{Y}_{..} \\ \mathbf{Y}_{1.} \\ \mathbf{Y}_{2.} \\ \cdot \\ \cdot \\ \cdot \\ \mathbf{Y}_{t.} \end{pmatrix}$$

Also $E[\mathbf{Y}_{p.}] = E\left[\sum_j^{n_p} \mathbf{y}_{pj}\right] = E\left[\sum_j (\mu + \tau_p + \mathbf{e}_{pj})\right] = n_p\mu + n_p\tau_p$ and

$$E[\mathbf{Y}_{..}] = N\mu + \sum_{p=1}^{t} n_p \tau_p$$

where $\sum_{p=1}^{t} n_p = N$. Consequently the normal equations are

$$\begin{aligned}
N\hat{\boldsymbol{\mu}} + n_1\hat{\boldsymbol{\tau}}_1 + n_2\hat{\boldsymbol{\tau}}_2 + \cdots + n_t\hat{\boldsymbol{\tau}}_t &= \mathbf{Y}_{..} \\
n_1\hat{\boldsymbol{\mu}} + n_1\hat{\boldsymbol{\tau}}_1 \qquad\qquad\qquad\qquad &= \mathbf{Y}_{1.} \\
n_2\hat{\boldsymbol{\mu}} \qquad + n_2\hat{\boldsymbol{\tau}}_2 \qquad\qquad &= \mathbf{Y}_{2.} \\
\cdots\cdots\cdots\cdots\cdots\cdots\cdots\cdots\cdots & \\
n_t\hat{\boldsymbol{\mu}} \qquad\qquad\qquad\qquad + n_t\hat{\boldsymbol{\tau}}_t &= \mathbf{Y}_{t.}
\end{aligned} \tag{2}$$

We can write the normal equations corresponding to μ and to τ_p in more compact form:

$$\begin{aligned}
\mu:&\quad N\hat{\boldsymbol{\mu}} + \sum_{i=1}^{t} n_i\hat{\boldsymbol{\tau}}_i = \mathbf{Y}_{..} \\
\tau_p:&\quad n_p\hat{\boldsymbol{\mu}} + n_p\hat{\boldsymbol{\tau}}_p \quad = \mathbf{Y}_{p.} \qquad p = 1, 2, \cdots, t
\end{aligned} \tag{3}$$

There are $t + 1$ normal equations, but the sum of the last t equations in (2) is equal to the first equation. If all $n_i \neq 0$, the rank of the normal equations is equal to t. Also $\mu + \tau_p$ is estimable for each $p = 1, 2, \cdots, t$, and the estimate is $\bar{\mathbf{y}}_{p.}$. The linear combination $\sum_{p=1}^{t} a_p(\mu + \tau_p)$ is also estimable, where the a_p are known constants, and the estimate is $\sum_{p=1}^{t} a_p\bar{\mathbf{y}}_{p.}$. But $\Sigma a_p(\mu + \tau_p) = \mu\Sigma a_p + \Sigma a_p\tau_p$, and so $\Sigma a_p\tau_p$ is estimable only if $\Sigma a_p = 0$, since then $\mu \Sigma a_p = 0$. The quantity $\Sigma a_p \tau_p$ is called a *contrast* among the parameters τ_p if $\Sigma a_p = 0$.

The hypothesis H_0: $\tau_1 = \tau_2 = \cdots = \tau_t$ can be tested by using Theorem 14.7. The identity

$$\sum \mathbf{y}_{ij}^2 = \frac{\mathbf{Y}_{..}^2}{N} + \sum_{ij} (\bar{\mathbf{y}}_{i.} - \bar{\mathbf{y}}_{..})^2 + \sum_{ij} (\mathbf{y}_{ij} - \bar{\mathbf{y}}_{i.})^2 = \text{MSS} + \text{TSS} + \text{ESS}$$

(where MSS stands for the sum of squares for the mean, ESS for the error sum of squares, etc.) can be readily established and put into an analysis-of-variance table, as in Table 14.1. The F column gives the u

TABLE 14.1. ANALYSIS OF VARIANCE

Source	Degrees of freedom	Sum of squares	Mean square	F
Total...........	N	$\Sigma \mathbf{y}_{ij}^2$		
Mean...........	1	$\mathbf{Y}_{..}^2/N = \text{MSS}$		
Treatments (τ)...	$t - 1$	$\sum_{ij} (\bar{\mathbf{y}}_{i.} - \bar{\mathbf{y}}_{..})^2 = \text{TSS}$	$\text{TSS}/(t-1)$	$\frac{\text{TSS}}{\text{ESS}} \cdot \frac{N-t}{t-1}$
Error...........	$N - t$	$\sum_{ij} (\mathbf{y}_{ij} - \bar{\mathbf{y}}_{i.})^2 = \text{ESS}$	$\text{ESS}/(N-t)$	

statistic in Theorem 14.7. To set a confidence interval on any contrast $\Sigma a_p \tau_p$, we note that $\Sigma a_p \hat{\tau}_p = \Sigma a_p \bar{\mathbf{y}}_{p.}$ is distributed normally with mean $\Sigma a_p \tau_p$ and variance $\sigma^2 \Sigma a_p^2 / n_p$, and $\text{ESS}/(N - t) = \hat{\sigma}^2$. These quantities can be used in Theorem 14.8.

14.4 Two-way Classification Model

It may have been noticed that the experiment described in Example 14.1 was very poorly designed. The trouble is that there is an extraneous factor, ability of the various workmen, which must necessarily enter into the experiment. If, in the experiment of Example 14.1, the production from one machine turned out to be relatively large, was it due to the machine or to the excellence of the particular group of workmen assigned to it? There is no way to tell from that experiment. In the language of experimental design, the effects due to machines and the effects due to groups of workmen are completely *confounded;* there is no way to differentiate the two factors.

The difficulty is removed by redesigning the experiment as a two-factor experiment. Let, for example, only five men be involved in the experiment and let each of the five men work one day on each of the three machines. The order in which a given man works on the three machines would be assigned by a random process. The data are now classified in a two-way table in accordance with the two factors and might appear as in Table 14.2. When a two-factor experiment is used to control an extraneous factor, as in the case here, the design is referred to as a *randomized block design.* The factor of interest is compared in blocks (men, in the present instance) so that conditions of the comparison are homogeneous within each block although they differ from block to block.

TABLE 14.2

		Machine		
		1	2	3
Man	1	53	47	57
	2	56	50	63
	3	45	47	54
	4	52	47	57
	5	49	53	58

The model can be written as

$$\mathbf{y}_{ij} = \mu + \alpha_i + \tau_j + \mathbf{e}_{ij} \qquad \begin{aligned} i &= 1, 2, \cdots, r \\ j &= 1, 2, \cdots, c \end{aligned} \tag{1}$$

where $\mathbf{y}_{ij}$ is the observation in the ith row and jth column, μ is a general mean, α_i is the effect of the ith level of the A factor, τ_j is the effect of the jth level of the B factor, and $\mathbf{e}_{ij}$ is an unobservable random error which we assume fits either Case A or Case B.

To find the normal equations we proceed by the rule in Sec. 14.2. Since μ appears in *every* equation in (1), the term in $X'\mathbf{Y}$ corresponding to μ is summed over *every* subscript, which gives $\mathbf{Y}_{...}$. α_p appears in those equations in (1) for which the first subscript of $\mathbf{y}_{ij}$ is p; that is, $\mathbf{y}_{pj}$; thus summing gives $\mathbf{Y}_{p..}$. Similarly, for τ_q the term in $X'\mathbf{Y}$ is $\mathbf{Y}_{.q}$ and so we get for the normal equations (we take expected value of $X'\mathbf{Y}$)

$$\begin{aligned} \mu&: \quad rc\hat{\mathbf{u}} + c\Sigma\hat{\boldsymbol{\alpha}}_i + r\Sigma\hat{\boldsymbol{\tau}}_j = \mathbf{Y}_{..} \\ \alpha_p&: \quad c\hat{\mathbf{u}} + c\hat{\boldsymbol{\alpha}}_p + \Sigma\hat{\boldsymbol{\tau}}_j = \mathbf{Y}_{p.} \qquad p = 1, 2, \cdots, r \\ \tau_q&: \quad r\hat{\mathbf{u}} + \Sigma\hat{\boldsymbol{\alpha}}_i + r\hat{\boldsymbol{\tau}}_q = \mathbf{Y}_{.q} \qquad q = 1, 2, \cdots, c \end{aligned} \tag{2}$$

There are c equations for τ, r equations for α, and one equation for μ, or $r + c + 1$ equations in all. Since the sum of the equations for τ equals the equation for μ and the sum of the equations for α also equals the equation for μ, there are at least two linear dependencies in the normal equations and so the rank must be less than or equal to

$$(r + c + 1) - 2 = r + c - 1$$

In models such as this it is generally desired to estimate contrasts of the α_p and the τ_q. Multiply the α_p equation in (2) by a_p and sum over p to obtain

$$\Sigma a_p c\hat{\mu} + \Sigma a_p c\hat{\alpha}_p + \Sigma a_p(\Sigma\hat{\tau}_j) = \Sigma a_p Y_{p.}$$

If $\Sigma a_p = 0$, we get

$$\Sigma a_p \hat{\alpha}_p = \Sigma a_p \bar{y}_{p.}$$

and so the ML (and LS) estimator of the contrast $\Sigma a_p \alpha_p$ is $\Sigma a_p \bar{y}_{p.}$. Similarly, $\Sigma b_q \hat{\tau}_q = \Sigma b_q \bar{y}_{.q}$ if $\Sigma b_q = 0$. Since every contrast of the α_p and τ_q is estimable, these represent $(r - 1) + (c - 1)$ linearly independent estimable functions. Further, by the first equation of (2), $rc\mu + c\Sigma\alpha_p + r\Sigma\tau_q$ is estimable and is linearly independent of the contrasts of α_p and τ_q. Hence there are at least $r + c - 1$ linearly independent estimable functions. By the discussion above, it then follows that there are exactly $r + c - 1$ linearly independent estimable functions. Consequently the rank of the normal equations is $r + c - 1$.

To obtain $\hat{\sigma}^2 = (Y - X\hat{\beta})'(Y - X\hat{\beta})/(rc - r - c + 1)$, we need to find *any* solution of the normal equations. An easy solution to obtain is to let $\Sigma\hat{\alpha}_p = \Sigma\hat{\tau}_q = 0$. Then

$$\begin{aligned} \hat{\mu} &= \bar{y}_{..} \\ \hat{\alpha}_p &= \bar{y}_{p.} - \bar{y}_{..} \qquad p = 1, 2, \cdots, r \\ \hat{\tau}_q &= \bar{y}_{.q} - \bar{y}_{..} \qquad q = 1, 2, \cdots, c \end{aligned}$$

Thus

$$\begin{aligned} (Y - X\hat{\beta})'(Y - X\hat{\beta}) &= Y'Y - \hat{\beta}'X'Y = \sum_{ij} y_{ij}^2 - \hat{\mu}Y_{..} - \sum_p \hat{\alpha}_p(Y_{p.}) \\ &\quad - \sum_q \hat{\tau}_q Y_{.q} = \sum y_{ij}^2 - \frac{Y_{..}^2}{rc} - \left(\sum_p \frac{Y_{p.}^2}{c} - \frac{Y_{..}^2}{rc}\right) - \left(\sum_q \frac{Y_{.q}^2}{r} - \frac{Y_{..}^2}{rc}\right) \\ &= \sum_{ij} (y_{ij} - \bar{y}_{i.} - \bar{y}_{.j} + \bar{y}_{..})^2 = \text{error sum of squares} \end{aligned}$$

and

$$\hat{\sigma}^2 = \frac{\sum_{ij} (y_{ij} - \bar{y}_{i.} - \bar{y}_{.j} + \bar{y}_{..})^2}{(r - 1)(c - 1)}$$

To test the hypothesis H_0: $\alpha_1 = \alpha_2 = \cdots = \alpha_r = \alpha$, we set $\alpha_i = \alpha$ in (1) and replace $\mu + \alpha$ with μ^*. The reduced model is

$$\mathbf{y}_{ij} = \mu^* + \tau_j + \mathbf{e}_{ij} \qquad \begin{array}{l} i = 1, 2, \cdots, r \\ j = 1, 2, \cdots, c \end{array}$$

and the normal equations are

$$\begin{array}{ll} \mu^*: & rc\tilde{\mathbf{u}}^* + r\Sigma\tilde{\boldsymbol{\tau}}_j = \mathbf{Y}_{..} \\ \tau_q: & r\tilde{\mathbf{u}}^* + r\tilde{\boldsymbol{\tau}}_q \quad = \mathbf{Y}_{.q} \qquad q = 1, 2, \cdots, c \end{array}$$

The rank is clearly c, and a solution is

$$\tilde{\mathbf{u}}^* = \bar{\mathbf{y}}_{..} \qquad \tilde{\boldsymbol{\tau}}_q = \bar{\mathbf{y}}_{.q} - \bar{\mathbf{y}}_{..}$$

and so

$$\tilde{\boldsymbol{\gamma}}'Z'\mathbf{Y} = \tilde{\mathbf{u}}^*\mathbf{Y}_{..} + \sum \tilde{\boldsymbol{\tau}}_q\mathbf{Y}_{.q} = \frac{\mathbf{Y}_{..}^2}{rc} + \left(\sum_q \frac{\mathbf{Y}_{.q}^2}{r} - \frac{\mathbf{Y}_{..}^2}{rc}\right)$$

and

$$\hat{\boldsymbol{\beta}}'X'\mathbf{Y} - \tilde{\boldsymbol{\gamma}}'Z'\mathbf{Y} = \sum_p \frac{\mathbf{Y}_{p.}^2}{c} - \frac{\mathbf{Y}_{..}^2}{rc} = \sum_{ij} (\bar{\mathbf{y}}_{i.} - \bar{\mathbf{y}}_{..})^2$$

By Theorem 14.7, we get

$$\mathbf{u} = \frac{\sum_{ij} (\bar{\mathbf{y}}_{i.} - \bar{\mathbf{y}}_{..})^2/(r-1)}{\sum_{ij} (\mathbf{y}_{ij} - \bar{\mathbf{y}}_{i.} - \bar{\mathbf{y}}_{.j} + \bar{\mathbf{y}}_{..})^2/(r-1)(c-1)}$$

distributed as F if H_0 is true, and H_0 is rejected if $\mathbf{u} > F_\alpha$.

By a similar procedure, we obtain a test of the hypothesis H_0:

$$\tau_1 = \tau_2 = \cdots = \tau_c$$

which is

$$\mathbf{u} = \frac{\sum_{ij} (\bar{\mathbf{y}}_{.j} - \bar{\mathbf{y}}_{..})^2/(c-1)}{\Sigma(\mathbf{y}_{ij} - \bar{\mathbf{y}}_{i.} - \bar{\mathbf{y}}_{.j} + \bar{\mathbf{y}}_{..})^2/(r-1)(c-1)}$$

It is interesting to note the identity

$$\sum_{ij} \mathbf{y}_{ij} = \frac{\mathbf{Y}_{..}^2}{rc} + \sum_{ij} (\bar{\mathbf{y}}_{i.} - \bar{\mathbf{y}}_{..})^2 + \sum_{ij} (\bar{\mathbf{y}}_{.j} - \bar{\mathbf{y}}_{..})^2 + \sum_{ij} (\mathbf{y}_{ij} - \bar{\mathbf{y}}_{i.} - \bar{\mathbf{y}}_{.j} + \bar{\mathbf{y}}_{..})^2$$

This is often put into a table as in Table 14.3.

TABLE 14.3. ANALYSIS-OF-VARIANCE TABLE FOR A TWO-WAY CLASSIFICATION

Source	Degrees of freedom	Sum of squares	Mean square	F
Total	rc	$\Sigma \mathbf{y}_{ij}^2$		
Mean	1	$\dfrac{\mathbf{Y}_{..}^2}{rc}$		
A class (α)	$r - 1$	$\sum_{ij} (\bar{\mathbf{y}}_{i.} - \bar{\mathbf{y}}_{..})^2$	$\mathbf{s}_1^2$	$\mathbf{s}_1^2/\mathbf{s}_3^2$
B class (τ)	$c - 1$	$\sum_{ij} (\bar{\mathbf{y}}_{.j} - \bar{\mathbf{y}}_{..})^2$	$\mathbf{s}_2^2$	$\mathbf{s}_2^2/\mathbf{s}_3^2$
Error	$(r - 1)(c - 1)$	$\sum_{ij} (\mathbf{y}_{ij} - \bar{\mathbf{y}}_{i.} - \bar{\mathbf{y}}_{.j} + \bar{\mathbf{y}}_{..})^2$	$\mathbf{s}_3^2$	

14.5 Other Models

The one-way classification model $\mathbf{y}_{ij} = \mu + \tau_i + \mathbf{e}_{ij}$ and the two-way classification model $\mathbf{y}_{ij} = \mu + \alpha_i + \tau_j + \mathbf{e}_{ij}$ are special cases of the more general model which can be written

$$\mathbf{y}_{ij\ldots t} = \mu_{ij\ldots t} + \mathbf{e}_{ij\ldots t}$$

where $\mu_{ij\ldots t}$ is an unknown constant and $\mathbf{e}_{ij\ldots t}$ is a random variable. This is known as an Eisenhart Model I.

Other special cases are:

Three-way classification (no interaction):

$$\mathbf{y}_{ijk} = \mu + \alpha_i + \gamma_j + \tau_k + \mathbf{e}_{ijk}$$

Two-way classification (with interaction):

$$\mathbf{y}_{ijk} = \mu + \alpha_i + \tau_j + (\alpha\tau)_{ij} + \mathbf{e}_{ijk}$$

These will not be discussed, but methods for estimating the parameters and testing hypotheses for these and other special cases are similar to those explained in the preceding sections.

14.6 Problems

1. Let a simple model be given by

$$\begin{aligned}
\mathbf{y}_{11} &= \mu + \alpha_1 + \mathbf{e}_{11} \\
\mathbf{y}_{12} &= \mu + \alpha_1 + \mathbf{e}_{12} \\
\mathbf{y}_{21} &= \mu + \alpha_2 + \mathbf{e}_{21} \\
\mathbf{y}_{31} &= \mu + \alpha_3 + \mathbf{e}_{31}
\end{aligned}$$

(*a*) Write out the X matrix and the β vector if this model is represented in matrix form as $\mathbf{Y} = X\beta + \mathbf{e}$.

(*b*) Find $X'X$.

(*c*) Show that

$$X'\mathbf{Y} = \begin{pmatrix} \mathbf{Y}_{..} \\ \mathbf{Y}_{1.} \\ \mathbf{y}_{21} \\ \mathbf{y}_{31} \end{pmatrix}$$

(*d*) Write out the normal equations.
(*e*) Find the rank of $X'X$.
(*f*) Find the ML (or LS) estimate of $\alpha_1 - \alpha_2$.

2. The one-way classification model describes the data in Sec. 14.1 where $n_i = 2$, $t = 3$. By the method described in Sec. 14.3

(*a*) Show that

$$X'Y = \begin{pmatrix} 314 \\ 103 \\ 89 \\ 122 \end{pmatrix}$$

(*b*) Using equation (14.3.1), write out explicitly the normal equations.
(*c*) Find any solution $\hat{\boldsymbol{\beta}}$ of the normal equations, and compute

$$\hat{\sigma}^2 = \frac{(\mathbf{Y} - X\hat{\boldsymbol{\beta}})'(\mathbf{Y} - X\hat{\boldsymbol{\beta}})}{3}$$

(*d*) Show that $\hat{\tau}_1 - \hat{\tau}_2 = 7.0$; $\hat{\tau}_3 - \hat{\tau}_1 = 9.5$; $\hat{\tau}_3 - \hat{\tau}_2 = 16.5$.
(*e*) Compute the entries in Table 14.1.
(*f*) In part (*e*), verify that $ESS/(N - t)$ equals the quantity in part (*c*).
(*g*) Use part (*e*) to test H_0: $\tau_1 = \tau_2 = \tau_3$, using a Type I error probability of .05.
(*h*) Is $\tau_1/2 + \tau_2/3 + \tau_3/6 + \mu$ estimable?

3. In Prob. 2, find the estimate of var $(\hat{\tau}_1 - \hat{\tau}_2)$.

4. In Prob. 2, use Theorem 14.8 to set a .95 confidence interval on $\tau_1 - \tau_2$.

5. The following data satisfy the two-way classification model

$$\mathbf{y}_{ij} = \mu + \alpha_i + \theta_j + \mathbf{e}_{ij} \qquad \begin{matrix} i = 1, 2, 3, 4 \\ j = 1, 2, 3, 4, 5, 6 \end{matrix}$$

Factor A (θ)

		1	2	3	4	5	6	Total
	1	21	17	56	59	41	51	
Factor B (α)	2	20	19	61	62	46	55	
	3	24	23	54	54	39	50	
	4	14	18	56	55	42	48	
Total								

(*a*) Write out the 11×1 vector β.

(*b*) Use equations (14.4.2) and write out the 11 normal equations with the values of r, c, $Y_{i.}$, $Y_{.j}$, etc., corresponding to the data in the table.

6. In Prob. 5, find the value of $\hat{\alpha}_1 - \hat{\alpha}_2$; of $\hat{\alpha}_1 + \hat{\alpha}_2 - 2\hat{\alpha}_3$; and of $\hat{\theta}_1 + 2\hat{\theta}_3 + \hat{\theta}_4 - 4\hat{\theta}_5$.

7. Compute the quantities in Table 14.3, using the data in Prob. 5.

8. In a two-way classification model $y_{ij} = \mu + \alpha_i + \theta_j + e_{ij}$, $i = 1, 2, \cdots, r$; $j = 1, 2, \cdots, c$, show from the normal equations (14.4.2) that

(*a*) $\hat{\theta}_1 - \hat{\theta}_2 = \bar{y}_{.1} - \bar{y}_{.2}$.

(*b*) $\hat{\theta}_1 + \hat{\theta}_2 - 2\hat{\theta}_3 = \bar{y}_{.1} + \bar{y}_{.2} - 2\bar{y}_{.3}$.

(*c*) The two estimators in parts (*a*) and (*b*) are uncorrelated when the random variables e_{ij} satisfy the specifications in either Case A or Case B.

9. Let the model be the two-way classification as given in Prob. 8, and let the random variables satisfy the specifications in either Case A or Case B. By the theory in Sec. 14.4, the contrast $\sum_{p=1}^{c} a_p\theta_p$ is estimated by $\Sigma a_p\bar{y}_{.p}$, and the contrast $\sum_{k=1}^{c} b_k\theta_k$ is estimated by $\Sigma b_p\bar{y}_{.p}$.

(*a*) Show that $\text{var}\left(\sum a_p\bar{y}_{.p}\right) = \frac{\sigma^2}{r}\sum_{p=1}^{c} a_p^2$.

(*b*) Show that $\Sigma a_p\bar{y}_{.p}$ and $\Sigma b_k\bar{y}_{.k}$ are uncorrelated if $\sum_{p=1}^{c} a_pb_p = 0$.

10. In Prob. 5, show that $\theta_1 - \bar{\theta}_.$ is estimable $\left(\bar{\theta}_. = 1/6 \sum_{i=1}^{6} \theta_i\right)$. Find the value of the "best" linear unbiased estimate.

11. In Prob. 5, set a .95 confidence interval on $\alpha_1 + \alpha_2 - 2\alpha_3$.

12. In the three-way classification model with no interaction

$$y_{ijk} = \mu + \alpha_i + \theta_j + \tau_k + e_{ijk} \qquad \begin{aligned} i &= 1, 2, \cdots, a \\ j &= 1, 2, \cdots, b \\ k &= 1, 2, \cdots, c \end{aligned}$$

show that the normal equations are

$$\begin{aligned} abc\hat{\mu} + bc\Sigma\hat{\alpha}_i + ac\Sigma\hat{\theta}_j + ab\Sigma\hat{\tau}_k &= Y_{...} \\ bc\hat{\mu} + bc\hat{\alpha}_p + c\Sigma\hat{\theta}_j + b\Sigma\hat{\tau}_k &= Y_{p..} \qquad p = 1, 2, \cdots, a \\ ac\hat{\mu} + c\Sigma\hat{\alpha}_i + ac\hat{\theta}_q + a\Sigma\hat{\tau}_k &= Y_{.q.} \qquad q = 1, 2, \cdots, b \\ ab\hat{\mu} + b\Sigma\hat{\alpha}_i + a\Sigma\hat{\theta}_j + ab\hat{\tau}_r &= Y_{..r} \qquad r = 1, 2, \cdots, c \end{aligned}$$

13. Show that a solution of the normal equations in Prob. 12 is

$$\begin{aligned} \hat{\beta}' &= (\hat{\mu}, \hat{\alpha}_1, \cdots, \hat{\alpha}_a, \hat{\theta}_1, \cdots, \hat{\theta}_b, \hat{\tau}_1, \cdots, \hat{\tau}_c) \\ &= (\bar{y}_{...}, \bar{y}_{1..} - \bar{y}_{...}, \cdots, \bar{y}_{a..} - \bar{y}_{...}, \bar{y}_{.1.} - \bar{y}_{...}, \cdots, \bar{y}_{.b.} - \bar{y}_{...}, \\ &\qquad \bar{y}_{..1} - \bar{y}_{...}, \cdots, \bar{y}_{..c} - \bar{y}_{...}) \end{aligned}$$

that is, $\hat{\mu} = \bar{y}_{...}$; $\hat{\alpha}_p = \bar{y}_{p..} - \bar{y}_{...}$; $\hat{\theta}_q = \bar{y}_{.q.} - \bar{y}_{...}$; $\hat{\tau}_r = \bar{y}_{..r} - \bar{y}_{...}$.

14. In Probs. 12 and 13, show that

$$\begin{aligned}
\hat{\boldsymbol{\beta}}'X'\mathbf{Y} &= \hat{\boldsymbol{\mu}}\mathbf{Y}_{...} + \sum_{p=1}^{a} \hat{\boldsymbol{\alpha}}_p\mathbf{Y}_{p..} + \sum_{q=1}^{b} \hat{\boldsymbol{\theta}}_q\mathbf{Y}_{.q.} + \sum_{r=1}^{c} \hat{\boldsymbol{\tau}}_r\mathbf{Y}_{..r} \\
&= \bar{\mathbf{y}}_{...}\mathbf{Y}_{...} + \sum_{p=1}^{a} (\bar{\mathbf{y}}_{p..} - \bar{\mathbf{y}}_{...})\mathbf{Y}_{p..} + \sum_{q=1}^{b} (\bar{\mathbf{y}}_{.q.} - \bar{\mathbf{y}}_{...})\mathbf{Y}_{.q.} \\
&\qquad + \sum_{r=1}^{c} (\bar{\mathbf{y}}_{..r} - \bar{\mathbf{y}}_{...})\mathbf{Y}_{..r} \\
&= \frac{\mathbf{Y}_{...}^2}{abc} + \left(\sum_{p=1}^{a} \frac{\mathbf{Y}_{p..}^2}{bc} - \frac{\mathbf{Y}_{...}^2}{abc}\right) + \left(\sum_{q=1}^{b} \frac{\mathbf{Y}_{.q.}^2}{ac} - \frac{\mathbf{Y}_{...}^2}{abc}\right) \\
&\qquad + \left(\sum_{r=1}^{c} \frac{\mathbf{Y}_{..r}^2}{ab} - \frac{\mathbf{Y}_{...}^2}{abc}\right) \\
&= \frac{\mathbf{Y}_{...}^2}{abc} + \sum_{pqr} (\bar{\mathbf{y}}_{p..} - \bar{\mathbf{y}}_{...})^2 + \sum_{pqr} (\bar{\mathbf{y}}_{.q.} - \bar{\mathbf{y}}_{...})^2 + \sum_{pqr} (\bar{\mathbf{y}}_{..r} - \bar{\mathbf{y}}_{...})^2
\end{aligned}$$

15. To test the hypothesis $\alpha_1 = \alpha_2 = \cdots = \alpha_a = \alpha$ (unknown), the reduced model is

$$\mathbf{y}_{ijk} = \mu^* + \theta_j + \tau_k + \mathbf{e}_{ijk}$$

where $\mu^* = \mu + \alpha$. Find the normal equations $Z'Z\tilde{\boldsymbol{\gamma}} = Z'\mathbf{Y}$ for the model, and show that (using the symbols in Theorem 14.7) a solution is

$$\begin{aligned}
\tilde{\boldsymbol{\gamma}} &= (\tilde{\boldsymbol{\mu}}^*, \tilde{\boldsymbol{\theta}}_1, \cdots, \tilde{\boldsymbol{\theta}}_b, \tilde{\boldsymbol{\tau}}_1, \cdots, \tilde{\boldsymbol{\tau}}_c) \\
&= (\bar{\mathbf{y}}_{...}, \bar{\mathbf{y}}_{.1.} - \bar{\mathbf{y}}_{...}, \cdots, \bar{\mathbf{y}}_{.b.} - \bar{\mathbf{y}}_{...}, \bar{\mathbf{y}}_{..1} - \bar{\mathbf{y}}_{...}, \cdots, \bar{\mathbf{y}}_{..c} - \bar{\mathbf{y}}_{...})
\end{aligned}$$

In other words,

$$\tilde{\boldsymbol{\mu}}^* = \bar{\mathbf{y}}_{...} \qquad \tilde{\boldsymbol{\theta}}_q = \bar{\mathbf{y}}_{.q.} - \bar{\mathbf{y}}_{...} \qquad \tilde{\boldsymbol{\tau}}_r = \bar{\mathbf{y}}_{..r} - \bar{\mathbf{y}}_{...}$$

16. In Prob. 15, find $\tilde{\boldsymbol{\gamma}}'Z'\mathbf{Y}$.

17. In Prob. 16, show that $\hat{\boldsymbol{\beta}}'X'\mathbf{Y} - \tilde{\boldsymbol{\gamma}}'Z'\mathbf{Y} = \sum_{ijk} (\bar{\mathbf{y}}_{i..} - \bar{\mathbf{y}}_{...})^2$.

18. In Prob. 13, show that, to test the hypothesis

$$H_0\colon \alpha_1 = \alpha_2 = \cdots = \alpha_a$$

by using Theorem 14.7, the quantity

$$\mathbf{u} = \frac{\sum_{ijk} (\bar{\mathbf{y}}_{i..} - \bar{\mathbf{y}}_{...})^2/(a-1)}{\sum_{ijk} (\mathbf{y}_{ijk} - \bar{\mathbf{y}}_{i..} - \bar{\mathbf{y}}_{.j.} - \bar{\mathbf{y}}_{..k} + 2\bar{\mathbf{y}}_{...})^2/T}$$

where $T = abc - a - b - c + 2$, is distributed as F with $a - 1$ and T degrees of freedom when H_0 is true.

19. Find the quantity $\mathbf{u}$ to test the hypothesis $H_0: \theta_1 = \theta_2 = \cdots = \theta_c$ in Prob. 12.

20. In the two-way classification model with interaction

$$\mathbf{y}_{ijk} = \mu + \alpha_i + \theta_j + (\alpha\theta)_{ij} + \mathbf{e}_{ijk}$$

find the normal equations.

14.7 Bibliography

1. Anderson, R. L., and T. A. Bancroft: "Statistical Theory in Research," McGraw-Hill Book Company, Inc., New York, 1952.
2. Bennett, C. A., and N. L. Franklin: "Statistical Analysis in Chemistry and the Chemical Industry," John Wiley & Sons, Inc., New York, 1954.
3. Cochran, W. G., and G. M. Cox: "Experimental Designs," John Wiley & Sons, Inc., New York, 1957.
4. Davies, O. L.: "Design and Analysis of Industrial Experiments," Oliver & Boyd, Ltd., Edinburgh and London, 1954.
5. Federer, W. T.: "Experimental Design, Theory and Application," The Macmillan Company, New York, 1955.
6. Goulden, C. H.: "Methods of Statistical Analysis," John Wiley & Sons, Inc., New York, 1939.
7. Graybill, F. A.: "An Introduction to Linear Statistical Models," Vol. I., McGraw-Hill Book Company, Inc., New York, 1961.
8. Kempthorne, O.: "Design and Analysis of Experiments," John Wiley & Sons, Inc., New York, 1952.
9. Rao, C. R.: "Advanced Statistical Methods in Biometric Research," John Wiley & Sons, Inc., New York, 1952.
10. Scheffé, H.: "The Analysis of Variance," John Wiley & Sons, Inc., New York, 1959.
11. Snedecor, G. W.: "Statistical Methods," Iowa State College Press, Ames, Iowa, 1956.

15

Sequential Tests of Hypotheses

15.1 Sequential Analysis

Sequential analysis refers to techniques for testing hypotheses or estimating parameters when the sample size is not fixed in advance but is determined during the course of the experiment by criteria which depend on the observations as they occur.

In Chap. 12 we considered the test $H_0: \theta = \theta_0$ against $H_1: \theta = \theta_1$. It was shown that for samples of size n, $(\mathbf{x}_1, \mathbf{x}_2, \cdots, \mathbf{x}_n)$, the test which minimizes the Type II error for fixed Type I error is the likelihood-ratio test. Thus if the Type I error is chosen to be α, then α determines a number A by virtue of the equation

$$\iint_{\lambda_n > A} \cdots \int f_0(x_1)f_0(x_2) \cdots f_0(x_n)\, dx_1 \cdots dx_n = \alpha \tag{1}$$

where

$$\lambda_n = \prod_1^n \frac{f_1(\mathbf{x}_i)}{f_0(\mathbf{x}_i)} \tag{2}$$

and the critical region for rejection of H_0 is the region

$$\lambda_n > A \tag{3}$$

This critical region minimizes the probability β (Type II error) of accepting H_0 when H_1 is true. We write $f(x; \theta_i)$ as $f_i(x)$.

Suppose that it is desired to fix both α and β in advance. One could do so as follows if the sample size were at his disposal: First determine A_n as a function of n by means of (1), then determine β as a function of n,

$$\beta_n = \iint_{\lambda_n < A_n} \cdots \int f_1(x_1)f_1(x_2) \cdots f_1(x_n)\, dx_1 \cdots dx_n \tag{4}$$

and finally select n so that β_n has the desired value.

Suppose further that for, say, $\alpha = .01$ and $\beta = .01$ and for particular functions f_0 and f_1 we had worked through the computation and found n

to be 100. The following considerations make sequential analysis interesting both from the theoretical and practical viewpoint: In drawing the 100 observations to test H_0, it is possible that among the first few observations there may be one or more that have values such that eventual rejection of H_0 is out of the question and it would be a waste of time to make the remaining observations. In other instances the first 20 or first 30 or first 40 observations may provide quite sufficient evidence, relative to α and β, for accepting or rejecting H_0. In short, the possibility is raised that, by constructing the test in a fashion which permits termination of the sampling at any observation, one can test H_0 with fixed errors α and β and yet do so with fewer than 100 observations, on an average. This is in fact the case, although it may at first appear surprising in view of the fact that the best test for fixed sample size requires 100 observations. The saving in observations is often quite large, sometimes more than 50 per cent. That is, in repeated tests of H_0 against H_1 for fixed control of both errors, 100 observations per test may be required for fixed sample sizes, but for sequential sampling and the same control of the errors, only 50 observations per test may be required, on an average.

15.2 Construction of Sequential Tests

In this section the theory of sequential testing will be developed for the case of testing a null hypothesis H_0 against a single alternative H_1. It

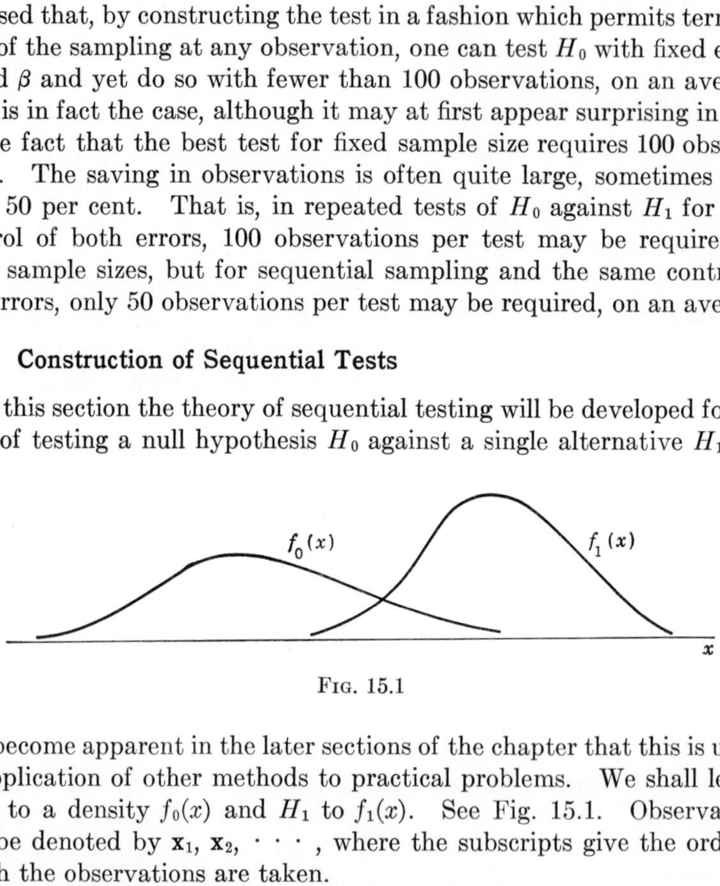

FIG. 15.1

will become apparent in the later sections of the chapter that this is useful in application of other methods to practical problems. We shall let H_0 refer to a density $f_0(x)$ and H_1 to $f_1(x)$. See Fig. 15.1. Observations will be denoted by $\mathbf{x}_1, \mathbf{x}_2, \cdots$, where the subscripts give the order in which the observations are taken.

The sequential test employs the likelihood-ratio

$$\lambda_m = \prod_{i=1}^{m} \frac{f_1(\mathbf{x}_i)}{f_0(\mathbf{x}_i)} \tag{1}$$

and two positive numbers A and B, with $A > 1$ and $B < 1$. As observations are made, one computes the ratios $\lambda_1, \lambda_2, \lambda_3, \cdots$ and continues taking observations as long as

$$B < \lambda_m < A \tag{2}$$

If, for some m, λ_m is less than or equal to B, H_0 is accepted and the test is completed. If λ_m becomes greater than or equal to A at some stage, H_0 is rejected and the test is completed. The procedure then is to continue sampling until λ_m falls outside the interval specified by (2), at which time the sampling ceases.

The first question that naturally arises is, What is to prevent the sampling from going on forever? It can be shown that this cannot happen—that the probability is 1 that the process will terminate whatever the distribution of **x**. Let

$$\mathbf{z} = \log\left[\frac{f_1(\mathbf{x})}{f_0(\mathbf{x})}\right] \tag{3}$$

Assume **z** has a density $g(z)$ (with positive variance) determined by the density of **x** [which need not be $f_0(x)$ or $f_1(x)$]. The sequence of observations $\mathbf{x}_1, \mathbf{x}_2, \cdots$ determines a sequence of **z** observations $\mathbf{z}_1, \mathbf{z}_2, \cdots$. The sequence of inequalities (2) becomes

$$\log B < \sum_1^m \mathbf{z}_i < \log A \tag{4}$$

where $\log B$ is negative and $\log A$ is positive. Let $c = \log A - \log B$ and let p be the area under $g(z)$ between $-c$ and c. Now if any one of the $\mathbf{z}_i$ falls outside the interval $-c$ to c, one of the inequalities in (4) will necessarily be violated either at that stage or, if not then, at some

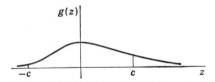

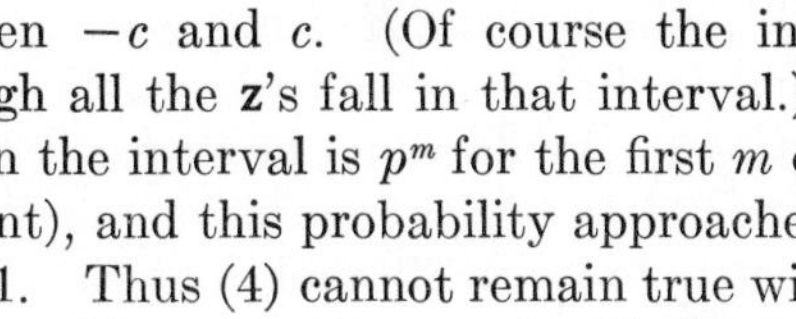

previous stage. Hence if (4) is to hold for all m, at the very least every $\mathbf{z}_i$ must fall between $-c$ and c. (Of course the inequalities may be violated even though all the **z**'s fall in that interval.) The probability that every $\mathbf{z}_i$ falls in the interval is p^m for the first m observations (since they are independent), and this probability approaches 0 as m increases, since p is less than 1. Thus (4) cannot remain true with probability one. [In case $g(z)$ is 0 outside $-c$ to c, one would define new variables $\mathbf{y}_i$, letting $\mathbf{y}_1$ be the sum of the first r **z**'s, $\mathbf{y}_2$ the sum of the next r **z**'s, and so forth, taking r to be large enough that the probability is positive that a value of **y** falls outside $-c$ to c.]

We turn now to the determination of A and B. The probability α that H_0 will be rejected when it is true is found by computing the probability that λ_m will exceed A before it becomes less than B. It is clear that

$$\alpha = P(\lambda_1 \geq A) + P(B < \lambda_1 < A, \lambda_2 \geq A) + P(B < \lambda_1 < A, B < \lambda_2 < A, \lambda_3 \geq A) + \cdots \quad (5)$$

Similarly the probability β that H_0 will be accepted when H_1 is true is

$$\beta = P(\lambda_1 \leq B) + P(B < \lambda_1 < A, \lambda_2 \leq B) + P(B < \lambda_1 < A, B < \lambda_2 < A, \lambda_3 \leq B) + \cdots \quad (6)$$

For two specified densities $f_0(x)$ and $f_1(x)$ one could compute all these probabilities, using $f_0(x)$ in (5) and $f_1(x)$ in (6). It follows then that α and β are known functions of A and B; hence if α and β are specified in advance, A and B are determined by (5) and (6).

As might be anticipated, the actual determination of A and B from (5) and (6) can be a major computational project. In practice, they are never determined that way because a very simple and accurate approximation is available. The approximate formulas are

$$A \cong \frac{1 - \beta}{\alpha} \quad (7)$$

$$B \cong \frac{\beta}{1 - \alpha} \quad (8)$$

and they arise from the following considerations. Suppose that λ_m is a continuous function of a continuous variate $\mathbf{m}$ so that λ_m is plotted as a function of $\mathbf{m}$, and suppose that the test is performed by moving out along the m axis until λ_m first equals A or B. That is, the test is continued as long as (2) is true and ceases when either $\lambda_m = B$ (H_0 accepted) or $\lambda_m = A$ (H_1 accepted). At all points of the $(\mathbf{x}_1, \mathbf{x}_2, \cdots)$ space where H_0 is accepted, the likelihood of H_1, say L_1, is exactly B times the likelihood L_0 of H_0, since $\lambda = L_1/L_0 = B$ at those points. Hence the integral of L_1 over those points is exactly equal to B times the integral of L_0 over those points. But the first integral is β, and the second is $1 - \alpha$ (the probability of accepting H_0 when it is true). Thus we would have β exactly equal to $B(1 - \alpha)$ and (8) would hold exactly. By a similar argument at $\lambda_m = A$, (7) would be an exact equality. Since the error of using (7) and (8) is merely a consequence of the discreteness of $\mathbf{m}$, one would expect it to be small, and analytical investigation shows that it is quite small when both α and β are less than $\frac{1}{2}$. We shall not, however, look into this matter.

Equations (7) and (8) make the actual performance of a sequential test astonishingly simple. It is not necessary to develop any sampling distribution theory at all; one merely selects α and β arbitrarily, computes A and B, and proceeds at once with the test. We shall state this result as a rule.

Rule 1. To perform a likelihood-ratio sequential test of the hypothesis H_0: $\theta = \theta_0$ against H_1: $\theta = \theta_1$ in the density $f(x; \theta)$, with approximate Type I error probability of α and Type II error probability of β, compute

1. A, where $A = (1 - \beta)/\alpha$.
2. B, where $B = \beta/(1 - \alpha)$.
3. Take an observation $\mathbf{x}_1$ at random from $f(x:\theta)$ and compute

$$\lambda_1 = \frac{f(\mathbf{x}_1:\theta_1)}{f(\mathbf{x}_1:\theta_0)}$$

4. If $\lambda_1 \leq B$, accept H_0.
5. If $\lambda_1 \geq A$, reject H_0.
6. If $B < \lambda_1 < A$, then take another observation at random from $f(x:\theta)$ and compute

$$\lambda_2 = \frac{f(\mathbf{x}_1:\theta_1)f(\mathbf{x}_2:\theta_1)}{f(\mathbf{x}_1:\theta_0)f(\mathbf{x}_2:\theta_0)}$$

7. Repeat 4 and 5 with λ_1 replaced by λ_2.
8. Continue taking observations until either 4 or 5 is satisfied for some λ_m.

Example 15.1. Let $\mathbf{x}$ be distributed normally with variance 1 and mean θ. Suppose that we wish to test the hypothesis H_0: $\theta = 6$ against the alternative H_1: $\theta = 8$, and we desire a Type I error probability of .03 and a Type II error probability of .10. By the rule, we get $\theta_0 = 6$; $\theta_1 = 8$; $\alpha = .03$; $\beta = .10$, and

$$f(x:\theta) = \frac{1}{\sqrt{2\pi}} e^{-(\frac{1}{2})(x-\theta)^2}$$

Also

$$A = \frac{1 - \beta}{\alpha} = \frac{.90}{.03} = 30 \qquad B = \frac{\beta}{1 - \alpha} = \frac{.10}{.97} = .103$$

and

$$\lambda_m = \frac{f(\mathbf{x}_1:\theta_1) \cdots f(\mathbf{x}_m:\theta_1)}{f(\mathbf{x}_1:\theta_0) \cdots f(\mathbf{x}_m:\theta_0)} = \frac{\exp[-(\frac{1}{2})\Sigma(\mathbf{x}_i - 8)^2]}{\exp[-(\frac{1}{2})\Sigma(\mathbf{x}_i - 6)^2]}$$

$$\log \lambda_m = 2\Sigma\mathbf{x}_i - 14\mathrm{m}$$

Then $\log B < \log \lambda_m < \log A$ becomes

$$7\mathrm{m} + (\tfrac{1}{2}) \log .103 < \sum_{i=1}^{\mathrm{m}} \mathbf{x}_i < 7\mathrm{m} + (\tfrac{1}{2}) \log 30$$

Since the inequalities $B < \lambda_m < A$ are equivalent to $\log B < \log \lambda_m < \log A$, the latter can be used.

15.3 Power Functions

Let a density $f(x; \theta)$ have one parameter θ, and let us test the null hypothesis, H_0: $\theta = \theta_0$, against the alternative hypothesis, H_1: $\theta = \theta_1$. We are interested in the behavior of the test for all possible values of θ.

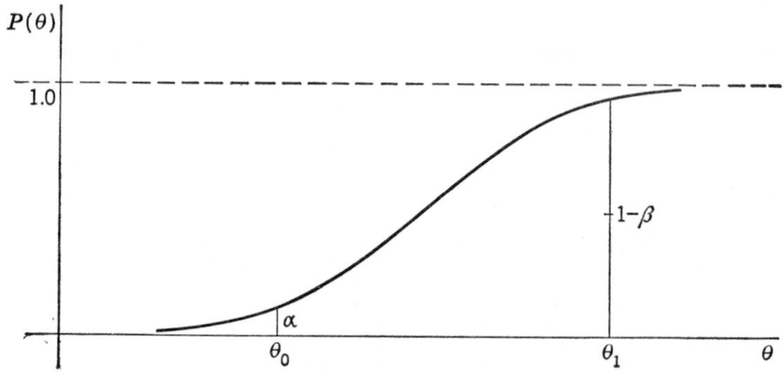

FIG. 15.2

In particular, we shall examine the power of the test, $P(\theta)$, which is the probability that θ_0 will be rejected when θ is the true parameter value. Of course

$$P(\theta_0) = \alpha \tag{1}$$

$$P(\theta_1) = 1 - \beta \tag{2}$$

and (supposing for definiteness that $\theta_0 < \theta_1$) we should expect the power function to have somewhat the shape of the curve of Fig. 15.2.

The straightforward way to compute $P(\theta)$ is simply to add the probabilities that H_0 will be rejected at each observation. Thus

$$P(\theta) = P(\lambda_1 \geq A) + P(B < \lambda_1 < A, \lambda_2 \geq A) + P(B < \lambda_1 < A, B < \lambda_2 < A, \lambda_3 \geq A) + \cdots \tag{3}$$

where, for example,

$$P(B < \lambda_1 < A, \lambda_2 \geq A) = \iint_R f(x_1; \theta) f(x_2; \theta)\, dx_1\, dx_2 \tag{4}$$

and the double integral is taken over the region R in the x_1x_2 plane defined by the inequalities

$$B < \frac{f(x_1; \theta_1)}{f(x_1; \theta_0)} < A \qquad \frac{f(x_1; \theta_1) f(x_2; \theta_1)}{f(x_1; \theta_0) f(x_2; \theta_0)} \geq A \tag{5}$$

This procedure for determining the power function is tedious, to say the least, and is usually so troublesome as to be completely out of the question in practice.

To avoid the use of (3), a very ingenious device has been developed. This method assumes certain regularity conditions on f and we shall present it without a formal proof of its correctness, merely giving the general pattern of the proof. The argument requires first the existence of a nonzero number h such that

$$g(x; \theta) = \left[\frac{f(x; \theta_1)}{f(x; \theta_0)}\right]^h f(x; \theta) \tag{6}$$

is a density, i.e., a number h such that

$$\int_{-\infty}^{\infty} g(x; \theta)\, dx = 1 \tag{7}$$

Of course $h = 0$ will make $g(x; \theta)$ a density, because $f(x; \theta)$ is a density. To show that such a nonzero value of h exists, we consider the expected value of $[f(\mathbf{x}; \theta_1)/f(\mathbf{x}; \theta_0)]^u$ as a function of u, say $\phi(u)$,

$$\phi(u) = \int_{-\infty}^{\infty} \left[\frac{f(x; \theta_1)}{f(x; \theta_0)}\right]^u f(x; \theta)\, dx \tag{8}$$

Obviously $\phi(u)$ is always positive, and furthermore $\phi(0) = 1$. We can also argue that $\phi(u)$ becomes infinite when u approaches infinity in either the positive or negative direction. Since $f(x; \theta_1)$ and $f(x; \theta_0)$ differ, there will be an interval or set of intervals where their ratio is greater than 1. Over such intervals the integrand becomes large with increasing u, and $\phi(u) \to \infty$ as $u \to \infty$. Similarly there will be intervals where the inverse ratio is greater than 1 and the integrand becomes large for large negative values of u. This is enough to show the existence of h. [Of course, $\phi(u)$ may have a minimum at $u = 0$, in which case h would not exist, but this can happen only for particular values of θ, not in general.] So far as our argument goes, there may be several values of u for which $\phi(u) = 1$. Actually there is only one, for the shape of $\phi(u)$ is as illustrated in Fig. 15.3; the minimum, though, may be to the left of the origin so that h may be negative. Thus there exists a nonzero h in general such that $\phi(h) = 1$, and the function defined in (6) is therefore a density.

One now sets up a sequential test of the null hypothesis H_0' that the density is $f(x; \theta)$ against the alternative hypothesis H_1' that the density is $g(x; \theta)$. Of course the null hypothesis here is true by assumption. The limits for the likelihood-ratio are taken to be A^h and B^h. Thus the test continues as long as

$$B^h < \frac{g(\mathbf{x}_1; \theta)g(\mathbf{x}_2; \theta) \cdots g(\mathbf{x}_m; \theta)}{f(\mathbf{x}_1; \theta)f(\mathbf{x}_2; \theta) \cdots f(\mathbf{x}_m; \theta)} < A^h \tag{9}$$

and ceases when the ratio equals or falls outside these limits. We are assuming here that h is positive; if it is negative, A and B are interchanged. In view of (6), the test defined by (9) is exactly equivalent to the original sequential test under consideration; i.e., (9) is equivalent to

$$B < \frac{f(\mathbf{x}_1; \theta_1)f(\mathbf{x}_2; \theta_1) \cdots f(\mathbf{x}_m; \theta_1)}{f(\mathbf{x}_1; \theta_0)f(\mathbf{x}_2; \theta_0) \cdots f(\mathbf{x}_m; \theta_0)} < A \tag{10}$$

Thus the rejection of H_0 implies the rejection of H_0'. But we can compute at once the probability that H_0' will be rejected when H_0' is true

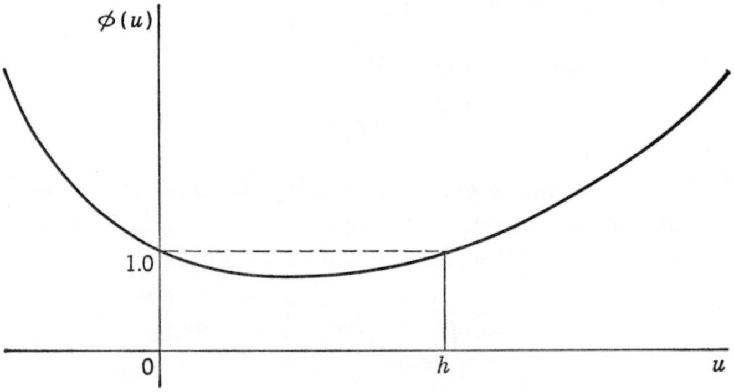

FIG. 15.3

[$f(x; \theta)$ is the true density]; hence we have $P(\theta)$ for $f(x; \theta)$. H_0' will be rejected when it is true with probability α' and accepted when H_1' is true with probability β', where, in accordance with (15.2.7) and (15.2.8),

$$A^h \cong \frac{1 - \beta'}{\alpha'} \tag{11}$$

$$B^h \cong \frac{\beta'}{1 - \alpha'} \tag{12}$$

On solving this pair of equations for α', we find

$$\alpha' = P(\theta) \cong \frac{1 - B^h}{A^h - B^h} \tag{13}$$

In summary:

Rule 2. To find the approximate power function of the sequential probability ratio test:

1. Find $\phi(u)$ defined by (8) for a particular θ^*.
2. Set $\phi(u) = 1$ and solve for u.
3. The nonzero root in 2 is the number h of (13).
4. Then the ordinate of the power function at θ^* is given in (13):

$$P(\theta^*) \cong \frac{1 - B^h}{A^h - B^h}$$

Example 15.2. As an illustration, let us consider the null hypothesis that the mean of a normal distribution is μ_0 against the alternative that the mean is μ_1 (with $\mu_0 < \mu_1$), assuming that the variance σ^2 is known. We wish to find the probability $P(\mu)$ that μ_0 will be rejected when the true mean is μ. $\phi(u)$ is

$$\phi(u) = \int_{-\infty}^{\infty} \frac{1}{\sqrt{2\pi}\,\sigma} e^{-[(x-\mu)^2/2\sigma^2]} \left(\frac{e^{-[(x-\mu_1)^2/2\sigma^2]}}{e^{-[(x-\mu_0)^2/2\sigma^2]}} \right)^u dx \tag{14}$$

The integral is easily evaluated, and on putting $\phi(u) = 1$ and solving for u, we find that one root is $u = 0$ while the other is

$$h = \frac{\mu_1 + \mu_0 - 2\mu}{\mu_1 - \mu_0} \tag{15}$$

On substituting this expression for h in (13), we have an explicit formula for $P(\mu)$ in terms of μ.

15.4 Average Sample Size

The sample size $\mathbf{n}$ in sequential testing is a random variable with a density, say $p(n)$, which may be determined in terms of the true density $f(x; \theta)$. Thus

$$p(1) = P(\lambda_1 \leq B) + P(\lambda_1 \geq A) \tag{1}$$
$$p(2) = P(B < \lambda_1 < A, \lambda_2 \leq B) + P(B < \lambda_1 < A, \lambda_2 \geq A) \tag{2}$$

and so forth, where the probabilities on the right are determined by integrals like that of equation (15.3.4). In this section we shall find an approximate expression for the expected sample size $E(\mathbf{n})$ and then illustrate the extent to which sequential methods may save observations.

Let

$$\mathbf{z} = \log \frac{f(\mathbf{x}; \theta_1)}{f(\mathbf{x}; \theta_0)} \tag{3}$$

and let $\mathbf{n}$ be the smallest integer for which $\mathbf{z}_1 + \mathbf{z}_2 + \cdots + \mathbf{z}_n = \mathbf{Z}_n^*$ does not satisfy

$$\log B < \mathbf{Z}_n^* < \log A \tag{4}$$

We shall show that the expected value of the variate $\mathbf{Z}_n^*$, which depends on the random $\mathbf{z}$'s and the random variate $\mathbf{n}$, is simply

$$E(\mathbf{Z}_n^*) = E(\mathbf{n})E(\mathbf{z}) \tag{5}$$

To do this, we let N be some very large but fixed value of $\mathbf{n}$ and disregard that part of the distribution of $\mathbf{n}$ to the right of N. The resulting error can be made arbitrarily small by taking N sufficiently large. Since

N is fixed, it follows that

$$E(\mathbf{Z}_N^*) = NE(\mathbf{z}) \tag{6}$$

The variate $\mathbf{Z}_N^*$ may be put in the form

$$\mathbf{Z}_N^* = \mathbf{Z}_n^* + \mathbf{W}_n \tag{7}$$

defining another variate $\mathbf{W}_n$, and by virtue of (6)

$$E(\mathbf{Z}_n^* + \mathbf{W}_n) = NE(\mathbf{z}) \tag{8}$$

The trouble with trying to get (5) directly is that the value of $\mathbf{z}_i$ depends on whether $i \leq \mathbf{n}$ or $i > \mathbf{n}$. In the latter case $E(\mathbf{z}_i) = E(\mathbf{z})$, but when $i < \mathbf{n}$, $\mathbf{z}_i$ is restricted by (4). Now in (8) the variate $\mathbf{W}_n$ consists of $\mathbf{z}$'s with $i > \mathbf{n}$, so that the expected value of each $\mathbf{z}$ in $\mathbf{W}_n$ is $E(\mathbf{z})$. Thus

$$E(\mathbf{W}_n) = E(\mathbf{z})E(N - \mathbf{n}) \tag{9}$$

where the second factor on the right depends only on the distribution of $\mathbf{n}$. Combining (8) and (9),

$$NE(\mathbf{z}) = E(\mathbf{Z}_n^*) + E(\mathbf{W}_n) \tag{10}$$
$$= E(\mathbf{Z}_n^*) + E(\mathbf{z})[N - E(\mathbf{n})] \tag{11}$$

which is the same as (5); solving for $E(\mathbf{n})$,

$$E(\mathbf{n}) = \frac{E(\mathbf{Z}_n^*)}{E(\mathbf{z})} \tag{12}$$

This last expression enables one to get a simple approximate formula for the expected sample size. The variate $\mathbf{Z}_n^*$ takes on only values beyond $\log A$ and smaller than $\log B$. If one ignores the amounts by which $\mathbf{Z}_n^*$ exceeds $\log A$ or falls short of $\log B$, he may say that $\mathbf{Z}_n^*$ takes essentially only two values, $\log A$ and $\log B$. When the true distribution is $f(x; \theta)$, the probability that $\mathbf{Z}_n^*$ takes the value $\log A$ is $P(\theta)$, while the probability that it takes the value $\log B$ is $1 - P(\theta)$. Hence

$$E(\mathbf{Z}_n^*) \cong P(\theta) \log A + [1 - P(\theta)] \log B \tag{13}$$

which together with (12) gives the following:

Theorem 15.1. *The approximate average sample size of the sequential likelihood-ratio test is*

$$E(\mathbf{n}) \cong \frac{P(\theta) \log A + [1 - P(\theta)] \log B}{E(\mathbf{z})} \tag{14}$$

This result enables one to compare sequential tests with fixed-sample-size tests.

Example 15.3. As an illustration, we shall consider the test that $\mu = 0$ against $\mu = 1$ for a normal population with unit variance. We shall choose $\alpha = .01$ and $\beta = .01$; then (15.2.7) and (15.2.8) give $A = 99$ and $B = 1/99$. Let us further assume that the true parameter value is 0 so that $P(\theta)$ in (14) is just .01. Also we need to compute the expected value of

$$\mathbf{z} = \log \frac{e^{-[(\mathbf{x}-1)^2/2]}}{e^{-(\mathbf{x}^2/2)}} = \mathbf{x} - \frac{1}{2} \tag{15}$$

which is $-\frac{1}{2}$ under the true distribution. Thus

$$\begin{aligned} E(\mathbf{n}) &\cong \frac{.01 \log 99 + .99 \log 1/99}{-\frac{1}{2}} \\ &\cong 1.96 \log 99 \cong 9 \end{aligned} \tag{16}$$

To get the same control of the two errors with a sample of fixed size, we recall that the best test is made by choosing a number c and accepting or rejecting $\mu = 0$ according as $\bar{\mathbf{x}}$ is less than or greater than c. The probability α that H_0 will be rejected (under $\mu = 0$) is

$$\alpha = \sqrt{\frac{n}{2\pi}} \int_c^\infty e^{-(n/2)\bar{x}^2}\, d\bar{x} = \frac{1}{\sqrt{2\pi}} \int_{\sqrt{n}c}^\infty e^{-t^2/2}\, dt$$

so that, for $\alpha = .01$,

$$\sqrt{n}\, c = 2.326 \tag{17}$$

The probability β that H_0 would be accepted under H_1 ($\mu = 1$) is

$$\beta = \sqrt{\frac{n}{2\pi}} \int_{-\infty}^c e^{-(n/2)(\bar{x}-1)^2}\, d\bar{x} = \frac{1}{\sqrt{2\pi}} \int_{-\infty}^{\sqrt{n}(c-1)} e^{-(t^2/2)}\, dt$$

so that, for $\beta = .01$,

$$\sqrt{n}\,(c - 1) = -2.326 \tag{18}$$

On solving (17) and (18) for n, we find it to be 22. Thus in repeated tests of the hypothesis in question, the sequential procedure would require, on an average, only $9/22$ or 41 per cent as many observations as the fixed-sample-size procedure.

15.5 Sampling Inspection

A particularly important application of sequential testing is in inspection of manufactured items. Large consumers such as retail chains, assembly plants, government agencies, and the like usually contract for periodic deliveries of items in large groups called *lots*. Certain specifications for the items in question are stipulated in the contract, and it is further stipulated that the items shall be inspected or partially inspected to ensure that only a small proportion of the delivered items fail to meet the specifications. Ordinarily, defective items are not so crucial as to warrant the expense of complete inspection of all items, and sampling inspection is used. That is, the supplier will inspect a sample of the items of a lot and estimate the proportion of the lot defective. If the quality of the lot appears satisfactory, it is delivered; otherwise it may be sold to a less exacting consumer or to the original consumer at a lower price, or it may be completely inspected (if the inspection is not destructive) and the defective items removed. When sampling inspection is to be used, the actual sampling procedure is often a part of the contract. The supplier does not guarantee that the proportion of defective items in submitted lots will be smaller than a given amount; he merely guarantees to submit only lots which have passed a specified sampling inspection test.

The simplest sort of sampling inspection plan is the so-called *single-sampling plan.* One inspects a sample of size n and accepts the lot as satisfactory if the number of defective items is less than or equal to a given number c; otherwise the lot is rejected. The probability of accepting a lot under such a plan depends, of course, on the proportion of defectives in the lot. The density for the number of defectives $\mathbf{x}$ is

$$g(x) = \frac{\binom{M}{x}\binom{N-M}{n-x}}{\binom{N}{n}} \tag{1}$$

where N is the lot size and M is the number of defectives in the lot. This distribution is somewhat troublesome to work with, and since n is usually quite small relative to N, it is customary to approximate this density by the binomial

$$f(x) = \binom{n}{x} p^x(1-p)^{n-x} \tag{2}$$

where $p = M/N$ is the proportion of defectives in the lot.

The performance of a sampling inspection plan may be portrayed by the *operating-characteristic* curve, which is simply a graph of the probability of accepting the lot plotted over the values of p. This probability for the single-sampling plan is

$$L(p) = \sum_{x=0}^{c} g(x) \cong \sum_{x=0}^{c} f(x) \tag{3}$$

using the binomial approximation as we shall do in this and the next section. An operating characteristic is plotted in Fig. 15.4. If, for example, one wished to pass all lots with 6 per cent or less defective and reject all lots with more than 6 per cent defective, the ideal operating characteristic would be the dashed curve of Fig. 15.4. This could not be achieved without complete inspection. Sampling inspection will necessarily reject some of the acceptable lots and will accept some lots which should be rejected. The more sampling one is willing to do, the more nearly he can force the operating characteristic to approximate the ideal operating characteristic. The actual extent of the sampling in any instance depends, of course, on various economic factors associated with the particular problem at hand—factors such as production cost per item,

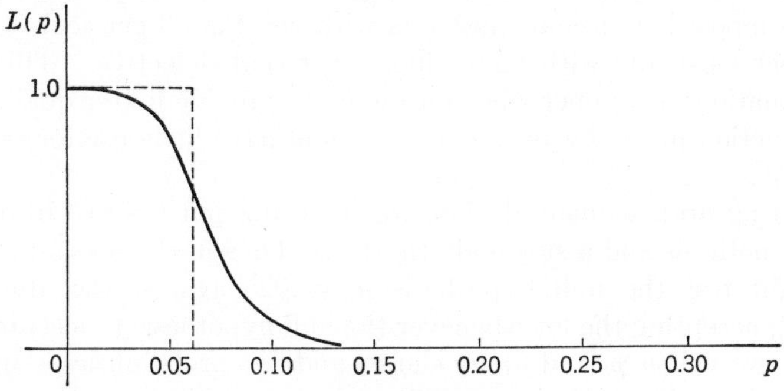

FIG. 15.4

inspection cost per item, difference in market value of accepted and rejected lots, etc.

Sampling inspection plans may be regarded as procedures for testing hypotheses. Thus the single-sampling plan is just the procedure one would use to test the null hypothesis that the parameter p of a binomial distribution has the value p_0 against alternatives $p > p_0$.

Somewhat more sophisticated inspection plans use *double sampling.* A small sample of size n_1 is examined, and the lot may be accepted or rejected on the basis of this sample. But in borderline cases a second sample of size n_2 is examined before the lot is finally classified one way or the other. Formally the procedure is:

1. Examine a sample of size n_1.
2. If $\mathbf{x}_1$ (number of defectives in n_1) $\leq c_1$, accept the lot.
3. If $\mathbf{x}_1 \geq c_2$, reject the lot.
4. If $c_1 < \mathbf{x}_1 < c_2$, examine a second sample of size n_2.
5. If $\mathbf{x}_1 + \mathbf{x}_2 \leq c_3$, accept the lot.
6. If $\mathbf{x}_1 + \mathbf{x}_2 > c_3$, reject the lot.

This procedure contains the germ of the sequential idea. It is better than single sampling in the following sense: Given a single-sampling plan with sample size n and a double-sampling plan with average sample size n, one can more nearly approximate the ideal operating characteristic with the latter. Or in other words, for a given operating characteristic, double sampling will require, on an average, fewer observations than single sampling.

15.6 Sequential Sampling Inspection

We shall suppose that large lots are being dealt with, so that the error of using the binomial distribution is of no practical importance. Let us further suppose that the supplier's production process, when all is well, produces about 2 per cent defectives and that the sampling inspection plan is supposed to accept most lots with less than 3 per cent defective and reject most lots with more than 3 per cent defective. This is the usual situation; a supplier who contracted to provide better quality than his production process was capable of would have little use for sampling inspection.

In setting up a sequential plan, we shall first put the test in terms of a null hypothesis and a single alternative. Thus in the present instance one might test the null hypothesis $p_0 = .025$ against the alternative $p_1 = .04$, accepting the lot whenever the null hypothesis is accepted. In general, two values p_0 and p_1 are chosen and two probabilities α and β for the Type I and Type II errors. Thus one has at his disposal two points on the operating characteristic: $(p_0, 1 - \alpha)$ and (p_1, β). One could make the inspection plan very critical at $p = .03$ by choosing, for example, the two points (.029, .999) and (.031, .001), but in doing so he would ensure that considerable sampling would be done. The actual choice of these two points depends on economic considerations.

The individual observations $\mathbf{y}_i$ have the density

$$f(y) = p^y(1 - p)^{1-y} \tag{1}$$

and if $\sum_1^n \mathbf{y}_i$ is denoted by $\mathbf{x}_n$, the likelihood-ratio is

$$\lambda_n = \frac{p_1^{\mathbf{x}_n}(1 - p_1)^{n-\mathbf{x}_n}}{p_0^{\mathbf{x}_n}(1 - p_0)^{n-\mathbf{x}_n}} \tag{2}$$

Observations are taken until either $\lambda_n \leq B$, in which case the lot is accepted, or $\lambda_n \geq A$, in which case the lot is rejected. A and B are computed from (15.2.7) and (15.2.8).

To get the operating characteristic, one first finds $\phi(u)$, which is

$$\phi(u) = E\left[\frac{p_1^{\mathbf{y}}(1 - p_1)^{1-\mathbf{y}}}{p_0^{\mathbf{y}}(1 - p_0)^{1-\mathbf{y}}}\right]^u \tag{3}$$

$$= \sum_{y=0}^{1} p^y(1 - p)^{1-y}\left(\frac{p_1}{p_0}\right)^{uy}\left(\frac{1 - p_1}{1 - p_0}\right)^{u(1-y)}$$

$$= p\left(\frac{p_1}{p_0}\right)^u + (1 - p)\left(\frac{1 - p_1}{1 - p_0}\right)^u \tag{4}$$

and the number h of Sec. 15.3 is the nonzero root of $\phi(u) = 1$, so that h is defined by

$$p\left(\frac{p_1}{p_0}\right)^h + (1-p)\left(\frac{1-p_1}{1-p_0}\right)^h = 1 \tag{5}$$

This equation together with

$$L(p) = \frac{A^h - 1}{A^h - B^h} \tag{6}$$

[obtained by subtracting (15.3.13) from 1] determine the approximate operating-characteristic function. Since the solution of (5) for h is a troublesome computation, one computes points on the curve by choosing values for h arbitrarily and calculating the corresponding values of p and $L(p)$ from (5) and (6).

Often a sufficient appraisal of the operating characteristic can be obtained from five easily computed points on the curve:

$$L(0) = 1 \tag{7}$$
$$L(1) = 0 \tag{8}$$
$$L(p_0) = 1 - \alpha \tag{9}$$
$$L(p_1) = \beta \tag{10}$$
$$L(p') = \frac{\log A}{\log A - \log B} \tag{11}$$

where

$$p' = \frac{\log [(1-p_0)/(1-p_1)]}{\log (p_1/p_0) - \log [(1-p_1)/(1-p_0)]} \tag{12}$$

The fifth point $[p', L(p')]$ is between p_0 and p_1 and corresponds to $h = 0$; the formulas (11) and (12) are obtained by letting h approach zero in (5) and (6), which become indeterminate at $h = 0$.

The average-sample-size curve may be plotted easily after $L(p)$ has been plotted. Referring to equation (15.4.14), the ordinate of this curve (Fig. 15.5) is given by

$$E(\mathbf{n}) \cong \frac{[1 - L(p)] \log A + L(p) \log B}{p \log (p_1/p_0) + (1-p) \log [(1-p_1)/(1-p_0)]} \tag{13}$$

where we have substituted $1 - L(p)$ for $P(p)$ and

$$E(\mathbf{z}) = E\left[\log \frac{p_1^{\mathbf{y}}(1-p_1)^{1-\mathbf{y}}}{p_0^{\mathbf{y}}(1-p_0)^{1-\mathbf{y}}}\right] \tag{14}$$

$$= p \log \frac{p_1}{p_0} + (1-p) \log \frac{1-p_1}{1-p_0} \tag{15}$$

The maximum value of $E(\mathbf{n})$ occurs very nearly at the point p' given by

(12). At that point, (13) is

$$\frac{\log A \log B}{\log (p_1/p_0) \log [(1 - p_1)/(1 - p_0)]} \tag{16}$$

This is approximately the maximum average sample size and occurs when the true proportion defective has the value given by (12).

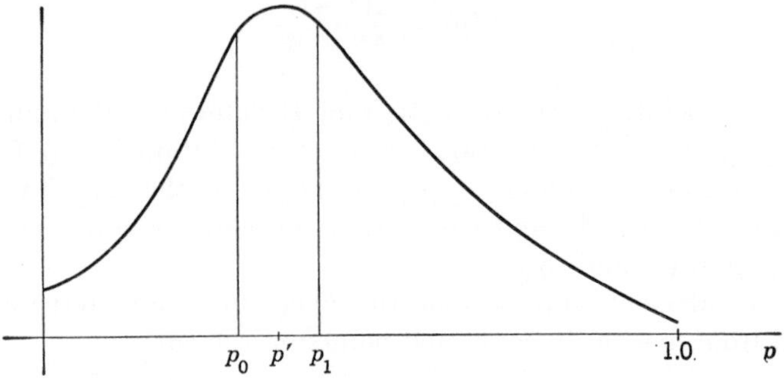

FIG. 15.5

15.7 Sequential Test for the Mean of a Normal Population

As a final example of sequential testing, we shall present without proof the two-sided test of the null hypothesis H_0 that the mean of a normal population has the value μ_0. It is assumed that the variance is one. It is necessary to frame the test in terms of a single alternative H_1. If we were interested in a one-sided test, say against alternatives $\mu > \mu_0$, we should simply choose some arbitrary value μ_1 (greater than μ_0) for the alternative. But that alternative will not serve for the two-sided test, because the power function approaches 0 as μ moves to the left.

Several devices are available to circumvent this difficulty. Perhaps the most satisfactory is a slight alteration of the likelihood-ratio function. Under H_0 the density is

$$f(x; \mu_0) = \frac{1}{\sqrt{2\pi}\,\sigma} e^{-[(x-\mu_0)^2/2]} \tag{1}$$

Instead of an alternative parameter $\mu \neq \mu_0$, we shall use a parameter $\delta_1 > 0$ and form the ratio

$$\lambda_n = \frac{\frac{1}{2} \prod_{i=1}^{n} f(\mathbf{x}_i; \mu_0 + \delta_1) + \frac{1}{2} \prod_{i=1}^{n} f(\mathbf{x}_i; \mu_0 - \delta_1)}{\prod_{i=1}^{n} f(\mathbf{x}_i; \mu_0)} \tag{2}$$

where the products are taken over the successive observations indexed by

$i = 1, 2, \cdots, n$. It is apparent that this ratio λ_n will behave as we wish. Under the null hypothesis, its numerator is equivalent to its denominator. If the alternative μ is actually to the left of μ_0, the second term in its numerator will eventually dominate the denominator, and if the alternative is to the right, the first term will do so.

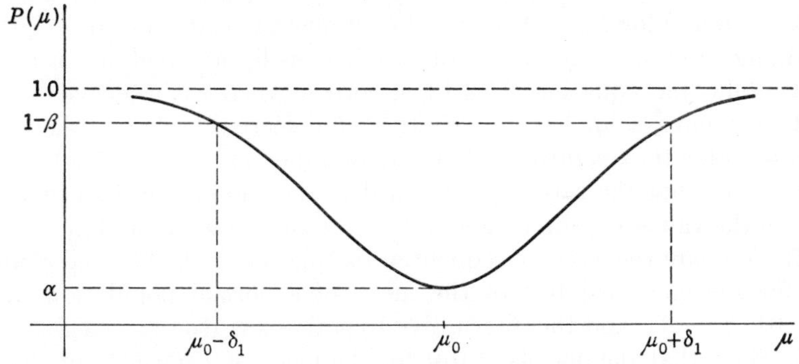

FIG. 15.6

The test is now performed in accordance with the usual procedure. One chooses probabilities α and β for the two types of error and computes A and B from (15.2.7) and (15.2.8). For a very sensitive test one would choose δ_1 as well as α and β to be small. Observations are made until λ_n exceeds A or becomes less than B. (See Fig. 15.6.)

When the variance is unknown, several tests are available; most of them use weight functions of one kind or another. Perhaps the simplest test is that based on the t distribution. If we denote by $g_n(t; \mu)$ the density for t with n degrees of freedom and with μ the mean of the normal population, then one may define

$$\lambda_n = \frac{g_n(\mathbf{t}; \mu_1)}{g_n(\mathbf{t}; \mu_0)} \tag{3}$$

with $n = 2, 3, 4, \cdots$. Although this function is not of the same type as the others that we have considered (because the numerator and denominator are not products of density functions of independent variates), it can be shown that the test terminates and that (15.2.7) and (15.2.8) determine A and B as before.

The criterion (3) refers, of course, to the one-sided test of $H_0: \mu = \mu_0$ against the alternative $H_1: \mu = \mu_1 > \mu_0$. For a two-sided test of μ_0, one may use

$$\lambda_n = \frac{\frac{1}{2}g_n(\mathbf{t}; \mu_0 + \delta_1) + \frac{1}{2}g_n(\mathbf{t}; \mu_0 - \delta_1)}{g_n(\mathbf{t}; \mu_0)} \tag{4}$$

where δ_1 has the same meaning as before.

15.8 Problems

1. Perform a sequential test of the null hypothesis that $p = .45$ against the alternative that $p = .30$. Let p refer to the probability of a head in tossing a coin, and carry through the test by tossing a coin, using $\alpha = .10$ and $\beta = .10$. The arithmetic is simplified by solving $\log \lambda_n = B$ and $\log \lambda_n = A$ for $\mathbf{x}_n$ (the number of heads in n tosses), thus obtaining acceptance and rejection numbers as linear functions of $\mathbf{n}$.

2. Show that equation (15.3.13) is correct when h is negative.

3. Assuming a lot has size N with M defectives, what is the exact expression for the operating-characteristic function?

4. Show that the ratio $9/22$ obtained at the end of Sec. 15.4 depends only on the values of α and β and not on the sizes of σ^2, μ_0, and μ_1.

5. Compare the average sequential sample size with the fixed sample size for the one-sided test of the mean of a normal population when $\alpha = .01$, $\beta = .05$, and the alternative hypothesis is true ($\sigma = 1$).

6. Show that the one-sided test for the mean of a normal population with known variance may be performed by plotting the two lines

$$y = \frac{\sigma^2}{\mu_1 - \mu_0} \log B + \frac{\mu_0 + \mu_1}{2} n$$

$$y = \frac{\sigma^2}{\mu_1 - \mu_0} \log A + \frac{\mu_0 + \mu_1}{2} n$$

in the ny plane; then plotting $\sum_1^n \mathbf{x}_i$ against n as the observations are made. The test ends when one of the lines is crossed.

7. Referring to Prob. 6, let $c = (\mu_0 + \mu_1)/2$, and let the two constants in the equations be denoted by b and a; that is,

$$a = \frac{\sigma^2 \log A}{\mu_1 - \mu_0} \qquad b = \frac{\sigma^2 \log B}{\mu_1 - \mu_0}$$

Show that the power function for the test may be put in the form

$$P(\mu) \cong \frac{1 - e^{2(c-\mu)b/\sigma^2}}{e^{2(c-\mu)a/\sigma^2} - e^{2(c-\mu)b/\sigma^2}}$$

8. Referring to Probs. 6 and 7, show that the expression for the average sample size may be written

$$E(\mathbf{n}) \cong \frac{b + P(\mu)(b - a)}{\mu - c}$$

9. Verify equations (15.6.11) and (15.6.12).

10. Plot the power function and average-sample-size function for the test of Prob. 1.

11. Plot the power function and the average-sample-size function for the test that the mean of a normal population is 0 against the alternative that it is 1. Let $\sigma^2 = 1$, $\alpha = .01$, $\beta = .05$.

12. Find formulas for the power function and average sample size for sequential tests on the mean of a Poisson distribution.

13. Suppose that a production process produces lots of size N with $\mathbf{M}$ defectives in such a way that $\mathbf{M}$ has a binomial distribution. Show that a sample of size n (with $\mathbf{x}$ defectives) can provide no information about the proportion of defectives in the remaining $N - n$ items of a lot.

14. Suppose that lots which are rejected under a sequential sampling inspection procedure are completely inspected and the defective items replaced by good items; this is a common practice. Let p be the proportion of defectives in the original lots. What will be the average proportion of defectives over all delivered lots counting both those completely inspected and those passed by the sampling plan? This function of p is called the *average outgoing quality* function; the maximum of the function is called the *average outgoing quality limit.* Make a rough sketch showing the general shape of the function.

15. Referring to the situation described in Prob. 14, find the average percentage of items inspected as a function of p, counting both passed and completely inspected lots. Make a rough sketch showing the general shape of the function.

16. Suppose that a uniform distribution is $f(x) = 1/\theta$, $0 < x < \theta$. Discuss the sequential test of $\theta = \theta_0$ against $\theta = \theta_1$ with $\theta_0 < \theta_1$. Be careful here; some of the general formulas may not be applicable.

17. By an argument similar to that used to obtain (15.4.5), Wald has shown that

$$E\{e^{\mathbf{Z}_n t}[\phi(t)]^{-\mathbf{n}}\} = 1$$

where $\phi(t)$ is the moment generating function of $\mathbf{z}$, that is, $\phi(t) = E(e^{\mathbf{z}t})$, and where the expectation E is over the joint distribution of the $\mathbf{z}$'s and the random variable $\mathbf{n}$. This is called the fundamental identity of sequential analysis. Use it to obtain (15.4.5).

18. Use the identity of Prob. 17 to show that

$$E(\mathbf{n}) = \frac{E(\mathbf{Z}_n^{*2})}{E(\mathbf{z}^2)}$$

when $E(\mathbf{z}) = 0$.

19. Use the result of Prob. 18 to obtain (15.6.16).

20. Use the result of Prob. 18 to show that the maximum average sample size for one-sided tests of the mean of a normal population is approximately $-ab/\sigma^2$, where a and b are defined in Prob. 7. Assume, do not try to prove, that the maximum occurs at $h = 0$.

15.9 Bibliography

1. Blackwell, D., and M. A. Girschick: "Theory of Games and Statistical Decisions," John Wiley & Sons, Inc., New York, 1954.
2. Brunk, H.: "An Introduction to Mathematical Statistics," Ginn & Company, Boston, 1960.
3. Fraser, D. A. S.: "Statistics—An Introduction," John Wiley & Sons, Inc., New York, 1959.
4. Freeman, H., M. Friedman, F. Mosteller, and W. Wallis: "Sampling Inspection," McGraw-Hill Book Company, Inc., New York, 1948.
5. Hoel, P. G.: "Introduction to Mathematical Statistics," 2d ed., John Wiley & Sons, Inc., New York, 1956.
6. Wald, A.: "Sequential Analysis," John Wiley & Sons, Inc., New York, 1947.

16

Nonparametric Methods

16.1 Introduction

The important place ascribed to the normal distribution in statistical theory is well justified on the basis of the central-limit theorem. However, often it is not known whether the basic distribution is such that the central-limit theorem applies or whether the approximation to the normal distribution is good enough that the resulting confidence intervals, and tests of hypotheses based on normal theory, are as accurate as desired. For example, if a random sample of size n is taken from a population with a normal density and a .95 confidence interval is set about the mean, then the frequency interpretation is: If repeated random samples are taken from this population and if a 95 per cent confidence interval is obtained for each random sample, in the long run 95 per cent of these intervals will contain the mean of the density. If sampling is from a density that is not normal, then instead of 95 per cent of the intervals containing the mean it may be 99 or 90 per cent or some other percentage. If it is close to 95 per cent, say 93 to 97, usually the experimenter will be satisfied. However, if it deviates a large amount from the desired percentage, then the experimenter will probably *not* be satisfied. In cases where it is known that the conventional methods based on the assumption of a normal density are not applicable, an alternative method is desired. If the basic distribution is known (but is not necessarily normal), one may be able to derive tests of hypotheses and confidence intervals based on that distribution. In many cases an experimenter does not know the form of the basic distribution and needs statistical techniques which are applicable regardless of the form of the density. These techniques are called *nonparametric* or *distribution-free* methods.

The term *nonparametric* arises from considerations of testing hypotheses (Chap. 12). In forming the likelihood-ratio, for example, one deals with a parameter space which defines a family of distributions as the parameters in the functional form of the distribution vary over the parameter space. The methods to be developed in this chapter make no use of functional forms or parameters of such forms. They apply to very wide families of distributions rather than only to families specified by a particular functional form. The term *distribution-free* is also often used to indicate similarly that the methods do not depend on the functional form of distribution functions.

Heretofore, in denoting a sample by $\mathbf{x}_1, \mathbf{x}_2, \cdots, \mathbf{x}_n$, the symbol $\mathbf{x}_1$ referred to the first observation, and so on. Throughout this chapter, unless otherwise stated, the $\mathbf{x}_i$ will be the ith ordered observation; i.e., the symbol $\mathbf{x}_1$ will refer to the smallest of the n observations, $\mathbf{x}_2$ will represent the second smallest of the observations, and so on, with $\mathbf{x}_n$ the largest. Thus, for the sample of four observations, 2, -4, -1, 1, $\mathbf{x}_1$ refers to the second observation, $\mathbf{x}_2$ to the third, $\mathbf{x}_3$ to the fourth, and $\mathbf{x}_4$ to the first. Nonparametric methods are based largely on these ordered observations, or *order statistics.*

The methods to be presented are applicable to both continuous and discrete variates, but we shall direct our attention almost entirely to the continuous case, merely pointing out occasionally the modifications that would be required in the case of discrete variates. Hence, unless specifically stated otherwise, *the basic random variables in this chapter will be assumed to be continuous.*

16.2 A Basic Distribution

Some of the structure of nonparametric methods rests on a simple property of order statistics: *The distribution of the area under the density function between any two ordered observations is independent of the form of the density function.* To show this, let $\mathbf{z}$ be a continuous random variable with density

$$f(z) \qquad -\infty < z < \infty \tag{1}$$

Let $\mathbf{z}_1, \mathbf{z}_2, \cdots, \mathbf{z}_n$ be a random sample from $f(z)$, and let $\mathbf{x}_1, \cdots, \mathbf{x}_n$ be the ordered sample. Then the joint density of the $\mathbf{x}_i$ is (Sec. 10.9)

$$q(x_1, x_2, \cdots, x_n) = n!f(x_1)f(x_2) \cdots f(x_n) \qquad -\infty < x_1 < x_2 < \cdots < x_n < \infty \tag{2}$$

where $f(x_i)$ is the density in (1).

We shall use the notation that $\mathbf{u}_i$ is the area of $f(z)$, which is less than the ith ordered observation $\mathbf{x}_i$, that is,

$$\mathbf{u}_i = \int_{-\infty}^{\mathbf{x}_i} f(z)\,dz = F(\mathbf{x}_i) \qquad i = 1, 2, \cdots, n \tag{3}$$

where $F(z)$ is the cumulative of $f(z)$.

Theorem 16.1. *The joint density of the random variables* $\mathbf{u}_1, \mathbf{u}_2, \cdots, \mathbf{u}_n$, *where* $\mathbf{u}_i$ *is given in* (3), *is*

$$g(u_1, u_2, \cdots, u_n) = n! \qquad 0 < u_1 < u_2 < \cdots < u_n < 1 \tag{4}$$

and does not depend on $f(z)$.

Proof. Use $q(x_1, \cdots, x_n)$ in (2) and transform to $\mathbf{u}_i$ by (3).

The density $g(u_1, \cdots, u_n)$ enables us to find the distribution of any set of areas under $f(z)$ between pairs of ordered observations. For example, we may desire the density of the area under $f(z)$ between the largest and smallest ordered observations, i.e., between $\mathbf{x}_n$ and $\mathbf{x}_1$.

Theorem 16.2. *The density of the random variable* $\mathbf{v}$, *which is the area under* $f(z)$ *between the largest and smallest observations in a sample of size* n *from* $f(z)$, *is the beta density:*

$$p(v) = n(n-1)v^{n-2}(1-v) \qquad 0 < v < 1 \tag{5}$$

Proof. We have let

$$\mathbf{v} = F(\mathbf{x}_n) - F(\mathbf{x}_1) = \mathbf{u}_n - \mathbf{u}_1 \tag{6}$$

The joint density of the $\mathbf{u}_i$ is given in (4), and we shall integrate out $u_2, u_3, \cdots, u_{n-1}$ to obtain the joint density of $\mathbf{u}_1$ and $\mathbf{u}_n$. Thus

$$h(u_1, u_n) = \int_{u_1}^{u_n} \cdots \int_{u_1}^{u_4} \int_{u_1}^{u_3} n!\, du_2\, du_3 \cdots du_{n-1} \tag{7}$$

$$= n! \frac{(u_n - u_1)^{n-2}}{(n-2)!} \qquad 0 < u_1 < u_n < 1 \tag{8}$$

and the density of $\mathbf{u}_1$ and $\mathbf{v}$ is

$$k(u_1, v) = n(n-1)v^{n-2} \qquad 0 < u_1 < (1-v) < 1 \tag{9}$$

On integrating out u_1, we obtain the required density.

More generally we have the following:

Theorem 16.3. *Let the random variable* $\mathbf{W}_{rs}$ *be the area under* $f(z)$ *between* $\mathbf{x}_r$ *and* $\mathbf{x}_s$ $(r < s)$; *then the density of* $\mathbf{W}_{rs}$ *is*

$$f(W_{rs}) = \frac{n!}{(s-r-1)!(n-s+r)!} (W_{rs})^{s-r-1}(1 - W_{rs})^{n-s+r}$$
$$0 < W_{rs} < 1 \tag{10}$$

The proof is similar to the proof for Theorem 16.2 and will be left for the reader.

The expected value of $\mathbf{u}_i$ is

$$E(\mathbf{u}_i) = \int_0^1 \cdots \int_0^{u_3} \int_0^{u_2} n! u_i\, du_1\, du_2 \cdots du_n$$
$$= \frac{i}{n+1} \tag{11}$$

Hence the expected area under $f(z)$ between two successive observations is

$$E(\mathbf{u}_i) - E(\mathbf{u}_{i-1}) = \frac{1}{n+1} \tag{12}$$

Thus, on an average, the n ordered observations divide the area under $f(z)$ into $n + 1$ equal parts of area $1/(n + 1)$ each.

16.3 Location and Dispersion

In the parametric case we have used the population mean and standard deviation as measures of location and dispersion. The nonparametric methods use other measures. The center of the population is often defined to be the median, say ν, which is the point that divides the area under the density in half. Thus ν is defined by

$$\tfrac{1}{2} = \int_{-\infty}^{\nu} f(z)\, dz = F(\nu) \tag{1}$$

where $f(z)$ is the density and $F(z)$ is the cumulative distribution. The median is often denoted by $\xi_{.50}$, and a similar notation is used for other percentage points; thus

$$F(\xi_{.15}) = .15 \tag{2}$$

defines the 15 per cent point, $\xi_{.15}$, of the population.

As a measure of dispersion one can use the distance between two percentage points. Thus, one frequently used measure of dispersion is

$$\tau_{.50} = \xi_{.75} - \xi_{.25} \tag{3}$$

which is called the 50 *per cent range*, or the *interquartile range*. But many other ranges are often used, for example, the 90 per cent range $\tau_{.90} = \xi_{.95} - \xi_{.05}$ or the $33\frac{1}{3}$ per cent range $\tau_{\frac{1}{3}} = \xi_{\frac{2}{3}} - \xi_{\frac{1}{3}}$.

Point Estimation. The population median ν is estimated by the sample median $\tilde{\mathbf{x}}$, which is the middle observation if the sample size is odd or the average of the two middle observations if the sample size is even. Thus

$$\begin{aligned} \tilde{\mathbf{x}} &= \mathbf{x}_{k+1} && \text{if } n = 2k + 1 && (4)\\ &= (\tfrac{1}{2})(\mathbf{x}_k + \mathbf{x}_{k+1}) && \text{if } n = 2k && (5) \end{aligned}$$

The sample median $\tilde{\mathbf{x}}$ is not ordinarily an unbiased estimate of ν even when n is odd, for the fact that $E[F(\tilde{\mathbf{x}})] = F(\nu)$ does not imply that $E(\tilde{\mathbf{x}}) = \nu$. However, the bias is usually not serious and for many useful densities it will approach 0 as the sample size increases.

To estimate percentage points, the $\mathbf{x}_i$ themselves furnish estimates of the $100i/(n + 1)$ per cent points. For other values one may use linear interpolation. Thus to estimate $\xi_{.25}$ from a sample of size $n = 10$, we observe that $\mathbf{x}_2$ estimates the $\frac{2}{11}$ point and $\mathbf{x}_3$ the $\frac{3}{11}$ point; hence we may use as the estimate

$$\tilde{\mathbf{x}}_{.25} = \mathbf{x}_2 + \frac{.25 - \frac{2}{11}}{\frac{1}{11}}(\mathbf{x}_3 - \mathbf{x}_2) \tag{6}$$

Given estimates of percentage points, one can obviously estimate the various ranges.

Confidence Intervals. A confidence interval for ν is easily constructed by means of the binomial distribution. The probability that an observation falls to the left or right of ν is $\frac{1}{2}$ in either case. The probability that exactly i observations in a random sample of n fall to the left of ν is just

$$\binom{n}{i}\left(\frac{1}{2}\right)^n \tag{7}$$

The probability that $\mathbf{x}_r$, the rth-order statistic, exceeds ν is then

$$P(\mathbf{x}_r > \nu) = \sum_{i=0}^{r-1} \binom{n}{i}\left(\frac{1}{2}\right)^n \tag{8}$$

and similarly

$$P(\mathbf{x}_s < \nu) = \sum_{i=s}^{n} \binom{n}{i}\left(\frac{1}{2}\right)^n \tag{9}$$

If we now suppose $s > r$, add (8) and (9), and subtract both sides from unity, we have

$$P(\mathbf{x}_r < \nu < \mathbf{x}_s) = \sum_{i=r}^{s-1} \binom{n}{i}\left(\frac{1}{2}\right)^n \tag{10}$$

which provides a confidence interval for ν. Ordinarily s is taken to be $n - r + 1$ so that the rth observations in order of magnitude from the top and from the bottom are used.

Theorem 16.4. *Let $\mathbf{x}_1, \mathbf{x}_2, \cdots, \mathbf{x}_n$ be an ordered sample from a population with density $f(z)$; then the probability that the random interval $\mathbf{x}_r < z < \mathbf{x}_{n-r+1}$ covers the median ν is*

$$\sum_{i=r}^{n-r} \binom{n}{i}\left(\frac{1}{2}\right)^n \tag{11}$$

If a confidence interval on the median ν with confidence coefficient $1 - \alpha$ is desired, the integer r is chosen so that (11) is nearest $1 - \alpha$ or so that the quantity in (11) is greater than $1 - \alpha$. If r' is the largest integer so that (11) is greater than or equal to $1 - \alpha$, then the confidence interval is

$$P(\mathbf{x}_{r'} < \nu < \mathbf{x}_{n-r'}) \geq 1 - \alpha$$

Thus for a sample of size 6, for a confidence interval on ν one could compute

$$P(\mathbf{x}_1 < \nu < \mathbf{x}_6) = 1 - (\tfrac{1}{2})^6 - (\tfrac{1}{2})^6 = \tfrac{31}{32} = .97 \tag{12}$$

and

$$P(\mathbf{x}_2 < \nu < \mathbf{x}_5) = 1 - 14/(2^6) = 50/64 = .78$$

If one were interested in a 95 per cent interval, (12) would probably be used. If, for instance, a 90 per cent interval were desired, one might use some randomized device between the two intervals.

If the sample size is small, one has only a few confidence levels available; in particular, when $n = 2$, there is only the 50 per cent confidence interval given by

$$P(\mathbf{x}_1 < \nu < \mathbf{x}_2) = .50 \tag{13}$$

For moderate sample sizes the binomial sum in (10) may be computed directly or found in tables. For large n one would use the normal approximation to the binomial. Since the index i in (7) is approximately normal with mean $n/2$ and standard deviation $\sqrt{n}/2$ for large n, a 95 per cent confidence interval, for example, is obtained by counting $1.96\sqrt{n}/2$ observations to the left and right of the sample median.

A similar technique is employed to obtain confidence intervals for percentage points. If ξ_p is the $100p$ per cent point of the distribution, then the same argument used to obtain (10) shows that

$$P(\mathbf{x}_r < \xi_p < \mathbf{x}_s) = \sum_{i=r}^{s-1} \binom{n}{i} p^i(1-p)^{n-i} \tag{14}$$

Thus for a sample of size 6, a possible confidence interval for the 25 per cent point is given by

$$P(\mathbf{x}_1 < \xi_{.25} < \mathbf{x}_4) = \sum_{1}^{3} \binom{6}{i} \left(\frac{1}{4}\right)^i \left(\frac{3}{4}\right)^{6-i} \cong .78 \tag{15}$$

A 96 per cent upper bound for $\xi_{.25}$ is given by

$$P(\xi_{.25} < \mathbf{x}_4) = \sum_{0}^{3} \binom{6}{i} \left(\frac{1}{4}\right)^i \left(\frac{3}{4}\right)^{6-i} \cong .96 \tag{16}$$

Tests of Hypotheses. To test the null hypothesis $\nu = \nu_0$ against alternatives $\nu > \nu_0$, one uses the relation (8), choosing in advance an integer r so that the probability of a Type I error will have as nearly as possible the desired value. Thus for a sample of size 6 one can make the probability of a Type I error $7/64 \cong .11$ by choosing $r = 2$. If after drawing the sample one finds $\mathbf{x}_2 < \nu_0$, the null hypothesis is accepted; if $\mathbf{x}_2 > \nu_0$, it is rejected. In the same fashion two-sided tests of $\nu = \nu_0$ may be constructed; the two-sided test is obviously equivalent to constructing a confidence interval for ν and accepting or rejecting $\nu = \nu_0$ according as the confidence interval does or does not cover ν_0. Tests on a percentage point ξ_p would be carried out by the same technique, using probabilities p and $(1 - p)$ instead of $\frac{1}{2}$ and $\frac{1}{2}$.

It is now apparent that nonparametric methods, besides being extremely general in that they require few assumptions about the form of the distribution function, are also extraordinarily simple. No complex analysis or distribution theory is needed; the simple binomial provides much of the necessary equipment for estimation and testing hypotheses when one is dealing with a single population. The only inconvenience is in the paucity of significance levels or confidence levels when the sample size is quite small.

A word about the discrete case is in order here. We have assumed that the density function was continuous. If it is discrete, then the equalities obtained in this section for confidence intervals and tests need to be replaced by inequalities. Thus (10), for example, becomes

$$P(\mathbf{x}_r < \nu < \mathbf{x}_s) \geq \sum_{r}^{s-1} \binom{n}{i} \left(\frac{1}{2}\right)^n \tag{17}$$

The reason for the inequality is the fact that certain observations may be duplicated. Thus suppose that one wished to estimate ν for a discrete distribution, using a sample of size 6 and a 78 per cent confidence interval given by $\mathbf{x}_2$ and $\mathbf{x}_5$. Now and then the two smallest observations $\mathbf{x}_1$ and $\mathbf{x}_2$ will be equal so that the $(\mathbf{x}_2, \mathbf{x}_5)$ interval is equivalent to the $(\mathbf{x}_1, \mathbf{x}_5)$ interval and hence corresponds to a probability larger than .78. The same thing may happen at the upper limit; $\mathbf{x}_5$ and $\mathbf{x}_6$ may be equal so that sometimes the $(\mathbf{x}_2, \mathbf{x}_5)$ interval is equivalent to the $(\mathbf{x}_2, \mathbf{x}_6)$ interval; occasionally it can even be the same as the $(\mathbf{x}_1, \mathbf{x}_6)$ interval and thus correspond to the 97 per cent rather than the 78 per cent level.

16.4 Comparison of Two Populations

A great many nonparametric methods have been developed for testing whether two populations have the same distribution. We shall consider only two of them, and at the end of this section we shall derive a confidence interval for the difference between two population medians. First, we shall obtain a simple result on the distribution of arrangements of two sets of observations from the same population.

Let $\mathbf{x}_1, \mathbf{x}_2, \cdots, \mathbf{x}_{n_1}$ be an ordered sample from a population with a density $f(x)$, and let $\mathbf{y}_1, \mathbf{y}_2, \cdots, \mathbf{y}_{n_2}$ be a second ordered sample from the same population. Let the two samples be combined and arranged in order of magnitude; thus, for example, one might have

$$\mathbf{y}_1, \mathbf{x}_1, \mathbf{x}_2, \mathbf{y}_2, \mathbf{x}_3, \mathbf{y}_3, \mathbf{y}_4, \mathbf{y}_5, \mathbf{x}_4, \cdots \tag{1}$$

We wish to find the probability of obtaining a specific arrangement of this kind.

If the **x**'s are transformed to **u**'s by the relation (16.2.3), and the **y**'s transformed to **v**'s by the same relation, the joint density of the **u**'s and **v**'s is

$$g(u_1, u_2, \cdots, u_{n_1}, v_1, v_2, \cdots, v_{n_2}) = n_1!n_2! \tag{2}$$

The probability of a given arrangement such as (1) is found by integrating (2) over the region defined by

$$0 < v_1 < u_1 < u_2 < v_2 < u_3 < \cdots < 1 \tag{3}$$

that is, v_1 is integrated from 0 to u_1, then u_1 from 0 to u_2, etc. It is readily seen that the value of the integral is $n_1!n_2!/(n_1 + n_2)!$, or simply $1\Big/\binom{n_1+n_2}{n_1}$. Since there are exactly $\binom{n_1+n_2}{n_1}$ arrangements of n_1 x's and n_2 y's, it follows that all arrangements of the x's and y's are equally likely.

Run Test. We now turn to the question of testing the null hypothesis that two samples have come from the same population. The observations in the two samples will be denoted by **x**'s and **y**'s as above. The two sets of observations are combined as in (1) and the number **d** of runs counted. A run is a sequence of letters of the same kind bounded by letters of the other kind. Thus (1) starts with a run of one **y**; then follows a run of two **x**'s, then a run of one **y**, and so on; six runs are exhibited in (1). It is apparent that, if the two samples are from the same population, the **x**'s and **y**'s will ordinarily be well mixed and **d** will be large. If the two populations are widely separated so that their ranges do not overlap, **d** will be only 2, and, in general, differences between the two populations will tend to reduce **d**. Thus the two populations may have the same mean or median, but if the **x** population is concentrated while the **y** population is dispersed, there will be a long **y** run on each end of the combined sample and there will thus be a tendency to reduce **d**. The test then is performed by observing the total number of runs in the combined sample, accepting the null hypothesis if **d** is greater than some specified number d_0, or rejecting the null hypothesis if $\mathbf{d} \leq d_0$. Our task now is to determine the distribution of **d** under the null hypothesis in order that we may specify d_0 for a given level of significance.

We have seen that all the $\binom{n_1+n_2}{n_1}$ arrangements of n_1 **x**'s and n_2 **y**'s are equally likely under the null hypothesis. It is necessary now to count all arrangements with exactly **d** runs. Suppose that **d** is even, say $2k$; then there must be k runs of **x**'s and k runs of **y**'s. To get k runs of **x**'s, the n_1 **x**'s must be divided into k groups, and we wish to count all permutations of the k numbers in each group. In short, we wish to count all the ordered k-part partitions of n_1 with zero parts excluded. This is readily done with the aid of the generating function described in Chap. 2 for enumerating the ways of getting a given total with a set of dice. The required number is the coefficient of t^{n_1} in

$$(t + t^2 + t^3 + \cdots)^k = \left(\frac{t}{1-t}\right)^k \tag{4}$$

$$= t^k \sum_{i=0}^{\infty} \binom{k-1+i}{k-1} t^i \tag{5}$$

which is $\binom{n_1-1}{k-1}$. Similarly there are $\binom{n_2-1}{k-1}$ k-part partitions of n_2, excluding zero parts. Any partition of the **x**'s may be combined in any partition of the **y**'s in two ways to form a sequence like (1); the first **x** partition or the first **y** partition may be put at the beginning of the sequence. Thus we have found the density for even values of **d**:

$$h(d) = 2\frac{\binom{n_1-1}{k-1}\binom{n_2-1}{k-1}}{\binom{n_1+n_2}{n_1}} \qquad k = \frac{d}{2} \tag{6}$$

and by similar reasoning one finds for odd values of **d**:

$$h(d) = \frac{\binom{n_1-1}{k}\binom{n_2-1}{k-1} + \binom{n_1-1}{k-1}\binom{n_2-1}{k}}{\binom{n_1+n_2}{n_1}} \qquad k = \frac{d-1}{2} \tag{7}$$

To test the null hypothesis in question with a probability α for the Type I error, one finds the integer d_0 so that (as nearly as possible)

$$\sum_{d=0}^{d_0} h(d) = \alpha \tag{8}$$

and rejects the null hypothesis if the observed **d** does not exceed d_0.

The computation involved in (8) can become quite tedious unless both n_1 and n_2 are small. The distribution of **d** becomes approximately normal for large samples, and in fact the approximation is usually good enough for practical purposes when both n_1 and n_2 exceed 10. The mean and variance of **d** are

$$E(\mathbf{d}) = \frac{2n_1n_2}{n_1 + n_2} + 1 \tag{9}$$

$$\sigma_{\mathbf{d}}^2 = \frac{2n_1n_2(2n_1n_2 - n_1 - n_2)}{(n_1 + n_2)^2(n_1 + n_2 - 1)} \tag{10}$$

and if we let

$$n_1 + n_2 = n \qquad n_1 = n\alpha \qquad n_2 = n\beta \tag{11}$$

these moments become, for large n, approximately

$$E(\mathbf{d}) \cong 2n\alpha\beta \tag{12}$$

$$\sigma_{\mathbf{d}}^2 \cong 4n\alpha^2\beta^2 \tag{13}$$

The large-sample normality of $h(d)$ is demonstrated by using Stirling's formula to evaluate the factorials in (6), substituting for d in terms of t defined by

$$t = \frac{d - 2n\alpha\beta}{2\alpha\beta\sqrt{n}} \tag{14}$$

and showing that the logarithm of the resulting expression approaches

$$-\log\sqrt{2\pi} - \tfrac{1}{2}t^2 \tag{15}$$

as n becomes infinite. We shall omit the details. Using this result, one would determine d_0 for testing the null hypothesis at the .05 level, for example, by putting the right-hand side of (14) equal to -1.645 and solving for d.

The run test is sensitive to both differences in shape and differences in location between two distributions. Often, however, in practice, one does not care about differences in shape; he is concerned only with location. That is to say, he would like to test merely the null hypothesis that the population medians are equal: $\nu_1 = \nu_2$. The following test of $f_1(x) = f_2(y)$ is sensitive primarily to differences in location and very little to differences in shape.

Median Test. As before, let there be an ordered sample $\mathbf{x}_1, \mathbf{x}_2, \cdots, \mathbf{x}_{n_1}$ from $f_1(x)$ and a sample $\mathbf{y}_1, \mathbf{y}_2, \cdots, \mathbf{y}_{n_2}$ from $f_2(y)$. Let $\mathbf{z}_1, \mathbf{z}_2, \cdots, \mathbf{z}_{n_1+n_2}$ be the ordered combined sample. The test of the null hypothesis $f_1(x) = f_2(x) = f(x)$ will consist in finding the median $\tilde{\mathbf{z}}$ of the combined sample, then counting the number of **x**'s, say $\mathbf{m}_1$, which exceed $\tilde{\mathbf{z}}$ and the number of **y**'s, say $\mathbf{m}_2$, which exceed $\tilde{\mathbf{z}}$. If the null hypothesis is true, we should expect $\mathbf{m}_1$ to be approximately $n_1/2$ and $\mathbf{m}_2$ approximately $n_2/2$. It is clear that this test will be sensitive to differences in location between

$f_1(x)$ and $f_2(x)$ but not to differences in their shape. Thus if $f_1(x)$ and $f_2(x)$ have the same median, we should expect the null hypothesis to be accepted ordinarily even though their shapes were quite different.

To make this test, the distribution of $\mathbf{m}_1$ and $\mathbf{m}_2$ under the null hypothesis is required. It can be shown that this density is

$$g(m_1, m_2) = \frac{\binom{n_1}{m_1}\binom{n_2}{m_2}}{\binom{n_1 + n_2}{a}} \tag{16}$$

where $a = \dfrac{n_1 + n_2 + 1}{2}$ if $n_1 + n_2$ is odd and $a = \dfrac{n_1 + n_2}{2}$ if $n_1 + n_2$ is even.

We observe that this expression is just the distribution of the cell frequencies in a 2×2 contingency table with all marginal totals fixed when there is independence. The contingency table is

m_1	m_2	$n_1 + n_2 - a$
$n_1 - m_1$	$n_2 - m_2$	a
n_1	n_2	

where the marginal totals are shown to the right of and below the closed part of the table. Thus the null hypothesis may be tested by using either the λ criterion or the chi-square criterion. If $n_1 + n_2$ were small, one would use (16) to compute the exact probabilities instead of using the approximate probability given by the chi-square distribution with one degree of freedom. The approximation is fairly good if both n_1 and n_2 exceed 10.

Confidence Intervals. In order to obtain exact confidence intervals for the difference between the medians of two populations, we shall assume that the distributions differ only in location. Letting $\mathbf{x}_1, \mathbf{x}_2, \cdots, \mathbf{x}_{n_1}$ be a sample from a population with median ν_1, and $\mathbf{y}_1, \mathbf{y}_2, \cdots, \mathbf{y}_{n_2}$ a sample from one with median ν_2, we assume that the variates

$$\mathbf{u}_i = \mathbf{x}_i - \nu_1 \qquad \text{and} \qquad \mathbf{v}_i = \mathbf{y}_i - \nu_2$$

have the same density, say $f(u)$, with median 0. The sample of $\mathbf{u}$'s and the sample of $\mathbf{v}$'s are then two samples from the same population. If one chooses two integers r and s, he may compute the probability that $\mathbf{u}_r$

exceeds $\mathbf{v}_s$ as follows:

$$P(\mathbf{u}_r > \mathbf{v}_s) = \int_{-\infty}^{\infty} s \binom{n_2}{s} [F(v_s)]^{s-1}[1 - F(v_s)]^{n_2-s} \sum_{i=0}^{r-1} \binom{n_1}{i} [F(v_s)]^i[1 - F(v_s)]^{n_1-i} f(v_s)\, dv_s \tag{17}$$

$$= \sum_{i=0}^{r-1} \frac{s\binom{n_2}{s}\binom{n_1}{i}}{(s+i)\binom{n_1+n_2}{s+i}} \tag{18}$$

$$= \sum_{i=0}^{r-1} \frac{\binom{s+i-1}{s-1}\binom{n_1+n_2-s-i}{n_2-s}}{\binom{n_1+n_2}{n_1}} \tag{19}$$

Similarly

$$P(\mathbf{u}_{r'} < \mathbf{v}_{s'}) = \sum_{i=r'}^{n_1} \frac{\binom{s'+i-1}{s'-1}\binom{n_1+n_2-s'-i}{n_2-s'}}{\binom{n_1+n_2}{n_1}} \tag{20}$$

If we now suppose $r < s$, $r' > s'$, and $\nu_2 > \nu_1$, then

$$P(\mathbf{y}_{s'} - \mathbf{x}_{r'} < \nu_2 - \nu_1 < \mathbf{y}_s - \mathbf{x}_r) = P(\mathbf{u}_r < \mathbf{v}_s \text{ and } \mathbf{u}_{r'} > \mathbf{v}_{s'}) \tag{21}$$

$$= 1 - P(\mathbf{u}_r > \mathbf{v}_s) - P(\mathbf{u}_{r'} < \mathbf{v}_{s'}) \tag{22}$$

and the left-hand side of this relation provides a confidence interval for $\nu_2 - \nu_1$ with a confidence level which is calculable by means of (19) and (20). The confidence interval provides a third test of the null hypothesis that the two distributions are the same; the hypothesis would be rejected if the interval did not include 0.

We shall outline a large-sample approximation which may be used when n_1 and n_2 both exceed 10. Since the sum expressed in (19) is 1 when taken over the whole range of i, we may regard the summand as a density for a variate **i** and find the normal approximation to that function. The sum may then be approximated by integrating the approximating function. The mean and variance of **i** are

$$E(\mathbf{i}) = \frac{sn_1}{n_2+1} \tag{23}$$

$$\sigma_i^2 = \frac{sn_1}{n_2+1}\left[\frac{(s+1)(n_2+3)}{n_2+2} + \frac{(s+1)n_1}{n_2+2} - (2s+1) - \frac{sn_1}{n_2+1}\right] \tag{24}$$

and their approximate values when n_1 and n_2 are large may be found by letting

$$n_1 + n_2 = n \qquad n_1 = n\alpha \qquad n_2 = n\beta \qquad s = \gamma n_2 = \beta\gamma n \tag{25}$$

and keeping only terms involving the highest power of n. The results are

$$E(\mathbf{i}) \cong n\alpha\gamma \tag{26}$$

$$\sigma_i^2 \cong n\alpha\gamma \frac{1-\gamma}{\beta} \tag{27}$$

The large-sample normality of $\mathbf{i}$ may be proved in the same manner as outlined for $\mathbf{d}$ in (6). The sum in (19) may then be approximated by

$$\int_{-\infty}^{A} \frac{1}{\sqrt{2\pi}} e^{-t^2/2}\, dt \tag{28}$$

where

$$A = \frac{(r - 1 + \frac{1}{2}) - n\alpha\gamma}{\sqrt{n\alpha\gamma(1-\gamma)/\beta}} \tag{29}$$

Given s, one would choose A to give the desired probability level (-1.96, for example, to make the probability .025) and solve for r.

The question arises as to how s should be chosen. Clearly s should be greater than $n_2/2$ and r should be less than $n_1/2$. One might, for example, make the two differences equal, but a shorter confidence interval may be expected by making the differences equal on "standard" scale. The number of $\mathbf{x}$ observations less than ν_1 is approximately normally distributed with mean $n_1/2$ and standard deviation $\sqrt{n_1}/2$; similarly the number of $\mathbf{y}$ observations exceeding ν_2 is approximately normally distributed with mean $n_2/2$ and standard deviation $\sqrt{n_2}/2$. We shall then determine s so that

$$\frac{(n_1/2) - r}{\sqrt{n_1}} = \frac{s - (n_2/2)}{\sqrt{n_2}} \tag{30}$$

If one substitutes for n_1, n_2, and s in this relation in terms of (25) and solves for r, then equates the result to the solution of (29) for r, he finds

$$\gamma \cong \frac{1}{2} + \frac{A}{2\sqrt{n}\,(\sqrt{\alpha\beta} + \beta)} \tag{31}$$

neglecting terms with higher powers of $1/\sqrt{n}$; in terms of the original symbols, this becomes

$$s \cong \frac{n_2}{2} + \frac{A\sqrt{n_2}\sqrt{n_1 + n_2}}{2(\sqrt{n_1} + \sqrt{n_2})} \tag{32}$$

and from (30)

$$r \cong \frac{n_1}{2} - \frac{A\sqrt{n_1}\sqrt{n_1+n_2}}{2(\sqrt{n_1}+\sqrt{n_2})} \tag{33}$$

In similar fashion one would argue that good choices for r' and s' in (22) are given by changing the signs in (32) and (33).

The technique presented here for finding confidence intervals for the difference of two medians can be used for any location parameters such as means or quartiles.

16.5 Tolerance Limits

An automatic machine in a ball-bearing factory is supposed to manufacture bearings .25 inch in diameter. The bearings are regarded as acceptable from an engineering standpoint if the diameter falls between the limits .249 and .251 inch. Production is regularly checked by measuring each day the diameter of a random sample of bearings and computing statistical tolerance limits, $\mathbf{L}_1$ and $\mathbf{L}_2$, from their samples. If $\mathbf{L}_1$ is above .249 and $\mathbf{L}_2$ is below .251, the production is accepted. How large should the sample be so that one can be assured with 90 per cent probability that the statistical tolerance limits will contain at least 99 per cent of the population of bearing diameters? There is a simple nonparametric solution of problems of this kind.

In more general terms, let $f(z)$ be a density, and on the basis of a sample of n values, it is desirable to determine two numbers $\mathbf{L}_1$ and $\mathbf{L}_2$ such that .99, say, of the area of $f(z)$ is between $\mathbf{L}_1$ and $\mathbf{L}_2$. On the basis of a sample we cannot be *certain* that .99 of the area of $f(z)$ is between $\mathbf{L}_1$ and $\mathbf{L}_2$, but we can specify a probability that it is so.

In other words, we want to find two functions $\mathbf{L}_1 = L_1(\mathbf{z}_1, \cdots, \mathbf{z}_n)$, $\mathbf{L}_2 = L_2(\mathbf{z}_1, \cdots, \mathbf{z}_n)$ of the random sample $\mathbf{z}_1, \cdots, \mathbf{z}_n$ such that the probability that

$$\int_{\mathbf{L}_1}^{\mathbf{L}_2} f(z)\,dz > \beta \tag{1}$$

is equal to $1 - \alpha$.

To put this another way, we want the probability to be $1 - \alpha$ that the area of $f(z)$ between $\mathbf{L}_1$ and $\mathbf{L}_2$ is greater than or equal to β. The limits $\mathbf{L}_1$ and $\mathbf{L}_2$ are called *tolerance limits*. There are many functions $\mathbf{L}_1$ and $\mathbf{L}_2$ that could be used, but we shall let $\mathbf{L}_1 = \mathbf{x}_1$, the smallest of the n observations, and let $\mathbf{L}_2 = \mathbf{x}_n$, the largest. Then the density of the area between $\mathbf{x}_1$ and $\mathbf{x}_n$ is given by Theorem 16.2; i.e., if

$$\mathbf{v} = \int_{\mathbf{x}_1}^{\mathbf{x}_n} f(z)\,dz \tag{2}$$

then the density of $\mathbf{v}$ is

$$p(v) = n(n-1)v^{n-2}(1-v) \qquad 0 < v < 1 \tag{3}$$

Example 16.1. Suppose that it is desired to determine how large a sample must be taken so that the probability is .90 that at least 99 per cent of a day's output of bearings will have diameters between the largest and smallest observations. The quantities are $1 - \alpha = .90$, $\beta = .99$, and we want to determine n such that

$$P(\mathbf{v} > \beta) = 1 - \alpha$$

where the density of $\mathbf{v}$ is given by (3). We get

$$1 - \alpha = P(\mathbf{v} > \beta) = \int_\beta^1 n(n - 1)v^{n-2}(1 - v)\, dv = 1 - n\beta^{n-1} + (n - 1)\beta^n$$

If we substitute for α and β, we get the equation

$$.90 = 1 - n(.99)^{n-1} + (n - 1)(.99)^n$$

which can be solved to determine n.

16.6 Rank Test for Two Samples

A very interesting nonparametric test for two samples was described by Wilcoxon and studied by Mann and Whitney. Given two random samples $\mathbf{x}_1, \mathbf{x}_2, \cdots, \mathbf{x}_n$ and $\mathbf{y}_1, \mathbf{y}_2, \cdots, \mathbf{y}_m$ from populations with continuous cumulative distributions $F(x)$ and $G(y)$, one arranges the $m + n$ sample observations in ascending order and then replaces the smallest by 1, the next by 2, and so on, with the largest being replaced by $m + n$. These integers are called the ranks of the observations. The test criterion is

$$\mathbf{T} = \text{sum of ranks of } \mathbf{y} \text{ observations}$$

and if $\mathbf{T}$ is significantly large or small, the null hypothesis that $F = G$ is rejected. The problem of statistical theory then is to find the distribution of $\mathbf{T}$ so that one can say what values of $\mathbf{T}$ are significant. It turns out to be a very troublesome problem to find the distribution of $\mathbf{T}$.

However, Mann and Whitney have calculated the distribution for small m and n, have found the moments of $\mathbf{T}$ in general, have shown that $\mathbf{T}$ is approximately normally distributed for large m and n, and have demonstrated that the normal approximation is quite accurate when m and n are larger than 7. We shall be content here merely to indicate how the moments of $\mathbf{T}$ are obtained by their methods.

Instead of $\mathbf{T}$, they use the criterion $\mathbf{U}$, which is defined as the total number of times that $\mathbf{y}$'s precede $\mathbf{x}$'s when the two samples are arranged in order. Thus, as a simple example, if the arrangement is

$$\mathbf{xyxyxx}$$

then $\mathbf{U} = 5$ because the first **y** precedes three **x**'s and the second **y** precedes two **x**'s. For this example, $\mathbf{T} = 2 + 4 = 6$. **U** and **T** have the simple linear relation

$$\mathbf{U} = mn + \frac{m(m+1)}{2} - \mathbf{T} \tag{1}$$

so that results for **U** can be immediately transformed to results for **T**.

Now let $N_{n,m}(U)$ be the number of arrangements in which **y**'s precede **x**'s exactly U times; by omitting the last letter of such arrangements, we find

$$N_{n,m}(U) = N_{n-1,m}(U - m) + N_{n,m-1}(U) \tag{2}$$

where the first term on the right arises when the omitted letter is an **x** and the second term when it is a **y**. Under the null hypothesis, the total number of arrangements is $(m + n)!/m!n!$ [that is, the number of ways of selecting m positions for **y**'s out of the $(m + n)$ positions]; hence the probability of obtaining U may be written

$$p_{n,m}(U) = \frac{N_{n,m}(U)}{(m+n)!/m!n!} \tag{3}$$

and, using this definition in (2), we obtain the relation

$$p_{n,m}(U) = \frac{n}{m+n}\, p_{n-1,m}(U - m) + \frac{m}{m+n}\, p_{n,m-1}(U) \tag{4}$$

If we denote the expectation of **U** for samples of size n and m by $E_{n,m}(\mathbf{U})$, then

$$E_{n,m}(\mathbf{U}) = \sum_U U p_{n,m}(U) \tag{5}$$

and, on multiplying (4) by U and summing on U, we have

$$\begin{aligned} E_{n,m}(\mathbf{U}) &= \frac{n}{m+n} \sum_U U p_{n-1,m}(U - m) + \frac{m}{m+n} \sum_U U p_{n,m-1}(U) \\ &= \frac{n}{m+n} \left[\sum_U (U - m) p_{n-1,m}(U - m) + m \sum_U p_{n-1,m}(U - m) \right] \\ &\qquad + \frac{m}{m+n} E_{n,m-1}(\mathbf{U}) \\ &= \frac{n}{m+n} [E_{n-1,m}(\mathbf{U}) + m] + \frac{m}{m+n} E_{n,m-1}(\mathbf{U}) \end{aligned}$$

or

$$(m + n)E_{n,m}(\mathbf{U}) = nE_{n-1,m}(\mathbf{U}) + mE_{n,m-1}(\mathbf{U}) + mn \tag{6}$$

This last relation may be regarded as a difference equation defining $E_{n,m}(\mathbf{U})$ as a function of m and n; according to the theory of such equations, it must be satisfied by a polynomial in m and n,

$$E_{n,m}(\mathbf{U}) = amn + bm + cn + d \tag{7}$$

On substituting (7) into (6) and equating coefficients of corresponding terms in m and n on the two sides, it is found that $a = \frac{1}{2}$ and that $b = c = d = 0$, so that

$$E_{n,m}(\mathbf{U}) = \frac{mn}{2} \tag{8}$$

To get the second moment of $\mathbf{U}$, one would multiply equation (4) by U^2 and sum on U to obtain, after some simplification, using (8),

$$E_{n,m}(\mathbf{U}^2) = \frac{n}{m+n} E_{n-1,m}(\mathbf{U}^2) + \frac{m}{m+n} E_{n,m-1}(\mathbf{U}^2) + \frac{m^2n^2}{m+n} \tag{9}$$

which is a difference equation in $E_{n,m}$ that must be satisfied by a polynomial quadratic in m and n. On substituting such a polynomial and equating coefficients, the second moment is found to be

$$E_{n,m}(\mathbf{U}^2) = \frac{m^2n^2}{4} + \frac{mn(m+n+1)}{12} \tag{10}$$

In view of (8), the variance of $\mathbf{U}$ is the second term on the right-hand side of (10). Using these results with equation (1), the mean and variance of $\mathbf{T}$ are found to be

$$E(\mathbf{T}) = \frac{m(m+n+1)}{2} \tag{11}$$

$$\sigma_{\mathbf{T}}^2 = \frac{mn(m+n+1)}{12} \tag{12}$$

and with these results the rank test can be carried out, using the normal approximation when m and n are greater than 7.

16.7 Asymptotic Efficiencies and the Randomization Test

The question naturally arises in connection with nonparametric tests whether one loses a great deal in efficiency in using such tests instead of the standard tests based on normal theory. There is no way to answer that question without knowing the population distributions with which one happens to be dealing. However, it is informative to compare some of these nonparametric tests with the t test under the assumption that the underlying population is normal. We shall make such a comparison for the rank test, assuming that **x** and **y** have the densities

$$f(x) = \frac{1}{\sqrt{2\pi}} e^{-x^2/2} \qquad \text{and} \qquad g(y) = \frac{1}{\sqrt{2\pi}} e^{-(y-\theta)^2/2} \tag{1}$$

Their cumulative forms will be denoted by $F(x)$ and $G(y)$.

In general, it is possible to show, under fairly general conditions (although we shall not do so here), that the power function for testing whether a parameter θ has the value θ_0 has for large samples the form of a parabola near the true value θ_0. More specifically, if the test criterion for testing θ is $\mathbf{S}_n$ for samples of size n, if $\mathbf{S}_n$ has mean μ_n and variance σ_n^2, and if $\mathbf{S}_n$ is approximately normally distributed for large sample size n, then the power function near θ_0 has the equation

$$\beta_n(\theta) = \alpha + \frac{k\phi(k)}{\sigma_n^2}\left(\frac{d\mu_n}{d\theta_0}\right)^2 (\theta - \theta_0)^2 \tag{2}$$

where $\beta_n(\theta)$ is the power function, α is the significance level of the test, k is the multiple of σ_n for the test (determined by α), and

$$\phi(k) = \frac{1}{\sqrt{2\pi}} e^{-k^2/2}$$

The steepness of the parabola is determined by the coefficient of $(\theta - \theta_0)^2$, and the larger this coefficient, the more powerful the test. Now suppose that one had a second statistic $\mathbf{S}_n^*$ for testing the same hypothesis and that it was approximately normally distributed for large samples with mean μ_n^* and variance σ_n^{*2}. Its power function would have an equation near θ_0 like (2) except that μ_n and σ_n would be replaced by μ_n^* and σ_n^*. A measure of the relative power of the two tests would be obtained by forming the ratio of the two coefficients of $(\theta - \theta_0)^2$. The *asymptotic relative efficiency* (ARE) of $\mathbf{S}_n$ to $\mathbf{S}_n^*$ is defined to be the limit as n becomes infinite of that ratio:

$$\text{ARE } (\mathbf{S}_n \text{ to } \mathbf{S}_n^*) = \lim_{n\to\infty} \frac{1/\sigma_n^2(d\mu_n/d\theta_0)^2}{1/\sigma_n^{*2}(d\mu_n^*/d\theta_0)^2} \tag{3}$$

What we now propose to do is to compute this ratio, taking $\mathbf{S}_n^*$ to be the t test and $\mathbf{S}_n$ to be the rank test.

In order to obtain the derivative of μ_n with respect to θ, it is necessary to find the expectation of the rank-test criterion **U** under the alternative hypothesis [$F \neq G$, that is, $\theta \neq 0$ in (1)]. Let

$$\begin{aligned} \mathbf{w}_{ij} &= 0 \qquad \text{if } \mathbf{x}_i < \mathbf{y}_i \\ &= 1 \qquad \text{if } \mathbf{x}_i \geq \mathbf{y}_i \end{aligned}$$

($\mathbf{x}_i$ refers to the ith $\mathbf{x}$ observation, not to the ith ordered value of the $\mathbf{x}$'s; similarly for $\mathbf{y}_i$);

$$\begin{aligned} E(\mathbf{w}_{ij}) &= P(\mathbf{x}_i \geq \mathbf{y}_i) \\ &= \int_{-\infty}^{\infty} [1 - F(v)]g(v)\,dv \\ &= \int_{-\infty}^{\infty} \left(\int_v^{\infty} \frac{1}{\sqrt{2\pi}} e^{-u^2/2}\,du \right) \frac{1}{\sqrt{2\pi}} e^{-(v-\theta)^2/2}\,dv \end{aligned}$$

and

$$\frac{dE(\mathbf{w}_{ij})}{d\theta} = \int_{-\infty}^{\infty} \int_v^{\infty} \frac{1}{2\pi} e^{-u^2/2}(v - \theta)e^{-(v-\theta)^2/2}\,du\,dv$$

On putting $\theta = \theta_0 = 0$

$$\frac{dE(\mathbf{w}_{ij})}{d\theta_0} = \int_{-\infty}^{\infty} \int_v^{\infty} \frac{v}{2\pi} e^{-(v^2+u^2)/2}\,du\,dv = -\frac{1}{2\sqrt{\pi}} \tag{4}$$

Hence it follows, since

$$\mu_n = E(\mathbf{U}) = E\Sigma\mathbf{w}_{ij} = mnE(\mathbf{w}_{ij})$$

that

$$\frac{d\mu_n}{d\theta_0} = -\frac{mn}{2\sqrt{\pi}} \tag{5}$$

Under the null hypothesis,

$$\sigma_n^2 = \frac{mn(m + n + 1)}{12} \tag{6}$$

For the t test,

$$\mu_n^* = \theta \tag{7}$$

$$\sigma_n^{*2} = \frac{1}{m} + \frac{1}{n} \tag{8}$$

$$\frac{d\mu_n^*}{d\theta_0} = 1 \tag{9}$$

On substituting (5), (6), (8), and (9) into (3), we find

$$\begin{aligned} \text{ARE } (\mathbf{S}_n \text{ to } \mathbf{S}_n^*) &= \lim \frac{[12/mn(m + n + 1)](mn/2\sqrt{\pi})^2}{\dfrac{1}{1/m + 1/n}} \\ &= \frac{3}{\pi} \end{aligned} \tag{10}$$

which is approximately 95 per cent. This means that if one uses the rank test instead of the t test when in fact the population is normally distributed he loses only about 5 per cent in efficiency for large samples; this is a small price to pay when the assumption of normality is suspect. However, this computation does not say anything about the relative efficiencies of the two tests for other than normal distributions, and it is to be expected that sometimes one and sometimes the other will be better, depending upon the distribution. In deciding which test to use, it is an important consideration, of course, that the significance levels of the rank test do not depend on the form of the distribution.

Incidentally, the median test given in Sec. 16.3 for two samples is known to have an asymptotic relative efficiency of $2/\pi$ with respect to the t test when the population distribution is, in fact, normal.

A natural question in this connection is whether there exists any nonparametric test which is equally efficient with the t test for normal populations. Lehmann and Stein have determined that there is such a test. It is the so-called randomization test. Assuming equal variances, this test is performed as follows: Compute the means $\bar{\mathbf{x}}$ and $\bar{\mathbf{y}}$ for the two samples $\mathbf{x}_1, \cdots, \mathbf{x}_n$ and $\mathbf{y}_1, \cdots, \mathbf{y}_m$ and the difference $\mathbf{d} = \bar{\mathbf{x}} - \bar{\mathbf{y}}$. Then divide the $m + n$ observations into two groups of size m and n in all possible ways [there are $(m + n)!/m!n!$ ways] and compute the differences $\mathbf{d}_i$ between the means of the two groups. Arrange these $(m + n)!/m!n!$ differences in ascending order. If the difference $\mathbf{d}$ falls among the lowest $2\frac{1}{2}$ per cent or the highest $2\frac{1}{2}$ per cent of these differences, then the null hypothesis is rejected at the 5 per cent level of significance. This nonparametric randomization test is therefore of quite important theoretical interest although it is of less practical interest because of the inordinate amount of computation often required.

16.8 Problems

1. Find the density function for $\mathbf{u} = F(\mathbf{x}_r)$, where $\mathbf{x}_r$ is the rth ordered observation of a sample of size n from a population with cumulative distribution $F(x)$.

2. Derive the density given in equation (16.2.10) by using (16.2.4).

3. Derive (16.2.10) by a geometrical argument, considering the x axis divided into five intervals as illustrated. The sample is regarded as coming from a multinomial population with five categories having probabilities $F(y - \Delta y/2)$, $f(y)\,\Delta y$, $F(z - \Delta z/2) - F(y + \Delta y/2)$, $f(z)\,\Delta z$,

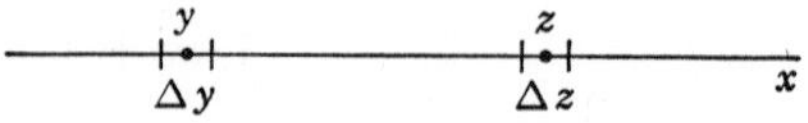

$1 - F(z + \Delta z/2)$, and in such a way that $r - 1$ observations fall in the first category, one in the second, and so on. The density of $\mathbf{x}$ is $f(x)$ with cumulative $F(x)$.

4. Use the geometrical method of Prob. 3 to find the joint density function of $\mathbf{u}$, the area between $\mathbf{x}_q$ and $\mathbf{x}_r$, and $\mathbf{v}$, the area between $\mathbf{x}_s$ and $\mathbf{x}_t$, with $q < r < s < t$.

5. Show that the expected value of the larger of a randon sample of two observations from a normal population with zero mean and unit variance is $1/\sqrt{\pi}$ and hence that for the general normal population the expected value is $\mu + (\sigma/\sqrt{\pi})$.

6. If $(\mathbf{x}, \mathbf{y})$ is an observation from a bivariate normal population with zero means, unit variances, and correlation ρ, show that the expected value of the larger of $\mathbf{x}$ and $\mathbf{y}$ is $\sqrt{(1 - \rho)/\pi}$.

7. Derive equation (16.4.7).

8. Verify equations (16.4.9) and (16.4.10).

9. Show that $\mathbf{t}$ defined by equation (16.4.14) is approximately normally distributed for large n.

10. Verify equations (16.4.23) and (16.4.24).

11. Verify equation (16.4.31).

12. If $\mathbf{x}_1, \mathbf{x}_2, \cdots, \mathbf{x}_n$ is an ordered sample from a population with cumulative distribution $F(x)$, find the density for

$$\mathbf{u} = \frac{F(\mathbf{x}_n) - F(\mathbf{x}_2)}{F(\mathbf{x}_n) - F(\mathbf{x}_1)}$$

13. The active life $\mathbf{x}$, in hours, of radioactive atoms has the density $(1/\theta)e^{-x/\theta}$. To estimate θ for a particular kind of atom, a sample of n atoms is put under observation, but the experiment is to stop when the rth atom has expired; i.e., it is intended not to wait until all the atoms have ceased activity but only until r of them (r chosen in advance) have done so. The data consist then of r measurements $\mathbf{x}_1, \mathbf{x}_2, \cdots, \mathbf{x}_r$ and $n - r$ measurements known only to exceed $\mathbf{x}_r$. Find the maximum-likelihood estimate of θ, and show that it has a chi-square distribution. Note that the likelihood contains the factor $[1 - F(\mathbf{x}_r)]^{n-r}$, where $F(x)$ is the cumulative distribution.

14. Referring to Prob. 13, must one start with newly activated atoms, or is it all right to start with atoms that have already been active for various lengths of time (and are still active)?

15. If $\mathbf{x}$ is uniformly distributed between $\theta - \frac{1}{2}$ and $\theta + \frac{1}{2}$, find the density for the median $\tilde{\mathbf{x}}$ for samples of size $2k + 1$.

16. Referring to Prob. 15, find the density for $\mathbf{z} = (\mathbf{x}_1 + \mathbf{x}_{2k+1})/2$. Is $\mathbf{z}$ or $\tilde{\mathbf{x}}$ the better estimator of θ?

17. Show that the sample median is a consistent estimator of the population median in Prob. 15.

18. We have seen that the sample mean for a distribution with infinite variance (such as the Cauchy distribution) is not necessarily a consistent estimator of the population mean. Is the sample median a consistent estimator of the population median?

19. If a population has a density

$$f(x) = \tfrac{1}{2}e^{-(x-\theta)} \qquad x > \theta$$
$$f(x) = \tfrac{1}{2}e^{+(x-\theta)} \qquad x \leq \theta$$

find the maximum-likelihood estimate of θ for samples of size n.

20. A common measure of association for two variates **x** and **y** is the *rank correlation*, or *Spearman's correlation*. The **x** values are ranked and the observations replaced by their ranks; similarly the **y** observations are replaced by their ranks. Thus for samples of size n one might have

X	1	2	3	. . .	n
y	7	4	11	. . .	6

Using these paired ranks, the ordinary correlation is computed:

$$\mathbf{S} = \frac{\Sigma(X_i - \bar{X})(\mathbf{y}_i - \bar{\mathbf{y}})}{\sqrt{\Sigma(X_i - \bar{X})^2\Sigma(\mathbf{y}_i - \bar{\mathbf{y}})^2}} = 1 - \frac{6\Sigma\mathbf{d}_i^2}{n^3 - n}$$

where the capital letters represent the ranks, and $\mathbf{d}_i = X_i - \mathbf{y}_i$. Verify that the given relation is true. $\left[\text{NOTE: } \sum_1^n i^2 = n(n+1)(2n+1)/6.\right]$

21. Show that the distribution of **S** of Prob. 20 is independent of the form of the distributions of **x** and **y**, provided that they are independently distributed, hence that **S** is a nonparametric criterion for testing the null hypothesis of independence.

22. Show that the mean and variance of **S** (in Prob. 21) under the hypothesis of independence are 0 and $1/(n - 1)$, respectively. To do this, show that **S** may be put in the form

$$\mathbf{S} = \frac{12}{n^3 - n}\left[\mathbf{Q} - \frac{n(n+1)^2}{4}\right]$$

where $\mathbf{Q} = \Sigma i\mathbf{y}_i$ (replacing X_i by i), and observe that the coefficient of $\prod_1^n u_i$ in

$$\phi(t) = \frac{1}{n!}\prod_{j=1}^{n}\left(\sum_{i=1}^{n} u_i t^{ij}\right)$$

is a factorial moment generating function for **Q**.

23. Find n in Example 16.1.

24. Use the rank test to test at the 5 per cent level the null hypothesis that these two samples came from the same population:

x	1.3	1.4	1.4	1.5	1.7	1.9	1.9
y	1.6	1.8	2.0	2.1	2.1	2.2	2.3

25. Use the randomization test instead of the rank test in Prob. 24.

26. Derive the relation between **U** and **T** given by equation (16.6.1).

27. Carry out the details involved in obtaining equations (16.6.9) and (16.6.10) from (16.6.4).

16.9 Bibliography

1. Fraser, D. A. S.: "Nonparametric Methods in Statistics," John Wiley & Sons, Inc., New York, 1957.
2. Hoeffding, W.: "Large sample power of tests based on permutations of observations," *Annals of Mathematical Statistics*, Vol. 23(1952), pp. 169–192.
3. Lehmann, E. L., and C. Stein: "On some theory of nonparametric hypotheses," *Annals of Mathematical Statistics*, Vol. 20(1949), pp. 28–46.
4. Lehmann, E. L.: "Testing Statistical Hypotheses," John Wiley & Sons, Inc., New York, 1959.
5. Mann, H. B., and D. R. Whitney: "On a test of whether one of two random variables is stochastically larger than the other," *Annals of Mathematical Statistics*, Vol. 18(1947), pp. 50–61.
6. Mood, A. M.: "On the asymptotic efficiency of certain nonparametric two-sample tests," *Annals of Mathematical Statistics*, Vol. 25(1954), pp. 514–522.
7. Siegel, S.: "Nonparametric Statistics for the Behavioral Sciences," McGraw-Hill Book Company, Inc., New York, 1956.
8. Wilcoxon, F.: "Individual comparisons by ranking methods," *Biometrics*, Vol. 1(1945), pp. 80–83.
9. Wilks, S. S.: "Order statistics," *Bulletin of the American Mathematical Society*, Vol. 54(1948), pp. 6–50.

Description of Tables

I. *Ordinates of the Normal Density Function.* This table gives values of

$$f(x) = \frac{1}{\sqrt{2\pi}} e^{-x^2/2}$$

for values of x between 0 and 4 at intervals of .01. For negative values of x one uses the fact that $f(-x) = f(x)$.

II. *Cumulative Normal Distribution.* This tabulates

$$F(x) = \int_{-\infty}^{x} \frac{1}{\sqrt{2\pi}} e^{-t^2/2}\, dt$$

for values of x between 0 and 3.5 at intervals of .01. For negative values of x, one uses the relation $F(-x) = 1 - F(x)$. Values of x corresponding to a few special values of F are given separately beneath the main table.

III. *Cumulative Chi-square Distribution.* This table gives values of u corresponding to a few selected values of $F(u)$, where

$$F(u) = \int_{0}^{u} \frac{x^{(n-2)/2} e^{-x/2}\, dx}{2^{n/2}[(n-2)/2]!}$$

for n, the number of degrees of freedom, equal to 1, 2, · · · , 30. For larger values of n, a normal approximation is quite accurate. The quantity $\sqrt{2u} - \sqrt{2n-1}$ is nearly normally distributed with zero mean and unit variance. Thus u_α, the α point of the distribution, may be computed by

$$u_\alpha = (\tfrac{1}{2})(x_\alpha + \sqrt{2n-1})^2$$

where x_α is the α point of the cumulative normal distribution. As an illustration, we may compute the .95 value of u for $n = 30$ degrees of freedom:

$$u_{.95} = \tfrac{1}{2}(1.645 + \sqrt{59})^2$$
$$= 43.5$$

which is in error by less than 1 per cent.

IV. *Cumulative "Student's" Distribution.* This table gives values of t corresponding to a few selected values of

$$F(t) = \int_{-\infty}^{t} \frac{\left(\frac{n-1}{2}\right)!}{\left(\frac{n-2}{2}\right)! \sqrt{\pi n} \left(1 + \frac{x^2}{n}\right)^{(n+1)/2}} dx$$

with $n = 1, 2, \cdots, 30, 40, 60, 120, \infty$. Since the density is symmetric in t, it follows that $F(-t) = 1 - F(t)$. One should not interpolate linearly between degrees of freedom but on the reciprocal of the degrees of freedom, if good accuracy in the last digit is desired. As an illustration, we shall compute the .975 value for 40 degrees of freedom. The values for 30 and 60 are 2.042 and 2.000. Using the reciprocals of n, the interpolated value is

$$2.042 - \frac{1/30 - 1/40}{1/30 - 1/60} (2.042 - 2.000) = 2.021$$

which is the correct value. Interpolating linearly, one would have obtained 2.028.

V. *Cumulative F Distribution.* This table gives values of F corresponding to five values of

$$G(F) = \int_0^F \frac{\left(\frac{m+n-2}{2}\right)! \, m^{m/2} n^{n/2} x^{(m-2)/2} (n + mx)^{-(m+n)/2} \, dx}{\left(\frac{m-2}{2}\right)! \left(\frac{n-2}{2}\right)!}$$

for selected values of m and n; m is the number of degrees of freedom in the numerator of F, and n is the number of degrees of freedom in the denominator of F. The table also provides values corresponding to $G = .10, .05, .025, .01$, and $.005$ because $F_{1-\alpha}$ for m and n degrees of freedom is the reciprocal of F_α for n and m degrees of freedom. Thus for $G = .05$ with three and six degrees of freedom, one finds

$$F_{.95}(3, 6) = \frac{1}{F_{.05}(6, 3)} = \frac{1}{8.94} = .112$$

One should interpolate on the reciprocals of m and n as in Table IV for good accuracy.

VI to VIII. *Studentized Range.* Let $\mathbf{x}_1, \mathbf{x}_2, \cdots, \mathbf{x}_n$ be normal and independent with mean μ and variance σ^2 and define the range $\mathbf{R}$ by

$$\mathbf{R} = \max_i \mathbf{x}_i - \min_i \mathbf{x}_i$$

Let $\nu \mathbf{s}^2/\sigma^2$ be a chi-square variate with ν degrees of freedom and be independent of the $\mathbf{x}_i$. Let $\mathbf{q} = \mathbf{R}/\mathbf{s}$; then Tables VI to VIII give values of $\mathbf{q}$ corresponding to

$$\int_{q_\alpha}^{\infty} f(q) \, dq = \alpha$$

for $\alpha = .01, .05$, and $.10$ for various values of n and ν.

Table I. Ordinates of the Normal Density Function

$$f(x) = \frac{1}{\sqrt{2\pi}} e^{-x^2/2}$$

x	.00	.01	.02	.03	.04	.05	.06	.07	.08	.09
.0	.3989	.3989	.3989	.3988	.3986	.3984	.3982	.3980	.3977	.3973
.1	.3970	.3965	.3961	.3956	.3951	.3945	.3939	.3932	.3925	.3918
.2	.3910	.3902	.3894	.3885	.3876	.3867	.3857	.3847	.3836	.3825
.3	.3814	.3802	.3790	.3778	.3765	.3752	.3739	.3725	.3712	.3697
.4	.3683	.3668	.3653	.3637	.3621	.3605	.3589	.3572	.3555	.3538
.5	.3521	.3503	.3485	.3467	.3448	.3429	.3410	.3391	.3372	.3352
.6	.3332	.3312	.3292	.3271	.3251	.3230	.3209	.3187	.3166	.3144
.7	.3123	.3101	.3079	.3056	.3034	.3011	.2989	.2966	.2943	.2920
.8	.2897	.2874	.2850	.2827	.2803	.2780	.2756	.2732	.2709	.2685
.9	.2661	.2637	.2613	.2589	.2565	.2541	.2516	.2492	.2468	.2444
1.0	.2420	.2396	.2371	.2347	.2323	.2299	.2275	.2251	.2227	.2203
1.1	.2179	.2155	.2131	.2107	.2083	.2059	.2036	.2012	.1989	.1965
1.2	.1942	.1919	.1895	.1872	.1849	.1826	.1804	.1781	.1758	.1736
1.3	.1714	.1691	.1669	.1647	.1626	.1604	.1582	.1561	.1539	.1518
1.4	.1497	.1476	.1456	.1435	.1415	.1394	.1374	.1354	.1334	.1315
1.5	.1295	.1276	.1257	.1238	.1219	.1200	.1182	.1163	.1145	.1127
1.6	.1109	.1092	.1074	.1057	.1040	.1023	.1006	.0989	.0973	.0957
1.7	.0940	.0925	.0909	.0893	.0878	.0863	.0848	.0833	.0818	.0804
1.8	.0790	.0775	.0761	.0748	.0734	.0721	.0707	.0694	.0681	.0669
1.9	.0656	.0644	.0632	.0620	.0608	.0596	.0584	.0573	.0562	.0551
2.0	.0540	.0529	.0519	.0508	.0498	.0488	.0478	.0468	.0459	.0449
2.1	.0440	.0431	.0422	.0413	.0404	.0396	.0387	.0379	.0371	.0363
2.2	.0355	.0347	.0339	.0332	.0325	.0317	.0310	.0303	.0297	.0290
2.3	.0283	.0277	.0270	.0264	.0258	.0252	.0246	.0241	.0235	.0229
2.4	.0224	.0219	.0213	.0208	.0203	.0198	.0194	.0189	.0184	.0180
2.5	.0175	.0171	.0167	.0163	.0158	.0154	.0151	.0147	.0143	.0139
2.6	.0136	.0132	.0129	.0126	.0122	.0119	.0116	.0113	.0110	.0107
2.7	.0104	.0101	.0099	.0096	.0093	.0091	.0088	.0086	.0084	.0081
2.8	.0079	.0077	.0075	.0073	.0071	.0069	.0067	.0065	.0063	.0061
2.9	.0060	.0058	.0056	.0055	.0053	.0051	.0050	.0048	.0047	.0046
3.0	.0044	.0043	.0042	.0040	.0039	.0038	.0037	.0036	.0035	.0034
3.1	.0033	.0032	.0031	.0030	.0029	.0028	.0027	.0026	.0025	.0025
3.2	.0024	.0023	.0022	.0022	.0021	.0020	.0020	.0019	.0018	.0018
3.3	.0017	.0017	.0016	.0016	.0015	.0015	.0014	.0014	.0013	.0013
3.4	.0012	.0012	.0012	.0011	.0011	.0010	.0010	.0010	.0009	.0009
3.5	.0009	.0008	.0008	.0008	.0008	.0007	.0007	.0007	.0007	.0006
3.6	.0006	.0006	.0006	.0005	.0005	.0005	.0005	.0005	.0005	.0004
3.7	.0004	.0004	.0004	.0004	.0004	.0004	.0003	.0003	.0003	.0003
3.8	.0003	.0003	.0003	.0003	.0003	.0002	.0002	.0002	.0002	.0002
3.9	.0002	.0002	.0002	.0002	.0002	.0002	.0002	.0002	.0001	.0001

Table II. Cumulative Normal Distribution

$$F(x) = \int_{-\infty}^{x} \frac{1}{\sqrt{2\pi}} e^{-t^2/2}\, dt$$

x	.00	.01	.02	.03	.04	.05	.06	.07	.08	.09
.0	.5000	.5040	.5080	.5120	.5160	.5199	.5239	.5279	.5319	.5359
.1	.5398	.5438	.5478	.5517	.5557	.5596	.5636	.5675	.5714	.5753
.2	.5793	.5832	.5871	.5910	.5948	.5987	.6026	.6064	.6103	.6141
.3	.6179	.6217	.6255	.6293	.6331	.6368	.6406	.6443	.6480	.6517
.4	.6554	.6591	.6628	.6664	.6700	.6736	.6772	.6808	.6844	.6879
.5	.6915	.6950	.6985	.7019	.7054	.7088	.7123	.7157	.7190	.7224
.6	.7257	.7291	.7324	.7357	.7389	.7422	.7454	.7486	.7517	.7549
.7	.7580	.7611	.7642	.7673	.7704	.7734	.7764	.7794	.7823	.7852
.8	.7881	.7910	.7939	.7967	.7995	.8023	.8051	.8078	.8106	.8133
.9	.8159	.8186	.8212	.8238	.8264	.8289	.8315	.8340	.8365	.8389
1.0	.8413	.8438	.8461	.8485	.8508	.8531	.8554	.8577	.8599	.8621
1.1	.8643	.8665	.8686	.8708	.8729	.8749	.8770	.8790	.8810	.8830
1.2	.8849	.8869	.8888	.8907	.8925	.8944	.8962	.8980	.8997	.9015
1.3	.9032	.9049	.9066	.9082	.9099	.9115	.9131	.9147	.9162	.9177
1.4	.9192	.9207	.9222	.9236	.9251	.9265	.9279	.9292	.9306	.9319
1.5	.9332	.9345	.9357	.9370	.9382	.9394	.9406	.9418	.9429	.9441
1.6	.9452	.9463	.9474	.9484	.9495	.9505	.9515	.9525	.9535	.9545
1.7	.9554	.9564	.9573	.9582	.9591	.9599	.9608	.9616	.9625	.9633
1.8	.9641	.9649	.9656	.9664	.9671	.9678	.9686	.9693	.9699	.9706
1.9	.9713	.9719	.9726	.9732	.9738	.9744	.9750	.9756	.9761	.9767
2.0	.9772	.9778	.9783	.9788	.9793	.9798	.9803	.9808	.9812	.9817
2.1	.9821	.9826	.9830	.9834	.9838	.9842	.9846	.9850	.9854	.9857
2.2	.9861	.9864	.9868	.9871	.9875	.9878	.9881	.9884	.9887	.9890
2.3	.9893	.9896	.9898	.9901	.9904	.9906	.9909	.9911	.9913	.9916
2.4	.9918	.9920	.9922	.9925	.9927	.9929	.9931	.9932	.9934	.9936
2.5	.9938	.9940	.9941	.9943	.9945	.9946	.9948	.9949	.9951	.9952
2.6	.9953	.9955	.9956	.9957	.9959	.9960	.9961	.9962	.9963	.9964
2.7	.9965	.9966	.9967	.9968	.9969	.9970	.9971	.9972	.9973	.9974
2.8	.9974	.9975	.9976	.9977	.9977	.9978	.9979	.9979	.9980	.9981
2.9	.9981	.9982	.9982	.9983	.9984	.9984	.9985	.9985	.9986	.9986
3.0	.9987	.9987	.9987	.9988	.9988	.9989	.9989	.9989	.9990	.9990
3.1	.9990	.9991	.9991	.9991	.9992	.9992	.9992	.9992	.9993	.9993
3.2	.9993	.9993	.9994	.9994	.9994	.9994	.9994	.9995	.9995	.9995
3.3	.9995	.9995	.9995	.9996	.9996	.9996	.9996	.9996	.9996	.9997
3.4	.9997	.9997	.9997	.9997	.9997	.9997	.9997	.9997	.9997	.9998

x	1.282	1.645	1.960	2.326	2.576	3.090	3.291	3.891	4.417
$F(x)$	.90	.95	.975	.99	.995	.999	.9995	.99995	.999995
$2[1 - F(x)]$	.20	.10	.05	.02	.01	.002	.001	.0001	.00001

Table III. Cumulative Chi-square Distribution*

$$F(u) = \int_0^u \frac{x^{(n-2)/2}e^{-x/2}\,dx}{2^{n/2}[(n-2)/2]!}$$

n \ F	.005	.010	.025	.050	.100	.250	.500	.750	.900	.950	.975	.990	.995
1	$.0^4393$	$.0^3157$	$.0^3982$	$.0^2393$	.0158	.102	.455	1.32	2.71	3.84	5.02	6.63	7.88
2	.0100	.0201	.0506	.103	.211	.575	1.39	2.77	4.61	5.99	7.38	9.21	10.6
3	.0717	.115	.216	.352	.584	1.21	2.37	4.11	6.25	7.81	9.35	11.3	12.8
4	.207	.297	.484	.711	1.06	1.92	3.36	5.39	7.78	9.49	11.1	13.3	14.9
5	.412	.554	.831	1.15	1.61	2.67	4.35	6.63	9.24	11.1	12.8	15.1	16.7
6	.676	.872	1.24	1.64	2.20	3.45	5.35	7.84	10.6	12.6	14.4	16.8	18.5
7	.989	1.24	1.69	2.17	2.83	4.25	6.35	9.04	12.0	14.1	16.0	18.5	20.3
8	1.34	1.65	2.18	2.73	3.49	5.07	7.34	10.2	13.4	15.5	17.5	20.1	22.0
9	1.73	2.09	2.70	3.33	4.17	5.90	8.34	11.4	14.7	16.9	19.0	21.7	23.6
10	2.16	2.56	3.25	3.94	4.87	6.74	9.34	12.5	16.0	18.3	20.5	23.2	25.2
11	2.60	3.05	3.82	4.57	5.58	7.58	10.3	13.7	17.3	19.7	21.9	24.7	26.8
12	3.07	3.57	4.40	5.23	6.30	8.44	11.3	14.8	18.5	21.0	23.3	26.2	28.3
13	3.57	4.11	5.01	5.89	7.04	9.30	12.3	16.0	19.8	22.4	24.7	27.7	29.8
14	4.07	4.66	5.63	6.57	7.79	10.2	13.3	17.1	21.1	23.7	26.1	29.1	31.3
15	4.60	5.23	6.26	7.26	8.55	11.0	14.3	18.2	22.3	25.0	27.5	30.6	32.8
16	5.14	5.81	6.91	7.96	9.31	11.9	15.3	19.4	23.5	26.3	28.8	32.0	34.3
17	5.70	6.41	7.56	8.67	10.1	12.8	16.3	20.5	24.8	27.6	30.2	33.4	35.7
18	6.26	7.01	8.23	9.39	10.9	13.7	17.3	21.6	26.0	28.9	31.5	34.8	37.2
19	6.84	7.63	8.91	10.1	11.7	14.6	18.3	22.7	27.2	30.1	32.9	36.2	38.6
20	7.43	8.26	9.59	10.9	12.4	15.5	19.3	23.8	28.4	31.4	34.2	37.6	40.0
21	8.03	8.90	10.3	11.6	13.2	16.3	20.3	24.9	29.6	32.7	35.5	38.9	41.4
22	8.64	9.54	11.0	12.3	14.0	17.2	21.3	26.0	30.8	33.9	36.8	40.3	42.8
23	9.26	10.2	11.7	13.1	14.8	18.1	22.3	27.1	32.0	35.2	38.1	41.6	44.2
24	9.89	10.9	12.4	13.8	15.7	19.0	23.3	28.2	33.2	36.4	39.4	43.0	45.6
25	10.5	11.5	13.1	14.6	16.5	19.9	24.3	29.3	34.4	37.7	40.6	44.3	46.9
26	11.2	12.2	13.8	15.4	17.3	20.8	25.3	30.4	35.6	38.9	41.9	45.6	48.3
27	11.8	12.9	14.6	16.2	18.1	21.7	26.3	31.5	36.7	40.1	43.2	47.0	49.6
28	12.5	13.6	15.3	16.9	18.9	22.7	27.3	32.6	37.9	41.3	44.5	48.3	51.0
29	13.1	14.3	16.0	17.7	19.8	23.6	28.3	33.7	39.1	42.6	45.7	49.6	52.3
30	13.8	15.0	16.8	18.5	20.6	24.5	29.3	34.8	40.3	43.8	47.0	50.9	53.7

* This table is abridged from "Tables of percentage points of the incomplete beta function and of the chi-square distribution," *Biometrika*, Vol. 32 (1941). It is here published with the kind permission of the author, Catherine M. Thompson, and the editor of *Biometrika*.

TABLE IV. CUMULATIVE "STUDENT'S" DISTRIBUTION*

$$F(t) = \int_{-\infty}^{t} \frac{\left(\frac{n-1}{2}\right)!}{\left(\frac{n-2}{2}\right)!\,\sqrt{\pi n}\left(1+\frac{x^2}{n}\right)^{(n+1)/2}}\,dx$$

n \ F	.75	.90	.95	.975	.99	.995	.9995
1	1.000	3.078	6.314	12.706	31.821	63.657	636.619
2	.816	1.886	2.920	4.303	6.965	9.925	31.598
3	.765	1.638	2.353	3.182	4.541	5.841	12.941
4	.741	1.533	2.132	2.776	3.747	4.604	8.610
5	.727	1.476	2.015	2.571	3.365	4.032	6.859
6	.718	1.440	1.943	2.447	3.143	3.707	5.959
7	.711	1.415	1.895	2.365	2.998	3.499	5.405
8	.706	1.397	1.860	2.306	2.896	3.355	5.041
9	.703	1.383	1.833	2.262	2.821	3.250	4.781
10	.700	1.372	1.812	2.228	2.764	3.169	4.587
11	.697	1.363	1.796	2.201	2.718	3.106	4.437
12	.695	1.356	1.782	2.179	2.681	3.055	4.318
13	.694	1.350	1.771	2.160	2.650	3.012	4.221
14	.692	1.345	1.761	2.145	2.624	2.977	4.140
15	.691	1.341	1.753	2.131	2.602	2.947	4.073
16	.690	1.337	1.746	2.120	2.583	2.921	4.015
17	.689	1.333	1.740	2.110	2.567	2.898	3.965
18	.688	1.330	1.734	2.101	2.552	2.878	3.922
19	.688	1.328	1.729	2.093	2.539	2.861	3.883
20	.687	1.325	1.725	2.086	2.528	2.845	3.850
21	.686	1.323	1.721	2.080	2.518	2.831	3.819
22	.686	1.321	1.717	2.074	2.508	2.819	3.792
23	.685	1.319	1.714	2.069	2.500	2.807	3.767
24	.685	1.318	1.711	2.064	2.492	2.797	3.745
25	.684	1.316	1.708	2.060	2.485	2.787	3.725
26	.684	1.315	1.706	2.056	2.479	2.779	3.707
27	.684	1.314	1.703	2.052	2.473	2.771	3.690
28	.683	1.313	1.701	2.048	2.467	2.763	3.674
29	.683	1.311	1.699	2.045	2.462	2.756	3.659
30	.683	1.310	1.697	2.042	2.457	2.750	3.646
40	.681	1.303	1.684	2.021	2.423	2.704	3.551
60	.679	1.296	1.671	2.000	2.390	2.660	3.460
120	.677	1.289	1.658	1.980	2.358	2.617	3.373
∞	.674	1.282	1.645	1.960	2.326	2.576	3.291

* This table is abridged from the "Statistical Tables" of R. A. Fisher and Frank Yates published by Oliver & Boyd, Ltd., Edinburgh and London, 1938. It is here published with the kind permission of the authors and their publishers.

Table V. Cumulative F Distribution*

m degrees of freedom in numerator; n in denominator

$$G(F) = \int_0^F \frac{[(m+n-2)/2]!\, m^{m/2} n^{n/2} x^{(m-2)/2} (n+mx)^{-(m+n)/2}\, dx}{[(m-2)/2]!\,[(n-2)/2]!}$$

G	n \ m	1	2	3	4	5	6	7	8	9	10	12	15	20	30	60	120	∞
.90		39.9	49.5	53.6	55.8	57.2	58.2	58.9	59.4	59.9	60.2	60.7	61.2	61.7	62.3	62.8	63.1	63.3
.95		161	200	216	225	230	234	237	239	241	242	244	246	248	250	252	253	254
.975	1	648	800	864	900	922	937	948	957	963	969	977	985	993	1000	1010	1010	1020
.99		4,050	5,000	5,400	5,620	5,760	5,860	5,930	5,980	6,020	6,060	6,110	6,160	6,210	6,260	6,310	6,340	6,370
.995		16,200	20,000	21,600	22,500	23,100	23,400	23,700	23,900	24,100	24,200	24,400	24,600	24,800	25,000	25,200	25,400	25,500
.90		8.53	9.00	9.16	9.24	9.29	9.33	9.35	9.37	9.38	9.39	9.41	9.42	9.44	9.46	9.47	9.48	9.49
.95		18.5	19.0	19.2	19.2	19.3	19.3	19.4	19.4	19.4	19.4	19.4	19.4	19.5	19.5	19.5	19.5	19.5
.975	2	38.5	39.0	39.2	39.2	39.3	39.3	39.4	39.4	39.4	39.4	39.4	39.4	39.4	39.5	39.5	39.5	39.5
.99		98.5	99.0	99.2	99.2	99.3	99.3	99.4	99.4	99.4	99.4	99.4	99.4	99.4	99.5	99.5	99.5	99.5
.995		199	199	199	199	199	199	199	199	199	199	199	199	199	199	199	199	199
.90		5.54	5.46	5.39	5.34	5.31	5.28	5.27	5.25	5.24	5.23	5.22	5.20	5.18	5.17	5.15	5.14	5.13
.95		10.1	9.55	9.28	9.12	9.01	8.94	8.89	8.85	8.81	8.79	8.74	8.70	8.66	8.62	8.57	8.55	8.53
.975	3	17.4	16.0	15.4	15.1	14.9	14.7	14.6	14.5	14.5	14.4	14.3	14.3	14.2	14.1	14.0	13.9	13.9
.99		34.1	30.8	29.5	28.7	28.2	27.9	27.7	27.5	27.3	27.2	27.1	26.9	26.7	26.5	26.3	26.2	26.1
.995		55.6	49.8	47.5	46.2	45.4	44.8	44.4	44.1	43.9	43.7	43.4	43.1	42.8	42.5	42.1	42.0	41.8
.90		4.54	4.32	4.19	4.11	4.05	4.01	3.98	3.95	3.93	3.92	3.90	3.87	3.84	3.82	3.79	3.78	3.76
.95		7.71	6.94	6.59	6.39	6.26	6.16	6.09	6.04	6.00	5.96	5.91	5.86	5.80	5.75	5.69	5.66	5.63
.975	4	12.2	10.6	9.98	9.60	9.36	9.20	9.07	8.98	8.90	8.84	8.75	8.66	8.56	8.46	8.36	8.31	8.26
.99		21.2	18.0	16.7	16.0	15.5	15.2	15.0	14.8	14.7	14.5	14.4	14.2	14.0	13.8	13.7	13.6	13.5
.995		31.3	26.3	24.3	23.2	22.5	22.0	21.6	21.4	21.1	21.0	20.7	20.4	20.2	19.9	19.6	19.5	19.3
.90		4.06	3.78	3.62	3.52	3.45	3.40	3.37	3.34	3.32	3.30	3.27	3.24	3.21	3.17	3.14	3.12	3.11
.95		6.61	5.79	5.41	5.19	5.05	4.95	4.88	4.82	4.77	4.74	4.68	4.62	4.56	4.50	4.43	4.40	4.37
.975	5	10.0	8.43	7.76	7.39	7.15	6.98	6.85	6.76	6.68	6.62	6.52	6.43	6.33	6.23	6.12	6.07	6.02
.99		16.3	13.3	12.1	11.4	11.0	10.7	10.5	10.3	10.2	10.1	9.89	9.72	9.55	9.38	9.20	9.11	9.02
.995		22.8	18.3	16.5	15.6	14.9	14.5	14.2	14.0	13.8	13.6	13.4	13.1	12.9	12.7	12.4	12.3	12.1
.90		3.78	3.46	3.29	3.18	3.11	3.05	3.01	2.98	2.96	2.94	2.90	2.87	2.84	2.80	2.76	2.74	2.72
.95		5.99	5.14	4.76	4.53	4.39	4.28	4.21	4.15	4.10	4.06	4.00	3.94	3.87	3.81	3.74	3.70	3.67
.975	6	8.81	7.26	6.60	6.23	5.99	5.82	5.70	5.60	5.52	5.46	5.37	5.27	5.17	5.07	4.96	4.90	4.85
.99		13.7	10.9	9.78	9.15	8.75	8.47	8.26	8.10	7.98	7.87	7.72	7.56	7.40	7.23	7.06	6.97	6.88
.995		18.6	14.5	12.9	12.0	11.5	11.1	10.8	10.6	10.4	10.2	10.0	9.81	9.59	9.36	9.12	9.00	8.88
.90		3.59	3.26	3.07	2.96	2.88	2.83	2.78	2.75	2.72	2.70	2.67	2.63	2.59	2.56	2.51	2.49	2.47
.95		5.59	4.74	4.35	4.12	3.97	3.87	3.79	3.73	3.68	3.64	3.57	3.51	3.44	3.38	3.30	3.27	3.23
.975	7	8.07	6.54	5.89	5.52	5.29	5.12	4.99	4.90	4.82	4.76	4.67	4.57	4.47	4.36	4.25	4.20	4.14
.99		12.2	9.55	8.45	7.85	7.46	7.19	6.99	6.84	6.72	6.62	6.47	6.31	6.16	5.99	5.82	5.74	5.65
.995		16.2	12.4	10.9	10.1	9.52	9.16	8.89	8.68	8.51	8.38	8.18	7.97	7.75	7.53	7.31	7.19	7.08
.90		3.46	3.11	2.92	2.81	2.73	2.67	2.62	2.59	2.56	2.54	2.50	2.46	2.42	2.38	2.34	2.31	2.29
.95		5.32	4.46	4.07	3.84	3.69	3.58	3.50	3.44	3.39	3.35	3.28	3.22	3.15	3.08	3.01	2.97	2.93
.975	8	7.57	6.06	5.42	5.05	4.82	4.65	4.53	4.43	4.36	4.30	4.20	4.10	4.00	3.89	3.78	3.73	3.67
.99		11.3	8.65	7.59	7.01	6.63	6.37	6.18	6.03	5.91	5.81	5.67	5.52	5.36	5.20	5.03	4.95	4.86
.995		14.7	11.0	9.60	8.81	8.30	7.95	7.69	7.50	7.34	7.21	7.01	6.81	6.61	6.40	6.18	6.06	5.95

.90		3.36	3.01	2.81	2.69	2.61	2.55	2.51	2.47	2.44	2.42	2.38	2.34	2.30	2.25	2.21	2.18	2.16
.95		5.12	4.26	3.86	3.63	3.48	3.37	3.29	3.23	3.18	3.14	3.07	3.01	2.94	2.86	2.79	2.75	2.71
.975	9	7.21	5.71	5.08	4.72	4.48	4.32	4.20	4.10	4.03	3.96	3.87	3.77	3.67	3.56	3.45	3.39	3.33
.99		10.6	8.02	6.99	6.42	6.06	5.80	5.61	5.47	5.35	5.26	5.11	4.96	4.81	4.65	4.48	4.40	4.31
.995		13.6	10.1	8.72	7.96	7.47	7.13	6.88	6.69	6.54	6.42	6.23	6.03	5.83	5.62	5.41	5.30	5.19
.90		3.29	2.92	2.73	2.61	2.52	2.46	2.41	2.38	2.35	2.32	2.28	2.24	2.20	2.15	2.11	2.08	2.06
.95		4.96	4.10	3.71	3.48	3.33	3.22	3.14	3.07	3.02	2.98	2.91	2.84	2.77	2.70	2.62	2.58	2.54
.975	10	6.94	5.46	4.83	4.47	4.24	4.07	3.95	3.85	3.78	3.72	3.62	3.52	3.42	3.31	3.20	3.14	3.08
.99		10.0	7.56	6.55	5.99	5.64	5.39	5.20	5.06	4.94	4.85	4.71	4.56	4.41	4.25	4.08	4.00	3.91
.995		12.8	9.43	8.08	7.34	6.87	6.54	6.30	6.12	5.97	5.85	5.66	5.47	5.27	5.07	4.86	4.75	4.64
.90		3.18	2.81	2.61	2.48	2.39	2.33	2.28	2.24	2.21	2.19	2.15	2.10	2.06	2.01	1.96	1.93	1.90
.95		4.75	3.89	3.49	3.26	3.11	3.00	2.91	2.85	2.80	2.75	2.69	2.62	2.54	2.47	2.38	2.34	2.30
.975	12	6.55	5.10	4.47	4.12	3.89	3.73	3.61	3.51	3.44	3.37	3.28	3.18	3.07	2.96	2.85	2.79	2.72
.99		9.33	6.93	5.95	5.41	5.06	4.82	4.64	4.50	4.39	4.30	4.16	4.01	3.86	3.70	3.54	3.45	3.36
.995		11.8	8.51	7.23	6.52	6.07	5.76	5.52	5.35	5.20	5.09	4.91	4.72	4.53	4.33	4.12	4.01	3.90
.90		3.07	2.70	2.49	2.36	2.27	2.21	2.16	2.12	2.09	2.06	2.02	1.97	1.92	1.87	1.82	1.79	1.76
.95		4.54	3.68	3.29	3.06	2.90	2.79	2.71	2.64	2.59	2.54	2.48	2.40	2.33	2.25	2.16	2.11	2.07
.975	15	6.20	4.77	4.15	3.80	3.58	3.41	3.29	3.20	3.12	3.06	2.96	2.86	2.76	2.64	2.52	2.46	2.40
.99		8.68	6.36	5.42	4.89	4.56	4.32	4.14	4.00	3.89	3.80	3.67	3.52	3.37	3.21	3.05	2.96	2.87
.995		10.8	7.70	6.48	5.80	5.37	5.07	4.85	4.67	4.54	4.42	4.25	4.07	3.88	3.69	3.48	3.37	3.26
.90		2.97	2.59	2.38	2.25	2.16	2.09	2.04	2.00	1.96	1.94	1.89	1.84	1.79	1.74	1.68	1.64	1.61
.95		4.35	3.49	3.10	2.87	2.71	2.60	2.51	2.45	2.39	2.35	2.28	2.20	2.12	2.04	1.95	1.90	1.84
.975	20	5.87	4.46	3.86	3.51	3.29	3.13	3.01	2.91	2.84	2.77	2.68	2.57	2.46	2.35	2.22	2.16	2.09
.99		8.10	5.85	4.94	4.43	4.10	3.87	3.70	3.56	3.46	3.37	3.23	3.09	2.94	2.78	2.61	2.52	2.42
.995		9.94	6.99	5.82	5.17	4.76	4.47	4.26	4.09	3.96	3.85	3.68	3.50	3.32	3.12	2.92	2.81	2.69
.90		2.88	2.49	2.28	2.14	2.05	1.98	1.93	1.88	1.85	1.82	1.77	1.72	1.67	1.61	1.54	1.50	1.46
.95		4.17	3.32	2.92	2.69	2.53	2.42	2.33	2.27	2.21	2.16	2.09	2.01	1.93	1.84	1.74	1.68	1.62
.975	30	5.57	4.18	3.59	3.25	3.03	2.87	2.75	2.65	2.57	2.51	2.41	2.31	2.20	2.07	1.94	1.87	1.79
.99		7.56	5.39	4.51	4.02	3.70	3.47	3.30	3.17	3.07	2.98	2.84	2.70	2.55	2.39	2.21	2.11	2.01
.995		9.18	6.35	5.24	4.62	4.23	3.95	3.74	3.58	3.45	3.34	3.18	3.01	2.82	2.63	2.42	2.30	2.18
.90		2.79	2.39	2.18	2.04	1.95	1.87	1.82	1.77	1.74	1.71	1.66	1.60	1.54	1.48	1.40	1.35	1.29
.95		4.00	3.15	2.76	2.53	2.37	2.25	2.17	2.10	2.04	1.99	1.92	1.84	1.75	1.65	1.53	1.47	1.39
.975	60	5.29	3.93	3.34	3.01	2.79	2.63	2.51	2.41	2.33	2.27	2.17	2.06	1.94	1.82	1.67	1.58	1.48
.99		7.08	4.98	4.13	3.65	3.34	3.12	2.95	2.82	2.72	2.63	2.50	2.35	2.20	2.03	1.84	1.73	1.60
.995		8.49	5.80	4.73	4.14	3.76	3.49	3.29	3.13	3.01	2.90	2.74	2.57	2.39	2.19	1.96	1.83	1.69
.90		2.75	2.35	2.13	1.99	1.90	1.82	1.77	1.72	1.68	1.65	1.60	1.54	1.48	1.41	1.32	1.26	1.19
.95		3.92	3.07	2.68	2.45	2.29	2.18	2.09	2.02	1.96	1.91	1.83	1.75	1.66	1.55	1.43	1.35	1.25
.975	120	5.15	3.80	3.23	2.89	2.67	2.52	2.39	2.30	2.22	2.16	2.05	1.94	1.82	1.69	1.53	1.43	1.31
.99		6.85	4.79	3.95	3.48	3.17	2.96	2.79	2.66	2.56	2.47	2.34	2.19	2.03	1.86	1.66	1.53	1.38
.995		8.18	5.54	4.50	3.92	3.55	3.28	3.09	2.93	2.81	2.71	2.54	2.37	2.19	1.98	1.75	1.61	1.43
.90		2.71	2.30	2.08	1.94	1.85	1.77	1.72	1.67	1.63	1.60	1.55	1.49	1.42	1.34	1.24	1.17	1.00
.95		3.84	3.00	2.60	2.37	2.21	2.10	2.01	1.94	1.88	1.83	1.75	1.67	1.57	1.46	1.32	1.22	1.00
.975	∞	5.02	3.69	3.12	2.79	2.57	2.41	2.29	2.19	2.11	2.05	1.94	1.83	1.71	1.57	1.39	1.27	1.00
.99		6.63	4.61	3.78	3.32	3.02	2.80	2.64	2.51	2.41	2.32	2.18	2.04	1.88	1.70	1.47	1.32	1.00
.995		7.88	5.30	4.28	3.72	3.35	3.09	2.90	2.74	2.62	2.52	2.36	2.19	2.00	1.79	1.53	1.36	1.00

* This table is abridged from "Tables of percentage points of the inverted beta distribution," *Biometrika*, Vol. 33 (1943). It is here published with the kind permission of the authors, Maxine Merrington and Catherine M. Thompson, and the editor of *Biometrika*.

Table VI. Upper 1 Per Cent Points of the Studentized Range*

The entries are $q_{.01}$, where $P(q < q_{.01}) = .99$

ν \ n	2	3	4	5	6	7	8	9	10	11	12	13	14	15	16	17	18	19	20
1	90.03	135.0	164.3	185.6	202.2	215.8	227.2	237.0	245.6	253.2	260.0	266.2	271.8	277.0	281.8	286.3	290.4	294.3	298.0
2	14.04	19.02	22.29	24.72	26.63	28.20	29.53	30.68	31.69	32.59	33.40	34.13	34.81	35.43	36.00	36.53	37.03	37.50	37.95
3	8.26	10.62	12.17	13.33	14.24	15.00	15.64	16.20	16.69	17.13	17.53	17.89	18.22	18.52	18.81	19.07	19.32	19.55	19.77
4	6.51	8.12	9.17	9.96	10.58	11.10	11.55	11.93	12.27	12.57	12.84	13.09	13.32	13.53	13.73	13.91	14.08	14.24	14.40
5	5.70	6.98	7.80	8.42	8.91	9.32	9.67	9.97	10.24	10.48	10.70	10.89	11.08	11.24	11.40	11.55	11.68	11.81	11.93
6	5.24	6.33	7.03	7.56	7.97	8.32	8.61	8.87	9.10	9.30	9.48	9.65	9.81	9.95	10.08	10.21	10.32	10.43	10.54
7	4.95	5.92	6.54	7.01	7.37	7.68	7.94	8.17	8.36	8.55	8.71	8.86	9.00	9.12	9.24	9.35	9.46	9.55	9.65
8	4.75	5.64	6.20	6.62	6.96	7.24	7.47	7.68	7.86	8.03	8.18	8.31	8.44	8.55	8.66	8.76	8.85	8.94	9.03
9	4.60	5.43	5.96	6.35	6.66	6.91	7.13	7.33	7.49	7.65	7.78	7.91	8.03	8.13	8.23	8.33	8.41	8.49	8.57
10	4.48	5.27	5.77	6.14	6.43	6.67	6.87	7.05	7.21	7.36	7.49	7.60	7.71	7.81	7.91	7.99	8.08	8.15	8.23
11	4.39	5.15	5.62	5.97	6.25	6.48	6.67	6.84	6.99	7.13	7.25	7.36	7.46	7.56	7.65	7.73	7.81	7.88	7.95
12	4.32	5.05	5.50	5.84	6.10	6.32	6.51	6.67	6.81	6.94	7.06	7.17	7.26	7.36	7.44	7.52	7.59	7.66	7.73
13	4.26	4.96	5.40	5.73	5.98	6.19	6.37	6.53	6.67	6.79	6.90	7.01	7.10	7.19	7.27	7.35	7.42	7.48	7.55
14	4.21	4.89	5.32	5.63	5.88	6.08	6.26	6.41	6.54	6.66	6.77	6.87	6.96	7.05	7.13	7.20	7.27	7.33	7.39
15	4.17	4.84	5.25	5.56	5.80	5.99	6.16	6.31	6.44	6.55	6.66	6.76	6.84	6.93	7.00	7.07	7.14	7.20	7.26
16	4.13	4.79	5.19	5.49	5.72	5.92	6.08	6.22	6.35	6.46	6.56	6.66	6.74	6.82	6.90	6.97	7.03	7.09	7.15
17	4.10	4.74	5.14	5.43	5.66	5.85	6.01	6.15	6.27	6.38	6.48	6.57	6.66	6.73	6.81	6.87	6.94	7.00	7.05
18	4.07	4.70	5.09	5.38	5.60	5.79	5.94	6.08	6.20	6.31	6.41	6.50	6.58	6.65	6.73	6.79	6.85	6.91	6.97
19	4.05	4.67	5.05	5.33	5.55	5.73	5.89	6.02	6.14	6.25	6.34	6.43	6.51	6.58	6.65	6.72	6.78	6.84	6.89
20	4.02	4.64	5.02	5.29	5.51	5.69	5.84	5.97	6.09	6.19	6.28	6.37	6.45	6.52	6.59	6.65	6.71	6.77	6.82
24	3.96	4.55	4.91	5.17	5.37	5.54	5.69	5.81	5.92	6.02	6.11	6.19	6.26	6.33	6.39	6.45	6.51	6.56	6.61
30	3.89	4.45	4.80	5.05	5.24	5.40	5.54	5.65	5.76	5.85	5.93	6.01	6.08	6.14	6.20	6.26	6.31	6.36	6.41
40	3.82	4.37	4.70	4.93	5.11	5.26	5.39	5.50	5.60	5.69	5.76	5.83	5.90	5.96	6.02	6.07	6.12	6.16	6.21
60	3.76	4.28	4.59	4.82	4.99	5.13	5.25	5.36	5.45	5.53	5.60	5.67	5.73	5.78	5.84	5.89	5.93	5.97	6.01
120	3.70	4.20	4.50	4.71	4.87	5.01	5.12	5.21	5.30	5.37	5.44	5.50	5.56	5.61	5.66	5.71	5.75	5.79	5.83
∞	3.64	4.12	4.40	4.60	4.76	4.88	4.99	5.08	5.16	5.23	5.29	5.35	5.40	5.45	5.49	5.54	5.57	5.61	5.65

* From E. S. Pearson and H. O. Hartley, "Biometrika Tables for Statisticians," Vol. 1, pp. 176–177, published by the Biometrika Trustees, Cambridge University Press, London, 1954. Reproduced with the permission of the authors and publishers. Corrections of ±1 in the last figure, supplied by Dr. Leon Harter, have been incorporated in some entries.

TABLE VII. UPPER 5 PER CENT POINTS OF THE STUDENTIZED RANGE*

The entries are $q_{.05}$, where $P(q < q_{.05}) = .95$

ν \ n	2	3	4	5	6	7	8	9	10	11	12	13	14	15	16	17	18	19	20
1	17.97	26.98	32.82	37.08	40.41	43.12	45.40	47.36	49.07	50.59	51.96	53.20	54.33	55.36	56.32	57.22	58.04	58.83	59.56
2	6.08	8.33	9.80	10.88	11.74	12.44	13.03	13.54	13.99	14.39	14.75	15.08	15.38	15.65	15.91	16.14	16.37	16.57	16.77
3	4.50	5.91	6.82	7.50	8.04	8.48	8.85	9.18	9.46	9.72	9.95	10.15	10.35	10.52	10.69	10.84	10.98	11.11	11.24
4	3.93	5.04	5.76	6.29	6.71	7.05	7.35	7.60	7.83	8.03	8.21	8.37	8.52	8.66	8.79	8.91	9.03	9.13	9.23
5	3.64	4.60	5.22	5.67	6.03	6.33	6.58	6.80	6.99	7.17	7.32	7.47	7.60	7.72	7.83	7.93	8.03	8.12	8.21
6	3.46	4.34	4.90	5.30	5.63	5.90	6.12	6.32	6.49	6.65	6.79	6.92	7.03	7.14	7.24	7.34	7.43	7.51	7.59
7	3.34	4.16	4.68	5.06	5.36	5.61	5.82	6.00	6.16	6.30	6.43	6.55	6.66	6.76	6.85	6.94	7.02	7.10	7.17
8	3.26	4.04	4.53	4.89	5.17	5.40	5.60	5.77	5.92	6.05	6.18	6.29	6.39	6.48	6.57	6.65	6.73	6.80	6.87
9	3.20	3.95	4.41	4.76	5.02	5.24	5.43	5.59	5.74	5.87	5.98	6.09	6.19	6.28	6.36	6.44	6.51	6.58	6.64
10	3.15	3.88	4.33	4.65	4.91	5.12	5.30	5.46	5.60	5.72	5.83	5.93	6.03	6.11	6.19	6.27	6.34	6.40	6.47
11	3.11	3.82	4.26	4.57	4.82	5.03	5.20	5.35	5.49	5.61	5.71	5.81	5.90	5.98	6.06	6.13	6.20	6.27	6.33
12	3.08	3.77	4.20	4.51	4.75	4.95	5.12	5.27	5.39	5.51	5.61	5.71	5.80	5.88	5.95	6.02	6.09	6.15	6.21
13	3.06	3.73	4.15	4.45	4.69	4.88	5.05	5.19	5.32	5.43	5.53	5.63	5.71	5.79	5.86	5.93	5.99	6.05	6.11
14	3.03	3.70	4.11	4.41	4.64	4.83	4.99	5.13	5.25	5.36	5.46	5.55	5.64	5.71	5.79	5.85	5.91	5.97	6.03
15	3.01	3.67	4.08	4.37	4.59	4.78	4.94	5.08	5.20	5.31	5.40	5.49	5.57	5.65	5.72	5.78	5.85	5.90	5.96
16	3.00	3.65	4.05	4.33	4.56	4.74	4.90	5.03	5.15	5.26	5.35	5.44	5.52	5.59	5.66	5.73	5.79	5.84	5.90
17	2.98	3.63	4.02	4.30	4.52	4.70	4.86	4.99	5.11	5.21	5.31	5.39	5.47	5.54	5.61	5.67	5.73	5.79	5.84
18	2.97	3.61	4.00	4.28	4.49	4.67	4.82	4.96	5.07	5.17	5.27	5.35	5.43	5.50	5.57	5.63	5.69	5.74	5.79
19	2 96	3.59	3.98	4.25	4.47	4.65	4.79	4.92	5.04	5.14	5.23	5.31	5.39	5.46	5.53	5.59	5.65	5.70	5.75
20	2.95	3.58	3.96	4.23	4.45	4.62	4.77	4.90	5.01	5.11	5.20	5.28	5.36	5.43	5.49	5.55	5.61	5.66	5.71
24	2.92	3.53	3.90	4.17	4.37	4.54	4.68	4.81	4.92	5.01	5.10	5.18	5.25	5.32	5.38	5.44	5.49	5.55	5.59
30	2.89	3.49	3.85	4.10	4.30	4.46	4.60	4.72	4.82	4.92	5.00	5.08	5.15	5.21	5.27	5.33	5.38	5.43	5.47
40	2.86	3.44	3.79	4.04	4.23	4.39	4.52	4.63	4.73	4.82	4.90	4.98	5.04	5.11	5.16	5.22	5.27	5.31	5.36
60	2.83	3.40	3.74	3.98	4.16	4.31	4.44	4.55	4.65	4.73	4.81	4.88	4.94	5.00	5.06	5.11	5.15	5.20	5.24
120	2.80	3.36	3.68	3.92	4.10	4.24	4.36	4.47	4.56	4.64	4.71	4.78	4.84	4.90	4.95	5.00	5.04	5.09	5.13
∞	2.77	3.31	3.63	3.86	4.03	4.17	4.29	4.39	4.47	4.55	4.62	4.68	4.74	4.80	4.85	4.89	4.93	4.97	5.01

* From E. S. Pearson and H. O. Hartley, "Biometrika Tables for Statisticians," Vol. 1, pp. 176–177, published by the Biometrika Trustees, Cambridge University Press, London, 1954. Reproduced with the permission of the authors and the publisher. Corrections of ±1 in the last figure, supplied by Dr. James Pachares, have been incorporated in some entries.

TABLE VIII. UPPER 10 PER CENT POINTS OF THE STUDENTIZED RANGE*

The entries are $q_{.10}$, where $P(q < q_{.10}) = .90$

ν \ n	2	3	4	5	6	7	8	9	10	11	12	13	14	15	16	17	18	19	20
1	8.93	13.44	16.36	18.49	20.15	21.51	22.64	23.62	24.48	25.24	25.92	26.54	27.10	27.62	28.10	28.54	28.96	29.35	29.71
2	4.13	5.73	6.77	7.54	8.14	8.63	9.05	9.41	9.72	10.01	10.26	10.49	10.70	10.89	11.07	11.24	11.39	11.54	11.68
3	3.33	4.47	5.20	5.74	6.16	6.51	6.81	7.06	7.29	7.49	7.67	7.83	7.98	8.12	8.25	8.37	8.48	8.58	8.68
4	3.01	3.98	4.59	5.03	5.39	5.68	5.93	6.14	6.33	6.49	6.65	6.78	6.91	7.02	7.13	7.23	7.33	7.41	7.50
5	2.85	3.72	4.26	4.66	4.98	5.24	5.46	5.65	5.82	5.97	6.10	6.22	6.34	6.44	6.54	6.63	6.71	6.79	6.86
6	2.75	3.56	4.07	4.44	4.73	4.97	5.17	5.34	5.50	5.64	5.76	5.87	5.98	6.07	6.16	6.25	6.32	6.40	6.47
7	2.68	3.45	3.93	4.28	4.55	4.78	4.97	5.14	5.28	5.41	5.53	5.64	5.74	5.83	5.91	5.99	6.06	6.13	6.19
8	2.63	3.37	3.83	4.17	4.43	4.65	4.83	4.99	5.13	5.25	5.36	5.46	5.56	5.64	5.72	5.80	5.87	5.93	6.00
9	2.59	3.32	3.76	4.08	4.34	4.54	4.72	4.87	5.01	5.13	5.23	5.33	5.42	5.51	5.58	5.66	5.72	5.79	5.85
10	2.56	3.27	3.70	4.02	4.26	4.47	4.64	4.78	4.91	5.03	5.13	5.23	5.32	5.40	5.47	5.54	5.61	5.67	5.73
11	2.54	3.23	3.66	3.96	4.20	4.40	4.57	4.71	4.84	4.95	5.05	5.15	5.23	5.31	5.38	5.45	5.51	5.57	5.63
12	2.52	3.20	3.62	3.92	4.16	4.35	4.51	4.65	4.78	4.89	4.99	5.08	5.16	5.24	5.31	5.37	5.44	5.49	5.55
13	2.50	3.18	3.59	3.88	4.12	4.30	4.46	4.60	4.72	4.83	4.93	5.02	5.10	5.18	5.25	5.31	5.37	5.43	5.48
14	2.49	3.16	3.56	3.85	4.08	4.27	4.42	4.56	4.68	4.79	4.88	4.97	5.05	5.12	5.19	5.26	5.32	5.37	5.43
15	2.48	3.14	3.54	3.83	4.05	4.23	4.39	4.52	4.64	4.75	4.84	4.93	5.01	5.08	5.15	5.21	5.27	5.32	5.38
16	2.47	3.12	3.52	3.80	4.03	4.21	4.36	4.49	4.61	4.71	4.81	4.89	4.97	5.04	5.11	5.17	5.23	5.28	5.33
17	2.46	3.11	3.50	3.78	4.00	4.18	4.33	4.46	4.58	4.68	4.77	4.86	4.93	5.01	5.07	5.13	5.19	5.24	5.30
18	2.45	3.10	3.49	3.77	3.98	4.16	4.31	4.44	4.55	4.65	4.75	4.83	4.90	4.98	5.04	5.10	5.16	5.21	5.26
19	2.45	3.09	3.47	3.75	3.97	4.14	4.29	4.42	4.53	4.63	4.72	4.80	4.88	4.95	5.01	5.07	5.13	5.18	5.23
20	2.44	3.08	3.46	3.74	3.95	4.12	4.27	4.40	4.51	4.61	4.70	4.78	4.85	4.92	4.99	5.05	5.10	5.16	5.20
24	2.42	3.05	3.42	3.69	3.90	4.07	4.21	4.34	4.44	4.54	4.63	4.71	4.78	4.85	4.91	4.97	5.02	5.07	5.12
30	2.40	3.02	3.39	3.65	3.85	4.02	4.16	4.28	4.38	4.47	4.56	4.64	4.71	4.77	4.83	4.89	4.94	4.99	5.03
40	2.38	2.99	3.35	3.60	3.80	3.96	4.10	4.21	4.32	4.41	4.49	4.56	4.63	4.69	4.75	4.81	4.86	4.90	4.95
60	2.36	2.96	3.31	3.56	3.75	3.91	4.04	4.16	4.25	4.34	4.42	4.49	4.56	4.62	4.67	4.73	4.78	4.82	4.86
120	2.34	2.93	3.28	3.52	3.71	3.86	3.99	4.10	4.19	4.28	4.35	4.42	4.48	4.54	4.60	4.65	4.69	4.74	4.78
∞	2.33	2.90	3.24	3.48	3.66	3.81	3.93	4.04	4.13	4.21	4.28	4.35	4.41	4.47	4.52	4.57	4.61	4.65	4.69

* From James Pachares, "Table of the upper 10% points of the Studentized range," *Biometrika*, Vol. 46, Pts. 3 and 4 (1959), pp. 461–466. Reproduced with the permission of the author and the Biometrika Trustees.

Index